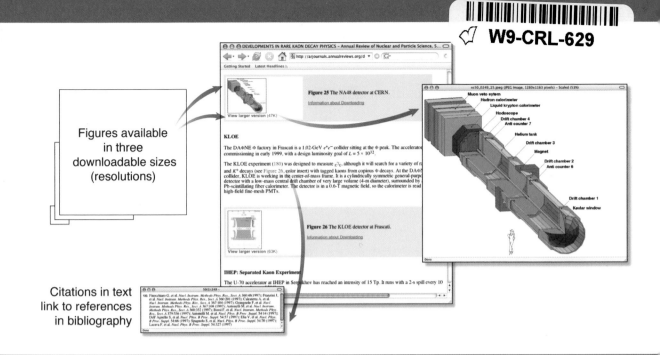

Figures available in three downloadable sizes (resolutions)

Citations in text link to references in bibliography

Figure 25 The NA48 detector at CERN.
Information about Downloading

View larger version (47K)

KLOE

The DAΦNE Φ factory in Frascati is a 1.02-GeV e^+e^- collider sitting at the Φ peak. The accelerator commissioning in early 1999, with a design luminosity goal of $L = 5 \times 10^{32}$.

The KLOE experiment (180) was designed to measure ε'/ε, although it will search for a variety of and K^+ decays (see Figure 26, color insert) with tagged kaons from copious Φ decays. At the DAΦ collider, KLOE is working in the center-of-mass frame. It is a cylindrically symmetric general-purpo detector with a low-mass central drift chamber of very large volume (4-m diameter), surrounded by Pb-scintillating fiber calorimeter. The detector is in a 0.6-T magnetic field, so the calorimeter is read high-field fine-mesh PMTs.

Figure 26 The KLOE detector at Frascati.
Information about Downloading

View larger version (63K)

IHEP: Separated Kaon Experiment

The U-70 accelerator at IHEP in Serpukhov has reached an intensity of 15 Tp. It runs with a 2-s spill every 10

References in Annual Reviews article bibliography link out to sources of cited articles online

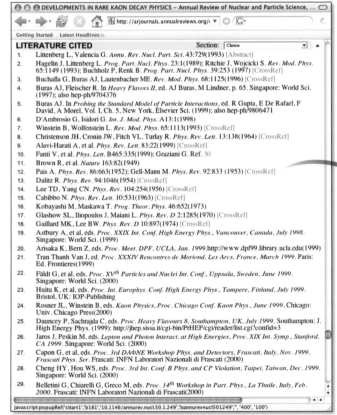

LITERATURE CITED   Section: Choose

1. Littenberg L, Valencia G. *Annu. Rev. Nucl. Part. Sci.* 43:729(1993) [Abstract]
2. Hagelin J, Littenberg L. *Prog. Part. Nucl. Phys.* 23:1(1989); Ritchie J, Wojcicki S. *Rev. Mod. Phys.* 65:1149 (1993); Buchholz P, Renk B. *Prog. Part. Nucl. Phys.* 39:253 (1997) [CrossRef]
3. Buchalla G, Buras AJ, Lautenbacher ME. *Rev. Mod. Phys.* 68:1125(1996) [CrossRef]
4. Buras AJ, Fleischer R. In *Heavy Flavors II*, ed. AJ Buras, M Lindner, p. 65. Singapore: World Sci. (1997); also hep-ph/9704376
5. Buras AJ. In *Probing the Standard Model of Particle Interactions*, ed. R Gupta, E De Rafael, F David, A Morel, Vol. I, Ch. 5, New York, Elsevier Sci. (1999); also hep-ph/9806471
6. D'Ambrosio G, Isidori G. *Int. J. Mod. Phys.* A13:1(1998)
7. Winstein B, Wolfenstein L. *Rev. Mod. Phys.* 65:1113(1993) [CrossRef]
8. Christenson JH, Cronin JW, Fitch VL, Turlay R. *Phys. Rev. Lett.* 13:138(1964) [CrossRef]
9. Alavi-Harati A, et al. *Phys. Rev. Lett.* 83:22(1999) [CrossRef]
10. Fanti V, et al. *Phys. Lett.* B465:335(1999); Graziani G. Ref. 30
11. Brown R, et al. *Nature* 163:82(1949)
12. Pais A. *Phys. Rev.* 86:663(1952); Gell-Mann M. *Phys. Rev.* 92:833 (1953) [CrossRef]
13. Dalitz R. *Phys. Rev.* 94:1046(1954) [CrossRef]
14. Lee TD, Yang CN. *Phys. Rev.* 104:254(1956) [CrossRef]
15. Cabibbo N. *Phys. Rev. Lett.* 10:531(1963) [CrossRef]
16. Kobayashi M, Maskawa T. *Prog. Theor. Phys.* 46:652(1973)
17. Glashow SL, Iliopoulos J, Maiani L. *Phys. Rev. D* 2:1285(1970) [CrossRef]
18. Gaillard MK, Lee BW. *Phys. Rev. D* 10:897(1974) [CrossRef]
19. Astbury A, et al, eds. *Proc. XXIX Int. Conf. High Energy Phys.*, Vancouver, Canada, July 1998. Singapore: World Sci. (1999)
20. Arisaka K, Bern Z, eds. *Proc. Meet. DPF*, UCLA, Jan. 1999.http://www.dpf99.library.ucla.edu(1999)
21. Tran Thanh Van J, ed. *XXXIV Rencontres de Moriond*, Les Arcs, France, March 1999. Paris: Ed. Frontieres(1999)
22. Fäldt G, et al, eds. *Proc. XVth Particles and Nuclei Int. Conf.*, Uppsala, Sweden, June 1999. Singapore: World Sci. (2000)
23. Huitu K, et al, eds. *Proc. Int. Europhys. Conf. High Energy Phys.*, Tampere, Finland, July 1999. Bristol, UK: IOP-Publishing
24. Rosner JL, Winstein B, eds. *Kaon Physics, Proc. Chicago Conf. Kaon Phys.*, June 1999, Chicago: Univ. Chicago Press(2000)
25. Dauncey P, Sachrajda C, eds. *Proc. Heavy Flavours 8*, Southampton, UK, July 1999. Southampton: J. High Energy Phys. (1999); http://jhep.sissa.it/cgi-bin/PrHEP/cgi/reader/list.cgi?confid=3
26. Jaros J, Peskin M, eds. *Lepton and Photon Interact. at High Energies, Proc. XIX Int. Symp.*, Stanford, CA 1999. Singapore: World Sci. (2000)
27. Capon G, et al, eds. *Proc. 3rd DAΦNE Workshop Phys. and Detectors*, Frascati, Italy, Nov. 1999, *Frascati Phys. Ser.* Frascati: INFN Laboratori Nazionali di Frascati (2000)
28. Cheng HY, Hou WS, eds. *Proc. 3rd Int. Conf. B Phys. and CP Violation*, Taipei, Taiwan, Dec. 1999. Singapore: World Sci. (2000)
29. Belletini G, Chiarelli G, Greco M, eds. *Proc. 14th Workshop in Part. Phys.*, La Thuile, Italy, Feb. 2000. Frascati: INFN Laboratori Nazionali di Frascati(2000)

javascript:popupRef('citart1','b181','10.1146/annurev.nucl.50.1.249','bannurevnucl501249','','400','100')

APS Journals Physical Review Online Archive
AMERICAN PHYSICAL SOCIETY

Phys. Rev. 86, 663–672 (1952)

[Issue 5 – 1 June 1952]

[Previous article | Next article | Issue 5 contents]

View Page Images, PDF (2100 kB), or Buy this Article

Some Remarks on the V-Particles

A. Pais
Institute for Advanced Study, Princeton, New Jersey

Received 22 January 1952

It is qualitatively investigated whether the abundance of V-particle production can be reconciled with their long lifetime by using only interactions of a conventional structure. This is possible, provided a V-particle is produced together with another heavy unstable particle (Sec. II). Two distinct groups of interactions are needed: for one, the coupling is strong (II); for the other, it is very weak (III). Two kinds of V-particles are considered, Fermions of mass ~2200m and Bosons (~800m). The arguments are somewhat different, according to whether the latter are nonpseudoscalar (III) or pseudoscalar (IV). The competition with processes involving μ-mesons is discussed (IV). Possible connections with the *tau*-meson are commented on in Sec. V. The preliminary nature of the present analysis is stressed (VI).

URL: http://link.aps.org/abstract/PR/v86/p663
DOI: 10.1103/PhysRev.86.663

Annual Review of
Nuclear and Particle Science

Annual Review of
Nuclear and Particle Science

Volume 58, 2008

Boris Kayser, *Editor*
Fermi National Accelerator Laboratory

Barry R. Holstein, *Associate Editor*
University of Massachusetts

Abolhassan Jawahery, *Associate Editor*
University of Maryland

www.annualreviews.org • science@annualreviews.org • 650-493-4400

Annual Reviews
4139 El Camino Way • P.O. Box 10139 • Palo Alto, California 94303-0139

Annual Reviews
Palo Alto, California, USA

International Standard Serial Number: 0163-8998
International Standard Book Number: 978-0-8243-1558-0
Library of Congress Catalog Card Number: 53-995

TYPESET BY APTARA
PRINTED AND BOUND BY FRIESENS CORPORATION, ALTONA, MANITOBA, CANADA

Contents

Annual Review of
Nuclear and
Particle Science

Volume 58, 2008

Indexes

Errata

An online log of corrections to *Annual Review of Nuclear and Particle Science* articles may be found at http://nucl.annualreviews.org/errata.shtml

Related Articles

Effective Field Theory and Finite-Density Systems

Richard J. Furnstahl,[1] Gautam Rupak,[2] and Thomas Schäfer[2]

[1] Department of Physics, Ohio State University, Columbus, Ohio 43210;
email: furnstahl.1@osu.edu

[2] Department of Physics, North Carolina State University, Raleigh, North Carolina 27695;
email: grupak@gmail.com, tmschaef@ncsu.edu

Annu. Rev. Nucl. Part. Sci. 2008. 58:1–25

First published online as a Review in Advance on April 17, 2008

The *Annual Review of Nuclear and Particle Science* is online at nucl.annualreviews.org

This article's doi:
10.1146/annurev.nucl.58.110707.171142

Key Words

nuclear matter, many-body physics, chiral symmetry

Abstract

This review gives an overview of effective field theory (EFT) as applied at finite density, with a focus on nuclear many-body systems. Uniform systems with short-range interactions illustrate the ingredients and virtues of many-body EFT; we also survey the varied frontiers of EFT for finite nuclei and nuclear matter.

Contents

1. INTRODUCTION

Calculating the properties of atomic nuclei and nuclear matter starting from microscopic internucleon forces is one of the oldest unsolved challenges of nuclear physics. Renewed interest in this problem has been fueled by experiments at rare isotope facilities, which are opening the door to new domains of unstable nuclides that are not all accessible in the lab, and by descriptions of astrophysical phenomena such as supernovae and neutron stars, which require controlled extrapolations of the equation of state of nuclear matter in density, temperature, and proton fraction (1). Despite decades of work and technological advances, however, there remain severe computational barriers and only limited control of uncertainties in conventional nuclear many-body calculations of all but the lightest nuclei. The difficulties are exacerbated by the need to supplement accurate phenomenological two-nucleon potentials with poorly understood many-body forces to achieve a quantitative (and in many cases qualitative) description of nuclei. Finally, conventional approaches are at best loosely connected to quantum chromodynamics (QCD), the underlying theory of the strong interaction.

Effective field theory (EFT) provides new tools to address these challenges. The goal of EFT applied to finite-density nuclear systems is to place nuclear many-body physics on a firm foundation so that it can be (*a*) systematically improved with associated theoretical error bars, (*b*) extended reliably to regimes where there are limited or no data, and (*c*) connected to QCD as well as to few-body experiments. In this review, we aim to describe how EFT can accomplish these goals in many-body systems and to survey the frontiers of EFT-based calculations of many-body nuclei and nuclear matter.

Any EFT builds on a basic physics principle that underlies every low-energy effective model or theory. A high-energy, short-wavelength probe reveals details down to scales comparable to the wavelength. Thus, electron scattering at sufficiently high energy reveals the quark substructure of protons and neutrons in a nucleus. At lower energies, however, details are not resolved, and one can replace short-distance structure with something simpler, as in a multipole expansion of a complicated charge or current distribution. This means that it is not necessary to calculate with full QCD to do accurate strong interaction physics at low energies; one can replace quarks and gluons by neutrons and protons (and maybe pions, nucleon resonances, etc.). EFT provides a systematic, model-independent way to carry out this program starting with a local Lagrangian framework.

An EFT is formulated by specifying appropriate low-energy degrees of freedom and then constructing the Lagrangian as a complete set of terms that embodies the symmetries of the underlying theory. (Note that the general Lagrangian will typically be overcomplete, but redundant terms can be removed by redefining the fields appropriately.) There is no unique EFT for nuclear physics. In different applications the relevant degrees of freedom might be neutrons and protons only; neutrons, protons, and pions; or neutrons, protons, pions, and Δs or quasi-nucleons. The form of the EFT can be chosen to readily expose universal behavior; for instance, dilute neutron matter has features in common with phenomena seen in cold atom experiments.

In applying an EFT Lagrangian, one must confront in a controlled way the impact of excluded short-distance physics. Quantum mechanics implies that sensitivity to short-distance physics is always present in a low-energy theory, but that it is made manifest in an EFT through dependence on a cutoff or other regulator instead of being hidden in phenomenological form factors. Removing this dependence necessitates a well-defined regularization and renormalization scheme as part of the EFT specification. This necessity becomes a virtue as residual regulator dependence can be used to assess truncation errors and many-body approximations. Furthermore, the freedom in regulating coupled with the freedom in making unitary transformations can be exploited by renormalization group (RG) methods to greatly simplify few- and many-body nuclear calculations.

For an EFT calculation to be improvable order by order, one needs a scheme to organize the infinite possible terms in the Lagrangian based on an expansion parameter (or parameters). Such a scheme is called a power counting. Power counting tells us what terms (or Feynman diagrams) to include at each order and lets us estimate the theoretical truncation error. The radius of convergence associated with the expansion means that the EFT predicts its own downfall, in contrast to phenomenological models. EFT expansion parameters most commonly arise as a ratio of disparate physical scales rather than as a small coupling constant (e.g., as in Coulomb systems); a many-body example is the ratio of the range of the interaction to the interparticle spacing in a dilute system. The power counting for this example is particularly simple when the scattering length is roughly the same size as the interaction range (called natural) but changes dramatically if the scattering length is much larger (called unnatural). We explore both scenarios below.

Chiral EFT is a faithful low-energy realization of QCD whose power counting takes advantage of the spontaneously broken chiral symmetry that gives rise to the almost massless (on hadronic scales) pion. It has the potential to bridge the gap between QCD and nuclei, letting us explore how nuclear properties depend on QCD parameters (e.g., how the binding energies of nuclei would change if the light quark masses were different or if the QCD scale parameter were time dependent) and opening a connection to ab initio QCD lattice calculations. Chiral EFT power counting explains the empirical hierarchy of many-body forces in nuclear physics, fixes their natural sizes, and gives an organizing principle for their construction. Other compelling features are the systematic inclusion of relativistic corrections and prescriptions for consistent currents needed to predict experimental observables.

A comprehensive treatment of EFT and finite-density nuclear systems would require several extended reviews covering EFT in general, EFT applied to internucleon interactions, and field theory at finite density. Fortunately, recent articles in this journal provide much of the background for the interested reader; these include an introduction to EFT by Burgess (2), an overview of chiral perturbation theory by Bernard & Meißner (3), and a review of EFT for few-nucleon systems by Bedaque & van Kolck (4) (see also References 5 and 6). We focus here on illustrating how the basic principles of EFT can be realized at finite density and on surveying various applications to nuclear matter and finite nuclei. Our treatment is schematic in most cases and we refer the reader to the literature for details.

In Section 2, we consider uniform systems with short-range interactions. The dilute Fermi gas with repulsive interactions serves as a prototype for EFT at finite density, whereas new features and techniques arise when we study physics near the Fermi surface. Many-body systems with unnatural scattering lengths, which manifest various forms of universal physics, are attacked by a variety of nonperturbative EFT techniques. Actual applications of EFT to nuclear many-body systems are in their infancy and there are multiple frontiers; we describe a range of examples in Section 3. These include the use of chiral EFT interactions as input to conventional many-body wave function methods applicable to light nuclei and a pioneering attempt to apply EFT to the methods themselves. Lattice calculations provide a complementary nonperturbative approach. Perturbative chiral EFT calculations for nuclei may be possible, however, if the power counting differs at nuclear densities. This may be justified by RG transformations that soften the chiral interactions. Finally we discuss density functional theory (DFT), which is computationally tractable for all nuclides and is naturally cast in EFT form using effective actions. In Section 4 we conclude with a summary of the current status of EFT for nuclear systems, ongoing developments, important open questions, and a brief discussion of omitted topics.

2. EFFECTIVE FIELD THEORY FOR UNIFORM SYSTEMS

In this section, we illustrate the ideas of EFT at finite density for uniform systems with short-range interactions.

2.1. Prototype Many-Body Effective Field Theory

We start with the simplest possible application, a dilute Fermi system with repulsive, spin-independent interactions of range R. A concrete example is "hard-sphere" repulsion at radius R, which can be viewed as a caricature of the short-range part of the nuclear force. In perturbation theory all matrix elements of this potential are infinite; whereas a more realistic potential would not be so extreme, textbook treatments of this many-body problem all start with nonperturbative summations and then expansions at low density (7). In contrast, the EFT approach directly exploits the essential physics result that low-momentum nucleons do not resolve the hard core.

With either approach, the end result for free-space, two-particle scattering at low energies ($\lambda = 2\pi/k \gg 1/R$) is the effective range expansion; e.g., the s-wave phase shift $\delta_0(k)$ satisfies:

$$k \cot \delta_0(k) \overset{k \to 0}{\to} -\frac{1}{a_0} + \frac{1}{2}r_0 k^2 + \dots, \qquad 1.$$

where a_0 is the scattering length and r_0 is the effective range. The system is said to have a natural scattering length if it is the same order as the range of the interaction (e.g., $a_0 = R$ and $r_0 = 2R/3$ for hard spheres). Below we consider the case of unnatural scattering length, with $a_0 \gg R$, which is relevant for dilute neutron matter and cold atom systems. For a natural system, the dilute expansion of the energy density for a uniform system starts as (s-wave only here)

$$\mathcal{E} = \rho \frac{k_{\mathrm{F}}^2}{2M} \left[\frac{3}{5} + (\nu - 1) \left\{ \frac{2}{3\pi}(k_{\mathrm{F}}a_0) + \frac{4}{35\pi^2}(11 - 2\ln 2)(k_{\mathrm{F}}a_0)^2 + \frac{1}{10\pi}(k_{\mathrm{F}}r_0)(k_{\mathrm{F}}a_0)^2 \right\} + \cdots \right],$$

$$2.$$

where k_F is the Fermi momentum, ν is the spin degeneracy, and $\rho = \nu k_F^3/6\pi^2$. This result arises very cleanly from an EFT treatment (8).

Consider the ingredients for any EFT along with the specifics for this example:

1. Use the most general $\mathcal{L}$ with low-energy degrees of freedom consistent with global and local symmetries of the underlying theory. Here we have nucleons only with Galilean invariance and discrete symmetries. A general interaction is then a sum of δ functions and derivatives of δ functions with two-body interactions (four fields), three-body interactions (six fields), and so on. Therefore, $\mathcal{L}_{\mathrm{eft}}$ is

$$\mathcal{L}_{\mathrm{eft}} = \psi^\dagger \left[i\frac{\partial}{\partial t} + \frac{\nabla^2}{2M} \right] \psi - \frac{C_0}{2}(\psi^\dagger\psi)^2 + \frac{C_2}{16}[(\psi\psi)^\dagger(\psi \overleftrightarrow{\nabla}^2 \psi) + \mathrm{h.c.}] - \frac{D_0}{6}(\psi^\dagger\psi)^3 + \dots,$$

3.

where ... indicates terms with more derivatives and more fields. (We have eliminated higher-order time derivatives using the equations of motion; see Reference 8.) The ψs have ν components and spin-indices are implicit (and contracted between $\psi^\dagger$ and ψ).

2. Declare a regularization and renormalization scheme. One choice is to smear out the δ functions (e.g., as Gaussians in momentum space) to introduce a cutoff; renormalization would remove cutoff dependence. However, for a natural a_0, using dimensional regularization and minimal subtraction (rather than a cutoff) is particularly convenient and efficient.

3. Establish a well-defined power counting, which means identifying small expansion parameters, typically using a ratio of scales. In free space k/Λ with $\Lambda \sim 1/R$ is the clear choice, and then k_F/Λ is the corresponding parameter in the medium. Dimensional analysis, with some additional insight to give us the 4πs, implies ($2i$ denotes the number of gradients)

$$C_{2i} \sim \frac{4\pi}{M} R^{2i+1}, \qquad D_{2i} \sim \frac{4\pi}{M} R^{2i+4},$$

4.

which will enable us to make quantitative power-counting estimates.

Feynman diagrams and rules for the EFT follow from conventional formalism for free-space and many-body perturbation theory (see, e.g., References 7 and 9). The constants C_{2i} are determined by matching to the free-space scattering amplitude $f_0(k)$ in perturbation theory:

$$f_0(k) = \frac{4\pi}{M}\left(a_0 - ia_0^2 k - a_0^3 k^2 + a_0^2 r_0 k^2 + \cdots\right).$$

5.

The leading potential $V_{\mathrm{EFT}}^{(0)}(\mathbf{x}) = C_0\delta(\mathbf{x})$ or $\langle\mathbf{k}|V_{\mathrm{eft}}^{(0)}|\mathbf{k}'\rangle = C_0$, where $\mathbf{k}, \mathbf{k}'$ are relative momenta. Matching to $f_0(k)$ fixes $C_0 = 4\pi a_0/M$ at leading order (LO), which then determines the leading finite-density contribution (Hartree-Fock) in Equation 2 after sums over the Fermi sea:

$$\times \rightarrow C_0 \Rightarrow \infty \rightarrow \mathcal{E}_{\mathrm{LO}} = \frac{C_0}{2}\nu(\nu-1)\left(\sum_{\mathbf{k}}^{k_F} 1\right)^2 \propto a_0 k_F^6.$$

6.

Similar matching yields C_2 in terms of a_0 and r_0 and the corresponding Hartree-Fock contribution for the effective range.

At the next order is $\langle\mathbf{k}|V_{\mathrm{eft}}^{(0)}G_0 V_{\mathrm{eft}}^{(0)}|\mathbf{k}'\rangle$, which includes a linearly divergent loop integral:

$$\times \rightarrow C_0 M \int^{\Lambda_c} \frac{d^3q}{(2\pi)^3}\frac{1}{k^2 - q^2 + i\varepsilon}C_0 = C_0^2 M\left(\frac{\Lambda_c}{2\pi^2} - \frac{ik}{4\pi} + \mathcal{O}\left(\frac{k^2}{\Lambda_c}\right)\right).$$

7.

We can redefine (renormalize) C_0 to absorb the linear dependence on the cutoff Λ_c, but we will obtain higher powers of k from every diagram. A more efficient scheme is dimensional regularization with minimal subtraction (DR/MS), which implies that only one power of k survives:

$$\int \frac{d^D q}{(2\pi)^3} \frac{1}{k^2 - q^2 + i\varepsilon} \xrightarrow{D \to 3} -\frac{ik}{4\pi}. \qquad 8.$$

Thus we obtain the second term in Equation 5 automatically with no change in C_0. At higher orders there is exactly one power of k per diagram and natural coefficients (i.e., consistent with Equation 4), so we can estimate truncation errors from simple dimensional analysis.

The contribution to the energy density has two terms, one of which vanishes identically. In the other, we again obtain a linear divergence,

$$\Rightarrow \qquad \to \mathcal{E}_{\text{NLO}} \propto \int_{k_F}^{\infty} \frac{d^3 q}{(2\pi)^3} \frac{C_0^2}{k^2 - q^2}, \qquad 9.$$

but the same renormalization fixes it,

$$\int_{k_F}^{\infty} \frac{1}{k^2 - q^2} = \int_0^{\infty} \frac{1}{k^2 - q^2} - \int_0^{k_F} \frac{1}{k^2 - q^2} \xrightarrow{D \to 3} -\int_0^{k_F} \frac{1}{k^2 - q^2}, \qquad 10.$$

and particles become holes through the renormalization. Pauli blocking does not change the free-space UV (short-distance) renormalization as the density is a long-distance effect; after fixing free space, the in-medium renormalization is determined. We find $\mathcal{E}_{\text{NLO}} \propto a_0^2 k_F^7$.

The diagrammatic power counting with DR/MS is very simple, with each loop adding a power of k in free space. At finite density, a diagram with V_{2i}^n n–body vertices and $2i$ gradients scales as $(k_F)^\beta$ with

$$\beta = 5 + \sum_{n=2}^{\infty} \sum_{i=0}^{\infty} (3n + 2i - 5) V_{2i}^n. \qquad 11.$$

This reproduces, for example, the LO [$\beta = 5 + (3 \cdot 2 + 2 \cdot 0 - 5) \cdot 1 = 6$] and next-to-leading order (NLO) [$\beta = 5 + (3 \cdot 2 + 2 \cdot 0 - 5) \cdot 2 = 7$] dependencies. The power counting is exceptionally clean, with a separation of vertex factors $\propto a_0, r_0, \ldots$ and a dimensionless geometric integral multiplying k_F^β, with each diagram contributing to exactly one order in the expansion. There is a systematic hierarchy, as adding derivatives or higher-body interactions increases the power of k_F. The ratio of successive terms is $\sim k_F R$ (see, e.g., Equation 2), so we can estimate excluded contributions.

The energy density (2) looks like a power series in k_F, but at higher order there are logarithmic divergences from 3–3 scattering, which indicate new sensitivity to short-distance behavior. A cutoff Λ_c serves as a resolution scale; as we increase Λ_c, we see more of the short-distance details. Observables (such as scattering amplitudes) must not vary with Λ_c, so changes must be absorbed in a coupling. But the coupling cannot be from 2–2 scattering, as we already regularized all the divergences there. Instead, we must use the point-like three-body force, whose coupling $D_0(\Lambda_c)$ can absorb the dependence on Λ_c (10). The diagrams are $\propto (C_0)^4 \ln(k/\Lambda_c)$, which means that

$$\frac{d}{d\Lambda_c} \left[\text{} \right] = 0 \Rightarrow D_0(\Lambda_c) \propto (C_0)^4 \ln(a_0 \Lambda_c) \qquad 12.$$

fixes the coefficient $D_0(\Lambda_c)$. Dimensional regularization works similarly (8). In turn this implies the following result for the energy density:

$$\mathcal{O}\left(k_F^9 \ln(k_F)\right): \text{} + \cdots \propto (\nu - 2)(\nu - 1) k_F^5 (k_F a_0)^4 \ln(k_F a_0) \qquad 13.$$

without actually carrying out the calculation! Similar analyses can identify the higher logarithmic terms in the expansion of the energy density (8, 10). This example illustrates the inevitability of many-body forces in low-energy theories: When the resolution or degrees of freedom are changed, we will have many-body forces. Thus the question is not whether such forces are present, but how large they are. For nuclear physics, their natural size implies that they cannot be neglected.

This brief tour of the EFT for a natural dilute Fermi gas includes features common to many other applications. Even if we know that the underlying physics is a hard-sphere potential, the EFT is easier to calculate than conventional approaches (7). Further, the EFT directly reveals the universal nature of the many-body counterpart to the effective range expansion, which applies to any short-range repulsive potential. Of course, this example is very simple; there are many ways to generalize. Some are immediate: For instance, we can account for short-range spin-dependent interactions by adding terms such as $C_0^\sigma (\psi^\dagger \boldsymbol{\sigma} \psi) \cdot (\psi^\dagger \boldsymbol{\sigma} \psi)$. To consider unnatural scattering, however, we must revisit the power counting and consider alternative expansion parameters, as $k_F a_0$ is no longer small. But first we turn from EFT for bulk properties to EFT near the Fermi surface.

2.2. Effective Field Theory Near the Fermi Surface

The theory described in the last section is completely perturbative. At any order in the $k_F R$ expansion, only a finite number of diagrams need to be computed. There are two ways in which this expansion can fail. One possibility is that one of the effective range parameters (typically, the scattering length) is anomalously large, so that a certain class of diagrams must be summed to all orders. We examine this problem in Section 2.3. A second possibility is that the density (and the Fermi momentum) is too large and that $k_F R$ ceases to be a useful expansion parameter. In this case it is possible to construct a different kind of EFT by focusing on quasi-particles in the vicinity of the Fermi surface and using $|k - k_F|/\Lambda$ as an expansion parameter. This effective theory is known as Landau Fermi-liquid theory (11, 12). The Landau theory does not account for all properties of the many-body system, but it does describe phenomena that are sensitive to physics near the Fermi surface such as collective modes, pairing, and transport properties.

Fermi-liquid theory was originally developed by Landau using intuitive arguments. These arguments were later confirmed by Abrikosov and others using diagrammatic many-body perturbation theory (13). The modern view of Fermi-liquid theory as an EFT was advocated by Shankar, Polchinski, and others (14, 15). Consider the effective action of noninteracting, nonrelativistic fermions near a Fermi surface,

$$S = \int dt \int \frac{d^3p}{(2\pi)^3} \psi^\dagger(p) \left(i \frac{\partial}{\partial t} - v_F l_p \right) \psi(p).$$

14.

Here we have decomposed the momenta as $\mathbf{p} = \mathbf{k} + \mathbf{l}_p$, where $\mathbf{k}$ is on the Fermi surface, $|\mathbf{k}| = k_F$, and $\mathbf{l}_p$ is orthogonal to the Fermi surface. The Fermi velocity is defined as $v_F = \partial E_p/\partial p$, where E_p is the quasi-particle energy. The power counting can be established by studying the behavior of the operators under transformations $l_p \to s l_p$ that scale the momenta towards the Fermi surface. In writing $E_p = E_F + v_F l_p + \mathcal{O}(l_p^2)$, we see that as $s \to 0$ only the Fermi velocity survives, so the detailed form of the dispersion relation is irrelevant. Using $d^3p = k_F^2 (dl_p)(d\Omega)$, we observe that $d^3p \sim s$, $dt \sim s^{-1}$, $\psi \sim s^{-1/2}$, and that S in (14) is $\mathcal{O}(s^0)$.

We now turn to the importance of interactions between fermions near the Fermi surface. The most general four-fermion interaction is of the form

$$S_{4f} = \frac{1}{4} \int dt \left[\prod_{i=1}^{4} \int \frac{d^3p_i}{(2\pi)^3} \right] \psi^\dagger(\mathbf{p}_4) \psi^\dagger(\mathbf{p}_3) \psi(\mathbf{p}_2) \psi(\mathbf{p}_1) \delta^3 (\mathbf{p}_{tot}) U(\mathbf{p}_4, \mathbf{p}_3, \mathbf{p}_2, \mathbf{p}_1),$$

15.

where $\mathbf{p}_{tot}$ is the sum of the four momenta $\mathbf{p}_i$, and we have suppressed the spin labels on U. For a generic set of momenta $\mathbf{p}_i$ the δ function constrains the large components of the momenta and scales as $\delta^3(\mathbf{p}_{tot}) \sim s^0$. In this case the four-fermion interaction scales as s^1 and becomes irrelevant near the Fermi surface. Interactions involving more fermions are even more strongly suppressed.

An exception occurs if the large components of the momenta cancel. This happens for back-to-back momenta, $\mathbf{k}_1 = -\mathbf{k}_2$, and for generalized forward scattering, $\mathbf{k}_1 \cdot \mathbf{k}_2 = \mathbf{k}_3 \cdot \mathbf{k}_4$. In these cases one component of the δ functions constrains $\mathbf{l}$, the scaling of the δ function is changed to s^{-1}, and the four-fermion interaction is marginal, $S_{4f} \sim s^0$. Whether or not the four-fermion interaction qualitatively changes the theory of noninteracting quasi-particles described by Equation 14 depends on quantum corrections, which can change the scaling from marginal to marginally relevant [$S_{4f} \sim \log(s)$] or irrelevant [$S_{4f} \sim \log(s)^{-1}$].

The one-loop corrections to the four-fermion interaction are given by

$$\delta S_{BCS} \sim \quad , \quad \delta S_{ZS} \sim \quad , \quad \delta S_{ZS'} \sim \quad . \qquad 16.$$

There are two possible scenarios. One possibility is that the interaction in the Bardeen-Cooper-Schrieffer (BCS) channel ($\mathbf{k}_1 = -\mathbf{k}_2$) is attractive in some partial wave. In this case the first diagram in Equation 16 leads to a logarithmic growth of the interaction. We can illustrate this effect using the s-wave four-fermion interaction defined in Equation 3. For $\mathbf{p}_1 = -\mathbf{p}_2$ and $E_1 = E_2 = E$, the one-loop correction to C_0 is given by

$$-C_0^2 \left(\frac{k_F m}{2\pi^2} \right) \log \left(\frac{E_0}{E} \right), \qquad 17.$$

where E_0 is a UV cutoff. This result can be interpreted as an effective energy-dependent coupling. The coupling constant satisfies the RG equation

$$E \frac{dC_0}{dE} = C_0^2 \left(\frac{k_F m}{2\pi^2} \right) \Rightarrow C_0(E) = \frac{C_0(E_0)}{1 + N C_0(E_0) \log(E_0/E)}, \qquad 18.$$

where $N = k_F m / 2\pi^2$ is the density of states. Equation 18 shows that if the initial coupling is repulsive, $C_0(E_0) > 0$, then the RG evolution will drive the effective coupling to zero. If, on the other hand, the initial coupling is attractive, $C_0(E_0) < 0$, then the effective coupling will grow and reach a pole (called a Landau pole) at $E_{crit} \sim E_0 \exp(-1/(N|C_0(E_0)))$. At the Landau pole the effective theory defined by Equations 14 and 15 has to break down. The RG equation does not determine what happens at this point, but we can assume that the strong attractive interaction leads to the formation of a fermion pair condensate in the BCS channel $\langle \psi(\mathbf{p}) \psi(-\mathbf{p}) \rangle$. The magnitude of the difermion condensate as well as the corresponding gap in the energy spectrum is easiest to compute if the microscopic interaction is weak (i.e., if $k_f R < 1$). Employing standard methods, we derive the gap equation

$$1 = \frac{|C_0|}{2} \int \frac{d^3 p}{(2\pi)^3} \frac{1}{\sqrt{(E_p - E_F)^2 + \Delta^2}}. \qquad 19.$$

The infrared divergence in the BCS channel is regulated by the energy gap Δ. The gap equation also has a logarithmic UV divergence. This divergence can be treated consistently with the relation between C_0 and a_0 derived in Section 2.1 by using dimensional regularization (16, 17). The result is

$$\Delta = \frac{8 E_F}{e^2} \exp \left(-\frac{\pi}{2 k_F |a_0|} \right). \qquad 20.$$

The term in the exponent represents the leading term in an expansion in $k_F|a_0|$. This means that in order to determine the pre-exponent in Equation 20 we must solve the gap equation at NLO. This correction corresponds to keeping the zero sound diagram in Equation 16. In nuclear physics this term is known as the induced interaction (18). For zero-range potentials, the induced interaction was first computed by Gorkov & Melik-Barkhudarov (19). It leads to a suppression of the s-wave gap by a factor $(4e)^{1/3} \simeq 2.2$.

For nuclear matter the result given in Equation 20 is not very useful, both because the scattering length is large and because effective range corrections are not negligible. We discuss the pairing gap in the limit $a_0 \to \infty$ in Section 2.3. Range corrections in the case of a normal scattering length were studied in Reference 16. A rough estimate of the gap at moderate densities can be obtained by replacing $1/(k_F a)$ with $\cot[\delta_0(k_F)]$, where $\delta_0(k)$ is the s-wave phase shift. This estimate gives neutron gaps on the order of 1 MeV at nuclear-matter density.

The second scenario arises if the interaction in the BCS channel is either repulsive or very weak. In this case the forward-scattering amplitudes are important. The interaction is

$$U(\hat{p}_4,\ \hat{p}_3,\ \hat{p}_2,\ \hat{p}_1)|_{\hat{p}_1 \cdot \hat{p}_2 = \hat{p}_3 \cdot \hat{p}_4} = F(\hat{p}_1 \cdot \hat{p}_2, \phi_{12,34}), \qquad 21.$$

where $\phi_{12,34}$ is the angle of the plane spanned by $\mathbf{p}_{1,2}$ and $\mathbf{p}_{3,4}$. The function $F(x,0)$ is called the Landau function and its Legendre coefficients are referred to as Landau parameters. If spin dependence is included, there is a second set of Landau parameters commonly denoted F_l'. The Landau parameters remain marginal at one-loop order.

The EFT characterized by v_F and F_l is called the Landau Fermi-liquid theory (11, 12). The Landau parameters can be related to compressibility, the velocity of zero and first sound, transport coefficients, etc. The compressibility of nuclear matter, for example, is given by

$$\frac{dP}{d\rho} = \frac{k_F^2}{m^2} \frac{1 + F_0}{3 + F_1}. \qquad 22.$$

The coefficient F_i can be extracted from experiment, but ultimately we would like to find a systematic method for computing the Landau parameters from the underlying nucleon-nucleon interaction. One possibility is to use the RG to integrate out modes far away from the Fermi surface. A difficulty with this strategy is the problem of finding suitable initial conditions for the RG flow. Schwenk et al. (20) proposed to use a free-space RG to generate a universal low-momentum effective interaction $V_{\text{low }k}$ (which we discuss in more detail in Section 3.2). This interaction, evolved to a scale $\Lambda \sim 2k_F$, can be used as a starting point for the determination of the Landau parameters (20).

2.3. Unnatural Scattering Length

An important aspect of nuclear physics is the fact that the nucleon scattering lengths are anomalously large. The neutron-proton scattering length in the $^1S_0$ channel is -23.71 fm, and the binding energy in the $^3S_1$ (deuteron) channel is 2.2 MeV. This implies that expanding the scattering amplitudes in powers of the momentum (as in Equation 5) is not useful, and that powers of $a_0 k$ have to be kept to all orders. Keeping the first two terms in the effective range expansion, the scattering amplitude can be written as

$$f_0(k) \sim \frac{1}{-1/a_0 + r_0 k^2/2 - ik} = \frac{1}{-1/a_0 - ik} \left\{ 1 + \frac{r_0/2}{-1/a_0 - ik} + \ldots \right\}. \qquad 23.$$

This expansion can be reproduced by keeping the s-wave contact interaction proportional to C_0 to all orders, and treating C_{2i} ($i > 0$) perturbatively as before. This procedure gives the correct result, but in dimensional regularization (with minimal subtraction) or cutoff regularization the power counting of individual diagrams is not manifest. This is readily seen in dimensional regularization where $C_0 \to \infty$ as $a_0 \to \infty$. As a consequence, individual diagrams diverge in the limit of a large scattering length even though the sum of all diagrams is finite. Kaplan et al. proposed a modified version of dimensional regularization (power divergence subtraction, or PDS) in which poles in lower dimensions are subtracted and power counting is manifest (21).

Interest in many-body systems with a large two-particle scattering length arises not only in nuclear physics, but also in atomic physics. It is now possible to create cold atomic gases in which the scattering length a_0 of the atoms can be adjusted experimentally using Feshbach resonances (see Reference 22 for a review). If the density is low, the atoms can be described as pointlike nonrelativistic particles that carry a "spin" label that characterizes the hyperfine quantum numbers of the atoms. A Feshbach resonance arises if a molecular bound state in a closed hyperfine channel crosses near the threshold of a lower "open" channel. Because the magnetic moments of the open and closed states are usually different, Feshbach resonances can be tuned using an applied magnetic field. At resonance the two-body scattering length in the open channel diverges, and the cross section σ is limited only by unitarity; $\sigma(k) = 4\pi/k^2$ for low momenta k. In the unitarity limit, details about the microscopic interaction are lost, and the system displays universal properties.

A dilute gas of any fermions in the unitarity limit is a strongly coupled quantum liquid that exhibits universality. At low density the limit $k_F a_0 \to \infty$ and $k_F r_0 \to 0$ is particularly interesting. From dimensional analysis it is clear that the energy per particle at zero temperature must be proportional to the energy per particle of a free Fermi gas at the same density:

$$\frac{E}{A} = \xi \left(\frac{E}{A} \right)_0 = \xi \frac{3}{5} \left(\frac{k_F^2}{2m} \right). \qquad 24.$$

The constant ξ is universal, that is, independent of the details of the system. Similar universal constants govern the magnitude of the gap in units of Fermi energy and the equation of state at finite temperature.

Calculating these universal constants is clearly a very challenging task—many-body diagrams containing C_0 must be summed to all orders. One possible solution is to do the calculation numerically, using diffusion or imaginary time path–integral Monte Carlo methods as described in Section 3.3. It would be desirable to find systematically improvable analytical approaches. Analytical methods offer the ability to systematically include higher-order terms in the interaction (range corrections, explicit pions, three-body forces, etc.) and to determine real-time properties that are hard to access numerically. A few analytical methods have been considered, such as an expansion in the number of fermion species (23, 24) or the number of spatial dimensions (which is related to the hole-line expansion of Brueckner, Bethe, and Goldstone; see References 25 and 26). Below, we discuss a proposal to perform an expansion around $d = 4 - \varepsilon$ spatial dimensions. ε expansions are well known in the theory of critical phenomena. An interesting aspect of the ε expansion in nuclear physics is that both many-body and few-body systems can be studied (27).

Nussinov & Nussinov observed that the fermion many-body system in the unitarity limit reduces to a free Fermi gas near $d = 2$ spatial dimensions and to a free Bose gas near $d = 4$ (28). Their argument was based on the behavior of the two-body wave function as the binding energy goes to zero. For $d = 2$ it is well known that the limit of zero binding energy corresponds to an arbitrarily weak potential. In $d = 4$ the two-body wave function at $a_0 = \infty$ displays a $1/r^2$ behavior and the normalization is concentrated near the origin. These observations suggest that the many-body system is equivalent to a gas of noninteracting bosons. A systematic expansion based on the observation of Nussinov & Nussinov was studied by Nishida & Son (29). In this section we explain their approach.

We begin by restating the argument of Nussinov & Nussinov in the language of EFT. For the sake of simplicity we work with dimensional regularization and minimal subtraction. In this case $a_0 \to \infty$ corresponds to $C_0 \to \infty$. The fermion-fermion scattering amplitude is given by

$$f(p_0, \mathbf{p}) = \left(\frac{4\pi}{m}\right)^{d/2} \left[\Gamma\left(1 - \frac{d}{2}\right)\right]^{-1} \frac{i}{(-p_0 + E_p/2 - i\delta)^{\frac{d}{2}-1}}, \qquad 25.$$

where $\delta \to 0+$. As a function of d the gamma function has poles at $d = 2, 4, \dots$ and the scattering amplitude vanishes at these points. Near $d = 2$ the scattering amplitude is independent of energy and momentum. For $d = 4 - \varepsilon$ we find

$$f(p_0, \mathbf{p}) = \frac{8\pi^2 \varepsilon}{m^2} \frac{i}{p_0 - E_p/2 + i\delta} + \mathcal{O}(\varepsilon^2). \qquad 26.$$

We observe that at LO in ε the scattering amplitude resembles the propagator of a boson with mass $2m$. The boson-fermion coupling is $g^2 = (8\pi^2\varepsilon)/m^2$ and vanishes as $\varepsilon \to 0$. This suggests that we can set up a perturbative expansion involving fermions of mass m weakly coupled to bosons of mass $2m$. A difermion field can be introduced using the Hubbard-Stratonovich trick. The difermion self-coupling is proportional to $1/C_0$ and vanishes in the unitarity limit. The Lagrangian is

$$\mathcal{L} = \Psi^\dagger \left[i\partial_0 + \sigma_3 \frac{\nabla^2}{2m}\right]\Psi + \mu\Psi^\dagger\sigma_3\Psi + (\Psi^\dagger\sigma_+\Psi\phi + h.c.), \qquad 27.$$

where $\Psi = (\psi_\uparrow, \psi_\downarrow^\dagger)^T$ is a two-component Nambu-Gorkov field, σ_i are Pauli matrices acting in the Nambu-Gorkov space, and $\sigma_\pm = (\sigma_1 \pm i\sigma_2)/2$.

In the superfluid phase ϕ acquires an expectation value. We write

$$\phi = \phi_0 + g\varphi, \qquad g = \frac{\sqrt{8\pi^2\varepsilon}}{m}\left(\frac{m\phi_0}{2\pi}\right)^{\varepsilon/4}, \qquad 28.$$

where $\phi_0 = \langle\phi\rangle$. The scale $M^2 = m\phi_0/(2\pi)$ was introduced in order to have a correctly normalized boson field. The scale parameter is arbitrary, but this particular choice simplifies some of the algebra. In order to obtain a well-defined perturbative expansion we add and subtract a kinetic term for the boson field to the Lagrangian. We include the kinetic term in the free part of the Lagrangian

$$\mathcal{L}_0 = \Psi^\dagger \left[i\partial_0 + \sigma_3 \frac{\nabla^2}{2m} + \phi_0(\sigma_+ + \sigma_-)\right]\Psi + \varphi^\dagger\left(i\partial_0 + \frac{\nabla^2}{4m}\right)\varphi, \qquad 29.$$

and the interacting part is

$$\mathcal{L}_I = g\left(\Psi^\dagger\sigma_+\Psi\varphi + h.c.\right) + \mu\Psi^\dagger\sigma_3\Psi - \varphi^\dagger\left(i\partial_0 + \frac{\nabla^2}{4m}\right)\varphi. \qquad 30.$$

Note that the interacting part generates self-energy corrections to the boson propagator, which, by virtue of Equation 26, cancels against the kinetic term of boson field. We also include the chemical potential term in $\mathcal{L}_I$. This is motivated by the fact that near $d = 4$ the system reduces to a noninteracting Bose gas and $\mu \to 0$. We count μ as a quantity of $\mathcal{O}(\varepsilon)$.

The Feynman rules are quite simple. The fermion and boson propagators are

$$G(p_0, \mathbf{p}) = \frac{i}{p_0^2 - E_p^2 - \phi_0^2}\begin{bmatrix} p_0 + E_p & -\phi_0 \\ -\phi_0 & p_0 - E_p \end{bmatrix}, \qquad D(p_0, \mathbf{p}) = \frac{i}{p_0 - E_p/2}, \qquad 31.$$

and the fermion-boson vertices are $ig\sigma_\pm$. Insertions of the chemical potential are $i\mu\sigma_3$. Both g^2 and μ are corrections of order ε. There are a finite number of one-loop diagrams that generate $1/\varepsilon$ terms. All other diagrams are finite, and the ε expansion is well defined.

The ground-state energy is determined by diagrams with no external legs. The first diagram is the free fermion loop, which is $\mathcal{O}(1)$ in the ε expansion. We obtain

$$\bigcirc = -\int \frac{d^d p}{(2\pi)^d} \sqrt{E_p^2 + \phi_0^2} = \frac{\phi_0}{3}\left[1 + \frac{7 - 3(\gamma + \log(2))}{6}\varepsilon\right]\left(\frac{m\phi_0}{2\pi}\right)^{d/2}. \qquad 32.$$

An insertion of μ is also $\mathcal{O}(1)$ because the loop diagram is divergent in $d = 4$. We find

$$\bigcirc\!\!\times = \mu \int \frac{d^d p}{(2\pi)^d} \frac{E_p}{\sqrt{E_p^2 + \phi_0^2}} = -\frac{\mu}{\varepsilon}\left[1 + \frac{1 - 2(\gamma + \log(2))}{4}\varepsilon\right]\left(\frac{m\phi_0}{2\pi}\right)^{d/2}. \qquad 33.$$

Graphs with extra insertions of μ follow the naive ε counting and are at least $\mathcal{O}(\varepsilon^2)$. Nishida & Son (29) also computed the leading two-loop contribution, which is $\mathcal{O}(\varepsilon)$ because of the factor of g^2 from the vertices. The result is

$$\bigcirc\!\!\cdots = -C_\varepsilon \left(\frac{m\phi_0}{2\pi}\right)^{d/2}, \qquad 34.$$

where the dashed line denotes the difermion propagator and $C \simeq 0.14424$.

We can now determine the minimum of the effective potential. We find $\phi_0 = (2\mu)/\varepsilon(1 + C'\varepsilon + \mathcal{O}(\varepsilon^2))$ with $C' = 3C - 1 + \log(2)$. The value of the effective potential at ϕ_0 determines the pressure and $n = \partial P/\partial \mu$ gives the density. From the density we can compute the Fermi momentum ($n \sim k_F^d$ in d dimensions), and the relationship between the Fermi energy $\varepsilon_F = k_F^2/2m$ and μ determines the universal parameter $\xi = \mu/\varepsilon_F$. We find

$$\xi = \frac{1}{2}\varepsilon^{3/2} + \frac{1}{16}\varepsilon^{5/2}\log(\varepsilon) - 0.025\varepsilon^{5/2} + \cdots = 0.475 \quad (\varepsilon = 1), \qquad 35.$$

which agrees quite well with the result of fixed-node quantum Monte Carlo calculations. The calculation was extended to $\mathcal{O}(\varepsilon^{7/2})$ by Arnold et al. (30). Unfortunately, the next term is very large and it appears necessary to combine the expansion in $4 - \varepsilon$ dimensions with a $2 + \varepsilon$ expansion in order to extract useful results. The ε expansion has also been applied to the calculation of the gap (29). At NLO the result is $\Delta = 0.62\varepsilon_F$. Somewhat surprisingly, this result is quite close to the naive $a_0 \to \infty$ limit of the BCS result given in Equation 20, provided that the induced interaction term is taken into account.

3. EFFECTIVE FIELD THEORY FOR FINITE NUCLEI AND NUCLEAR MATTER

In this section, we survey the wide range of pioneering applications of EFT to nonrelativistic finite-density nuclear systems. These frontiers are rapidly evolving and most results are immature, so we focus on general illustrative aspects.

3.1. Pion Physics from Chiral Effective Field Theory

To apply EFT to finite nuclei and nuclear matter, we must first consider the appropriate degrees of freedom. Applications to sufficiently low density systems such as dilute neutron matter are possible with nucleons as the only degrees of freedom. These are called pionless EFTs. In such an EFT, the pion is a heavy degree of freedom whose effects are mimicked by contact terms. This EFT breaks down when external momenta are comparable to the pion mass, and pion exchange is resolved. This criterion does not automatically translate into a clear limit on the applicability of pionless EFT to finite nuclei; pionless EFT is successful for at least the ground states of the deuteron and triton, and its limits for heavier nuclei are not yet known (4).

However, given that the Fermi momentum k_F for the interior of heavy nuclei is about twice the pion mass, one expects that the pion would have to be treated as a long-range degree of freedom in a free-space EFT applicable to most nuclei. Chiral EFTs for nucleons incorporate the pion systematically as the (near) Goldstone boson of approximate and spontaneously broken chiral symmetry, expanding about the massless pion limit. The functional dependence on the QCD quark masses is captured in perturbation theory and the dependence on the strong coupling is contained in universal parameters to be determined from data or direct numerical calculations of QCD. Chiral EFT in nuclear physics originated with the seminal work of Weinberg and van Kolck and collaborators in the early 1990s (31–37), and the field has been active ever since (4–6).

Currently the most commonly applied chiral EFT Lagrangians have nonrelativistic nucleons and pions as degrees of freedom based on the "heavy-baryon" formalism, which eliminates anti-nucleons and organizes relativistic corrections (4). As usual, renormalization can be carried out because all interactions consistent with QCD symmetries are included, which allows regulator dependence to be absorbed. To organize the EFT in a systematic hierarchy we need a power counting, but the optimal scheme is not yet settled. Both practical and formal questions are being argued and different schemes are under investigation (38–42). In all cases, chiral symmetry dictates that pion interactions be accompanied by derivatives (because they are Goldstone bosons) or powers of the pion mass (Ward identity constraints from QCD), thus yielding ratios of characteristic momenta and m_π to the scale of excluded physics, such as heavier meson exchange, as expansion parameters. Relativistic corrections are organized in powers of momenta over the nucleon mass.

For applications to nuclear structure, an energy-independent nucleons-only potential is desirable (and required for many of the methods discussed below); it can be derived from the chiral Lagrangian by a unitary transformation method that decouples the nucleons from explicit pion fields, leaving static pion-exchange interactions and regulated contact terms (6). At present these potentials are organized by a power counting proposed by Weinberg, then iterated with either a Lippmann-Schwinger equation for two-body scattering or another nonperturbative method for bound-state properties with more nucleons. A momentum-space cutoff is used for technical reasons, which means that the advantages of dimensional regularization we saw for short-range interactions at finite density are not available.

For Weinberg power counting there is a formula analogous to Equation 11 that identifies the order in the EFT expansion at which a given term in the potential contributes. This formula yields a hierarchy of terms with increasing derivatives and pion exchanges and, perhaps most important for finite-density applications to be tractable, a hierarchy of many-body forces. At LO, there is one pion exchange and two no-derivative contact terms. The NLO adds the first two-pion exchange contributions, which are important for the mid-range nuclear attraction. At present, NN interactions go to up to N^3LO, which includes 24 constants for the contact terms (not including isospin violation) that are determined by fits to NN scattering. The best fits have a χ^2/dof comparable to the best phenomenological potentials (43, 44).

Three-nucleon forces (3NF) appear first at N^2LO and are shown on the left in **Figure 1**. There are parameters associated with long-range two-pion exchange (four constants fit to πN or NN scattering), mid-range one-pion exchange (one constant), and purely short-range (one constant) parts. The extension to N^3LO is in progress and involves many additional diagrams but no additional parameters. However, there are sizable uncertainties at present in determining the long-range 3NF parameters from πN or NN scattering, which translate into significant

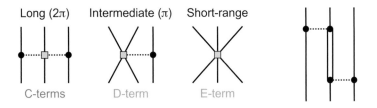

Long (2π)   **Intermediate (π)**   **Short-range**

C-terms   D-term   E-term

Figure 1

Leading three-body contributions in chiral effective field theory (EFT). *Left*: N²LO terms in an EFT without Δs (dashed line represents the pion). *Right*: NLO contribution with explicit Δs (*double line*). Abbreviation: NLO, next-to-leading-order.

uncertainties at finite density. The four-nucleon (4N) interaction appears first at N^3LO in the form of long-range pion exchange and is parameter free (45). The quantitative suppression of many-nucleon forces predicted by chiral power counting is consistent with binding-energy calculations in light nuclei (6, 46), but much remains to be tested in larger systems.

Even after we specify a power counting and the order in the expansion, there is no unique EFT potential because one can choose different cutoffs. Calculations of observables should be independent of the cutoff at the level of the truncation error determined by the missing orders. By comparing calculations with varied cutoffs one can test whether the EFT is working and then put a bound on the theoretical error. The precision EFT potentials currently available for nuclear structure have cutoffs in a rather narrow range close to the expected breakdown scale of the EFT, about 450–600 MeV (cf. the ρ or ω meson mass), which is consistent with the prescription of Lepage (47, 48). In practice, lower cutoffs mean large truncation errors (i.e., the expansion parameter q/Λ_c gets too small), whereas larger cutoffs create implementation problems with increasingly singular (at short distances) potentials from multiple pion exchange. Within this cutoff range there is no penalty for iterating subleading potential terms, which violates some power countings, because the truncation and iteration errors are the same size (4).

Recent surveys of ongoing applications of chiral potentials to scattering and to properties of few-body nuclei can be found in References 4 and 6. Among the developments most relevant to finite density is work to add the $\Delta(1232)$-isobar resonance explicitly to the chiral EFT Lagrangian; this research formed part of the original explorations by van Kolck et al. (35–37), but has only recently been reconsidered for energy-independent potentials (49, 50). The Δ is considered important because of its low excitation energy (the mass difference to the nucleon is about 300 MeV) and its strong coupling to the πN system. Including Δ would resum important contributions and improve the pattern of convergence. In this scheme, the leading 3NF term comes from pion exchange with an intermediate Δ (**Figure 1**, *right*) and appears at NLO. As this and other developments mature, in parallel there will be applications to finite nuclei. Indeed, because the energy-independent potentials take the same form as phenomenological nonlocal potentials, almost all conventional few- and many-body methods are immediately available.

3.2. Wave Function Methods

There are a wide variety of methods available to determine properties of few-body systems given an internucleon potential. Each in some way involves solving for the approximate wave function of the system. If we arbitrarily set the crossover from few-body to many-body nuclei at $A = 8$, the choice of methods dwindles to a few: Green's function Monte Carlo (GFMC), no-core shell model (NCSM), and coupled cluster (CC). The GFMC approach (51, 52) has had great success up to $A = 12$ (and extensions using auxiliary field methods promise to go much further), but is

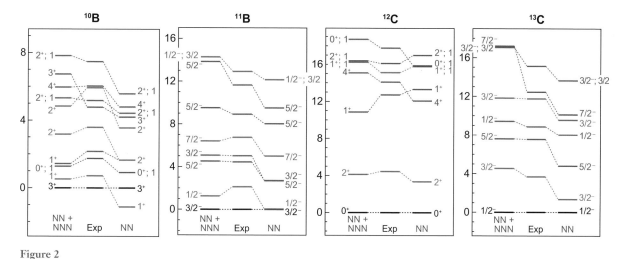

Figure 2

Excitation energies (in MeV) of selected levels in four p-shell nuclei (55) calculated using the N^{3}LO potential of Reference 43. Calculations with nucleon-nucleon- (NN-)only and with N^{3}LO NN plus N^{2}LO three-nucleon forces are compared to experiment. Abbreviation: NLO, next-to-leading-order.

limited at present to local potentials, i.e., diagonal in coordinate representation, which excludes current chiral EFT interactions. However, both the NCSM and CC methods are compatible with energy-independent chiral potentials including many-body forces (53, 54).

The NCSM diagonalizes the Hamiltonian in a harmonic oscillator basis with all nucleons active (hence no core). Lanczos methods allow the extraction of the lowest eigenvalues and eigenvectors from spaces up to dimension 10^9 (and growing, given the advances in computer hardware and software), but the matrix size grows rapidly with A and the maximum oscillator excitation energy $N_{max} \hbar \Omega$. For a given A, the convergence of observables with N_{max} depends strongly on the nature of the potential. Chiral EFT Hamiltonians are softer than conventional nuclear potentials (i.e., smaller high-momentum contributions, which means less coupling to high oscillator states), but adequate convergence with 3NF still requires too large a basis beyond the lightest nuclei. Therefore Lee-Suzuki transformations of the potential, which are unitary order by order in a cluster expansion, are applied to decouple included and excluded oscillator states, greatly reducing the size of the model space needed. This procedure has many demonstrated successes (53, 55) although there are drawbacks, such as distortions of long-range physics, problems with extrapolations of energies, and the loss of the variational principle (56).

Recent state-of-the-art NCSM calculations of excitation energies for four p-shell nuclei are shown in **Figure 2** for a single N^{3}LO potential with and without the N^{2}LO 3NF (55). (The mismatch in orders means that this calculation is not yet completely consistent from the EFT perspective.) It is evident that the fine structure of the nuclear spectra is uniformly improved with the three-body contribution. Of particular note is the ground state of ^{10}B and the splittings of spin-orbit partners throughout. The sensitivity of three-body parameters to particular observables (e.g., ^{6}Li quadrupole moment, the lowest 1^+ states in ^{10}B) suggests that fits of 3NF parameters will improve with input from more than $A = 3, 4$ systems (55).

How can we tell if an EFT-based interaction used by a wave function method is working as expected? One way is to do comparative calculations at different orders in the EFT with a range of cutoffs. Because cutoff variation is absorbed by the contact interactions, which scale as powers of the inverse cutoff, the relative variation of the potential energies over this range should decrease systematically according to the power of omitted contact interactions (and assuming a typical momentum scale ≈ 130 MeV). Binding-energy variations will be larger because of cancellations in nuclear systems, which amplify the role of higher orders (including many-body forces). Nogga has shown that such estimates are consistent with calculations in ^{3}H (57). For ^{4}He, he concludes that the EFT estimate of 2% for the ratio of 3NF to NN potential energies is consistent with observed ratios of roughly 5% (57), and preliminary calculations of the 4NF contribution were found to be as small as expected (46). All of these tests will need to be repeated for larger nuclei as reliable calculations become possible.

RG methods applied in free space to chiral EFT interactions are a promising means of calculating larger nuclei. These methods prescribe how each matrix element of the potential (and other operators) in a discretized momentum basis must evolve under changes in the resolution scale so that observables remain unchanged. (Because the potential is not an observable, we are always free to make unitary transformations.) The resolution scale is changed by lowering a cutoff in relative momentum ($V_{\text{low}\,k}$) (58), by using a flow equation for the Hamiltonian (similarity RG) (59) or by using tailored unitary transformations (UCOM) (60). The result is a decoupling of high- and low-momentum dependence without modification of long-distance interactions, leading to low-momentum potentials that are more perturbative, such that convergence in harmonic oscillator bases is dramatically accelerated (61). Such potentials can be applied without Lee-Suzuki transformations in the NCSM and can maintain the variational principle. Because the transformations are unitary, the EFT truncation error is unchanged, in contrast to the RG evolution of a chiral EFT at fixed order to low cutoff. However, the evolution of the NN potential is inevitably accompanied by the evolution of the three- and higher-body potentials. The latter has not yet been implemented but is instead approximated by fitting the N^2LO chiral interaction at each cutoff (62), which introduces a theoretical error.

These low-momentum potentials show great promise for the CC method, which has been highly developed in ab initio quantum chemistry but has only recently been revived for nuclear applications, including the development of CC theory for three-body Hamiltonians (54, 63). CC calculations are based on a potent exponential ansatz for the ground-state wave function $|\psi\rangle = e^{\hat{T}}|\phi\rangle$, where $|\phi\rangle$ is a simple reference state (typically a harmonic oscillator Slater determinant). The operator $\hat{T}$ is specified by amplitudes for a truncated sum of operators creating one-particle–one-hole, two-particle–two-hole, etc. excitations. The amplitudes are found from nonlinear equations whose solution scales vary gently with the size of the nucleus and model space.

As with the NCSM, convergence is accelerated with low-momentum potentials; particularly promising is the calculation of 3NF contributions, which are the most expensive component. The 3NF potential is rewritten in terms of normal-ordered creation and destruction operators with respect to $|\phi\rangle$ (instead of the vacuum), which recasts the 3NF into an expectation value in $|\phi\rangle$, one- and two-body pieces, and the remaining 3NF part. In the hierarchy of contributions to a CC calculation, only the last piece is expensive to calculate, but recent CC calculations of ^{4}He found it to be negligible (54). If this result persists for larger nuclei, calculations of $A = 100$ or beyond will be feasible in the near future! The present limit for NCSM is much lower, around $A = 16$, but could be extended using importance-sampling methods that select the most important basis states (64), if such methods can be implemented in a size-extensive way.

The NCSM and CC wave function methods apply EFT (and RG) only to create the input potential and not to solve the many-body problem. There is also the possibility of a more EFT-like treatment, such as the pioneering work to apply EFT to the shell model by Stetcu et al. (65). (See Reference 66 for a completely different application of EFT methods to the shell model.) These authors formulate an EFT in the harmonic oscillator basis, where the restricted model space generates all interactions consistent with the underlying symmetries. The parameters are directly determined in the model space rather than fitting in free space and transforming the interaction. The oscillator frequency sets an infrared cutoff $\lambda \sim \sqrt{M_N \hbar \Omega}$ whereas the UV cutoff is $\Lambda \sim \sqrt{M_N(N_{max} + 3/2)\hbar \Omega}$. Within each model space, a set of observables is used to fix the EFT parameters, then other observables are calculated. The EFT works if cutoff dependence decreases with decreasing λ and increasing Λ; in that case one makes an extrapolation to the continuum limit $\hbar \Omega \to 0$ with $N_{max} \to 0$ with Λ fixed. At the end, one takes $\Lambda \to \infty$. The first application with a pionless theory up to $A = 6$ is encouraging and motivates generalizations to the pionful theory and to other many-body methods (65).

3.3. Effective Field Theory on the Lattice

We have seen that chiral EFT potentials have been used successfully in connection with standard numerical many-body approaches such as CC or the NCSM. A disadvantage of these methods is that they rely on the existence of a potential, which is not an observable, and as a consequence scheme and renormalization scale invariance are not manifest. A numerical few- and many-body method that is based directly on the effective Lagrangian is the Euclidean lattice path integral Monte Carlo method. Euclidean lattice calculations are standard in the context of QCD but, except for some isolated attempts (67, 68), have been applied in nuclear physics only recently (69–71).

In the following paragraphs we introduce the Euclidean lattice method in the case of a simple s-wave contact interaction $\mathcal{L} = -C_0(\psi^\dagger \psi)^2/2$. More sophisticated interactions involving higher partial-wave terms and explicit pions are discussed in Reference 72. The usual strategy for dealing with the four-fermion interaction is to use a Hubbard-Stratonovich transformation. The partition function can be written (69) as

$$Z = \int Ds \, Dc \, Dc^* \, \exp[-S],\qquad 36.$$

where s is the Hubbard-Stratonovich field and c is a Grassmann field. S is a discretized Euclidean action

$$S = \sum_{n,i} \left[e^{-\hat{\mu}\alpha_t} c_i^*(\mathbf{n})c_i(\mathbf{n}+\hat{\mathbf{0}}) - e^{\sqrt{-C_0\alpha_t}s(\mathbf{n})+\frac{C_0\alpha_t}{2}}(1-6h)c_i^*(\mathbf{n})c_i(\mathbf{n}) \right]$$

$$- h \sum_{n,l_s,i} [c_i^*(\mathbf{n})c_i(\mathbf{n}+\hat{\mathbf{l}}_s) + c_i^*(\mathbf{n})c_i(\mathbf{n}-\hat{\mathbf{l}}_s)] + \frac{1}{2}\sum_n s^2(\mathbf{n}).\qquad 37.$$

Here i labels spin and $\mathbf{n}$ labels lattice sites. Spatial and temporal unit vectors are denoted by $\hat{\mathbf{l}}_s$ and $\hat{\mathbf{0}}$, respectively. The temporal and spatial lattice spacings are b_τ and b, and the dimensionless chemical potential is given by $\hat{\mu} = \mu b_\tau$. We define α_t as the ratio of the temporal and spatial lattice spacings and $h = \alpha_t/(2\hat{m})$. The action (37) is quadratic in the fermion fields, and can be simulated using a variety of methods such as determinant or hybrid Monte Carlo. Note that for $C_0 < 0$ the action is real and importance sampling is possible.

The four-fermion coupling is fixed by computing the sum of all particle-particle bubbles as in Section 2.3, but with the elementary loop function regularized on the lattice. Schematically,

$$\frac{m}{4\pi a_0} = \frac{1}{C_0} + \frac{1}{2}\sum_p \frac{1}{E_p},\qquad 38.$$

where the sum runs over discrete momenta on the lattice and E_p is the lattice dispersion relation. A detailed discussion of the lattice regularized scattering amplitude can be found in References 69, 74, and 75. For a given scattering length a_0 the four-fermion coupling is a function of the lattice

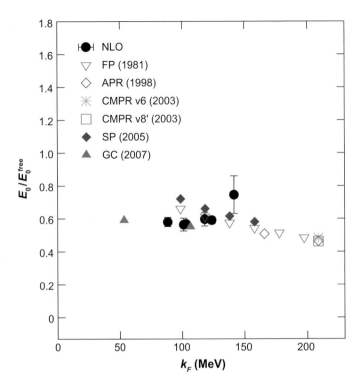

Figure 3

Lattice results for the energy per particle of a dilute Fermi gas from Borasoy et al. (72, 73). We show the energy per particle in units of the same ratio for the free system as a function of the Fermi momentum. The solid dots represent the lattice results. For comparison, we also show results from wave function–based many-body calculations (72). Abbreviation: NLO, next-to-leading-order.

spacing. The continuum limit corresponds to taking the temporal and spatial lattice spacings b_τ, b to zero,

$$b_\tau \mu \to 0, \quad b n^{1/3} \to 0, \tag{39.}$$

keeping $a_0 n^{1/3}$ fixed. Here μ is the chemical potential and n is the density. Numerical results for the energy per particle of dilute neutron matter are shown in **Figure 3**. We observe that the results agree quite well with traditional many-body calculations. We also note that even when higher-order corrections are taken into account, the equation of state exhibits approximate universal behavior, with an effective $\xi \simeq (0.5-0.6)$. For applications of the lattice method to finite nuclei, see Reference 76.

3.4. Perturbative Effective Field Theory for Nuclear Matter

The nuclear calculations discussed so far have all been nonperturbative. However, RG methods have been used to show that the perturbativeness of internucleon interactions depends strongly on the momentum cutoff and the density (58, 77). Lowering the resolution via an RG evolution leaves observables and EFT truncation errors unchanged by construction (up to approximation errors and omitted many-body contributions) but shifts contributions between the potential and the sums over intermediate states in loop integrals. These shifts can weaken or even eliminate sources of nonperturbative behavior such as strong short-range repulsion (e.g., from singular

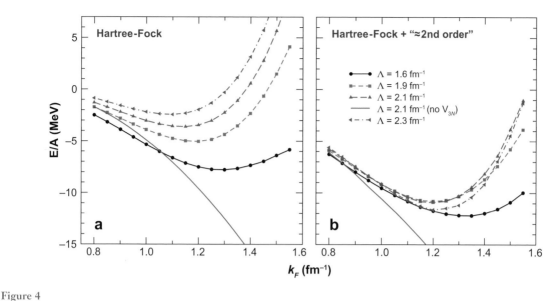

Figure 4

Nuclear matter energy per particle using renormalization-group evolved low-momentum potentials with a range of cutoffs with three-nucleon forces fit to few-body binding energies (78).

chiral two-pion exchange) or the tensor force. At sufficient density, effective range corrections and beyond suppress the effects of large s-wave scattering lengths (78).

Consequently, although nuclear matter is generally considered to be nonperturbative, it is also resolution dependent. **Figure 4** shows the energy per particle in nuclear matter for several values of the RG cutoff Λ calculated in leading-order (Hartree-Fock) and second-order many-body perturbation theory (78). (Note: The initial potential used in these figures is not a chiral EFT NN potential. However, all NN potentials fit to scattering phase shifts flow to very similar low-momentum potentials by this range of cutoffs, so similar results are expected.) The three-body potential is of the N^2LO form, fit at each cutoff to the binding energies of the triton and ^{4}He. As the RG only changes short-distance physics, the procedure for determining the 3NF is argued to be a good approximation to the consistently evolved 3NF (62).

There are several encouraging features of perturbative many-body calculations with RG evolved potentials. First, Hartree-Fock is a reasonable starting point for the description of nuclear matter; this is patently false for conventional phenomenological potentials, which do not even bind. Second, the dependence on the cutoff is greatly reduced going to second order. Further calculations show that the third-order ladder diagrams make a very small contribution (78). Third, with a fit to few-body properties, the minimum is reasonably close to the empirical saturation point of (roughly) 16 MeV per particle with $k_F \approx 1.35$ fm^{-1} (indeed, the discrepancy is the order of uncertainties in the three-body force). These results motivate a program to study nuclear matter with chiral EFT internucleon forces evolved to lower resolution (which should also include studying unevolved chiral EFT potentials fit with a lower cutoff).

The increased perturbativeness in nuclear matter with increased density and lower cutoff can be understood physically from reduced phase space due to Pauli blocking and the cutoff, combined with the favorable momentum dependence of the low-momentum interaction (77, 78). Pauli blocking means that particles with momenta below k_F must forward scatter (Hartree-Fock) or be excited out of the Fermi sea. The latter amplitude is limited by the weakened coupling of occupied and unoccupied states, which in turn limits the volume of available momentum states (this is the phase space restriction). A consequence is that the saturation mechanism is now dominated by the three-body force contribution (cf. the NN-only curves in the figure), rather than by the density dependence of two-body tensor contributions. For cutoffs in the range shown, the three-body contribution still remains natural-sized according to chiral EFT power counting (78), but it is clearly quantitatively important. The implication is that the 4NF contribution will also be important at the level of about 1 MeV per particle at saturation, but this conjecture has yet to be tested.

These results suggest that an alternative EFT power counting may be appropriate at nuclear matter densities. Kaiser and collaborators have proposed a perturbative chiral EFT approach to nuclear matter and then to finite nuclei through an energy functional (79–81; see also 82, 84). They consider Lagrangians both for nucleons and pions and for nucleons, pions, and Δs, and fit parameters to nuclear saturation properties. They construct a loop expansion for the nuclear matter energy per particle, which leads to an energy expansion of the form

$$E(k_F) = \sum_{n=2}^{\infty} k_F^n \, f_n(k_F/m_\pi, \, \Delta/m_\pi), \quad [\Delta = M_\Delta - M_N \approx 300\,\text{MeV}] \qquad 40.$$

where each f_n is determined from a finite number of in-medium Feynman diagrams. All powers of k_F/m_π and Δ/m_π are kept in the f_ns because these ratios are not small quantities (83). A semi-quantitative description of nuclear matter is found even with just the lowest two terms without Δs, and adding Δs brings uniform improvement (e.g., in the neutron matter equation of state). There remain open questions about power counting and convergence, and there are many promising avenues to pursue.

3.5. Density Functional Theory as an Effective Field Theory

DFT (85–87) is widely used in condensed-matter and quantum chemistry to treat large many-body systems. It is based on the response of the ground-state energy to external perturbations of the density, with fermion densities as the fundamental variables. This means that the computational cost for DFT is far less than for wave function methods, and the calculations can be applied to heavy nuclei. DFT is naturally formulated in an effective action framework (88) and is carried out using an inversion method implemented with EFT power counting (89–91).

The simple prototype EFT for a dilute system (see Section 2) can be revisited in DFT by placing the fermions in a trap potential $v_{\text{ext}}(\mathbf{x})$ (e.g., a harmonic oscillator) and adding sources coupled to external densities (92). Consider a single external source $J(\mathbf{x})$ coupled to the density operator $\hat{\rho}(x) \equiv \psi^\dagger(x)\psi(x)$ in the partition function (neglecting normalization and factors of the temperature and volume and suppressing v_{ext}),

$$\mathcal{Z}[J] = e^{-W[J]} \sim \text{Tr}\, e^{-\beta(\hat{H}+J\hat{\rho})} \sim \int \mathcal{D}[\psi^\dagger]\mathcal{D}[\psi]\, e^{-\int[\mathcal{L}+J\psi^\dagger\psi]}, \qquad 41.$$

with the Lagrangian from Section 2.1. The static density $\rho(\mathbf{x})$ in the presence of $J(\mathbf{x})$ is

$$\rho(\mathbf{x}) \equiv \langle \hat{\rho}(\mathbf{x}) \rangle_J = \frac{\delta W[J]}{\delta J(\mathbf{x})}, \qquad 42.$$

which we invert to find $J[\rho]$ and then Legendre transform from J to ρ:

$$\Gamma[\rho] = -W[J] + \int d^3x J(\mathbf{x})\rho(\mathbf{x}) \quad \text{with} \quad J(\mathbf{x}) = \frac{\delta \Gamma[\rho]}{\delta \rho(\mathbf{x})} \rightarrow \left.\frac{\delta \Gamma[\rho]}{\delta \rho(\mathbf{x})}\right|_{\rho_{\text{gs}}(\mathbf{x})} = 0. \qquad 43.$$

For static $\rho(\mathbf{x})$, $\Gamma[\rho]$ is proportional to the Hohenberg-Kohn energy functional, which by Equation 43 is extremized at the ground state density $\rho_{\text{gs}}(\mathbf{x})$.

With $W[J]$ constructed as a diagrammatic expansion, EFT power counting provides us with a means of inverting from $W[J]$ to $\Gamma[\rho]$ (89, 90). It proceeds by substituting the decomposition $J(\mathbf{x}) = J_0(\mathbf{x}) + J_1(\mathbf{x}) + J_2(\mathbf{x}) + \ldots$ (where 1 stands for LO, 2 stands for NLO, and so on) and corresponding expansions for W and Γ into Equation 43 and matching order by order with ρ treated as order unity. Here J_0 is chosen so that there are no corrections to the zeroth order density at each order in the expansion; the interpretation is that J_0 is the external potential that yields for a noninteracting system the exact density of the interacting system. Zeroth order is the noninteracting system with potential $J_0(x)$,

$$\Gamma_0[\rho] = -W_0[J_0] + \int d^3x \, J_0(\mathbf{x})\rho(\mathbf{x}) \Rightarrow \rho(\mathbf{x}) = \frac{\delta W_0[J_0]}{\delta J_0(\mathbf{x})}, \qquad 44.$$

which is the so-called Kohn-Sham system with the exact density! To evaluate $W_0[J_0]$, we introduce orbitals $\{\psi_\alpha\}$ satisfying (with v_{ext} made explicit)

$$\left[-\frac{\nabla^2}{2M} + v_{\text{ext}}(\mathbf{x}) - J_0(\mathbf{x}) \right] \psi_\alpha(\mathbf{x}) = \varepsilon_\alpha \psi_\alpha(\mathbf{x}), \qquad 45.$$

which diagonalizes W_0, so that it yields a sum of ε_αs for the occupied states. We calculate the W_is and Γ_is up to a given order as functionals of J_0 and then determine J_0 for the ground state via a self-consistency loop:

$$J_0 \to W_1 \to \Gamma_1 \to J_1 \to W_2 \to \Gamma_2 \to \cdots \Rightarrow J_0(\mathbf{x})|_{\rho=\rho_{\text{gs}}} = \left. \frac{\delta \Gamma_{\text{interacting}}[\rho]}{\delta \rho(\mathbf{x})} \right|_{\rho=\rho_{\text{gs}}}. \qquad 46.$$

Adding sources coupled to other currents improves the functional variationally and allows pairing to be treated within the same framework (93, 94).

Figure 5 shows how EFT power-counting estimates predict the hierarchy of contributions to a DFT energy functional. Shown at left are the results for the energy per particle of $A = 140$ fermions in a trap with short-range repulsive interactions. The a priori estimates from terms at three different orders in the EFT expansion (the counterparts to the terms in Equation 2 plus gradient corrections) are shown with error bars that reflect a natural range for the unknown coefficients (in this case from 1/2 to 2). These are compared to actual values, with good agreement (93). A similar exercise using a chiral EFT–inspired power counting has been applied to phenomenological nonrelativistic (Skyrme) and covariant density functionals. Results for terms organized by powers of the density in each term are shown on the right in **Figure 5** and show that the predicted hierarchy is realized (91, 95).

The apparent success of many-body perturbation theory for nuclear matter using low-momentum potentials RG-evolved from chiral EFT input enables the construction of a nuclear DFT functional in the effective action formalism that is compatible with nonrelativistic Skyrme energy functional technology (96, 97). A large-scale five-year project to develop a universal nuclear energy density functional (UNEDF) that will cover the entire table of nuclides (98) is under way. The goal is to generate systematically improved energy functionals based on chiral EFT/RG input potentials, including theoretical error estimates so that extrapolation to the driplines is under control.

The density matrix expansion (DME) of Negele & Vautherin (99, 100) has been extended to three-body force contributions and applied in momentum space to provide the first-generation functional (91, 101). This construction is facilitated by analytic expressions for the long-range pion contributions derived by Kaiser et al. (80, 81). The functional has the form of a generalized Skyrme functional with density-dependent coefficients, including all allowed terms up to two derivatives, which means it can be directly incorporated into existing computer codes. Cutoff dependence can be used as a diagnostic tool for assessing missing elements of the interaction, the many-body

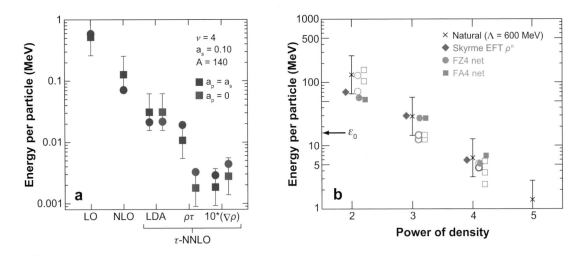

Figure 5

Estimates for energy functionals for a dilute fermion in a harmonic trap (*a*) and three phenomenological energy functionals for nuclei (*b*).

approximations, and the performance of the energy functional. It is possible to benchmark against NCSM and CC calculations for light- and medium-mass nuclei by calculating the energy with an additional external field, i.e., putting the nuclei in theoretically adjustable traps.

4. SUMMARY AND OUTLOOK

EFT is a well-established technique with demonstrated success in all branches of physics. Applications of EFT to finite-density systems have many precursors going back decades, but implementations are relatively recent. Many-body systems with short-range interactions are an ideal testing ground for many-body EFT because of the universal nature of the systems and the connection to experiment through cold atom physics.

Far less developed is the application of EFT methods to nuclear many-body systems. The immediate impact of EFT on nuclear many-body calculations is through the systematic organization of effective Hamiltonians for low-energy QCD using chiral EFT. Of particular importance is the role of many-body forces. We emphasize that although these Hamiltonians have been successful in describing scattering and properties of light nuclei, they are largely untested at the densities that are relevant for most nuclei and nuclear matter. Fortunately, computational tools such as the NCSM, CC, and lattice methods, RG techniques, and DFT will funnel advances in chiral EFT to new predictions, so that true tests are forthcoming. More direct applications of EFT methods to many-body calculations are in their infancy, but there are clear incentives to pursue them.

This has necessarily been a shallow survey, but the breadth of activity should be clear. Key developments are expected in the next few years. These include improvements to the chiral EFT potentials such as full N^3LO three-body interactions and the corresponding N^3LO Hamiltonian with Δ degrees of freedom and the subsequent testing of power counting in light- to medium-mass systems. In addition, the consistent evolution of many-body forces with RG methods will open the door to the full range of nuclei and nuclear matter.

Beyond the calculational tools, EFT provides a new perspective for nuclear many-body calculations. Whereas traditionally one sought a universal Hamiltonian for all problem and energy length scales, EFT exploits the infinite number of low-energy potentials: Rather than finding the "best" potential, we use a convenient or efficient one or work directly from a Lagrangian. For a long time it was hoped that two-body data would be sufficient for nuclear systems; many-body forces were treated as a last resort, to be considered as an add-on. In EFT it is inevitable that many-body forces and data are needed and that they are directly tied to the two-body interaction. Whereas researchers used to avoid divergences and hide them in form factors, with EFT they now confront and exploit them (e.g., using cutoff dependence as a tool). Finally, instead of choosing diagrams to sum by "art," power counting determines what to sum and establishes theoretical truncation errors.

Many relevant and interesting topics were not treated here because of space limitations. Two major (related) areas largely unaddressed are (*a*) the response to external probes and (*b*) nuclear reactions. Another area is EFT at high temperature for many-body systems with large scattering length, which has been formulated using the virial expansion (102, 103) (see References 104 and 105 for recent applications of the virial expansion to hot dilute nuclear matter). The EFT formulation of the finite temperature nuclear many-body system with long-range pion interaction is a frontier. Other nuclear systems wherein EFT can play a particular role are hypernuclei (57) and halo nuclei (106). Work to apply EFT methods to covariant hadronic field theories strives to understand the successes of relativistic mean-field phenomenology (107). Finally, there is the challenge of making the connection to lattice QCD (108) (as opposed to EFT on the lattice).

DISCLOSURE STATEMENT

The authors are not aware of any biases that might be perceived as affecting the objectivity of this review.

ACKNOWLEDGMENTS

This work was supported in part by the National Science Foundation under grant nos. PHY-0354916 and PHY-0653312, the Department of Energy under grant no. DE-FG02-03ER4126, and the UNEDF SciDAC Collaboration under DOE grant DE-FC02-07ER41457.

LITERATURE CITED

1. Natl. Res. Counc. *Nuclear Physics: The Core of Matter, the Fuel of Stars.* Washington, DC: Natl. Acad. (1999)
2. Burgess CP. *Annu. Rev. Nucl. Part. Sci.* 57:329 (2007)
3. Bernard V, Meißner U-G. *Annu. Rev. Nucl. Part. Sci.* 57:33 (2007)
4. Bedaque PF, van Kolck U. *Annu. Rev. Nucl. Part. Sci.* 52:339 (2002)
5. Beane SR, et al. nucl-th/0008064 (2000)
6. Epelbaum E. *Prog. Part. Nucl. Phys.* 57:654 (2006)
7. Fetter AL, Walecka JD. *Quantum Many-Particle Systems.* New York: McGraw-Hill (1971)
8. Hammer HW, Furnstahl RJ. *Nucl. Phys. A* 678:277 (2000)
9. Negele JW, Orland H. *Quantum Many-Particle Systems.* Redwood City, CA: Addison-Wesley (1988)
10. Braaten E, Nieto A. *Phys. Rev. B* 56:14745 (1997)
11. Pines D. *The Theory of Quantum Liquids.* Menlo Park, CA: Addison-Wesley (1966)
12. Baym G, Pethick C. *Landau Fermi Liquid Theory.* New York: Wiley (1991)
13. Abrikosov AA, Gorkov LP, Dzyaloshinski IE. *Methods of Quantum Field Theory in Statistical Physics.* Englewood Cliffs, NJ: Prentice Hall (1963)
14. Shankar R. *Rev. Mod. Phys.* 66:129 (1994)
15. Polchinski J. hep-th/9210046 (1992)
16. Papenbrock T, Bertsch GF. *Phys. Rev. C* 59:2052 (1999)

17. Marini M, Pistolesi F, Strinati GC. *Eur. Phys. J. B* 1:151 (1998)
18. Wambach J, Ainsworth TL, Pines D. *Nucl. Phys. A* 555:128 (1993)
19. Gorkov LP, Melik-Barkhudarov TK. *Sov. Phys. JETP* 13:1018 (1961)
20. Schwenk A, Friman B, Brown GE. *Nucl. Phys. A* 713:191 (2003)
21. Kaplan DB, Savage MJ, Wise MB. *Nucl. Phys. B* 534:329 (1998)
22. Regal C. *Experimental realization of BCS-BEC crossover physics with a Fermi gas of atoms*. PhD thesis. Univ. Colo., Boulder (2005)
23. Furnstahl RJ, Hammer HW. *Ann. Phys.* 302:206 (2002)
24. Nikolic P, Sachdev S. *Phys. Rev. A* 75:033608 (2007)
25. Steele JV. nucl-th/0010066 (2000)
26. Schäfer T, Kao CW, Cotanch SR. *Nucl. Phys. A* 762:82 (2005)
27. Rupak G. nucl-th/0605074 (2006)
28. Nussinov Z, Nussinov S. *Phys. Rev. A* 74:053622 (2006)
29. Nishida Y, Son DT. *Phys. Rev. Lett.* 97:050403 (2006)
30. Arnold P, Drut JE, Son DT. *Phys. Rev. A* 75:043605 (2007)
31. Weinberg S. *Phys. Lett. B* 251:288 (1990)
32. Weinberg S. *Nucl. Phys. B* 363:3 (1991)
33. Ordonez C, van Kolck U. *Phys. Lett. B* 291:459 (1992)
34. Weinberg S. *Phys. Lett. B* 295:114 (1992)
35. Ordonez C, Ray L, van Kolck U. *Phys. Rev. Lett.* 72:1982 (1994)
36. van Kolck U. *Phys. Rev. C* 49:2932 (1994)
37. Ordonez C, Ray L, van Kolck U. *Phys. Rev. C* 53:2086 (1996)
38. Beane SR, Bedaque PF, Savage MJ, van Kolck U. *Nucl. Phys. A* 700:377 (2002)
39. Nogga A, Timmermans RGE, van Kolck U. *Phys. Rev. C* 72:054006 (2005)
40. Birse MC. *Phys. Rev. C* 74:014003 (2006)
41. Epelbaum E, Meißner U-G. nucl-th/0609037 (2006)
42. Pavon Valderrama M, Ruiz Arriola E. *Phys. Lett. B* 580:149 (2004)
43. Entem DR, Machleidt R. *Phys. Rev. C* 68:041001 (2003)
44. Epelbaum E, Glockle W, Meißner U-G. *Nucl. Phys. A* 747:362 (2005)
45. Epelbaum E. *Eur. Phys. J. A* 34:197 (2007)
46. Rozpedzik D, et al. *Acta Phys. Polon. B* 37:2889 (2006)
47. Lepage GP. In *Proc. TASI 1989: From Actions to Answers*, ed. T DeGrand, D. Toussaint, 23 pp. Singapore: World Sci. (1990)
48. Lepage GP. nucl-th/9706029 (1997)
49. Krebs H, Epelbaum E, Meißner U-G. *Eur. Phys. J. A* 32:127 (2007)
50. Epelbaum E, Krebs H, Meißner U-G. arXiv:0712.1969 (2007)
51. Pieper SC. *Nucl. Phys. A* 751:516 (2005)
52. Pieper SC. arXiv:0711.1500 (2007)
53. Nogga A, Navratil P, Barrett BR, Vary JP. *Phys. Rev. C* 73:064002 (2006)
54. Hagen G, et al. *Phys. Rev. C* 76:044305 (2007)
55. Navratil P, et al. *Phys. Rev. Lett.* 99:042501 (2007)
56. Stetcu I, Barrett BR, Navratil P, Vary JP. *Phys. Rev. C* 73:037307 (2006)
57. Nogga A. nucl-th/0611081 (2006)
58. Bogner SK, Kuo TTS, Schwenk A. *Phys. Rep.* 386:1 (2003)
59. Bogner SK, Furnstahl RJ, Perry RJ. *Phys. Rev. C* 75:061001 (2007)
60. Roth R, et al. *Phys. Rev. C* 72:034002 (2005)
61. Bogner SK, et al. *Nucl. Phys. A* 801:21 (2008)
62. Nogga A, Bogner SK, Schwenk A. *Phys. Rev. C* 70:061002 (2004)
63. Hagen G, et al. *Phys. Rev. C* 76:034302 (2007)
64. Roth R, Navratil P. *Phys. Rev. Lett.* 99:092501 (2007)
65. Stetcu I, Barrett BR, van Kolck U. *Phys. Lett. B* 653:358 (2007)
66. Haxton WC. arXiv:0710.0289 (2007)
67. Brockmann R, Frank J. *Phys. Rev. Lett.* 68:1830 (1992)

68. Muller HM, Koonin SE, Seki R, van Kolck U. *Phys. Rev. C* 61:044320 (2000)
69. Lee D, Schäfer T. *Phys. Rev. C* 72:024006 (2005)
70. Lee D, Schäfer T. *Phys. Rev. C* 73:015202 (2006)
71. Seki R, van Kolck U. *Phys. Rev. C* 73:044006 (2006)
72. Borasoy B, et al. arXiv:0712.2990 (2007)
73. Borasoy B, Epelbaum E, Krebs H, Lee D, Meissner U-G. nucl-th/0712.2993 (2007)
74. Chen JW, Kaplan DB. *Phys. Rev. Lett.* 92:257002 (2004)
75. Beane SR, Bedaque PF, Parreno A, Savage MJ. *Phys. Lett. B* 585:106 (2004)
76. Borasoy B, et al. *Eur. Phys. J. A* 31:105 (2007)
77. Bogner SK, Furnstahl RJ, Ramanan S, Schwenk A. *Nucl. Phys. A* 773:203 (2006)
78. Bogner SK, Schwenk A, Furnstahl RJ, Nogga A. *Nucl. Phys. A* 763:59 (2005)
79. Kaiser N, Fritsch S, Weise W. *Nucl. Phys. A* 697:255 (2002)
80. Kaiser N, Fritsch S, Weise W. *Nucl. Phys. A* 724:47 (2003)
81. Fritsch S, Kaiser N, Weise W. *Nucl. Phys. A* 750:259 (2005)
82. Lutz M, Friman B, Appel C. *Phys. Lett. B* 474:7 (2000)
83. Kaiser N, Muhlbauer M, Weise W. *Eur. Phys. J. A* 31:53 (2007)
84. Saviankou P, Krewald S, Epelbaum E, Meissner U-G. nucl-th/0802.3782 (2008)
85. Dreizler RM, Gross E. *Density Functional Theory.* Berlin: Springer-Verlag (1990)
86. Argaman N, Makov G. *Am. J. Phys.* 68:69 (2000)
87. Fiolhais C, Nogueira F, Marques M, eds. *A Primer in Density Functional Theory.* Berlin: Springer-Verlag (2003)
88. Polonyi J, Sailer K. *Phys. Rev. B* 66:155113 (2002)
89. Fukuda R, Kotani T, Suzuki Y, Yokojima S. *Prog. Theor. Phys.* 92:833 (1994)
90. Valiev M, Fernando GW. *Phys. Lett. A* 227:265 (1997)
91. Furnstahl RJ. nucl-th/0702040 (2007)
92. Puglia SJ, Bhattacharyya A, Furnstahl RJ. *Nucl. Phys. A* 723:145 (2003)
93. Bhattacharyya A, Furnstahl RJ. *Nucl. Phys. A* 747:268 (2005)
94. Furnstahl RJ, Hammer HW, Puglia SJ. *Ann. Phys.* 322:2703 (2007)
95. Furnstahl RJ. *J. Phys. G* 31:S1357 (2005)
96. Dobaczewski J, Nazarewicz W, Reinhard PG. *Nucl. Phys. A* 693:361 (2001)
97. Bender M, Heenen PH, Reinhard PG. *Rev. Mod. Phys.* 75:121 (2003)
98. Bertsch GF, Dean DJ, Nazarewicz W. *SciDAC Rev.* 6:42 (2007)
99. Negele JW, Vautherin D. *Phys. Rev. C* 5:1472 (1972)
100. Negele JW, Vautherin D. *Phys. Rev. C* 11:1031 (1975)
101. Bogner SK, Furnstahl RJ, Platter L. Manuscript in preparation (2008)
102. Bedaque PF, Rupak G. *Phys. Rev. B* 67:174513 (2003)
103. Rupak G. *Phys. Rev. Lett.* 98:090403 (2007)
104. Horowitz CJ, Schwenk A. *Nucl. Phys. A* 776:55 (2006)
105. Horowitz CJ, Schwenk A. *Phys. Lett. B* 638:153 (2006)
106. Bertulani CA, Hammer HW, Van Kolck U. *Nucl. Phys. A* 712:37 (2002)
107. Furnstahl RJ. *Lect. Notes Phys.* 641:1 (2004)
108. Savage MJ. nucl-th/0611038 (2006)

Nuclear Many-Body Scattering Calculations with the Coulomb Interaction

A. Deltuva,[1] A.C. Fonseca,[1] and P.U. Sauer[2]

[1]Centro de Física Nuclear da Universidade de Lisboa, P-1649-003 Lisboa, Portugal;
email: deltuva@cii.fc.ul.pt; fonseca@cii.fc.ul.pt

[2]Institut für Theoretische Physik, Leibniz Universität Hannover, D-30167 Hannover, Germany;
email: sauer@itp.uni-hannover.de

Annu. Rev. Nucl. Part. Sci. 2008. 58:27–49

The *Annual Review of Nuclear and Particle Science* is online at nucl.annualreviews.org

This article's doi:
10.1146/annurev.nucl.58.110707.171203

Key Words

Coulomb interaction, screening and renormalization, momentum-space scattering equations, three-nucleon, four-nucleon, nuclear reactions

Abstract

Recent progress in the solution of three- and four-particle scattering equations including the Coulomb interaction is reviewed. The method of screening and renormalization in the framework of momentum-space integral equations is used and its reliability demonstrated. We also review results for observables in three- and four-nucleon scattering as well as applications to nuclear reactions that display three-body degrees of freedom.

Contents

1. INTRODUCTION

Microscopic studies of nuclear structure and nuclear reactions assume, as nuclear constituents, point-like nucleons that interact nonrelativistically by means of a two-nucleon (2N) force and additional many-nucleon forces when necessary. The interactions among nucleons cannot yet be uniquely derived from first principles. Owing to the nonperturbative nature of quantum chromo-dynamics (QCD) at low energy, the interaction between hadrons has to be defined phenomeno-logically. This definition is still ambiguous and has led to two conceptually different approaches.

2N potential forms, mediated by meson exchange, are fitted to the same deuteron properties and nucleon-nucleon (NN) elastic scattering data up to laboratory energies $E_{Lab} \leq 350$ MeV, usually with high precision (χ^2/degree of freedom ∼1). Potentials of this type are Nijmegen (1), Argonne V18 (2), and CD-Bonn (3). Irreducible three-nucleon (3N) forces such as Urbana IX (4), Tucson-Melbourne (5), and Brazil (6) are added, extending the 2N phenomenology to the 3N system. Nevertheless, the definitions of 2N and 3N potentials are not fully consistent. Still in the framework of meson-exchange potentials, the coupled-channel approach to the NN interaction— explicitly allowing the excitation of a nucleon to a Δ isobar—represents the first attempt to obtain consistent 2N and 3N forces. An example of this approach is the CD-Bonn + Δ potential (7), which also has a precise fit to the NN data with χ^2/degree of freedom ∼1.

The modern approach to consistency between 2N and 3N forces is based on QCD-inspired effective field theory (EFT) (8). This theory is derived from a local Lagrangian with nucleon and pion fields and all possible interactions consistent with the (broken) chiral symmetry of QCD. In the framework of EFT, researchers have developed 2N and 3N forces (9–11) that are consistent with each other and that satisfy a hierarchy in terms of a power counting scheme; however, they also have to be fitted to the NN data like the meson-exchange potentials discussed before.

Although all these potentials share a common treatment of the one pion–exchange (OPE) inter-action and are fitted to the same low-energy data, each displays different short-distance behavior and high-momentum components. Therefore, the ultimate test for these hadronic interactions in the form of 2N-plus-3N force models is how well they describe nuclear-bound and excited states as well as scattering observables resulting from nuclear collisions. This test requires not only sophis-ticated theoretical tools to handle the nonrelativistic quantum-mechanical many-body problem for the chosen nuclear interactions, but also the ability to include the long-range Coulomb force between charged particles.

The Coulomb repulsion between protons can easily be included into bound-state calculations, but it constitutes a severe conceptual problem in many-body scattering calculations. Therefore, al-though at present there exist numerous successful microscopic structure calculations using Green's function Monte Carlo (GFMC) methods (12, 13) and No-Core Shell Model techniques (14) up to nuclei of mass $A = 12$, ab initio studies of nuclear reactions are still limited to a small number of specific few-nucleon systems. The greater complexity involved in the solution of n-body scattering equations ($n > 2$), together with the difficulties associated with the presence of the long-range Coulomb force between the protons, has until recently restricted precise three-body calculations to neutron-deuteron (n-d) elastic scattering and breakup (15), proton-deuteron (p-d) elastic scattering (16), and p-d capture (17) at low energies. Likewise, four-body scattering was restricted to four-nucleon (4N) calculations of neutron-^{3}H (n-^{3}H) (18) and proton-^{3}He (p-^{3}He) (19) elastic observables at low energies. Most p-d data at energies above breakup threshold were analyzed through n-d calculations wherein the Coulomb force was neglected (15, 20). An obvious consequence of such limited analyses is that large discrepancies between data and theory, such as those observed in p-d breakup or three-body photodisintegration of ^{3}He, cannot be attributed solely to the inadequacy of the nuclear force models used in the calculations, but also to the neglect of the Coulomb repulsion between the protons. This serious drawback has now been overcome, enabling detailed analyses of the abundant p-d data with realistic calculations that have the same degree of accuracy as the equivalent n-d calculations.

In this article, we review the recent progress that has been achieved on the precise treatment of the Coulomb force in ab initio 3N (21–24) and 4N (25–27) calculations in the framework of momentum-space n-body scattering equations. Investigations have also progressed in the treatment of complex nuclear reactions, where few-body degrees of freedom are dominant. One example is d-α (28) elastic scattering and breakup below the ^{3}H + ^{3}He threshold, where three particles ($p + n + \alpha$) interact through real potentials. The same technical developments have also been applied to d-^{12}C, d-^{58}Ni, and ^{11}Be-p scattering (29), where ^{12}C, ^{58}Ni, and ^{10}Be nuclei are taken as inert cores and optical potentials are used between some of the pairs. Our proposed method is general enough to accommodate any number of charged particles of the same sign, but it is restricted to elastic, transfer, and breakup reactions where no more than two charged objects (nucleons or nuclei) appear in the exit channel.

In contrast to the hadronic interactions mentioned above, the Coulomb potential between two charged particles presents a significant challenge for the theoretical description of many-body reactions, including the simplest three-body system for which there is a well-established theoretical framework (30) based on the Faddeev equation (31) or the equivalent Alt, Grassberger, and Sandhas (AGS) equations (32). The Coulomb interaction is well known; however, due to its $1/r$ behavior, it does not satisfy the mathematical properties required for the formulation of standard scattering theory. When the theoretical description of three-particle scattering is attempted in integral form, the Coulomb interaction renders the standard equations ill defined: The kernel of the equations is noncompact. When the theoretical description is based on differential equations, the asymptotic boundary conditions for the wave function must be numerically imposed on the trial solutions; in the presence of the Coulomb interaction, those boundary conditions are nonstandard (33–35).

There is a long history of theoretical prescriptions for the solution of the Coulomb problem in three-particle scattering, where each research group followed a different procedure. Some investigators have used a modified momentum-space integral equation approach (36–39), whereas others have used the configuration-space differential equation approach in a variational framework (16) and in the framework of the coordinate-space Faddeev equations (40–43). Except for the work presented in References 16, 17, 40, and 41, all other calculations have thus far relied on simplified NN interactions or approximations in the treatment of the Coulomb potential, leading to results that are not well converged or are misleading in terms of the conclusions one could reach by comparing them with experimental data. There are more recent formulations (44–46) of modified scattering equations with the Coulomb interaction; however, they have not yet matured into practical applications, except to calculate numerically the two-body S-wave Coulomb phase shifts over a wide range of energies (47).

In 1974, Taylor (48) suggested that even for the description of systems with the Coulomb interaction, it may be sufficient to solve the standard scattering equations, as in nature the Coulomb potential is always screened. The study of the two-particle system with the screened Coulomb interaction revealed that, as expected, the physical observables become insensitive to screening, provided that it takes place at sufficiently large distances R and, in the $R \to \infty$ limit, coincides with the corresponding quantities known from the analytical solution of the two-particle Coulomb problem. That is, the screened Coulomb scattering amplitude renormalized by a diverging phase factor in the limit of vanishing screening converges as a distribution to the well-known pure Coulomb amplitude. The technique of screening and renormalization could be extended to more complicated systems, as was done for three-particle scattering (49, 50); even practical calculations were performed (36–39), albeit with additional approximations both at the level of the hadronic interaction and on the treatment of the Coulomb interaction itself.

Our treatment of the Coulomb interaction is based on momentum-space integral equations together with the method of screening and renormalization, but with novel technical implementations that allow the use of realistic force models along with the full treatment of the Coulomb interaction between charged particles of equal sign. We choose the screened Coulomb potential w_R in configuration space as

$$w_R(r) = w(r)e^{-(r/R)^n}, \qquad\qquad 1.$$

where $w(r) = \alpha_e Z_1 Z_2 / r$ is the true Coulomb potential, $\alpha_e \approx 1/137$ the fine structure constant, Z_i the charge of each particle in units of the proton charge, R the screening radius, and n controls the smoothness of the screening. One major difference relative to previous works (36–39) is that we use a sharper screening than the Yukawa screening ($n = 1$). We want to ensure that the screened Coulomb potential w_R closely approximates the true Coulomb potential w for distances $r < R$ and simultaneously vanishes rapidly for $r > R$, providing a comparatively fast convergence of the partial-wave expansion. In contrast, the sharp cutoff ($n \to \infty$) displays an unwanted oscillatory behavior in the momentum-space representation, thereby leading to convergence problems. We find that values of $3 \le n \le 8$ provide a sufficiently smooth yet rapid screening around $r = R$. The screening functions for different n values are compared in **Figure 1**, which shows that the

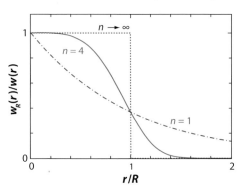

Figure 1

Screening function $w_R(r)/w(r)$ as a function of the distance between two charged particles r for characteristic values of the parameter n in Equation 1. $n = 1$ (*blue dashed-dotted curve*) corresponds to Yukawa screening, $n = 4$ (*solid red curve*) is the standard choice in this review, and $n \to \infty$ (*dotted gray curve*) corresponds to a sharp cutoff.

choice $n = 4$ includes much more of the exact Coulomb potential at short distances than does the Yukawa screening. For example, Yukawa screening requires a screening radius of $R = 1280$ fm to approximate the true Coulomb at relative distance $r = 5$ fm as well as the $n = 4$ choice does with $R = 20$ fm. Therefore the Yukawa screening (36–39) requires very large values of R for convergence compared to those used by us (21–29).

The screening radius R is chosen to be much larger than the range of the strong interaction, which is of the order of the pion wavelength $\hbar/m_\pi c \approx 1.4$ fm. Nevertheless, the screened Coulomb potential, w_R, is short range in the sense of scattering theory; therefore, standard scattering theory is applicable. Of course, the partial-wave expansion of the pair interaction requires much higher angular momenta than does the hadronic potential alone, but not as high as Yukawa screening would require.

Moreover, our theoretical framework is based on a "two-potential formula" (21, 22, 49, 50) where, in elastic scattering, one separates the long-range Coulomb amplitude between the two charged objects (nucleons or nuclei) in the entrance channel from the remainder that constitutes the Coulomb-modified short-range part of the scattering amplitude. For finite R, both terms satisfy well-defined integral equations and after renormalization have well-defined $R \to \infty$ limits.

In Section 2, we review the two-charged-particle problem in a pedagogical form suitable to readers with basic knowledge of quantum mechanics. In Section 3, we present a method for three-particle scattering and show some results for p-d, d-α, and d-^{12}C scattering. We review 4N results in Section 4 and, finally, present some conclusions in Section 5.

2. TWO-PARTICLE SCATTERING

This section sets forth the essential physics ideas for our treatment of Coulomb effects in many-body scattering calculations. The ideas are presented for a two-particle system with charges of equal sign. For such systems, exact scattering results are available and serve as benchmarks for the validity of our Coulomb treatment. The non–theoretically minded reader, equipped with an understanding of our technique for two-particle scattering, will be able to study and appreciate all of the results for three- and four-particle systems given in this review because all of the many-particle scattering problems we discuss can, in their asymptotic Coulomb behavior, be related back to a two-particle system.

Consider that two charged particles interact through the strong potential v and the Coulomb potential w. We introduce the full resolvent

$$g^{(R)}(z) = (z - h_0 - v - w_R)^{-1} \qquad \text{2a.}$$

for the auxiliary situation, in which the Coulomb potential w is replaced by the screened potential w_R, and h_0 is the kinetic energy operator. The full resolvent $g^{(R)}(z)$ yields the full scattering state when acting on a plane-wave state $|\mathbf{p}\nu\rangle$ of relative momentum $\mathbf{p}$, energy $e(p)$, and discrete two-particle quantum numbers ν, in the appropriate limit $z = e(p) + i0$. The full resolvent, therefore, also yields the desired S matrix. The full resolvent $g^{(R)}(z)$ depends on the screening radius R for Coulomb and that dependence is notationally indicated.

Next we discuss formal manipulations of the full resolvent. It can be decomposed according to

$$g^{(R)}(z) = g_0(z) + g_0(z)t^{(R)}(z)g_0(z), \qquad \text{2b.}$$

with the free resolvent $g_0(z) = (z - h_0)^{-1}$ and the full transition matrix

$$t^{(R)}(z) = (v + w_R) + (v + w_R)g_0(z)t^{(R)}(z). \qquad \text{3.}$$

Of course, $t^{(R)}(z)$ must contain the transition matrix

$$t_R(z) = w_R + w_R g_0(z) t_R(z) \qquad\qquad 4.$$

derived from the screened Coulomb potential alone. Therefore, an alternative decomposition of the full resolvent (Equation 2b) that isolates $t_R(z)$ appears conceptually neater. Instead of correlating the plane-wave state $|\mathbf{p}\nu\rangle$ in a single step to the full scattering state by $g^{(R)}(z)$, we may correlate it first to a screened Coulomb state by the screened Coulomb potential w_R through

$$g_R(z) = (z - h_0 - w_R)^{-1}, \qquad\qquad 5a.$$
$$g_R(z) = g_0(z) + g_0(z) t_R(z) g_0(z). \qquad\qquad 5b.$$

In such a case the full resolvent can alternatively be decomposed into

$$g^{(R)}(z) = g_R(z) + g_R(z)\tilde{t}^{(R)}(z) g_R(z), \qquad\qquad 6.$$

with the short-range operator $\tilde{t}^{(R)}(z)$ satisfying

$$\tilde{t}^{(R)}(z) = v + v g_R(z)\tilde{t}^{(R)}(z). \qquad\qquad 7.$$

Using Equation 5b in Equation 6 and comparing the result with Equation 2b, after some elementary algebraic manipulations, one obtains an alternative form for the difference of transition matrices $[t^{(R)}(z) - t_R(z)]$, i.e.,

$$t^{(R)}(z) - t_R(z) = [1 + t_R(z)g_0(z)]\tilde{t}^{(R)}(z)[1 + g_0(z)t_R(z)]. \qquad\qquad 8.$$

The above equation is the well-known two-potential formula that achieves a clean separation of the full transition matrix $t^{(R)}(z)$ into a long-range part $t_R(z)$ and a short-range part $[t^{(R)}(z) - t_R(z)]$. Although the left-hand side of Equation 8 can be calculated directly from the potentials v and w_R according to Equations 3 and 4, Equation 8 is introduced to demonstrate that $[t^{(R)}(z) - t_R(z)]$, even in the infinite R limit, is a short-range operator with a limited partial-wave expansion due to the short-range nature of v and $\tilde{t}^{(R)}(z)$. However, on-shell, it is externally distorted due to the screened Coulomb wave generated by $[1 + g_0(z)t_R(z)]$ which, together with the long-range part $t_R(z)$, does not have a proper limit as $R \to \infty$. This difficulty brings about the concept of renormalization of on-shell matrix elements of the operators (48–50) in order to recover the proper results in the unscreened Coulomb limit. As has been proven elsewhere (48, 51), after renormalization with an equally diverging phase factor $z_R(p_i)$, the screened Coulomb amplitude $\langle \mathbf{p}_f\, \nu_f | t_R(e(p_i) + i0) | \mathbf{p}_i \nu_i\rangle$, $p_f = p_i$, and wave function in the $R \to \infty$ limit converge to the analytically known proper Coulomb amplitude $\langle \mathbf{p}_f\, \nu_f | t_C | \mathbf{p}_i \nu_i\rangle$ and proper Coulomb wave function $|\psi_C^{(+)}(\mathbf{p}_i)\nu_i\rangle$, respectively:

$$\lim_{R\to\infty} \langle \mathbf{p}_f\, \nu_f | t_R(e(p_i) + i0) | \mathbf{p}_i \nu_i\rangle z_R^{-1}(p_i) = \langle \mathbf{p}_f\, \nu_f | t_C | \mathbf{p}_i \nu_i\rangle, \qquad\qquad 9a.$$

and

$$\lim_{R\to\infty} [1 + g_0(e(p_i) + i0)t_R(e(p_i) + i0)] | \mathbf{p}_i \nu_i\rangle z_R^{-\frac{1}{2}}(p_i) = |\psi_C^{(+)}(\mathbf{p}_i)\nu_i\rangle. \qquad\qquad 9b.$$

Therefore, the renormalization of the on-shell $t^{(R)}(z)$ yields the transition amplitude

$$\langle \mathbf{p}_f\nu_f | t | \mathbf{p}_i \nu_i\rangle = \lim_{R\to\infty} z_R^{-\frac{1}{2}}(p_f)\langle \mathbf{p}_f\, \nu_f | t^{(R)}(e(p_i) + i0) | \mathbf{p}_i \nu_i\rangle z_R^{-\frac{1}{2}}(p_i), \qquad\qquad 10a.$$

which refers to the strong potential v and the unscreened Coulomb potential w. In general, the renormalized screened Coulomb amplitudes in Equations 9a and 10a converge as distributions to proper Coulomb amplitudes but, as discussed in Reference 48, this is fully sufficient for the description of real experiments. Nevertheless, in our numerical calculations those limits are not taken numerically. We split the full transition matrix $t^{(R)}(z)$ into the long-range part $t_R(z)$ and the

Coulomb distorted short-range part $[t^{(R)}(z) - t_R(z)]$. After renormalization by $z_R^{-1}(p_i)$, the $R \to \infty$ limit is taken implicitly for $t_R(z)$, according to Equation 9a, whereas for $[t^{(R)}(z) - t_R(z)]$ it is done explicitly, yielding

$$
\begin{aligned}
\langle \mathbf{p}_f \nu_f | t | \mathbf{p}_i \nu_i \rangle &= \langle \mathbf{p}_f \nu_f | t_C | \mathbf{p}_i \nu_i \rangle \\
&+ \lim_{R \to \infty} \left\{ z_R^{-\frac{1}{2}}(p_f) \langle \mathbf{p}_f \nu_f | [t^{(R)}(e(p_i) + i0) - t_R(e(p_i) + i0)] | \mathbf{p}_i \nu_i \rangle z_R^{-\frac{1}{2}}(p_i) \right\}.
\end{aligned}
\tag{10b.}
$$

The first term in Equation 10b is known analytically, whereas the second term is calculated numerically from the solutions presented in Equations 3 and 4 at given R. The $R \to \infty$ limit must be performed numerically but, due to the short-range nature of the operator $[t^{(R)}(z) - t_R(z)]$ demonstrated in Equation 8, it is reached with sufficient accuracy at finite screening radii R. In contrast to $\langle \mathbf{p}_f \nu_f | t_C | \mathbf{p}_i \nu_i \rangle$, the short-range part $[t^{(R)}(z) - t_R(z)]$ can be calculated using the partial-wave expansion of Equations 3 and 4.

The renormalization factor for $R \to \infty$ is a diverging phase factor

$$
z_R(p) = e^{-2i\delta_R(p)},
\tag{11a.}
$$

where $\delta_R(p)$, although independent of the relative orbital angular momentum L in the infinite R limit, is realized at finite R (48) by

$$
\delta_R(p) = \sigma_L(p) - \eta_{LR}(p),
\tag{11b.}
$$

with the diverging screened Coulomb phase shift $\eta_{LR}(p)$ corresponding to standard boundary conditions and the proper Coulomb phase shift $\sigma_L(p)$ referring to the logarithmically distorted proper Coulomb boundary conditions. We can readily understand the form of the renormalization phase in Equation 11b by looking back to Equation 8 and realizing that the external distortion generated by the screened Coulomb wave function $[1 + g_0(e(p) + i0)t_R(e(p) + i0)] | \mathbf{p} \nu \rangle$ carries, in each partial wave, the overall phase factor $e^{i\eta_{LR}(p)}$ (52). Except for this overall phase factor, the screened Coulomb wave approximates the proper Coulomb wave $| \psi_C^{(+)}(\mathbf{p}) \nu \rangle$, well within the range required by the operator $\tilde{t}^{(R)}(z)$ (Equation 8), i.e., for distances $r < R$. Therefore, through the renormalization, the unwanted phase factor is replaced by the appropriate phase factor $e^{i\sigma_L(p)}$ for the unscreened Coulomb wave.

For the screened Coulomb potential of Equation 1 the infinite R limit of $\delta_R(p)$ is known analytically (48) as

$$
\delta_R(p) = \kappa(p)[\ln(2pR) - C/n],
\tag{11c.}
$$

where $\kappa(p) = \alpha_e Z_1 Z_2 \mu / p$ is the Coulomb parameter, μ is the reduced mass, $C \approx 0.5772156649$ is the Euler number, and n is the exponent in Equation 1. The renormalization phase $\delta_R(p)$ to be used in the actual calculations with finite screening radii R is not unique because only the infinite R limit matters, but the converged results must be independent of the chosen form of $\delta_R(p)$. According to our investigations, this independence holds. The results presented here are based on the partial-wave dependent form (Equation 11b) of the renormalization factor, for which we find the convergence with R to be slightly faster than for the form presented in Equation 11c.

To convince the reader of the numerical reliability of our technique, we calculate the Coulomb effect on the hadronic pp phase shift η, which is most important in the $^1S_0$ partial wave. The convergence with R for the $^1S_0$ phase shift, shown in **Figure 2**, is impressive. The convergence is faster at higher energies. A screening radius of $R = 20$ fm (10 fm) suffices for an agreement within 0.01 deg with the exact phase-shift values at all energies above 5 MeV (25 MeV). In contrast, to reproduce the $^1S_0$ pp scattering length $a_{pp}^C = -7.815$ fm and the effective range $r_{pp}^C = 2.773$ fm within 0.010 fm, screening radii larger than $R = 100$ fm are required. Compared with the screening

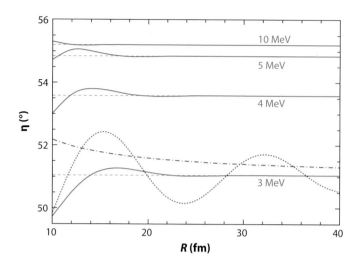

Figure 2

Convergence of the $^1S_0$ pp phase shift η with screening radius R for proton lab energies 3, 4, 5, and 10 MeV. Our results derived from Equation 10b (*solid red curves*) are compared with the exact results (*dashed orange lines*). Also shown at 3 MeV are the results obtained with Yukawa screening (*blue dashed-dotted curve*) and with a sharp cutoff (*gray dotted curve*), demonstrating the superiority of the chosen screening function.

function adopted by us, **Figure 2** also shows the convergence with R to be rather slow for the Yukawa screening and to exhibit unwanted oscillatory behavior for a sharp cutoff.

As demonstrated above, our technique is applicable at all energies, but it becomes more cumbersome as the energy decreases. In two-particle scattering, even the extrapolation to zero energy is achieved. However, as discussed below, in 3N and 4N scattering we consider the application of our Coulomb treatment to be technically too demanding at extremely low energies.

3. THREE-PARTICLE SCATTERING

In this section, we review our treatment of the Coulomb interaction for three-particle scattering. The theory we have developed applies to reactions in which no more than two free objects (nucleons or nuclei) in the physically observable initial and final channels have charges of equal sign. In the case of the 3N system with two protons, all physically possible reactions are described up to pion-production threshold, i.e., p-d elastic scattering and breakup. When one, two, or all three particles are nuclei, each is assumed inert (as in the d-α reaction, which may be considered as a three-particle system consisting of $p + n + \alpha$ as long as one assumes the α-particle to be inert). This section is highly technical; readers who are not interested in lengthy derivations may skip to Equations 21 and 27 below for the major technical results that lead to the applications reviewed in Sections 3.1 and 3.2.

Consider a system of three particles where each pair $(\beta\gamma)$ interacts through the strong potential v_α and the Coulomb potential w_α, $(\alpha\beta\gamma = (123))$, according to the standard "odd man out" notation of the three-body problem. We introduce the full resolvent

$$G^{(R)}(Z) = \left(Z - H_0 - \sum_\sigma v_\sigma - \sum_\sigma w_{\sigma R} \right)^{-1} \qquad 12.$$

for the auxiliary situation in which the Coulomb potential is screened; H_0 is the three-particle kinetic energy operator. The full resolvent yields the full particle-pair scattering state when acting

Figure 3

For $\alpha = 3$, we show the screened Coulomb potential $W_{3R}^{\text{c.m.}}$ between particle α and the center of mass of the remaining pair. The full circles indicate charged particles, whereas the open circle represents a neutral particle.

on the channel state $|\phi_\alpha(\mathbf{q})\nu_\alpha\rangle$ of relative momentum $\mathbf{q}$, energy $E_\alpha(q)$, and additional discrete quantum numbers ν_α in the appropriate limit $Z = E_\alpha(q) + i0$. The full resolvent $G^{(R)}(Z)$ and related operators depend on the screening radius R. The full resolvent, following the standard AGS notation (32) for three-particle scattering, may be decomposed into channel resolvents

$$G_\alpha^{(R)}(Z) = (Z - H_0 - v_\alpha - w_{\alpha R})^{-1}, \qquad 13.$$

and into the full multichannel three-particle transition matrix $U_{\beta\alpha}^{(R)}(Z)$ according to

$$G^{(R)}(Z) = \delta_{\beta\alpha} G_\alpha^{(R)}(Z) + G_\beta^{(R)}(Z) U_{\beta\alpha}^{(R)}(Z) G_\alpha^{(R)}(Z). \qquad 14.$$

The full multichannel transition matrix satisfies the AGS equations (32)

$$U_{\beta\alpha}^{(R)}(Z) = \bar{\delta}_{\beta\alpha} G_0^{-1}(Z) + \sum_\sigma \bar{\delta}_{\beta\sigma} T_\sigma^{(R)}(Z) G_0(Z) U_{\sigma\alpha}^{(R)}(Z), \qquad 15a.$$

with the two-particle transition matrix, $T_\alpha^{(R)}$, derived from the full channel interaction, $v_\alpha + w_{\alpha R}$, through

$$T_\alpha^{(R)}(Z) = (v_\alpha + w_{\alpha R}) + (v_\alpha + w_{\alpha R}) G_0(Z) T_\alpha^{(R)}(Z), \qquad 15b.$$

where $G_0(Z) = (Z - H_0)^{-1}$ is the free resolvent and $\bar{\delta}_{\beta\alpha} = 1 - \delta_{\beta\alpha}$. Of course, the full multichannel transition matrix $U_{\alpha\alpha}^{(R)}(Z)$ must contain the screened Coulomb transition matrix

$$T_{\alpha R}^{\text{c.m.}}(Z) = W_{\alpha R}^{\text{c.m.}} + W_{\alpha R}^{\text{c.m.}} G_\alpha^{(R)}(Z) T_{\alpha R}^{\text{c.m.}}(Z), \qquad 16.$$

which is derived from the screened Coulomb potential $W_{\alpha R}^{\text{c.m.}}$ between the spectator particle α and the center of mass of the remaining pair (**Figure 3**). The same screening function is used for both Coulomb potentials $w_{\alpha R}$ and $W_{\alpha R}^{\text{c.m.}}$.

As shown in Section 2, an alternative decomposition of the full resolvent may be developed based on the following idea: Instead of correlating the plane-wave channel state $|\phi_\alpha(\mathbf{q})\nu_\alpha\rangle$ in a single step to the full scattering state by $G^{(R)}(Z)$, it may be correlated first to the screened Coulomb state generated by the potential $W_{\alpha R}^{\text{c.m.}}$. The corresponding resolvent is

$$G_{\alpha R}(Z) = (Z - H_0 - v_\alpha - w_{\alpha R} - W_{\alpha R}^{\text{c.m.}})^{-1}, \qquad 17a.$$

$$G_{\alpha R}(Z) = G_\alpha^{(R)}(Z) + G_\alpha^{(R)}(Z) T_{\alpha R}^{\text{c.m.}}(Z) G_\alpha^{(R)}(Z). \qquad 17b.$$

Thus, the full resolvent can alternatively be decomposed into

$$G^{(R)}(Z) = \delta_{\beta\alpha} G_{\alpha R}(Z) + G_{\beta R}(Z) \tilde{U}_{\beta\alpha}^{(R)}(Z) G_{\alpha R}(Z), \qquad 18a.$$

$$\begin{aligned} G^{(R)}(Z) = {} & \delta_{\beta\alpha} G_\alpha^{(R)}(Z) + G_\beta^{(R)}(Z) \delta_{\beta\alpha} T_{\alpha R}^{\text{c.m.}}(Z) G_\alpha^{(R)}(Z) \\ & + G_\beta^{(R)}(Z)[1 + T_{\beta R}^{\text{c.m.}}(Z) G_\beta^{(R)}(Z)] \tilde{U}_{\beta\alpha}^{(R)}(Z) \\ & \times [1 + G_\alpha^{(R)}(Z) T_{\alpha R}^{\text{c.m.}}(Z)] G_\alpha^{(R)}(Z), \end{aligned} \qquad 18b.$$

where the operator $\tilde{U}_{\beta\alpha}^{(R)}(Z)$ may be calculated through the integral equation

$$
\tilde{U}_{\beta\alpha}^{(R)}(Z) = \bar{\delta}_{\beta\alpha}\left[G_{\alpha R}^{-1}(Z) + v_\alpha\right] + \delta_{\beta\alpha}\mathcal{W}_{\alpha R}
$$
$$
+ \sum_\sigma (\bar{\delta}_{\beta\sigma}v_\sigma + \delta_{\beta\sigma}\mathcal{W}_{\beta R})G_{\sigma R}(Z)\tilde{U}_{\sigma\alpha}^{(R)}(Z), \qquad 19.
$$

which is driven by the strong potential v_α and the potential of three-nucleon nature, $\mathcal{W}_{\alpha R} = \sum_\sigma (\bar{\delta}_{\alpha\sigma}w_{\sigma R} - \delta_{\alpha\sigma}W_{\sigma R}^{\text{c.m.}})$. The potential $\mathcal{W}_{\alpha R}$ accounts for the difference between the direct Coulomb interaction and that which takes place between the charged particle and the center of mass of the remaining pair. When calculated between on-shell screened Coulomb states, $\tilde{U}_{\beta\alpha}^{(R)}(Z)$ is of short range, even in the infinite R limit. Equation 18b, together with Equation 14, gives an alternative form for the difference of the transition matrices $[U_{\beta\alpha}^{(R)}(Z) - \delta_{\beta\alpha}T_{\alpha R}^{\text{c.m.}}(Z)]$, namely

$$
U_{\beta\alpha}^{(R)}(Z) - \delta_{\beta\alpha}T_{\alpha R}^{\text{c.m.}}(Z) = \left[1 + T_{\beta R}^{\text{c.m.}}(Z)G_\beta^{(R)}(Z)\right]\tilde{U}_{\beta\alpha}^{(R)}(Z)\left[1 + G_\alpha^{(R)}(Z)T_{\alpha R}^{\text{c.m.}}(Z)\right]. \qquad 20.
$$

Although we calculate this difference directly from the potentials v_α, $w_{\alpha R}$, and $W_{\alpha R}^{\text{c.m.}}$ through the numerical solutions of Equations 15a, 15b, and 16, Equation 20 demonstrates that, for initial and final particle-pair states, $[U_{\beta\alpha}^{(R)}(Z) - \delta_{\beta\alpha}T_{\alpha R}^{\text{c.m.}}(Z)]$ is a short-range operator, due to the nature of $\tilde{U}_{\beta\alpha}^{(R)}(Z)$, as discussed above; however, it is externally distorted due to the screened Coulomb wave generated by $[1 + G_\alpha^{(R)}(Z)T_{\alpha R}^{\text{c.m.}}(Z)]$.

The subtraction of $\delta_{\beta\alpha}T_{\alpha R}^{\text{c.m.}}(Z)$ is by no means an approximation; instead, it is an exact procedure that is validated by Equation 19 for $\tilde{U}_{\beta\alpha}^{(R)}(Z)$, where the subtracted term appears. A different subtraction leads to a different $\tilde{U}_{\beta\alpha}^{(R)}(Z)$, but only this one achieves a clean separation of the full on-shell transition matrix, $U_{\beta\alpha}^{(R)}(Z)$, into the long-range part $\delta_{\beta\alpha}T_{\alpha R}^{\text{c.m.}}(Z)$, and the Coulomb-distorted short-range part, $[U_{\beta\alpha}^{(R)}(Z) - \delta_{\beta\alpha}T_{\alpha R}^{\text{c.m.}}(Z)]$. On shell, neither part has a proper limit as $R \to \infty$ but, as discussed in Section 2, the limit emerges after renormalization by an appropriate phase factor. In close analogy with two-particle scattering (Equations 9a and 10a), the full transition amplitude for initial and final particle-pair states, $|\phi_\alpha(\mathbf{q}_i)\nu_{\alpha_i}\rangle$ and $|\phi_\beta(\mathbf{q}_f)\nu_{\beta_f}\rangle$, respectively, with $E_\beta(q_f) = E_\alpha(q_i)$, is obtained via the renormalization of the on-shell multichannel transition matrix $U_{\beta\alpha}^{(R)}(Z)$, with $Z = E_\alpha(q_i) + i0$, in the infinite R limit

$$
\langle\phi_\beta(\mathbf{q}_f)\nu_{\beta_f}|U_{\beta\alpha}|\phi_\alpha(\mathbf{q}_i)\nu_{\alpha_i}\rangle = \delta_{\beta\alpha}\langle\phi_\alpha(\mathbf{q}_f)\nu_{\alpha_f}|T_{\alpha C}^{\text{c.m.}}|\phi_\alpha(\mathbf{q}_i)\nu_{\alpha_i}\rangle
$$
$$
+ \lim_{R\to\infty}\left\{Z_{\beta R}^{-\frac{1}{2}}(q_f)\langle\phi_\beta(\mathbf{q}_f)\nu_{\beta_f}|[U_{\beta\alpha}^{(R)}(E_\alpha(q_i) + i0)\right. \qquad 21.
$$
$$
\left. - \delta_{\beta\alpha}T_{\alpha R}^{\text{c.m.}}(E_\alpha(q_i) + i0)]|\phi_\alpha(\mathbf{q}_i)\nu_{\alpha_i}\rangle Z_{\alpha R}^{-\frac{1}{2}}(q_i)\right\}.
$$

The first term on the right-hand side of Equation 21 is known analytically; it corresponds to the proper Coulomb transition amplitude between particle α and the center of mass of pair α, which results from the implicit renormalization of $T_{\alpha R}^{\text{c.m.}}(Z)$ (see Equation 9a) after splitting $U_{\beta\alpha}^{(R)}(Z)$ into the long-range term $\delta_{\beta\alpha}T_{\alpha R}^{\text{c.m.}}(Z)$, and the short-range part, $[U_{\beta\alpha}^{(R)}(Z) - \delta_{\beta\alpha}T_{\alpha R}^{\text{c.m.}}(Z)]$. The $R \to \infty$ limit for the remaining part of the multichannel transition matrix, $[U_{\beta\alpha}^{(R)}(Z) - \delta_{\beta\alpha}T_{\alpha R}^{\text{c.m.}}(Z)]$, is performed numerically. Due to the short-range nature of this term, as demonstrated in Equation 20, the limit is reached with sufficient accuracy at finite screening radii R; furthermore, it can be calculated using a partial-wave expansion.

The renormalization factor for $R \to \infty$ is a diverging phase factor,

$$
Z_{\alpha R}(q) = e^{-2i\delta_{\alpha R}(q)}, \qquad 22a.
$$

where $\delta_{\alpha R}(q)$, although independent of the particle-pair relative angular momentum l in the infinite R limit, is realized at finite R by

$$\delta_{\alpha R}(q) = \sigma_l^\alpha(q) - \eta_{lR}^\alpha(q),\qquad 22b.$$

with the diverging screened Coulomb phase shift, $\eta_{lR}(q)$, corresponding to standard boundary conditions and the proper Coulomb phase shift, $\sigma_l(q)$, referring to the logarithmically distorted proper Coulomb boundary conditions. In analogy with two-body scattering, the form of the renormalization phase given in Equation 22b is readily understood by looking back to Equation 20. For the screened Coulomb potential of Equation 1, the infinite R limit of $\delta_{\alpha R}(q)$ is known analytically as

$$\delta_{\alpha R}(q) = \kappa_\alpha(q)[\ln(2q\,R) - C/n],\qquad 22c.$$

where $\kappa_\alpha(q) = \alpha_e Z_\alpha(Z_\beta + Z_\gamma)M_\alpha/q$ is the Coulomb parameter and M_α is the reduced mass in channel α. The form of the renormalization phase $\delta_{\alpha R}(q)$ to be used in the actual calculations with finite screening radii R is not unique; however, like in two-body scattering, the converged results show independence of the chosen form of $\delta_{\alpha R}(q)$. The elastic scattering results presented below are based on the partial-wave dependent form of the renormalization factor given by Equation 22b, for which the convergence with R is slightly faster than for Equation 22c.

For breakup observables, one follows a very similar strategy where the starting point is the AGS equation for the breakup operator $U_{0\alpha}^{(R)}(Z)$ and the corresponding relation to the full resolvent

$$U_{0\alpha}^{(R)}(Z) = G_0^{-1}(Z) + \sum_\sigma T_\sigma^{(R)}(Z)G_0(Z)U_{\sigma\alpha}^{(R)}(Z),\qquad 23a.$$

$$G^{(R)}(Z) = G_0(Z)U_{0\alpha}^{(R)}(Z)G_\alpha^{(R)}(Z),\qquad 23b.$$

where $U_{\beta\alpha}^{(R)}(Z)$, $T_\alpha^{(R)}(Z)$, and $G_0(Z)$ are defined as above. In the same spirit, the final breakup state to be analyzed may not be reached in a single step; instead, it may be correlated first to a screened Coulomb state between the charged particles whose corresponding Coulomb resolvent,

$$G_R(Z) = \left(Z - H_0 - \sum_\sigma w_{\sigma R}\right)^{-1},\qquad 24a.$$

keeps only the screened Coulomb interaction. The proper three-body Coulomb wave function and its relation to the three-body screened Coulomb wave function generated by $G_R(Z)$ are unknown, thus preventing the application of the screening and renormalization method to the reactions involving three free charged particles (nucleons or nuclei) in the final state. However, in the system of two charged particles and one neutral particle, only the channel $\sigma = \rho$, corresponding to the correlated pair of charged particles, contributes to $G_R(Z)$, which simplifies to

$$G_R(Z) = G_0(Z) + G_0(Z)T_{\rho R}(Z)G_0(Z),$$

$$T_{\rho R}(Z) = w_{\rho R} + w_{\rho R}G_0(Z)T_{\rho R}(Z),\qquad 24b.$$

making channel ρ the most convenient choice for the description of the final breakup state. Thus, for the purpose of breakup, a decomposition of the full resolvent (an alternative to that presented in Equation 23b) is

$$G^{(R)}(Z) = G_R(Z)\tilde{U}_{0\alpha}^{(R)}(Z)G_{\alpha R}(Z),\qquad 25a.$$

$$G^{(R)}(Z) = G_0(Z)[1 + T_{\rho R}(Z)G_0(Z)]\tilde{U}_{0\alpha}^{(R)}(Z)\left[1 + G_\alpha^{(R)}(Z)T_{\alpha R}^{\text{c.m.}}(Z)\right]G_\alpha^{(R)}(Z),\qquad 25b.$$

where the full breakup transition matrix may be written as

$$U_{0\alpha}^{(R)}(Z) = [1 + T_{\rho R}(Z)G_0(Z)]\tilde{U}_{0\alpha}^{(R)}(Z)\left[1 + G_{\alpha}^{(R)}(Z)T_{\alpha R}^{\text{c.m.}}(Z)\right]. \qquad \text{26a.}$$

The reduced operator $\tilde{U}_{0\alpha}^{(R)}(Z)$ may be calculated through quadrature

$$\tilde{U}_{0\alpha}^{(R)}(Z) = \left[G_{\alpha R}^{-1}(Z) + v_\alpha\right] + \sum_\sigma v_\sigma G_{\sigma R}(Z)\tilde{U}_{\sigma\alpha}^{(R)}(Z) \qquad \text{26b.}$$

from the corresponding reduced operator of elastic/rearrangement scattering $\tilde{U}_{\beta\alpha}^{(R)}(Z)$. In Equation 26a for the full breakup transition matrix, the external distortions are made explicit due to the presence of the screened Coulomb interaction in both initial and final states. On shell, the reduced operator $\tilde{U}_{0\alpha}^{(R)}(Z)$, calculated between screened Coulomb distorted initial and final states, is of finite range, although the two contributions in Equation 26b have slightly different range properties (23). Again, no approximation occurs by the explicit use of the c.m. Coulomb potential $W_{\alpha R}^{\text{c.m.}}$.

In the full breakup operator $U_{0\alpha}^{(R)}(Z)$, the external distortions show up in screened Coulomb waves generated by $[1 + G_{\alpha}^{(R)}(Z)T_{\alpha R}^{\text{c.m.}}(Z)]$ in the initial state and by $[1 + T_{\rho R}(Z)G_0(Z)]$ in the final state; neither wave function has a proper limit as $R \to \infty$. Therefore, the full breakup transition amplitude, connecting initial and final states $|\phi_\alpha(\mathbf{q}_i)\nu_{\alpha_i}\rangle$ and $|\phi_0(\mathbf{p}_f \mathbf{q}_f)\nu_{0_f}\rangle$, respectively, with $E_\alpha(q_i) = E_0(p_f q_f)$, is obtained via the renormalization of the on-shell breakup transition matrix $U_{0\alpha}^{(R)}(E_\alpha(q_i) + i0)$ in the infinite R limit

$$\langle\phi_0(\mathbf{p}_f \mathbf{q}_f)\nu_{0_f}|U_{0\alpha}|\phi_\alpha(\mathbf{q}_i)\nu_{\alpha_i}\rangle = \lim_{R\to\infty}\left[z_R^{-\frac{1}{2}}(p_f)\langle\phi_0(\mathbf{p}_f \mathbf{q}_f)\nu_{0_f}|\right.$$
$$\left.\times U_{0\alpha}^{(R)}(E_\alpha(q_i) + i0)|\phi_\alpha(\mathbf{q}_i)\nu_{\alpha_i}\rangle Z_{\alpha R}^{-\frac{1}{2}}(q_i)\right], \qquad 27.$$

where $Z_{\alpha R}(q_i)$ and $z_R(p_f)$ are the renormalization factors defined in Equations 22 and 11a,b. The limit in Equation 27 must be performed numerically, but, due to the short-range nature of the breakup operator, it can be reached with sufficient accuracy at finite screening radii R. Unlike the work described in References 37 and 38, our method leads not only to fast convergence in R at all energies above breakup threshold, but also to the possibility of including realistic force models.

In conclusion, the new numerical procedure followed in References 21–24 and 28 consists of three steps: (a) to solve Equations 15a, 16, and 23a independently for increasing R; (b) to calculate the scattering amplitudes through Equations 21 and 27; (c) to establish the R-independence of the observables for sufficiently large R. As discussed above, this method cannot be used for reactions with three free charged bodies in the final state. In the following subsections, we illustrate the convergence in R and present selected results.

3.1. Three-Nucleon Scattering

We have studied p-d elastic scattering and breakup as well as p-d capture into ${}^3\text{He} + \gamma$ and the photo- and electro-disintegration of ${}^3\text{He}$ (21–23). The three nucleons are considered identical particles. Their charge difference is taken care of by the isospin dependence of the nuclear and Coulomb interactions. Equations 21 and 27 are symmetrized and therefore simplified; their actual forms can be found in References 21 and 23. In those studies, we demonstrated that the convergence with R is obtained at rather small finite R, as shown in **Figure 4** for elastic scattering, and in **Figure 5** for breakup in several kinematical configurations

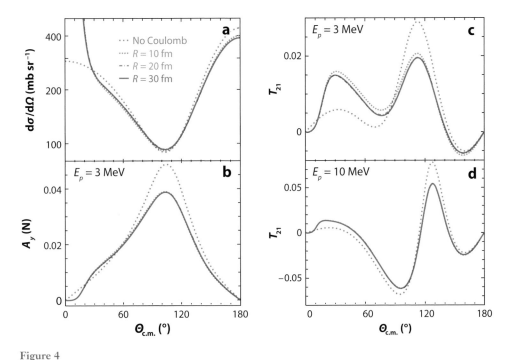

Figure 4

Convergence with the screening radius R of the differential cross section (a), proton analyzing power A_y (b), and deuteron tensor analyzing power T_{21} (c) for p-d elastic scattering at 3 MeV. Results for T_{21} are also shown at 10 MeV (d).

$(\theta_1, \theta_2, \varphi_2 - \varphi_1)$ characterized in a standard way by the polar and azimuthal angles (θ_i, φ_i) of the two protons. All of the observables shown converge at $R = 20$ fm except in the pp final-state interaction (FSI) configuration, where a pp-FSI peak in the absence of Coulomb effects becomes a pp-FSI depression with zero cross section at relative pp energy $E_{pp} = 0$ MeV when Coulomb is included. Although further details are available (21–23), it is worth mentioning that benchmark calculations were performed (53) by comparing the present results for p-d elastic scattering observables with those obtained by the Pisa group (16) using coordinate space methods and the Kohn variational principle (KVP). The agreement between the two calculations is excellent, as shown in **Figure 6** for $E_p = 3$ MeV, 10 MeV, and 65 MeV proton lab energy.

For breakup observables, there are at present no other reliable calculations to compare with ours. Therefore, the validity of the proposed method is based on the fast convergence with R of the calculated observables. **Figure 7** illustrates three examples of how Coulomb effects in p-d breakup and three-body photo-disintegration of ^{3}He are important when describing the data. The calculations are based on the charge-dependent coupled-channel potential CD-Bonn + Δ (7). In the 3N system, the Δ isobar mediates an effective 3N force and effective 2N and 3N currents, both of which are consistent with the underlying 2N force. In these observables the Coulomb effect is large, whereas the effect due to Δ excitation is small and therefore is not shown separately. Further studies may be found in Reference 54.

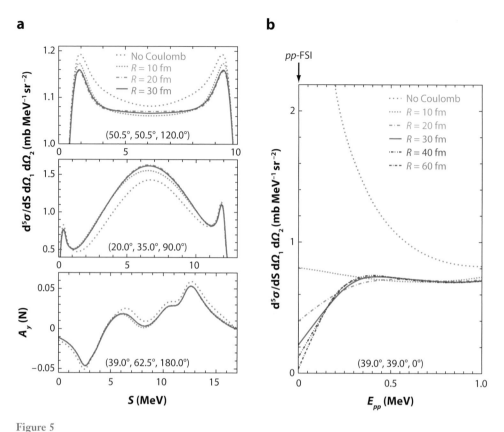

Figure 5

Convergence of *p-d* breakup observables with screening radius R at $E_p = 13$ MeV. Differential cross sections and proton analyzing power A_y in specified kinematical configurations are shown as functions of the arc length S along the kinematical curve (*a*) or the relative *pp* energy (*b*) for the *pp*-FSI configuration. Abbreviation: FSI, final-state interaction.

3.2. Three-Body-Like Nuclear Reactions

The possibility of including the Coulomb force in three-particle scattering opens the door to the study of nuclear reactions dominated by effective three-body degrees of freedom, namely the scattering of deuterons or light bound nuclear systems such as halo nuclei from a nuclear target. Thus at least one of the three particles is a nucleus that is considered inert vis-a-vis its internal excitation.

3.2.1. *d*-α Scattering. The study of *d*-α scattering as a $p + n + \alpha$ three-body system with the α-*p* Coulomb potential included is discussed in Reference 28. Below the ^{3}H + ^{3}He threshold, the α-*p* and α-*n* nuclear interactions are real and are fitted to the respective scattering data. Here we use the parametrization known as α-*N*-III (28). The Coulomb effect on the observables is large in elastic scattering at very low energies and in breakup, where the shift of the α-*p* *P*-wave resonance position leads to corresponding shifts of the differential cross section peaks; selected examples are presented in **Figure 8**.

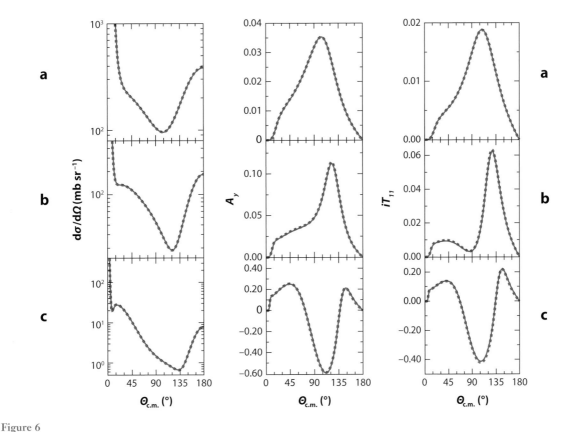

Figure 6

Differential cross section and the proton and deuteron analyzing powers A_y and iT_{11} are shown for p-d elastic scattering at 3 MeV (*a*), 10 MeV (*b*), and 65 MeV (*c*) lab energies as functions of the center of mass scattering angle. Results obtained using Kohn variational principle (*thin solid blue curves*) and integral equation approach (*thick dotted red curves*) are compared. Curves are coincident.

3.2.2. Scattering from heavier nuclei. Until recently, three-body-like nuclear reactions have been analyzed through the continuum-discretized coupled-channels (CDCC) method (58), although no realistic benchmark calculation exists to validate the accuracy of this method to describe, for example, deuteron elastic scattering and breakup from a stable nucleus such as ^{12}C. Therefore, the first studies (29) that utilized our Coulomb treatment concentrated on this reaction at $E_d = 56$ MeV. The n-^{12}C and p-^{12}C interactions are optical potentials that fit the elastic scattering at half the incident laboratory energy (59). A simple Gaussian potential fitted to the deuteron-binding energy is used for np. Both techniques, CDCC and our Faddeev/AGS approach, employ identical dynamics. Our calculations are meant to check the validity of CDCC and, at the same time, demonstrate that the proposed method to treat the Coulomb interaction is also feasible for reactions where $Z_i Z_j > 1$.

In the case of d-^{12}C scattering at $E_d = 56$ MeV, **Figure 9** shows that the Faddeev/AGS results describe the elastic data up to 60° and that the equivalent CDCC calculation coincides reasonably well with the exact results for both elastic and breakup scattering. In addition, we find that the Coulomb interaction also plays an important role in specific breakup configurations, in accordance with what we found in p-d breakup. In Reference 29 we present calculations for other reactions (not reviewed here) such as ^{11}Be scattering from protons where CDCC calculations seem to be

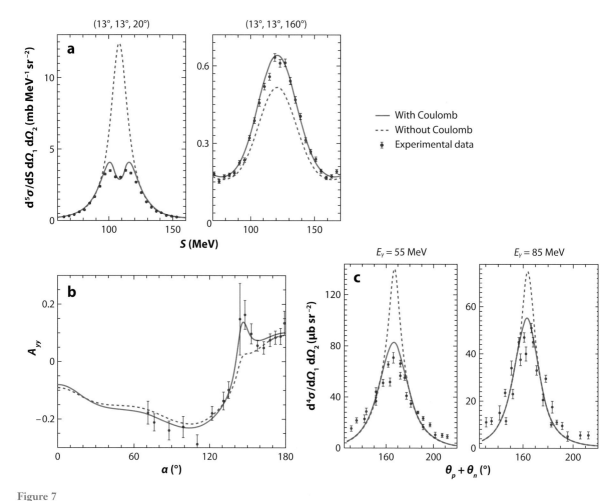

Figure 7

(*a*) Fivefold differential cross section for *d-p* breakup at $E_d = 130$ MeV. Experimental data reproduced from Reference 54 with permission. (*b*) Deuteron analyzing power A_{yy} for *d-p* breakup at $E_d = 94.5$ MeV in symmetric constant relative energy (SCRE) geometry. Curves as in panel *a*. Experimental data reproduced from Reference 55 with permission. (*c*) The semi-inclusive fourfold differential cross section for $^3\text{He}(\gamma, pn)p$ reaction at 55- and 85-MeV photon lab energy as a function of the *np* opening angle $\theta_p + \theta_n$ with $\theta_p = 81°$. Curves as in panel *a*. Experimental data reproduced from Reference 56 with permission.

less reliable for specific breakup configurations. Thus, the validity of CDCC appears to be mixed and, wherever possible, one should employ the Faddeev/AGS technique.

4. FOUR-NUCLEON SCATTERING

In this section, we review the application of four-body scattering theory to the 4N system, which concerns reactions involving two or three protons. In the former case, one is able to calculate all reactions leading to two, three, and four bodies in the final state because the renormalization procedure for the asymptotic wave function referring to two charged particles interacting through the screened Coulomb potential is well defined. Nevertheless, for 4N reactions involving three protons, for reasons mentioned before, one is only able to calculate elastic observables because each breakup channel contains three charged bodies. Unlike in Section 3, however, we develop

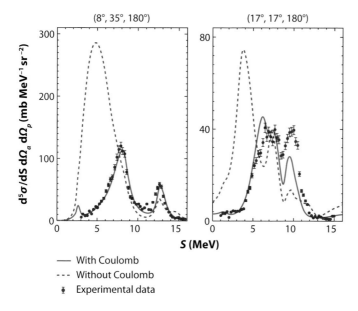

(8°, 35°, 180°)   (17°, 17°, 180°)

— With Coulomb
--- Without Coulomb
⊤ Experimental data

Figure 8

Fivefold differential cross section for *d*-*α* breakup at $E_\alpha = 15$ MeV. Data reproduced from Reference 57 with permission.

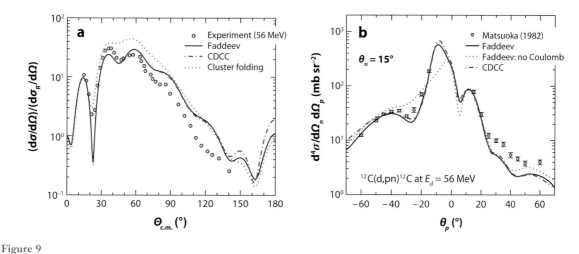

Figure 9

Deuteron scattering on ^{12}C at $E_d = 56$ MeV. (*a*) Elastic differential cross section divided by Rutherford cross section. (*b*) Semi-inclusive breakup cross section versus proton scattering angle. Experimental data for elastic scattering and breakup reproduced with permission from References 60 and 61, respectively. Abbreviation: CDCC, continuum-discretized coupled-channels.

scattering equations for four identical particles and provide them in symmetrized form at the outset. For nonidentical particles, we direct the interested reader to References 25 and 62.

The 4N scattering problem gives rise to the simplest set of nuclear reactions that shows the complexity of heavier systems. n-^{3}H and p-^{3}He scattering is dominated by the total isospin $\mathcal{T} = 1$ states, while elastic deuteron-deuteron (*d*-*d*) scattering is dominated by the $\mathcal{T} = 0$ states; the n-^{3}He and p-^{3}H reactions involve both $\mathcal{T} = 0$ and $\mathcal{T} = 1$ and are coupled to *d*-*d* in $\mathcal{T} = 0$. Due to the charge dependence of the hadronic and electromagnetic interaction, a small admixture of $\mathcal{T} = 2$ states is also present. In 4N scattering, the Coulomb interaction is crucial not only to treat p-^{3}He, p-^{3}H, and d-d elastic scattering, but also to separate the n-^{3}He and p-^{3}H thresholds, and avoid the presence of an excited state of the α particle a few keV below the lowest scattering threshold. All these complex features make the 4N scattering problem a natural theoretical laboratory to test different force models of the nuclear interaction, after the 3N system.

In this section, we solve the four-body AGS equations (62) in the symmetrized forms used in References 25 and 26 to study n-^{3}H and p-^{3}He elastic scattering and in Reference 27 to calculate all coupled reactions resulting from n-^{3}He, p-^{3}H, and d-d initial states. As in Equation 15a, the four-body AGS transition operators in the presence of screened Coulomb become R dependent. The transition operators $\mathcal{U}_{(R)}^{\beta\alpha}$, where $\alpha(\beta) = 1$ and 2 corresponds to initial/final $1 + 3$ and $2 + 2$ states, respectively, satisfy the symmetrized AGS equations

$$\mathcal{U}_{(R)}^{11} = -(G_0 T^{(R)} G_0)^{-1} P_{34} - P_{34} U_{(R)}^1 G_0 T^{(R)} G_0 \mathcal{U}_{(R)}^{11} + U_{(R)}^2 G_0 T^{(R)} G_0 \mathcal{U}_{(R)}^{21}, \qquad 28a.$$

$$\mathcal{U}_{(R)}^{21} = (G_0 T^{(R)} G_0)^{-1}(1 - P_{34}) + (1 - P_{34}) U_{(R)}^1 G_0 T^{(R)} G_0 \mathcal{U}_{(R)}^{11} \qquad 28b.$$

for $1 + 3$ as the initial state and

$$\mathcal{U}_{(R)}^{12} = (G_0 T^{(R)} G_0)^{-1} - P_{34} U_{(R)}^1 G_0 T^{(R)} G_0 \mathcal{U}_{(R)}^{12} + U_{(R)}^2 G_0 T^{(R)} G_0 \mathcal{U}_{(R)}^{22}, \qquad 29a.$$

$$\mathcal{U}_{(R)}^{22} = (1 - P_{34}) U_{(R)}^1 G_0 T^{(R)} G_0 \mathcal{U}_{(R)}^{12} \qquad 29b.$$

for $2 + 2$ as the initial state. In both sets of equations, G_0 is the free four-particle Green's function and $T^{(R)}$ is the 2N t-matrix derived from nuclear potential plus screened Coulomb between pp pairs. The operators $U_{(R)}^\alpha$, resulting from

$$U_{(R)}^\alpha = P_\alpha G_0^{-1} + P_\alpha T^{(R)} G_0 U_{(R)}^\alpha, \qquad 30a.$$

$$P_1 = P_{12} P_{23} + P_{13} P_{23}, \qquad \text{and} \qquad 30b.$$

$$P_2 = P_{13} P_{24}, \qquad 30c.$$

are the symmetrized AGS operators for the $1 + 3$ and $2 + 2$ subsystems and P_{ij} is the permutation operator of particles i and j.

The amplitudes for all possible transitions between two-cluster states with relative two-body momentum, $\mathbf{p}_i$ and $\mathbf{p}_f$, are obtained from

$$\langle \mathbf{p}_f | T_{(R)}^{\beta\alpha} | \mathbf{p}_i \rangle = S_{\beta\alpha} \langle \xi_\beta^{(R)}(\mathbf{p}_f) | \mathcal{U}_{(R)}^{\beta\alpha} | \xi_\alpha^{(R)}(\mathbf{p}_i) \rangle, \qquad 31.$$

where $|\xi_\alpha^{(R)}(\mathbf{p})\rangle = G_0 T^{(R)} P_\alpha |\xi_\alpha^{(R)}(\mathbf{p})\rangle$ represent the Faddeev components of the initial/final $1 + 3$ and $2 + 2$ states and $S_{11} = 3$, $S_{21} = \sqrt{3}$, $S_{22} = 2$, and $S_{12} = 2\sqrt{3}$ are the weight factors resulting from the symmetrization.

In close analogy with three-particle scattering, the full scattering amplitude, $T_{(R)}^{\beta\alpha}$, is decomposed into the long-range part $\delta_{\beta\alpha} T_{\alpha R}^{\text{c.m.}}$ and the remaining Coulomb-distorted short-range part $[T_{(R)}^{\beta\alpha} - \delta_{\beta\alpha} T_{\alpha R}^{\text{c.m.}}]$, with $T_{\alpha R}^{\text{c.m.}}$ being the two-body transition matrix derived from the screened Coulomb potential between the center of mass of two charged clusters (50). The renormalization procedure in the $R \to \infty$ limit yields the full transition amplitude in the presence of the Coulomb interaction

$$\langle \mathbf{p}_f | T^{\beta\alpha} | \mathbf{p}_i \rangle = \delta_{\beta\alpha} \langle \mathbf{p}_f | T_{\alpha C}^{\text{c.m.}} | \mathbf{p}_i \rangle + \lim_{R \to \infty} \left\{ \mathcal{Z}_{\beta R}^{-\frac{1}{2}}(p_f) \langle \mathbf{p}_f | [T_{(R)}^{\beta\alpha} - \delta_{\beta\alpha} T_{\alpha R}^{\text{c.m.}}] | \mathbf{p}_i \rangle \mathcal{Z}_{\alpha R}^{-\frac{1}{2}}(p_i) \right\}, \qquad 32.$$

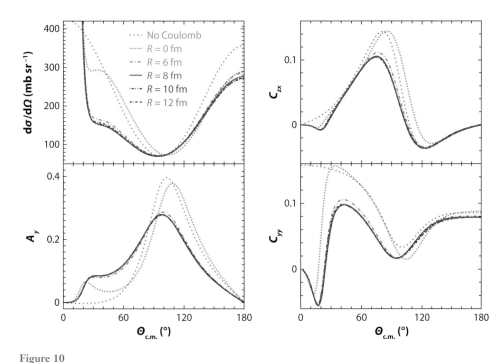

Figure 10

Convergence of the p-^{3}He scattering observables with screening radius R. Results for the differential cross section, proton analyzing power A_y, and p-^{3}He spin correlation coefficients C_{zx} and C_{yy} at 4 MeV proton lab energy are shown.

where $\langle \mathbf{p}_f | T_{\alpha C}^{\text{c.m.}} | \mathbf{p}_i \rangle$ is the pure Coulomb amplitude between the center of mass of two charged clusters; the renormalization factors are used in the partial-wave-dependent form of Equation 22b. Obviously, there is no long-range Coulomb force in the n-^{3}He states; in such cases $\langle \mathbf{p}_f | T_{\alpha C}^{\text{c.m.}} | \mathbf{p}_i \rangle = \langle \mathbf{p}_f | T_{\alpha R}^{\text{c.m.}} | \mathbf{p}_i \rangle = 0$, and $\mathcal{Z}_{\alpha R}(p) = 1$. The second term in Equation 32 represents the Coulomb-modified nuclear short-range amplitude. It must be calculated numerically; however, due to its short-range nature, the $R \rightarrow \infty$ limit is reached with sufficient accuracy at finite screening radii R, as we demonstrate for p-^{3}He scattering in **Figure 10**. The $R = 0$ curve corresponds to the usual approximation where the pure Coulomb amplitude is added to the nuclear amplitude multiplied by the Coulomb phases. Depending on the reaction and the energy, we obtain fully converged results with R ranging from 10 to 20 fm.

In **Figure 11** we show results for p-^{3}He and n-^{3}He elastic scattering as well as $d + d \rightarrow p + ^3$H and $d + d \rightarrow n + ^3$He transfer using AV18 (2), CD-Bonn (3), N3LO (11), and INOY04 (63) potentials between NN pairs plus Coulomb. The potentials are purely nucleonic ones, in contrast to the description of the 3N system with the coupled-channel potential CD-Bonn + Δ. Thus, we do not include here a 3N force, although this can be done as demonstrated in Reference 64. Nevertheless, the 3N force effect on the nuclear binding is simulated here by using the potential INOY04 that fits both ^{3}He and ^{3}H experimental binding energies (7.72 MeV and 8.48 MeV, respectively). Results indicate that in p-^{3}He scattering there is a stronger A_y deficiency than in n-^{3}He. Coulomb effects are also shown in **Figure 11c**, where a clear difference between $d + d \rightarrow p + ^3$H and $d + d \rightarrow n + ^3$He transfer is observed. Other considerations and examples may be found in References 25–27.

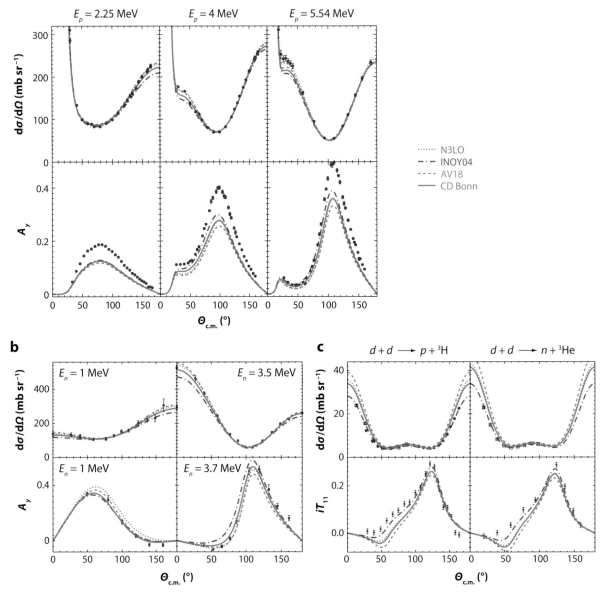

Figure 11

(*a*) The differential cross section and proton analyzing power A_y for p-^{3}He elastic scattering at 2.25, 4.0, and 5.54 MeV proton lab energy. Results including the Coulomb interaction obtained with potentials CD Bonn (*solid orange curves*), AV18 (*dashed blue curves*), INOY04 (*dashed-dotted purple curves*), and N3LO (*dotted green curves*) are compared. Data reproduced with permission from References 65–67. (*b*) Differential cross section and neutron analyzing power for elastic n-^{3}He scattering at 1, 3.5, and 3.7 MeV neutron lab energy. Curves as in panel *a*. The cross section data, A_y data at 1 MeV, and A_y data at 3.7 MeV are reproduced with permission from References 68, 69, and 70, respectively. (*c*) Differential cross section and deuteron vector analyzing power for $d + d \rightarrow p + {}^3$H and $d + d \rightarrow n + {}^3$He transfer reactions at 3 MeV deuteron lab energy. Curves as in panel *a*. Cross section data reproduced from References 71 (*squares*) and 72 (*circles*). Analyzing power data for $d + d \rightarrow p + {}^3$H and $d + d \rightarrow n + {}^3$He reproduced with permission from References 72 and 73, respectively.

5. CONCLUSIONS

This article reviews the recent developments in the solution of the n-body scattering problem (n equals three and four) with charged particles of equal sign in the framework of momentum-space integral equations. The long-range Coulomb interaction is treated by screening and renormalization. The three most important technical features of this treatment are: (*a*) a new screening function that preserves the properties of the Coulomb potential at short distances, but cuts off the long-range tail for $r > R$ faster than Yukawa screening to improve convergence, but slower than a sharp cutoff so as to avoid unwanted oscillatory behavior; (*b*) the use of a "two-potential" formula for the elastic scattering of two charged bodies in which the full scattering amplitude is split into a pure Coulomb amplitude and a Coulomb-modified nuclear short-range amplitude; (*c*) the obtaining of the latter term by calculating numerically, at sufficiently large screening radius R, the full many-body amplitude for nuclear plus screened Coulomb potentials, subtracting the screened Coulomb amplitude resulting from the screened Coulomb potential between the center of mass of the two charged bodies, and renormalizing that difference to obtain a result that is independent of R.

This approach has been applied to the solution of the three-nucleon scattering problem with two protons and the four-nucleon scattering problem with two and three protons, as well as to a number of nuclear reactions wherein effective three-body degrees of freedom play a dominant role, such as d-α or d-^{12}C elastic scattering and breakup. In those cases, the α and ^{12}C nuclei are taken as inert cores. When the number of charged particles (nucleons or nuclei) in the considered n-body system is limited to at most two, one is able to calculate all possible elastic, transfer, and breakup observables. If this number exceeds two, however, one may only be able to calculate observables corresponding to reactions where, in the initial and final physical channels, two bodies at most are charged. In other words, if ab initio calculations of the many-body scattering problem (74) were possible for larger nuclear systems beyond 3N or 4N, one could use the present method to calculate all elastic and transfer reactions, but not all breakup observables—only those leading to at most two charged bodies in the final state. For three or more charged bodies in the final state, the renormalization prescription cannot be applied as a result of the lack of knowledge of the proper three-body Coulomb wave function with three charged particles. Also outside the scope of the present review are systems with charged particles of different signs; we do not address these systems as we do not yet know all of the mathematical and numerical complications that could emerge from the possible formation of an infinite number of Coulomb bound states in the exit channels.

DISCLOSURE STATEMENT

The authors are not aware of any biases that might be perceived as affecting the objectivity of this review.

LITERATURE CITED

1. Stoks VGJ, Klomp RAM, Terheggen CPF, Swart JJ. *Phys. Rev. C* 49:2950 (1994)
2. Wiringa RB, Stoks VGJ, Schiavilla R. *Phys. Rev. C* 51:38 (1995)
3. Machleidt R. *Phys. Rev. C* 63:024001 (2001)
4. Pudliner BS, et al. *Phys. Rev. C* 56:1720 (1997)
5. Coon SA, et al. *Nucl. Phys. A* 317:242 (1979)
6. Coelho HT, Das TK, Robilotta MR. *Phys. Rev. C* 28:1812 (1983)
7. Deltuva A, Machleidt R, Sauer PU. *Phys. Rev. C* 68:024005 (2003)

8. Weinberg S. *Physica* 96A:327 (1979); *Phys. Lett. B* 251:288 (1990); *Nucl. Phys. B* 363:3 (1991); *Phys. Lett. B* 295:114 (1992)
9. van Kolck U. *Prog. Part. Nucl. Phys.* 43:337 (1999)
10. Epelbaum E, Glockle W, Meissner U-G. *Nucl. Phys. A* 671:295 (1998); *Nucl. Phys. A* 671:295 (2000)
11. Entem DR, Machleidt R. *Phys. Rev. C* 68:041001(R) (2003)
12. Pieper SC, Pandharipande VR, Wiringa RB, Carlson J. *Phys. Rev. C* 64:014001 (2001)
13. Pieper SC, Varga K, Wiringa RB. *Phys. Rev. C* 66:044310 (2002)
14. Caurier E, Navratil P, Ormand WE, Vary JP. *Phys. Rev. C* 66:024314 (2002)
15. Glöckle W, et al. *Phys. Rep.* 274:107 (1996)
16. Kievsky A, Viviani M, Rosati S. *Phys. Rev. C* 64:024002 (2001)
17. Viviani M, et al. *Phys. Rev. C* 61:064001 (2000); Marcucci LE, et al. *Phys. Rev. C* 72:014001 (2005)
18. Lazauskas R, Carbonell J. *Phys. Rev. C* 70:044002 (2004); Lazauskas R, et al. *Phys. Rev. C* 71:034004 (2005)
19. Viviani M, et al. *Phys. Rev. Lett.* 86:3739 (2001)
20. Golak J, et al. *Phys. Rep.* 4 15:89 (2005)
21. Deltuva A, Fonseca AC, Sauer PU. *Phys. Rev. C* 71:054005 (2005)
22. Deltuva A, Fonseca AC, Sauer PU. *Phys. Rev. Lett.* 95:092301 (2005)
23. Deltuva A, Fonseca AC, Sauer PU. *Phys. Rev. C* 72:054004 (2005)
24. Deltuva A, Fonseca AC, Sauer PU. *Phys. Rev. C* 73:057001 (2006)
25. Deltuva A, Fonseca AC. *Phys. Rev. C* 75:014005 (2007)
26. Deltuva A, Fonseca AC. *Phys. Rev. Lett.* 98:162502 (2007)
27. Deltuva A, Fonseca AC. *Phys. Rev. C* 76:021001(R) (2007)
28. Deltuva A. *Phys. Rev. C* 74:064001 (2006)
29. Deltuva A, et al. *Phys. Rev. C* 76:064602 (2007); Fonseca AC. *Proc. Int. IUPAP Nucl. Phys. Conf., Tokyo* (2007)
30. Glöckle W. *The Quantum Mechanical Few-Body Problem*. Berlin/Heidelberg: Springer-Verlag (1983)
31. Faddeev LD. *Zh. Eksp. Theor. Fiz.* 39:1459 (1960) [*Sov. Phys. JETP* 12:1014 (1961)]
32. Alt EO, Grassberger P, Sandhas W. *Nucl. Phys.* B2:167 (1967)
33. Merkuriev SP. *Ann. Phys. (NY)* 130:395 (1980)
34. Faddeev LD, Merkuriev SP. *Quantum Scattering Theory for Several Particle System*. London: Kluwer Academic Publishers (1993)
35. Kuperin Yu A, Merkuriev SP, Kvitsinskii AA. *Sov. J. Nucl. Phys.* 37:857 (1983)
36. Berthold GH, Stadler A, Zankel H. *Phys. Rev. C* 41:1365 (1990)
37. Alt EO, Mukhamedzhanov AM, Sattarov AI. *Phys. Rev. Lett.* 81:4820 (1998)
38. Alt EO, Rauh M. *Few-Body Syst.* 17:121 (1994)
39. Alt EO, Mukhamedzhanov AM, Nishonov MM, Sattarov AI. *Phys. Rev. C* 65:064613 (2002)
40. Chen CR, Friar JL, Payne GL. *Few-Body Syst.* 31:13 (2001)
41. Ishikawa S. *Few-Body Syst.* 32:229 (2003)
42. Papp Z. *Phys. Rev. C* 55:1080 (1997)
43. Suslov VM, Vlahovic B. *Phys. Rev. C* 69:044003 (2004)
44. Alt EO, Levin SB, Yakovlev SL. *Phys. Rev. C* 69:034002 (2004)
45. Oryu S. *Few-Body Syst.* 34:113 (2004); Oryu S. *Phys. Rev. C* 73:054001 (2006)
46. Kadyrov AS, Bray I, Mukhamedzhanov AM, Stelbovics AT. *Phys. Rev. A* 72:032712 (2005)
47. Oryu S, Nishinohara S, Shiiki N, Chiba S. *Phys. Rev. C* 75:021001(R) (2007)
48. Taylor JR. *Nuovo Cimento B* 23:313 (1974); Semon MD, Taylor JR. *Nuovo Cimento A* 26:48 (1975)
49. Alt EO, Sandhas W, Ziegelmann H. *Phys. Rev. C* 17:1981 (1978)
50. Alt EO, Sandhas W. *Phys. Rev. C* 21:1733 (1980)
51. Gorshkov VG. *Sov. Phys.-JETP* 13:1037 (1961)
52. Rodberg LS, Thaler RM. *Introduction to the Quantum Theory of Scattering*. New York: Academic (1967)
53. Deltuva A, et al. *Phys. Rev. C* 71:064003 (2005)
54. Kistryn St, et al. *Phys. Lett. B* 641:23 (2006)
55. Low DA, et al. *Phys. Rev. C* 44:2276 (1991)
56. Kolb NR, et al. *Phys. Rev. C* 44:37 (1991)
57. Koersner I, et al. *Nucl. Phys. A* 286:431 (1977)

58. Austern N, et al. *Phys. Rep.* 154:125 (1987)

59. Watson BA, Singh PP, Segel RE. *Phys. Rev.* 182:977 (1969)

60. Matsuoka N, et al. *Nucl. Phys. A* 455:413 (1986)

61. Matsuoka N, et al. *Nucl. Phys. A* 391:357 (1982)

62. Grassberger P, Sandhas W. *Nucl. Phys. B* 2:181 (1967); Alt EO, Grassberger P, Sandhas W. JINR report No. E4–6688 (1972)

63. Doleschall P. *Phys. Rev. C* 69:054001 (2004)

64. Deltuva A, Fonseca AC, Sauer PU. *Phys. Lett. B* 660:471 (2008)

65. Fisher BM, et al. *Phys. Rev. C* 74:034001 (2006)

66. McDonald DG, Haeberli W, Morrow LW. *Phys. Rev.* 133:B1178 (1964)

67. Alley MT, Knutson LD. *Phys. Rev. C* 48:1890 (1993)

68. Seagrave JD, Cranberg L, Simmons JE. *Phys. Rev.* 119:1981 (1960)

69. Jany P, et al. *Nucl. Phys. A* 483:269 (1988)

70. Klages HO, et al. *Nucl. Phys. A* 443:237 (1985)

71. Blair JM, et al. *Phys. Rev.* 74:1599 (1948)

72. Grüebler W, et al. *Nucl. Phys. A* 193:129 (1972)

73. Dries LJ, Clark HW, Detomo R, Donoghue TR. *Phys. Lett.* 80B:176 (1979)

74. Yakubovsky OA. *Sov. J. Nucl. Phys.* 5:937 (1967)

The Exotic *XYZ* Charmonium-Like Mesons

Stephen Godfrey[1] and Stephen L. Olsen[2,3]

[1] Ottawa-Carleton Institute for Physics, Department of Physics, Carleton University, Ottawa, Ontario K1S 5B6, Canada; email: godfrey@physics.carleton.ca

[2] Institute of High Energy Physics, Beijing, China 100049

[3] Department of Physics and Astronomy, University of Hawaii at Manoa, Honolulu, Hawaii 96822; email: solsen@phys.hawaii.edu

Annu. Rev. Nucl. Part. Sci. 2008. 58:51–73

First published online as a Review in Advance on May 22, 2008

The *Annual Review of Nuclear and Particle Science* is online at nucl.annualreviews.org

This article's doi:
10.1146/annurev.nucl.58.110707.171145

Key Words

mesons, charmonium, hybrids, molecules, tetraquarks

Abstract

Charmonium, the spectroscopy of $c\bar{c}$ mesons, has recently enjoyed a renaissance with the discovery of several missing states and numerous unexpected charmonium-like resonances. These discoveries were made possible by the extremely large data samples made available by the *B* factories at SLAC and KEK, as well as CESR. Conventional $c\bar{c}$ states are well described by quark potential models; however, many of the newly discovered charmonium-like mesons do not seem to fit into the conventional $c\bar{c}$ spectrum. There is growing evidence that at least some of these new states are exotic, e.g., new forms of hadronic matter such as mesonic molecules, tetraquarks, and/or hybrid mesons. In this review we describe expectations for the properties of conventional charmonium states and the predictions for molecules, tetraquarks, and hybrids and the various processes that produce them. We examine the evidence for the new candidate exotic mesons, possible explanations, and experimental measurements that might reveal the nature of these states.

Contents

1. INTRODUCTION

Meson: a bound state of a quark and antiquark ($q\bar{q}$)

Baryon: a bound state of three quarks (qqq)

CQM: constituent quark model

QCD: quantum chromodynamics, the theory of strong interactions

Lattice QCD: a numerical approach to calculate hadronic properties wherein spacetime is discretized and Monte Carlo techniques are used to calculate expectation values of various operators by integrating over the quark gluon configurations

In 1964, faced with a large proliferation of strongly interacting subatomic particles, Murray Gell-Mann (1) and George Zweig (2) independently hypothesized the existence of three fractionally charged constituent fermions called quarks, the charge $= +\frac{2}{3}e$ up (u) quark and the charge $= -\frac{1}{3}e$ down (d) and strange (s) quarks and their antiparticles ($e = +1.6 \times 10^{-19}$ Coulombs). In the Gell-Mann–Zweig scheme, mesons are formed from quark and antiquark ($q\bar{q}$) pairs and baryons from three-quark triplets (qqq). This picture was remarkably successful; it accounted for all of the known hadrons at that time and predicted the existence of additional hadrons that were subsequently discovered.

More than 40 years later, the Gell-Mann–Zweig idea (also known as the constituent quark model, or CQM) remains an effective scheme for classifying all of the known hadrons, although the number of quarks has expanded to include the charge $= +\frac{2}{3}e$ charm (c) and top (t) quarks and the charge $= -\frac{1}{3}e$ bottom (b) quark.

Our current understanding is that the forces that bind quarks into hadrons are described by the non-Abelian field theory called quantum chromodynamics (QCD). At distance scales that correspond to the separations between quarks inside hadrons, QCD is a strongly coupled theory and perturbation theory is of limited applicability. It is expected that ultimately, numerical lattice QCD computations (3) will generate predictions for QCD observables such as masses, transitions, and decays. However, progress—while steady—is slow, and it will be some time before investigators are able to make precise reliable predictions for hadron masses. To date, models that incorporate general features of QCD have proven to be the most useful approach for describing the spectra and properties of hadrons. One prediction of these QCD-motivated models, supported by lattice QCD, is the existence of hadrons with more complex substructures than those of the simple

$q\bar{q}$ mesons and the qqq baryons. In spite of considerable experimental effort, however, no un-ambiguous evidence for hadrons with a non-CQM-like structure was found until recently, when studies of the spectrum of charmonium mesons (i.e., mesons formed from a $c\bar{c}$ pair) uncovered a number of meson candidates that do not seem to conform to CQM expectations. The status of these candidate non-$q\bar{q}$ particles, the so-called *XYZ* mesons, is the subject of this review.

We organize our discussion as follows: Section 2 provides a brief summary of theoretical expectations for charmonium mesons and the more complex structures that are expected in the context of QCD; Section 3 provides some experimental background of the recent observations; Section 4 forms the bulk of the review, describing the evidence for and measured properties of the *XYZ* states, why they defy any CQM assignment, and theoretical speculation about their nature and how to test these hypotheses; and Section 5 contains summary points and future issues. Recent related reviews on charmonium spectroscopy and the *XYZ* states may be found in References 4–8.

2. THEORETICAL BACKGROUND

QCD-motivated potential models successfully described the J/ψ and ψ' as $c\bar{c}$ states soon after they were discovered more than 30 years ago. These models have stood up quite well over the ensuing years, during which other low-lying $c\bar{c}$ states were discovered and were found to have properties that agree reasonably well with the models' predictions. Early pioneering papers also predicted the existence of mesons that are more complicated than conventional $q\bar{q}$ states such as multiquark states (9, 10) and hybrid mesons, which are states with an excited gluonic degree of freedom (11). Although corresponding exotic states are predicted to exist in the light meson spectrum, they are difficult to disentangle from the dense background of conventional states (12) therein. The charmonium spectrum provides a cleaner environment where (one might hope) nonconventional states containing $c\bar{c}$ pairs may be easier to identify. In this section we give a brief overview of the properties of conventional charmonium states and the nonconventional multiquark and hybrid states. In addition, we mention threshold effects that could masquerade as resonances.

2.1. Charmonium States and Properties

In QCD-motivated quark potential models, quarkonium states are described as a quark-antiquark pair bound by an interquark force with a short-distance behavior that is dominated by single-gluon exchange and is thus approximately Coulombic, plus a linearly increasing confining potential that dominates at large separations. Typically, one finds the energy levels by solving a nonrelativistic Schrödinger equation, although there are more sophisticated calculations that take into account relativistic corrections and other effects. These calculations yield energy levels that are charac-terized by the radial quantum number n and the relative orbital angular momentum between the quark and antiquark, L. The current status of this approach is shown in **Figure 1**, which also shows the observed charmonium levels. For those levels that have been assigned, the commonly used names of their associated mesons are indicated.

As indicated in **Figure 1**, the orbital levels are labeled by **S, P, D** and the quark and antiquark spins couple to give the total spin $S = 0$ (spin-singlet) or $S = 1$ (spin-triplet). S and L couple to give the total angular momentum of the state, J. The parity of a quark-antiquark state with orbital angular momentum L is $P = (-1)^{L+1}$ and the charge conjugation eigenvalue is given by $C = (-1)^{L+S}$. Quarkonium states are generally denoted by $^{2S+1}L_J$ with quantum numbers J^{PC}. Thus, the $L = 0$ states are $^1S_0$ and $^3S_1$ with $J^{PC} = 0^{-+}$ and 1^{--}, respectively; the $L = 1$ states are $^1P_1$ and $^3P_{0,1,2}$ with $J^{PC} = 1^{+-}$, 0^{++}, 1^{++}, and 2^{++}; the $L = 2$ states are $^1D_2$ and $^3D_{1,2,3}$ with $J^{PC} = 2^{-+}$, 1^{--}, 2^{--}, and 3^{--}; etc.

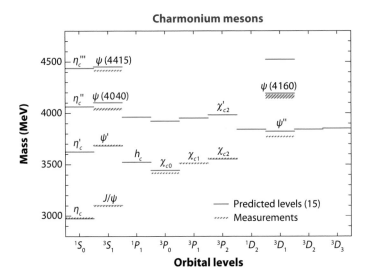

Figure 1

Diagram of charmonium levels. The commonly used names for the mesons associated with assigned states are indicated. The states are labeled by $^{2S+1}L_J$, where S is the total spin of the quark-antiquark pair; L is the relative angular momentum between the quark and antiquark labeled by S, P, D, corresponding to $L = 0, 1, 2$; and J is the total angular momentum of the meson.

In addition to the spin-independent potential, there are spin-dependent interactions that produce corrections of order $(v/c)^2$, where v is the quark speed and c is the speed of light. These are found by assuming a specific Lorentz structure for the quark-antiquark interactions. Typically the short-distance one-gluon exchange is taken to be a Lorentz vector interaction and the confinement piece is assumed to be a Lorentz scalar. The resulting potential gives rise to splittings within multiplets. For example, the $J/\psi(1^3S_1) - \eta_c(1^1S_0)$ splitting is attributed to a short-distance $\vec{S}_Q \cdot \vec{S}_{\bar{Q}}$ contact interaction arising from the one-gluon exchange, whereas the splittings of the P-wave $\chi_c(1^3P_{J=0,1,2})$ and higher L states are due to spin-orbit and tensor spin-spin interactions arising from one-gluon exchange and a relativistic spin-orbit Thomas precession term. The recent measurement of the h_c mass by CLEO (13, 14) is an important validation of this picture.

An important approach to understanding the charmonium spectrum is lattice QCD (3). There has been considerable recent progress in calculating the masses of excited $c\bar{c}$ states and radiative transitions (15), although the results are still not sufficient to make precision predictions for excited states. However, lattice QCD calculations of the static energy between a heavy quark-antiquark pair are in good agreement with phenomenological potentials (3), and lattice calculations of the spin-dependent potentials also support the phenomenological contact, tensor, and spin-orbit potentials (16).

All charmonium states below the $D\bar{D}$ "open-charm" mass threshold have been observed. The D-wave $c\bar{c}$ states lie just above this threshold[1] and thus far only the 1^3D_1 state, identified as the ψ'' [or $\psi(3770)$], has been observed. The remaining $n = 1$ D-wave charmonium states, the spin-triplet $^3D_2$ and $^3D_3$ states, and the spin singlet $^1D_2$ state are all expected to have masses near 3800 MeV/c^2 and to be narrow (17–20); therefore it should be possible to observe them (21). The $n = 2$ P states are the next highest multiplet, with masses predicted to lie in the range of

---

[1]D^0 and D^+ mesons: spin-singlet S-wave (1^1S_0) $c\bar{u}$ and $c\bar{d}$ quark states, respectively.

3800–3980 MeV/c^2 and with total widths of 80, 165, 30, and 87 MeV/c^2 for the $2^3 P_2$, $2^3 P_1$, $2^3 P_0$, and $2^1 P_1$, respectively. We also mention the $1^3 F_4$ as it is relatively narrow for a state so massive; it has a predicted mass and width of 4021 and ~ 8 MeV, respectively. The η_c'' ($3^1 S_0$) mass and width are predicted to be ~ 4050 MeV/c^2 and ~ 80 MeV/c^2.

Although the mass value is an important first element for the identification of a new state, more information is usually needed to distinguish among different possibilities. One therefore needs other measurements to form a detailed picture of the new state's internal structure. Decay properties provide important input for constructing this picture.

Electromagnetic transitions can potentially give information on the quantum numbers of a parent state when it decays to a final state with established quantum numbers such as the J/ψ or χ_{cJ}; studies of the angular correlations among the final-state decay particles provide additional information. Quark model predictions also provide an important benchmark against which to test a conventional quarkonium interpretation versus an exotic one. The theory of electromagnetic transitions between quarkonium states is straightforward, and potential models provide detailed predictions that can be compared to experimental measurements to test the internal structure of a state. The leading-order amplitudes are those for electric ($E1$) and magnetic ($M1$) dipole transitions; the $E1$ amplitude is the most relevant to our discussion. The predictions for the $^3 P_J \leftrightarrow {}^3 S_1$ transitions are in good agreement with experimental data (4). We can therefore expect that other electromagnetic transitions will also yield useful information, with possible exceptions for those cases in which there are large dynamical cancellations in the matrix elements (for instance those that involve higher radial excitations that have nodes in their wave functions). The status of electromagnetic transitions has been reviewed recently (4), and detailed predictions for charmonium states are given in References 17–20.

Charmonium states can also undergo hadronic transitions from one $c\bar{c}$ state to another via the emission of light hadrons. Examples of observed transitions include $\psi(2s) \rightarrow J/\psi \pi^+ \pi^-$, $\psi(2s) \rightarrow J/\psi \eta$, $\psi(2s) \rightarrow J/\psi \pi^0$, and $\psi(2s) \rightarrow h_c \pi^0$. The theoretical description of hadronic transitions uses a multipole expansion of the gluonic fields (22–27), which resembles the usual multipole expansion applied to electromagnetic transitions. Detailed predictions for hadronic transitions are given in References 28–35.

Charmonium states above the $D\bar{D}$ and/or $D\bar{D}^*$ mass threshold can decay to DD or $D\bar{D}^{(*)}$ final states.[2] These decays are well described by the $^3 P_0$ model, wherein a light $q\bar{q}$ pair is created out of the vacuum with the quantum numbers of the vacuum, 0^{++} (17, 18, 36–38). The partial decay widths have been calculated for many mesons using this model and the overall qualitative agreement with experiment is very good. Thus, the predictions can provide a useful means of identifying conventional charmonium states. Recent calculations of decay properties of excited charmonium states are given in References 17–20.

A final decay of charmonium states occurs via the annihilation of the $c\bar{c}$ into final states consisting of gluons and light quark pairs, sometimes with a photon (39, 40). So far, however, these processes have not proven to be very important for classifying charmonium states.

2.2. Multiquark States

An early quark model prediction posited the existence of multiquark states, specifically bound meson-antimeson molecular states (9, 10). In the light quark sector the $f_0(980)$ and $a_0(980)$ are considered to be strong candidates for $K\bar{K}$ molecules. In general, however, it is challenging to

---

[2] The D^* mesons are the spin-triplet $1^3 S_1$ partners of the D mesons.

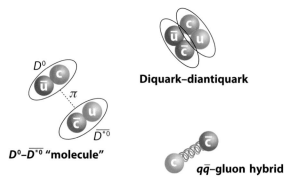

Diquark–diantiquark

D^0

π

$\bar{D}^{*0}$

D^0–$\bar{D}^{*0}$ "molecule"

$q\bar{q}$–gluon hybrid

Figure 2

Schematic representations of molecular states, diquark-diantiquark tetraquark mesons, and quark-antiquark-gluon hybrids.

identify unambiguously a light multiquark state in an environment of many broad and often overlapping conventional states. The charmonium spectrum is better defined, so new types of states can potentially be more easily delineated from conventional charmonium states. The observation of the $X(3872)$, the first of the XYZ particles to be seen, allowed researchers to hope that a multiquark state had definitively been observed.

Two generic types of multiquark states have been described in the literature. The first is a molecular state, sometimes referred to as a deuson (41), that comprises two charmed mesons bound together to form a molecule. These states are by nature loosely bound. Molecular states bind through two mechanisms: quark/color exchange interactions at short distances and pion exchange at large distance (5, 41, 42) (see **Figure 2**), although pion exchange is expected to dominate (5). Molecular states are generally not isospin eigenstates, resulting in distinctive decay patterns. Because the mesons inside the molecule are weakly bound, they tend to decay as if they are free. The details of this process are reviewed by Swanson (5).

The second type of multiquark state is a tightly bound four-quark state, known as a tetraquark, which is predicted to have properties different from those of a molecular state. In the model of Maiani et al. (43) the tetraquark is described as a diquark-diantiquark structure in which the quarks group into color-triplet scalar and vector clusters and in which the interactions are dominated by a simple spin-spin interaction (see **Figure 2**). Here, strong decays are expected to proceed via rearrangement processes, followed by dissociation, that give rise to (for example) decays such as $X \to \rho J/\psi \to \pi\pi J/\psi$ or $X \to D\bar{D}^* \to D\bar{D}\gamma$. A prediction that distinguishes multiquark states containing a $c\bar{c}$ pair from conventional charmonia is the possible existence of multiplets that include members with nonzero charge (e.g., $[cu\bar{c}\bar{d}]$), strangeness (e.g., $[cd\,\bar{c}\bar{s}]$), or both (e.g., $[cu\bar{c}\bar{s}]$) (44).

2.3. Charmonium Hybrids

Hybrid mesons are states characterized by an excited gluonic degree of freedom (see **Figure 2**), which have been described by many different models and calculational schemes (45). A compelling description, supported by lattice QCD (46, 47), views the quarks as moving in adiabatic potentials produced by gluons by analogy to the atomic nuclei in molecules moving in the adiabatic potentials produced by electrons. The lowest adiabatic surface leads to the conventional quarkonium spectrum, whereas the excited adiabatic surfaces result from putting the gluons into more complicated color configurations. In the flux-tube model (48), the lowest excited adiabatic surface corresponds to transverse excitations of the flux tube and leads to a doubly degenerate octet of the lowest mass hybrids with quantum numbers $J^{PC} = 0^{+-}, 0^{-+}, 1^{+-}, 1^{-+}, 2^{+-}, 2^{-+}, 1^{++}$, and 1^{--}. Quantum numbers $0^{+-}, 1^{-+}$, and 2^{+-} are not possible for a $c\bar{c}$ bound state in the quark model and are referred to as exotic quantum numbers. If observed, they would unambiguously signal the existence of an unconventional state. Lattice QCD and most models predict the lowest charmonium hybrid state to be roughly 4200 MeV/c^2 in mass (45, 48, 49).

Charmonium hybrids can decay via electromagnetic transitions, hadronic transitions such as $\psi_g \rightarrow J/\psi + \pi\pi$, or to open-charm final states such as $\psi_g \rightarrow D^{(*,**)}\bar{D}^{(*,**)}$.[3] The partial widths have been calculated using many different models. There are some general properties that seem to be supported by most models and by recent lattice QCD calculations. Nevertheless, because there are no experimental results against which to test these calculations, one should take their predictions with a grain of salt. Two important decay modes are:

1. $\psi_g \rightarrow D^{(*,**)}\bar{D}^{(**,*)}$. Most calculations predict that the ψ_g should decay to a P-wave plus an S-wave meson. In this case $D(L = 0) + D^{**}(L = 1)$ final states should dominate over decays to $D\bar{D}$ and the partial width to $D\bar{D}^*$ should be very small.
2. $\psi_g \rightarrow (c\bar{c})(gg) \rightarrow (c\bar{c}) + (\pi\pi, \eta\cdots)$. These modes offer clean experimental signatures. If the total width is small, they could have significant branching fractions. One recent lattice QCD calculation found that these types of decays are potentially quite large, with partial widths of order $\mathcal{O}(10 \text{ MeV}/c^2)$ (50).

2.4. Threshold Effects

In addition to various types of resonances, thresholds can also give rise to structures in cross sections and kinematic distributions. Possible thresholds include the DD^*, D^*D^*, DD_1, and D^*D_1 at $E_{cm} \sim 3872, 4020, 4287$, and 4430 MeV, respectively. At threshold, the cross section is typically dominated by S-wave ($L = 0$) scattering, although in some cases higher waves can be important. States in a relative S-wave with little relative momentum which live long on the timescale of strong interactions will have enough time to exchange pions and interact (51). Binding then becomes possible via an attractive π exchange that could occur via couplings such as $D \leftrightarrow D^*\pi^0$ and could lead to the molecular states discussed above. However, other strong interaction effects might also lead to a repulsive interaction that could result in a virtual state above threshold. Thus, passing through a kinematical threshold can lead to structure in the cross section that may or may not indicate a resonance. In addition, if there are nearby $c\bar{c}$ states they will interact with the threshold, resulting in mass shifts of both the $c\bar{c}$ resonance and the threshold-related enhancement. The effects of this channel coupling can be quite significant in the observed cross section, particularly close to thresholds (51, 52). These effects were studied for e^+e^- annihilation some time ago (53–55). Given the observation of new charmonium-like states in channels other than $J^{PC} = 1^{--}$, it would be useful to revisit these studies.

3. EXPERIMENTAL BACKGROUND

The observations described in this section were made possible by the extraordinary performance of the PEP-II B factory at the Stanford Linear Accelerator Center (SLAC) in the United States and the KEKB B factory at the High-Energy Accelerator Research Organization (KEK) in Japan.

---

[3] D^{**}: denotes mesons formed from P-wave $c\bar{q}$ ($q = u$ or d) pairs: $D_0^*(^3P_0)$, $D_2^*(^3P_2)$, and the D_1 and D_1' are $^3P_1 - ^1P_1$ mixtures.

Luminosity: measure
of the beam-beam
interaction intensity

B meson: particle
formed from a b quark
and a $\bar{d}$ or $\bar{u}$ quark in a
$1^1 S_0$ state

ISR: initial-state
radiation

These B factories, which were constructed to test the standard model mechanism for matter-antimatter asymmetries (so-called CP violation), are very high luminosity electron (e^-) positron (e^+) colliders operating at a center-of-mass (c.m.) energy near 10,580 MeV. Electron-positron annihilations at this c.m. energy produce large numbers of B meson–anti-B meson ($B\bar{B}$) pairs in a coherent quantum state. Measurements of the decay patterns of neutral $B^0 \bar{B}^0$ pairs by the BaBar experiment (56) at PEP-II and the Belle experiment (57) at KEKB have provided sensitive tests of the standard model mechanism for CP violation.

An unexpected bonus from the B factories has been a number of interesting contributions to the field of hadron spectroscopy, in particular the area of charmonium spectroscopy. At B factories, charmonium mesons are produced in a number of ways. Here we briefly describe the charmonium production mechanisms relevant to the XYZ states.

3.1. B Decays to Final States Containing $c\bar{c}$ Mesons

B mesons decay radioactively with a lifetime of approximately 1.5 ps. At the quark level, the dominant decay mechanism is the weak interaction transition of a b quark to a c quark accompanied by the emission of a virtual W^- boson, the mediator of the weak interaction. Approximately 15% of the time, the W^- boson materializes as a $s\bar{c}$ pair. As a result, around 15% of all B meson decays result in a final state that contains a c quark and a $\bar{c}$ quark. When these final state c and $\bar{c}$ quarks are produced close to each other in phase space, they can coalesce to form a $c\bar{c}$ charmonium meson.

The simplest charmonium-producing B meson decays are those wherein the s quark from the W^- combines with the parent B meson's $\bar{u}$ or $\bar{d}$ quark to form a K meson. In such decays, to the extent that the $\bar{u}$ or $\bar{d}$ quark acts as a passive spectator to the decay process, the possible J^{PC} quantum numbers of the produced $c\bar{c}$ charmonium system are 0^{-+}, 1^{--}, and 1^{++}. Experimenters have observed that decays of the type $B \to K(c\bar{c})$, where the $c\bar{c}$ pair forms a charmonium state with these J^{PC} values, occur with branching fractions that are all within about a factor of two of 1×10^{-3}. Because both of the B factory experiments detect more than a million B mesons a day, the number of detected charmonium states produced via the $B \to K(c\bar{c})$ process is substantial. In 2002, the Belle group discovered the η_c', the first radial excitation of the η_c meson, via the process $B \to K\eta_c'$, where $\eta_c' \to K_S K^- \pi^+$ (58).

3.2. Production of 1^{--} Charmonium States via Initial-State Radiation

In $e^+ e^-$ collisions at a c.m. energy of 10,580 MeV, the initial state e^+ or e^- occasionally radiates a high-energy γ ray, and the e^+ and e^- subsequently annihilate at a correspondingly reduced c.m. energy. When the c.m. energy of the radiated γ ray (γ_{ISR}) is between 4000 and 5000 MeV, the $e^+ e^-$ annihilation occurs at c.m. energies that correspond to the range of mc^2 values of charmonium mesons. Thus, the initial-state radiation (ISR) process can directly produce charmonium states with $J^{PC} = 1^{--}$. Although this is a suppressed higher-order QED process, the very high luminosities available at the B factories have made ISR a valuable research tool. For example, the BaBar group used the ISR technique to make measurements of J/ψ meson decay processes (59).

3.3. Charmonium-Associated Production with J/ψ Mesons in $e^+ e^-$ Annihilation

In studies of $e^+ e^-$ annihilations at c.m. energies near 10,580 MeV, the Belle group made the unexpected discovery that when a J/ψ meson is produced in the inclusive annihilation process $e^+ e^- \to J/\psi +$ anything, there is a high probability that the accompanying system will contain another $c\bar{c}$ meson system (60). Belle found, for example, cross sections for the annihilation processes $e^+e^- \rightarrow J/\psi\eta_c, J/\psi\chi_{c0}$, and $J/\psi\eta_c'$ that are more than an order of magnitude larger than previously expected (61). Thus the study of systems recoiling against the J/ψ in inclusive $e^+e^- \rightarrow J/\psi X$ annihilations is another source of $c\bar{c}$ states at a B factory. The very low cross sections for these processes are compensated by the very high luminosities. The conservation of charge-conjugation parity in electromagnetic processes guarantees that the C quantum number of the accompanying $c\bar{c}$ system will be $C = +$. Experimentally, only the 0^{-+} η_c and η_c' and the 0^{++} χ_{c0} are observed to be produced in association with a J/ψ. The 1^{++} χ_{c1} and 2^{++} χ_{c2} are not seen. This indicates that this process favors the production of $J = 0$ states over those with $J = 1$ and higher.

3.4. Two-Photon Collisions

In high-energy e^+e^- machines, photon-photon collisions are produced when both an incoming e^+ and an e^- radiate photons that subsequently interact with each other. Two-photon interactions can directly produce particles with $J^{PC} = 0^{-+}, 0^{++}, 2^{-+}$, and 2^{++}. For example, the CLEO group confirmed the existence of the η_c' charmonium state from studies of two-photon production of $K_S K^\pm \pi^\mp$ final states (62).

4. EXPERIMENTAL EVIDENCE AND THEORETICAL INTERPRETATIONS FOR THE *XYZ* MESONS

In this section we describe experimental characteristics of the *XYZ* mesons, discuss their various theoretical interpretations, and present measurements that can distinguish among possibilities and verify their nature.

4.1. *X*(3872)

In 2003, Belle first observed the $X(3872)$ as a narrow peak near $mc^2 = 3872$ MeV in the $\pi^+\pi^- J/\psi$ invariant mass distribution in $B^- \rightarrow K^-\pi^+\pi^- J/\psi$ decays (63). Shortly after the Belle announcement, it was observed by the Collider Detector at Fermilab (CDF) (64) and DØ (65) groups to be produced in high-energy proton-antiproton ($p\bar{p}$) collisions at the Fermilab Tevatron, and its production in B meson decays was subsequently confirmed by BaBar (66). Its current world average mass is (3871.4 ± 0.6) MeV/c^2, and its total width is less than 2.3 MeV/c^2 (67).

Both BaBar (68) and Belle (69) have reported evidence for the decay $X(3872) \rightarrow \gamma J/\psi$, which indicates that the $X(3872)$ has $C = +$. This evidence implies that the dipion in the $\pi^+\pi^- J/\psi$ mode has $C = -$, which suggests that it originates from a ρ. In fact, analyses of $X(3872) \rightarrow \pi^+\pi^- J/\psi$ decays by the CDF group have demonstrated that the dipion invariant mass distribution is most simply understood by the hypothesis that it originates from the decay $\rho \rightarrow \pi^+\pi^-$ (70). The decay of a charmonium state to $\rho J/\psi$ would violate isospin, and the evidence for this process provides an argument against a charmonium explanation for this state: Evidence for the decay $X(3872) \rightarrow \pi^+\pi^-\pi^0 J/\psi$ at a rate comparable to that of $\pi^+\pi^- J/\psi$ was reported by Belle (69), leading to speculation that the decay proceeds through a virtual ω, as had been predicted by Swanson (71). If confirmed, the coexistence of both the $X(3872) \rightarrow \pi^+\pi^- J/\psi$ and $X(3872) \rightarrow \pi^+\pi^-\pi^0 J/\psi$ transitions would imply that the $X(3872)$ is a mixture of both $I = 0$ and $I = 1$, as suggested by Close and Page (72). Angular correlations among the final-state particles from $X(3872) \rightarrow \pi^+\pi^- J/\psi$ decays rule out all J^{PC} assignments for the $X(3872)$ other than $J^{PC} = 1^{++}$ and 2^{-+} (73). Neither of the available charmonium assignments with these J^{PC} values—the 1^{++} χ_{c1}' (the 2^3P_1 $c\bar{c}$ state) and the 2^{-+} η_{c2} (the 1^1D_2 $c\bar{c}$ state)—is expected to have a large branching fraction for the isospin-violating $\rho J/\psi$ decay channel. Furthermore, a 2^{-+} assignment would require that the decay $X(3872) \to \gamma J/\psi$ be a highly suppressed higher multipole, and it is therefore unlikely. Finally, in the discussion below we identify the $Z(3930)$ as the 2^3P_2 state, thereby setting the 2^3P_2 mass at $\sim$3930 MeV/c^2; this measurement is inconsistent with the 2^3P_1 interpretation of the $X(3872)$, as the $2^3P_2 - 2^3P_1$ mass splittings are expected to be lower than $\sim$50 MeV/c^2 (17, 20).

An intriguing feature of the $X(3872)$ is that its measured mass value is nearly equal to the sum of the masses of the D^0 and D^{*0} mesons, which has recently been precisely measured by the CLEO experiment to be $m_{D^0} + m_{D^{*0}} = (3871.81 \pm 0.36)$ MeV/c^2 (74). This close correspondence has led to considerable speculation that the $X(3872)$ is a molecule-like bound state of a D^0 and a $\bar{D}^{*0}$ meson[4] (9, 10, 41, 71, 72, 75). The recent measurement of the D^0 mass implies a $D^{*0}\bar{D}^0$ binding energy of (0.4 ± 0.7) MeV/c^2.

A 1^{++} quantum number assignment for the $X(3872)$ implies that S-wave couplings of the X to $D^{*0}\bar{D}^0$ are permitted and that they result in a strong coupling between the X and the two mesons. This strong coupling can produce a bound state with a molecular structure just below the two-particle threshold. In this molecular scenario, the decays of the $X(3872)$ into $D^{*0}\bar{D}^0\pi^0$ and $D^*\bar{D}^0\gamma$ proceed through the decays of its constituent D^{*0} with branching ratios similar to those of the D^{*0} (72, 75). The $D^0\bar{D}^{0*}$ molecule wave function is expected to contain some admixture of $\rho J/\psi$ and $\omega J/\psi$, which explains the isospin-violating $\rho J/\psi$ decay mode and also successfully predicts the $\pi^+\pi^-\pi^-J/\psi$ decay width (71). This scenario further predicts the existence of a molecular $D^*\bar{D}^*$ state with mass 4019 MeV/c^2 and $J^{PC} = 0^{++}$ decaying to $\omega J/\psi$, $\eta\eta_c$, and $\eta'\eta_c$ (5). A related possibility is that the $X(3872)$ is dynamically generated (76).

Maiani et al. (43) advocate a tetraquark explanation for the $X(3872)$ (43, 77), which predicts the existence of a second neutral X state that is strongly produced in neutral B^0 meson decays to $K^0\pi^+\pi^-J/\psi$ with a mass that differs by 8 ± 3 MeV/c^2 from the mass of the $X(3872)$ produced in B^+ decays. This model also predicts the existence of charged isospin partner states.

Belle recently reported a $\sim$7σ signal for $X(3872)$ production in neutral B meson decays [i.e., $B^0 \to K^0_S X(3872)$], which is shown together with the signal from charged B meson decays in **Figure 3**. Belle determined a mass difference between the $X(3872)$ produced in charged versus neutral B decays of 0.9 ± 0.9 MeV/c^2 (78), which is consistent with zero and is inconsistent with the tetraquark model's prediction. This finding confirms an early lower-precision result from BaBar (79). The BaBar group also searched for a charged partner of the $X(3872)$ in the ρ^-J/ψ decay channel. They found no signal and excluded an isovector hypothesis for the $X(3872)$ with high confidence (80).

In studies of the decay process $B \to KD^0\bar{D}^0\pi^0$, both Belle (81) and BaBar (82) reported narrow enhancements just above the $m_{\pi^0} + 2m_{D^0}$ mass threshold. The peak mass values for the two observations [(3875.2 ± 1.9) MeV/c^2 for Belle and (3875.1 ± 1.2) MeV/c^2 for BaBar] are in good agreement with each other and are about four standard deviations higher than the $X(3872)$ mass measured with $\pi^+\pi^-J/\psi$ decays, which may be evidence for the second X state predicted in Reference 43. BaBar observed this enhancement in both the $D^0\bar{D}^0\pi^0$ and $D^0\bar{D}^0\gamma$ modes, which strongly supports the presence of the $D^0\bar{D}^{*0}$ intermediate state in the decay of this (possibly) new X (72, 75).

Dunwoodie and Ziegler argue that the mass shift between the two sets of observations is a result of the sensitivity of the peak position of the $D^*\bar{D}^0$ invariant mass distribution to the final-state orbital momentum because of the proximity of the $X(3872)$ to the $D^*\bar{D}^0$ threshold (83). Another

---

[4]In this review the inclusion of charge conjugate states is always implied, e.g., "a D^0 and a $\bar{D}^{*0}$ meson" could also mean "a D^{*0} and a $\bar{D}^0$ meson."

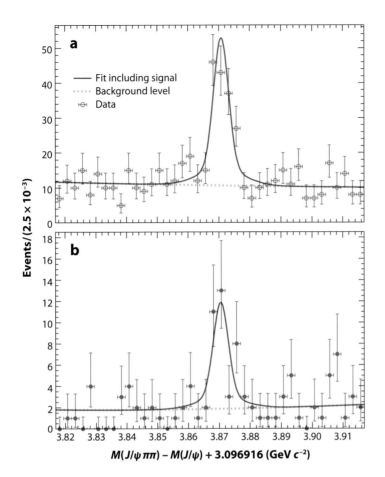

Figure 3

The $M(\pi^+\pi^- J/\psi)$ mass distributions produced in charge B^- (*a*) and neutral B^0 (*b*) decays to $K\pi^+\pi^- J/\psi$ final states (78).

explanation put forward in References 84–86 is that the line shapes of the $X(3872)$ depend on its decay channel and are different for the $J/\psi\pi^+\pi^-$, $J/\psi\pi^+\pi^-\pi^0$, and $D^0\bar{D}^0\pi^0$ channels. In both explanations the more massive enhancement is not regarded as a separate state, but as a manifestation of the $X(3872)$. In summary, there is an emerging consensus that the $X(3872)$ is a multiquark state; the molecular interpretation is favored due to its proximity to the DD^* threshold.

4.2. XYZ Particles with mc^2 Near 3940 MeV

Three apparently distinct XYZ candidate states have been observed with masses near $3940 \, \mathrm{MeV}/c^2$. These include the $X(3940)$, seen as a peak in the $D\bar{D}^*$ invariant mass in the process $e^+e^- \rightarrow J/\psi \, D\bar{D}^*$ (87); the $Y(3940)$, a peak in the $\omega J/\psi$ mass spectrum seen in $B \rightarrow K\omega J/\psi$ decays (88); and the $Z(3930)$, a peak in the invariant mass distribution of $D\bar{D}$ meson pairs produced in two-photon collisions (89).

4.2.1. The Z(3930). The $Z(3930)$ may be the easiest state to understand. It is a peak reported by Belle in the spectrum of $D\bar{D}$ mesons produced in $\gamma\gamma$ collisions, with mass and width measuring $M = 3929 \pm 6 \, \mathrm{MeV}/c^2$ and $\Gamma = 29 \pm 10 \, \mathrm{MeV}/c^2$ (89), respectively. The $D\bar{D}$ decay mode makes it impossible for the $Z(3930)$ to be the $\eta_c(3S)$ state. The two-photon production process can only produce $D\bar{D}$ in a 0^{++} or 2^{++} state. For these states the $dN/d\cos\theta^*$ distributions, where θ^* is the

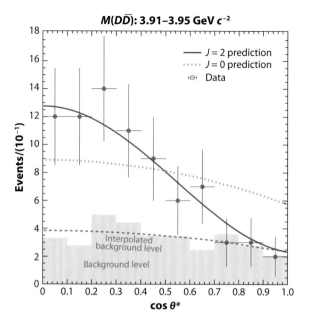

Figure 4

Belle's $\chi_{c2}(2P)$ candidate (89). $\cos\theta^*$ represents the angle of the D meson relative to the beam axis in the $\gamma\gamma$ center-of-mass frame for events with $3.91 < m(D\bar{D}) < 3.95$ GeV.

angle between the D meson and the incoming photon in the $\gamma\gamma$ c.m., are expected to be quite distinct: flat for 0^{++} and $\propto \sin^4\theta^*$ for 2^{++}. The Belle measurement strongly favors the 2^{++} hypothesis (see **Figure 4**), making the $Z(3930)$ a prime candidate for the χ'_{c2}, the $2^3 P_2$ charmonium state. The predicted mass of the $\chi_{c2}(2P)$ is 3972 MeV/c^2 and the predicted total width—assuming the observed mass value—is $\Gamma_{\rm total}(\chi_{c2}(2P)) = 28.6$ MeV/c^2 (17, 20, 90), which is in good agreement with the experimental measurement. Furthermore, the two-photon production rate for the $Z(3930)$ is also consistent with expectations for the χ'_{c2} (91). The $\chi_{c2}(2P)$ interpretation could be confirmed by observation of the $D\bar{D}^*$ final state, which is expected to have a $\mathcal{B} \sim 25\%$ (17, 20), and the radiative transition $\chi_{c2}(2P) \to \gamma\psi(2S)$, which is predicted to have a partial width of $\mathcal{O}(100 \text{ keV})$ (17, 20).

4.2.2. The $X(3940)$ and $X(4160)$. Belle observed the $X(3940)$ in double-charmonium production in the reaction $e^+e^- \to J/\psi + X$ with mass $M = 3943 \pm 8$ MeV/c^2 and intrinsic width $\Gamma < 52$ MeV/c^2 at 90% CL (87). In addition to the $X(3940)$, Belle observed the well-known charmonium states η_c, χ_{c0}, and $\eta_c(2S)$, which have properties consistent with other measurements of those states. Although a distinct signal for $X(3940) \to D\bar{D}^*$ has been observed, there is no evidence for the $X(3940)$ in either the $D\bar{D}$ or the $\omega J/\psi$ decay channels. If the $X(3940)$ has $J = 0$, as seems to be the case for mesons produced via this production mechanism, the absence of a substantial $D\bar{D}$ decay mode strongly favors $J^P = 0^{-+}$, for which the most likely charmonium assignment is the η''_c, the 3^1S_1 charmonium state. The fact that the lower mass $\eta_c(1S)$ and $\eta_c(2S)$ are also produced in double-charm production seems to support this assignment. The predicted width for a 3^1S_0 state with a mass of 3943 MeV/c^2 is $\sim$50 MeV/c^2 (20), which is in acceptable agreement with the measured $X(3940)$ width.

However, there are problems with this assignment. First, the measured mass of the $X(3940)$, recently updated by Belle to (3942 ± 8) MeV/c^2 (92), is below potential model estimates of $\sim$4050 MeV/c^2 or higher (17). Second, Belle recently observed a mass peak in the $D^*\bar{D}^*$ system recoiling from a J/ψ in the process $e^+e^- \to J/\psi D^* \bar{D}^*$ (92). This state, designated $X(4160)$, has a mass of (4156 ± 29) MeV/c^2 and a total width of $\Gamma = (139^{+113}_{-65})$ MeV/c^2. The production mechanism ensures that it has $C = +$. Using similar arguments, this latter state could also be attributed to the 3^1S_0 state. But the $X(4160)$ mass is well above expectations for the 3^1S_0 and well below those for the 4^1S_0, which is predicted to be near 4400 MeV/c^2 (17). Although either the $X(3940)$ *or* the $X(4160)$ might conceivably fit a charmonium assignment, it seems very unlikely that both of them could be accommodated as $c\bar{c}$ states. The η_c'' assignment can be tested by studying the angular distribution of the $D\bar{D}^*$ final state and by observing it in $\gamma\gamma \to D\bar{D}^*$.

4.2.3. The $Y(3940)$. Belle's observation of the $Y(3940) \to \omega J/\psi$ in $B \to K\omega J/\psi$ decays (88) has recently been confirmed by BaBar (93). Belle reports a mass and width of $M = (3943 \pm 17)$ MeV/c^2 and $\Gamma = (87 \pm 34)$ MeV/c^2, whereas BaBar reports values of $M = (3914.3^{+4.1}_{-3.8})$ MeV/c^2 and $\Gamma = (33^{+12}_{-8})$ MeV/c^2, both of which are somewhat smaller than Belle's values. The measured product branching fractions agree: $\mathcal{B}(B \to KY(3940))\mathcal{B}(X(3940) \to \omega J/\psi) = (7.1 \pm 3.4) \times 10^{-5}$ (Belle), and $\mathcal{B}(B \to KY(3940))\mathcal{B}(X(3940) \to \omega J/\psi) = (4.9 \pm 1.1) \times 10^{-5}$ (BaBar). These values, together with an assumption that the branching fraction $\mathcal{B}(B \to KY(3940))$ is less than or equal to 1×10^{-3} (a value that is typical for allowed $B \to K$+charmonium decays), imply a partial width $\Gamma(Y(3940) \to \omega J/\psi) > 1$ MeV/c^2, which is at least an order of magnitude higher than those for hadronic transitions between any of the established charmonium states. Belle's 90%-CL limit on $\mathcal{B}(X(3940) \to \omega J/\psi) < 26\%$ (87) is not stringent enough to rule out the possibility that the $X(3940)$ and the $Y(3940)$ are the same state.

The mass and width of the $Y(3940)$ suggest a radially excited P-wave charmonium state. We expect that $\chi_{c1}(2P) \to D\bar{D}^*$ would be the dominant decay mode, with a predicted partial width of 140 MeV/c^2 (94), which would be consistent with the width of the $Y(3940)$ within the theoretical and experimental uncertainties. Furthermore, the χ_{c1} is also seen in B decays. However, the large branching fraction for $Y \to \omega J/\psi$ is unusual for a $c\bar{c}$ state above open-charm threshold. A possible explanation for this unusual decay mode is that rescattering through $D\bar{D}^*$ is responsible: $1^{++} \to D\bar{D}^* \to \omega J/\psi$. Another contributing factor might be mixing with the molecular state that is tentatively identified with the $X(3872)$. The $\chi_{c1}(2P)$ assignment can be tested by searching for the $D\bar{D}$ and $D\bar{D}^*$ final states and by studying their angular distributions. With the present experimental data, a $\chi_{c0}(2P)$ assignment cannot be ruled out.

4.3. The $J^{PC} = 1^{--}$ States Produced via Initial-State Radiation

Using the ISR process, BaBar discovered unexpected peaks near 4300 MeV/c^2 in the $\pi^+\pi^- J/\psi$ and $\pi^+\pi^- \psi'$ channels. The partial widths for these decay channels are much larger than is usual for charmonium states. Because these states are produced via the ISR process, they have $J^{PC} = 1^{--}$. All of the 1^{--} charmonium levels in the 4000–4500 MeV/c^2 mass range have already been assigned to the well-established $\psi(4040)$, $\psi(4160)$, and $\psi(4415)$ mesons, which accords well with their assignments to the 3^3S_1, 2^3D_1, and 4^3S_1 $c\bar{c}$ states, respectively. The quark model predicts additional charmonium 1^{--} states, but at higher masses: $3^3D_1(4520)$, $5^3S_1(4760)$, $4^3D_1(4810)$, etc. (95). The experimental situation is likely complicated and obscured by interference among these resonances, which can affect the parameters extracted from the measurements.

4.3.1. The $Y(4260)$ $\pi^+\pi^- J/\psi$ resonance. The BaBar group measured the energy dependence of the cross section for $e^+e^- \to \pi^+\pi^- J/\psi$ using ISR radiation events at a primary c.m. energy of 10,580 MeV. They found a broad enhancement around 4260 MeV (96) that they called the

Y(4260). A fit to the peak with a single Breit-Wigner resonance shape yields mass $M = (4259 \pm 10)$ MeV/c^2 and full width $\Gamma = (88 \pm 24)$ MeV/c^2, values that are quite distinct from those of other established charmonium states. Although Y(4260) is well above the threshold for decaying into $D\bar{D}$, $D\bar{D}^*$, or $D^*\bar{D}^*$ meson pairs, there is no evidence for it in any of these channels (97). In fact, there appears to be a dip in the measured e^+e^- total annihilation cross section at this energy (98). An analysis using total cross section data for e^+e^- annihilation into hadrons at c.m. energies around 4260 MeV results in a 90%-CL lower limit on the partial decay width $\Gamma(Y(4260) \to \pi^+\pi^- J/\psi) > 1.6$ MeV/c^2 (99), which is much larger than the partial widths for equivalent transitions among established 1^{--} charmonium states. The Y(4260) peak was confirmed by both CLEO (100) and Belle (101). Belle reported a second, broader $\pi^+\pi^- J/\psi$ peak near 4008 MeV/c^2. It is currently not known whether this latter enhancement is due to the $\psi(4040)$, a dynamical threshold enhancement, or another meson state.

4.3.2. The $\pi^+\pi^-\psi'$ resonances at 4370 MeV/c^2 and 4660 MeV/c^2.

BaBar has also found a broad peak in the cross section for $e^+e^- \to \pi^+\pi^-\psi'$ that is distinct from the Y(4260); its peak position and width are not consistent with those of the Y(4260) (102). The BaBar observation was subsequently confirmed by a Belle study that used a larger data sample (103). Belle found that the $\pi^+\pi^-\psi'$ mass enhancement is, in fact, produced by two distinct peaks: (a) the Y(4360) with $M = (4361 \pm 13)$ MeV/c^2 and $\Gamma = (74 \pm 18)$ MeV/c^2 and (b) the Y(4660) with $M = (4664 \pm 12)$ MeV/c^2 and $\Gamma = (48 \pm 15)$ MeV/c^2 (103). These masses and widths are not consistent with any of the established 1^{--} charmonium states, and no sign of a peak at either of these masses is evident either in the e^+e^- total annihilation cross section (98) or in the exclusive cross sections $e^+e^- \to D\bar{D}$, $D\bar{D}^*$, or $D^*\bar{D}^*$ (97), which indicates that the $\pi^+\pi^-\psi'$ partial width for these states is unusually large (at least by charmonium standards). Moreover, as is evident in **Figure 5** there is no sign of either the Y(4360) or the Y(4660) in the $\pi^+\pi^- J/\psi$ channel, nor is there any sign of the Y(4260) peak in the $\pi^+\pi^-\psi'$ mass spectrum.

4.3.3. Discussion.

The discovery of the Y(4260), Y(4360), and Y(4660) appears to represent an overpopulation of the expected charmonium 1^{--} states. The absence of open-charm production is also inconsistent with a conventional $c\bar{c}$ explanation. Although Ding et al. (104) argue that the Y(4360) and Y(4660) are conventional $c\bar{c}$ states (in particular the 3^3D_1 and 5^3S_1, respectively), these states' masses are inconsistent with other quark model calculations (95). Other possible identities for these states include charmonium hybrids, S-wave charm meson thresholds, or multiquark states—either $cq\bar{c}\bar{q}$ tetraquarks or DD_1 and D^*D_0 molecules. Liu suggests that the peak at 4008 MeV/c^2 is related to the $D^*\bar{D}^*$ threshold and could be a $D^*\bar{D}^*$ molecule where the D^* and $\bar{D}^*$ are in a P-wave (105).

The Y(4260), the first state to be discovered, has received the most scrutiny. The first unaccounted-for $c\bar{c}$ state is the $\psi(3^3D_1)$, which is predicted to have a mass of $M(3^3D_1) \simeq 4500$ MeV/c^2—much too heavy to be the Y(4260). Numerous explanations of the Y(4260) have been proposed: It could be a $D\bar{D}_1(2420)$ threshold enhancement (106), a $D\bar{D}_1$ or $D^*\bar{D}_0^0$ bound state (51, 107, 108), or some sort of tetraquark (77, 109). In the latter cases, the Y would decay to $D\pi\bar{D}^*$, where the D and π are not from a D^*. One would expect this mode to have a large width, so its nonobservation disfavors the tetraquark/molecule explanations.

A plausible interpretation is that the Y(4260) is a charmonium hybrid (110–112). The flux tube model predicts the lowest $c\bar{c}$ hybrid to have a mass that is $\sim$4200 MeV/c^2 (45), which is consistent with lattice gauge theory predictions (49). Lattice gauge theory found that the $b\bar{b}$ hybrids have large partial widths for hadronic transitions (50); this finding accords with the BaBar observation of $Y \to J/\psi\pi^+\pi^-$ and is much larger than is typical for transitions involving conventional charmonium

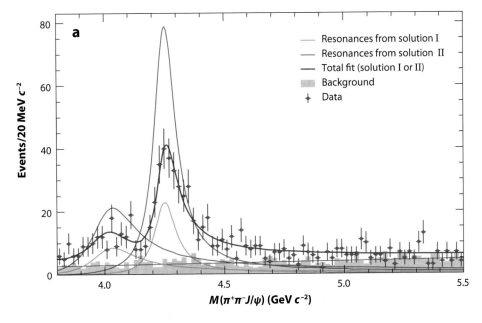

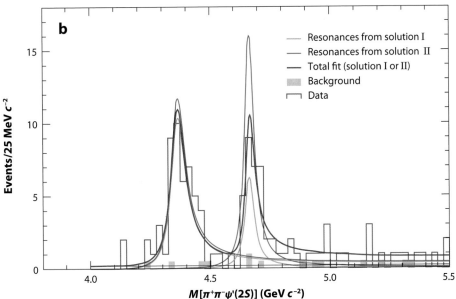

Figure 5

The $\pi^+\pi^- J/\psi$ (*a*) and $\pi^+\pi^- \psi'$ (*b*) invariant mass distributions for the initial-state radiation processes $e^+e^- \rightarrow \gamma\pi^+\pi^- J/\psi(\psi')$. These fits have two solutions with identical χ^2 values: the total fit (gray curve) is $|\text{Breit-Wigner } 1 + \text{Breit-Wigner } 2|^2$; the red (and orange) curves show $|\text{Breit-Wigner } 1|^2$ and $|\text{Breit-Wigner } 2|^2$ separately. Data reproduced from References 101 and 103 with permission.

states. A prediction of the hybrid hypothesis is that the dominant hybrid-charmonium open-charm decay modes are expected to be a meson pair with an S-wave (D, D^*, D_s, D_s^*) and a P-wave (D_J, D_{sJ}) in the final state (111). The dominant decay mode is expected to be $D\bar{D}_1$. Evidence for a large $D\bar{D}_1$ signal would be strong evidence for the hybrid interpretation. A complication is that the $D\bar{D}_1$ threshold is 4287 MeV/c^2 if we consider the lightest D_1 to be the narrow state at 2422 MeV/c^2 (67). Note that both the $Y(4370)$ and the $Y(4660)$ are well above the $D\bar{D}_1$ mass threshold. If the same hybrid interpretation were applied to them, decays to $D\bar{D}_1$ should be very strong and one would expect peaks in the exclusive cross sections for $e^+e^- \rightarrow D\bar{D}_1$ at these masses.

Lattice gauge theory also suggests that we search for other hadronic transitions with $J^{PC} = 1^{--}$: $J/\psi\eta, J/\psi\eta', \chi_{cJ}\omega$, and more. If the $Y(4260)$ is a hybrid it is expected to be a member of a multiplet consisting of eight states with masses in the 4000–4500 MeV/c^2 mass range. Discovery of some of these partners, especially those with exotic J^{PC} quantum numbers, would represent strong evidence for the hybrid theory. In the flux-tube model the exotic states have $J^{PC} = 0^{+-}, 1^{-+}$, and 2^{+-}, whereas the nonexotic low-lying hybrids have $0^{-+}, 1^{+-}, 2^{-+}, 1^{++}$, and 1^{--}.

Currently we do not have a good understanding of the Y states that are produced via ISR. Coupled-channel effects and rescattering of pairs of charmed mesons could play an important role (52) in understanding these peaks. Other phenomena that are not well understood include couplings to channels near thresholds that can interfere with conventional $c\bar{c}$ states. The challenge in extracting resonance parameters in this environment is highlighted by the recent Beijing Spectrometer Collaboration (BES) analysis, which found substantial variations in the resonance parameters from a fit that took into account the interference between these broad resonances compared to a fit that did not take interference into account (113). Clearly, more experimental information on the decay properties of these states and more theoretical work on coupled-channel and interference effects are needed if we are to achieve a better understanding of these states.

4.4. The $Z^+(4430) \rightarrow \pi^+\psi'$

In mid-2007, the Belle group reported on a study of the $B \rightarrow K\pi^+\psi'$ decay process wherein they observed a relatively narrow enhancement in the $\pi^+\psi'$ invariant mass distribution at $M = (4433 \pm 5)$ MeV/c^2 (114) (see **Figure 6**). The fitted width of $\Gamma = (45^{+35}_{-18})$ MeV/c^2 is too narrow to be caused by interference effects in the $K\pi$ channel. The B meson decay rate to this state, which is called

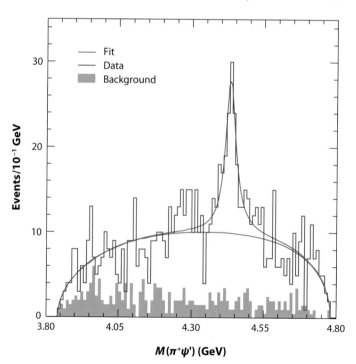

Figure 6

The $\pi^+\psi'$ invariant mass distribution for $B \rightarrow K\pi^+\psi'$ decays (114).

$Z^+(4430)$, is similar to that for decays to the $X(3872)$ and $Y(3940)$, suggesting that the $Z^+(4430)$ has a substantial branching fraction (i.e., greater than a few percent) to $\pi^+\psi'$ and, thus, a partial decay width for this mode that is on the MeV scale. There have been no reports of a $Z^+(4430)$ signal in the π^+J/ψ decay channel.

Among the XYZ exotic meson candidates the $Z^+(4430)$ is unique in that it has a nonzero electric charge, which is not possible for $c\bar{c}$ charmonium states or $c\bar{c}$-gluon hybrid mesons. It is, therefore, a prime candidate for a multiquark meson.

There have been a number of theoretical explanations. Because this candidate is close to the $D^*\bar{D}_1(2420)$ threshold, Rosner (115) and Bugg (116) suggest it is an S-wave threshold effect, whereas others consider it to be a strong candidate for a $D^*\bar{D}_1(2420)$ molecule (117–119). Maiani et al. (120) suggest that the $Z(4430)$ is a diquark-diantiquark state with flavor $[cu][\bar{c}\bar{d}]$ and is the radial excitation of an $X_{u\bar{d}}^+(1^{+-}; 1S)$ state with mass 3880 MeV/c^2. The tetraquark hypothesis suggests that the $Z(4430)^+$ will have neutral partners decaying to $\psi(2S)+\pi^0/\eta$ or $\eta_c(2S)+\rho^0/\omega$. If the $Z^+(4430)$ is a molecule, assuming that the $D^*\bar{D}_1$ is in a relative S-wave, it will have $J^P = 0^-$, 1^-, or 2^-, with the lightest state expected to be the 0^- (119). In contrast, a tetraquark would have $J^P = 1^+$. The molecule would decay via the decay of its constituent mesons into $D^*D^*\pi$ (117), whereas the tetraquark would fall apart into $D\bar{D}^*$, $D^*\bar{D}^*$, $J/\psi\pi$, $J/\psi\rho$, $\eta_c\rho$, and $\psi(2S)\pi$—but not into $D\bar{D}$ due to its unnatural spin parity (121).

4.5. Are There Corresponding States in the s and b Quark Sectors?

Many of the models proposed to explain the XYZ states predict analogous states in the $b\bar{b}$ and $s\bar{s}$ sectors. In the $s\bar{s}$ sector the $f_0(980)$ and $a_0(980)$ have long been identified as candidates for $K\bar{K}$ molecules. In the $b\bar{b}$ sector $B\bar{B}^*$, $B^*\bar{B}^*$ molecules (41) in addition to a $B^*\bar{B}_1$ molecule bound state are expected (118, 121, 122). In addition, threshold effects due to π exchange and hybrid states are also expected in both the $b\bar{b}$ and $s\bar{s}$ sectors (51). Therefore, it will be very interesting to see whether there are corresponding exotic meson candidates in the b quark and s quark sectors. Some recent results indicate that this may be the case.

4.5.1. An anomalous partial width for "$\Upsilon(nS)$" $\to \pi^+\pi^-\Upsilon(2S)$.
The bottomonium states are the $b\bar{b}$ counterparts of the charmonium mesons. For these, the $J^{PC} = 1^{--}$ states are the $\Upsilon(nS)$ mesons. Most of the data accumulated by the KEKB and PEP-II B factory experiments are at the c.m. energy that corresponds to the peak of the $\Upsilon(4S)$, the 4^3S_1 $b\bar{b}$ state at 10,580 MeV/c^2, which is just above the threshold for producing $B\bar{B}$ meson pairs. Using their large $\Upsilon(4S)$ data sample, the BaBar group measured the partial widths for $\Upsilon(4S) \to \pi^+\pi^-\Upsilon(2S)$ as well as $\pi^+\pi^-\Upsilon(1S)$ of (1.8 ± 0.4) keV/c^2 and (1.7 ± 0.5) keV/c^2 (123). The latter value has been confirmed by Belle (124) and both values are similar to those for dipion transitions from the $\Upsilon(3S)$ to the $\Upsilon(2S)$ $(0.6 \pm 0.2 \text{ keV}/c^2)$ and $\Upsilon(1S)$ $(1.2 \pm 0.2 \text{ keV}/c^2)$ (67).

Recently, Belle accumulated a much smaller data sample at 10,870 MeV, the peak of the $\Upsilon(5S)$, and found huge signals for $\pi^+\pi^-\Upsilon(1S)$, $\pi^+\pi^-\Upsilon(2S)$, and $\pi^+\pi^-\Upsilon(3S)$ (see **Figure 7**). If these are attributed to dipion transitions from the $\Upsilon(5S)$, the partial widths are (125)

$$\Gamma("\Upsilon(5S)" \to \pi^+\pi^-\Upsilon(1S)) = (590 \pm 100) \text{ keV}/c^2,$$
$$\Gamma("\Upsilon(5S)" \to \pi^+\pi^-\Upsilon(2S)) = (850 \pm 175) \text{ keV}/c^2, \text{ and}$$
$$\Gamma("\Upsilon(5S)" \to \pi^+\pi^-\Upsilon(3S)) = (520 \pm 220) \text{ keV}/c^2, \qquad\qquad 1.$$

which are more than two orders of magnitude larger than those for the corresponding transitions for the $\Upsilon(4S)$, $\Upsilon(3S)$, or $\Upsilon(2S)$. A likely interpretation is that a $b\bar{b}$ counterpart of the $Y(4260)$,

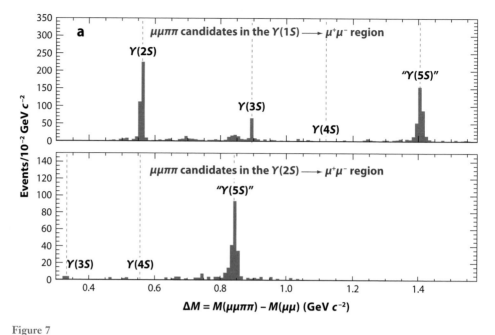

Figure 7

Belle's $M(\mu^+\mu^-\pi^+\pi^-) - M(\mu^+\mu^-)$ mass difference distributions for events with (*a*) $M(\mu^+\mu^-) = \Upsilon(1S)$ and (*b*) $M(\mu^+\mu^-) = \Upsilon(2S)$ (125). The vertical dashed lines indicate the expected locations for $\Upsilon(nS) \to \pi^+\pi^-\Upsilon(1, 2S)$ transitions. The $\Upsilon(2, 3S) \to \pi^+\pi^-\Upsilon(1S)$ signals in panel *a* are produced by initial-state radiation transitions $e^+e^- \to \gamma_{ISR}\Upsilon(2, 3S)$.

the Y_b, may be overlapping the $\Upsilon(5S)$, which could be the source of the anomalous $\pi^+\pi^-\Upsilon(nS)$ production (126).[5] As noted in Reference 125, this hypothesis could be verified by measuring the c.m.-energy dependence of the cross sections for $e^+e^- \to \pi^+\pi^-\Upsilon(nS)$ around 10,870 MeV. Another suggestion is that the anomalously high $\pi^+\pi^-$ transitions could be due to the mixing of conventional $b\bar{b}$ states with thresholds and subsequent rescattering (51). This interpretation could be tested by looking for other final states.

4.5.2. The $Y(2175) \to \phi f_0(980)$: an $s\bar{s}$ counterpart of the $Y(4260)$? In a study of the ISR process $e^+e^- \to \gamma_{ISR}\phi f_0(980)$, where $\phi \to K^+K^-$ and $f_0(980) \to \pi^+\pi^-$, the BaBar group observed a distinct resonance-like peak in the $\phi f_0(980)$ invariant mass distribution at a mass $M = (2175 \pm 18)$ MeV/c^2 with a full width $\Gamma = (58 \pm 26)$ MeV/c^2 (127). Recently, the BES group observed a $\phi f_0(980)$ invariant mass peak with mass and width values consistent with the BaBar observation in $J/\psi \to \phi f_0(980)\eta$ decays (128). The ϕ meson is the $s\bar{s}$ counterpart of the J/ψ, and the observed structure—called the $Y(2175)$—has production and decay characteristics similar to those of the $Y(4260)$. These similarities have prompted speculation that the $Y(2175)$ may be the Y_s, i.e., an s quark system counterpart to the $Y(4260)$ (129). Although this is an intriguing idea, the experimental situation is far from conclusive, and the $Y(2175)$ may very well be an excited state of the ϕ or some other $q\bar{q}$ meson. Ding & Yan (130) have suggested that studying the decay modes of the $Y(2175)$ can distinguish between the conventional $2^3 D_1(s\bar{s})$ and strangeonium hybrid explanations. Specifically, the dominant decay modes of an $s\bar{s}$ hybrid are $K_1(1400)\bar{K}$ and $K_1(1270)\bar{K}$

---

[5]This is the reason for the quotation marks around $\Upsilon(5S)$ in Equation 1.

Table 1 Properties of the candidate XYZ mesons

State	M (MeV)	Γ (MeV)	J^{PC}	Decay modes	Production modes	Reference(s)
$Y_s(2175)$	2175 ± 8	58 ± 26	1^{--}	$\phi f_0(980)$	e^+e^- (ISR), J/ψ decay	127, 128
$X(3872)$	3871.4 ± 0.6	<2.3	1^{++}	$\pi^+\pi^- J/\psi$, $\gamma J/\psi$	$B \to KX(3872)$, $p\bar{p}$	63–66
$X(3875)$	3875.5 ± 1.5	$3.0^{+2.1}_{-1.7}$		$D^0\bar{D}^0\pi^0$	$B \to KX(3875)$	81, 82
$Z(3940)$	3929 ± 5	29 ± 10	2^{++}	$D\bar{D}$	$\gamma\gamma$	89
$X(3940)$	3942 ± 9	37 ± 17	J^{P+}	$D\bar{D}^*$	$e^+e^- \to J/\psi X(3940)$	87, 92
$Y(3940)$	3943 ± 17	87 ± 34	J^{P+}	$\omega J/\psi$	$B \to KY(3940)$	88, 93
$Y(4008)$	4008^{+82}_{-49}	226^{+97}_{-80}	1^{--}	$\pi^+\pi^- J/\psi$	e^+e^- (ISR)	101
$X(4160)$	4156 ± 29	139^{+113}_{-65}	J^{P+}	$D^*\bar{D}^*$	$e^+e^- \to J/\psi X(4160)$	92
$Y(4260)$	4264 ± 12	83 ± 22	1^{--}	$\pi^+\pi^- J/\psi$	e^+e^- (ISR)	96, 100, 101
$Y(4350)$	4361 ± 13	74 ± 18	1^{--}	$\pi^+\pi^- \psi'$	e^+e^- (ISR)	102, 103
$Z(4430)$	4433 ± 5	45^{+35}_{-18}	?	$\pi^\pm \psi'$	$B \to KZ^\pm(4430)$	114
$Y(4660)$	4664 ± 12	48 ± 15	1^{--}	$\pi^+\pi^- \psi'$	e^+e^- (ISR)	103
Y_b	$\sim 10,870$	?	1^{--}	$\pi^+\pi^- \Upsilon(nS)$	e^+e^-	125

For simplicity, the quoted errors are quadratic sums of statistical and systematic uncertainties.

with, for example, the decays to $K\bar{K}$ or $K^*\bar{K}^*$ forbidden. In contrast the $2^3D_1(s\bar{s})$ is expected to have large branching fractions to $K\bar{K}$ and $K^*\bar{K}^*$. The $3^3S_1(s\bar{s})$ is not considered a candidate, as it is predicted to be quite broad. Further studies of the properties of the $Y(2175)$ and searches for s quark counterparts of other XYZ states could help clarify the situation.

5. SUMMARY

The B factory experiments have uncovered a large (and rapidly growing) number of candidates for charmonium and charmonium-like meson states, many of which cannot be easily accommodated by current theoretical expectations for $c\bar{c}$ mesons. Numerous models have been proposed to explain these states, including meson-antimeson molecules, diquark-diantiquark bound states, $c\bar{c}$ hybrids, and threshold effects. None of the proposed mechanisms easily accounts for all of the observations. Moreover, there is some evidence for similar behavior in the b and s quark sectors. As a summary, we list in **Table 1** all of the states discussed above along with some of their pertinent properties.

SUMMARY POINTS

1. QCD-motivated quark potential models describe the properties of the charmonium spectrum quite well.

2. Over the past few years researchers have discovered the η_c', h_c, and χ_{c2}' charmonium states and have found that their measured properties are in good agreement with the quark model predictions.

3. There is accumulating evidence for the existence of mesons with mass in the region between 3800 MeV/c^2 and 4700 MeV/c^2 that are not easily explained as simple quark-antiquark states of the charmonium model. These mesons have a number of intriguing and/or unexpected properties.

4. These states are relatively narrow, although many of them are well above relevant open-charm thresholds. Many of them have partial widths for decays to charmonium + light hadrons that are at the ~MeV scale, which is much larger than is typical for established $c\bar{c}$ charmonium meson states.

5. The $X(3872)$, which was first seen as a narrow peak in the invariant mass distribution of $\pi^+\pi^-J/\psi$ in $B^- \to K^-\pi^+\pi^-J/\psi$, is not easily described as a conventional $c\bar{c}$ state and is a strong candidate for a $D\bar{D}^*$ molecule.

6. The new 1^{--} charmonium states are not apparent in the $e^+e^- \to$ charmed-meson pair or the total hadronic cross sections and there are no evident changes in the properties of these states at the DD^{**} mass threshold. There seems to be some selectivity: States that are observed to decay to final states with a ψ' are not observed in the corresponding J/ψ channel, and vice versa. At least one of these states is regarded as a strong candidate for a charmonium hybrid.

7. At least one of these new states, the $Z(4430)$, is unique in that it has a nonzero electric charge.

8. There is some evidence that similar states exist in the s and b quark sectors.

FUTURE ISSUES

1. To confirm that these states are not conventional $c\bar{c}$ states, investigators must perform more detailed studies of their properties, especially measurements of their quantum numbers and of other decay modes.

2. It will also be important to have rigorous quantitative limits on the nonobservation of final states.

3. Researchers should verify the existence of similar states in the $s\bar{s}$ and $b\bar{b}$ sectors and measure their properties.

4. Because many of these states have been observed to have masses that are close to kinematic thresholds, it is necessary that we improve the theoretical understanding of threshold effects, including π-exchange contributions, coupled-channel effects, and the interaction between both resonances and thresholds via coupled channel effects and the resulting observed cross sections.

DISCLOSURE STATEMENT

The authors are not aware of any biases that might be perceived as affecting the objectivity of this review.

ACKNOWLEDGMENTS

We thank T. Barnes, K.-F. Chen, S.-K. Choi, F. Close, J. Rosner, E. Swanson, K. Trabelsi, S. Uehara, and C.Z. Yuan for helpful communications. This work was supported in part by the Natural Sciences and Engineering Research Council of Canada, the U.S. Department of Energy, and the Chinese Academy of Sciences.

LITERATURE CITED

1. Gell-Mann M. *Phys. Rev. Lett.* 8:214 (1964)
2. Zweig G. CERN Preprint 8182/TH401 (1964)
3. Bali GS. *Phys. Rep.* 343:1 (2001)
4. Eichten E, Godfrey S, Mahlke H, Rosner JL. arXiv:hep-ph/0701208 (2007)
5. Swanson ES. *Phys. Rep.* 429:243 (2006)
6. Godfrey S. The XYZ's of c anti-c: hints of exotic new mesons. *Proc. Flavor Phys. CP Viol. Conf., 4th, Vancouver, Can.* (2006)
7. Zhu SL. *Int. J. Mod. Phys. E* 17:283 (2008)
8. Brambilla N, et al. (Quarkonium Working Group) *CERN Yellow Report* CERN-2005-005. hep-ph/0412158 (2005)
9. Voloshin MB, Okun LB. *JETP Lett.* 23:333 (1976)
10. De Rujula A, Georgi H, Glashow SL. *Phys. Rev. Lett.* 38:317 (1977)
11. Buchmuller W, Tye SHH. *Phys. Rev. Lett.* 44:850 (1980)
12. Godfrey S, Napolitano J. *Rev. Mod. Phys.* 71:1411 (1999)
13. Rosner JL, et al. (CLEO Collab.) *Phys. Rev. Lett.* 95:102003 (2005)
14. Rubin P, et al. (CLEO Collab.) *Phys. Rev. D* 72:092004 (2005)
15. Dudek JJ. Charmonium from lattice QCD. In *Proc. Int. Workshop Charm Phys., Ithaca, New York.* hep-ph/0711.1600v1 (2008)
16. Koma M, Koma Y, Wittig H. *PoS LAT* 2005:216 (2006)
17. Barnes T, Godfrey S, Swanson ES. *Phys. Rev. D* 72:054026 (2005)
18. Barnes T, Godfrey S. *Phys. Rev. D* 69:054008 (2004)
19. Eichten EJ, Lane K, Quigg C. *Phys. Rev. D* 69:094019 (2004)
20. Eichten EJ, Lane K, Quigg C. *Phys. Rev. D* 73:014014 (2006); Erratum. *Phys. Rev. D* 73:079903 (2006)
21. Eichten EJ, Lane K, Quigg C. *Phys. Rev. Lett.* 89:162002 (2002)
22. Gottfried K. *Phys. Rev. Lett.* 40:598 (1978)
23. Bhanot G, Fischler W, Rudaz S. *Nucl. Phys. B* 155:208 (1979)
24. Peskin ME. *Nucl. Phys. B* 156:365 (1979)
25. Bhanot G, Peskin ME. *Nucl. Phys. B* 156:391 (1979)
26. Voloshin MB. *Nucl. Phys. B* 154:365 (1979)
27. Yan TM. *Phys. Rev. D* 22:1652 (1980)
28. Kuang YP, Yan TM. *Phys. Rev. D* 24:2874 (1980)
29. Voloshin MB. *Phys. Rev. D* 74:054022 (2006)
30. Voloshin MB. *Sov. J. Nucl. Phys.* 43:1011 (1986)
31. Kuang YP, Tuan SF, Yan TM. *Phys. Rev. D* 37:1210 (1988)
32. Kuang YP, Yan TM. *Phys. Rev. D* 41:155 (1990)
33. Kuang YP. *Phys. Rev. D* 65:094024 (2002)
34. Voloshin MB. *Phys. Lett. B* 562:68 (2003)
35. Kuang YP. *Front. Phys. China* 1:19 (2006)
36. Micu L. *Nucl. Phys. B* 10:521 (1969)
37. Colglazier EW, Rosner JL. *Nucl. Phys. B* 27:349 (1971)
38. Le Yaouanc A, Oliver L, Pène O, Raynal JC. *Phys. Rev. D* 8:2223 (1973)
39. Kwong W, Mackenzie PB, Rosenfeld R, Rosner JL. *Phys. Rev. D* 37:3210 (1988)
40. Petrelli A, et al. *Nucl. Phys. B* 514:245 (1998)
41. Tornqvist NA. *Z. Phys. C* 61:525 (1994)
42. Ericson TEO, Karl G. *Phys. Lett. B* 309:426 (1993)
43. Maiani L, Piccinini F, Polosa AD, Riquer V. *Phys. Rev. D* 71:014028 (2005)
44. Chiu T-W, Hsieh TH. *Phys. Rev. D* 73:111503 (2006)
45. Barnes T, Close FE, Swanson ES. *Phys. Rev. D* 52:5242 (1995)
46. Morningstar C. *Nucl. Phys. Proc. Suppl.* 90:214 (2000)
47. Bali GS, Pineda A. *Phys. Rev. D* 69:094001 (2004)
48. Isgur N, Paton JE. *Phys. Rev. D* 31:2910 (1985)

49. Lacock P, Michael C, Boyle P, Rowland P. (UKQCD Collab.) *Phys. Lett. B* 401:308 (1997)

50. McNeile C, Michael C, Pennanen P. (UKQCD Collab.) *Phys. Rev. D* 65:094505 (2002)

51. Close F. Three flavours of hybrid or pi exhange: Which is more attractive? In *Proc. Int. Conf. Hadron Spectrosc., 12th, Frascati, Italy, Oct. 8–13, 2007.* hep-ph/0801.2646 (2008)

52. Voloshin MB. arXiv:hep-ph/0602233 (2006)

53. Eichten E, et al. *Phys. Rev. Lett.* 36:500 (1976)

54. Eichten E, et al. *Phys. Rev. D* 17:3090 (1978); Erratum. *Phys. Rev. D* 21:313 (1980)

55. Eichten E, et al. *Phys. Rev. D* 21:203 (1980)

56. Aubert B, et al. (BaBar Collab.) *Phys. Rev. Lett.* 87:091801 (2001)

57. Abe K, et al. (Belle Collab.) *Phys. Rev. Lett.* 87:091802 (2001)

58. Choi S-K, et al. (Belle Collab.) *Phys. Rev. Lett.* 89:102001 (2002)

59. Aubert B, et al. (BaBar Collab.) *Phys. Rev. D* 70:072004 (2004)

60. Abe K, et al. (Belle Collab.) *Phys. Rev. Lett.* 89:142001 (2002)

61. Braaten E, Fleming S. *Phys. Rev. Lett.* 74:3327 (1995)

62. Asner D, et al. (CLEO Collab.) *Phys. Rev. Lett.* 92:142001 (2004)

63. Choi S-K, et al. (Belle Collab.) *Phys. Rev. Lett.* 91:262001 (2003)

64. Acosta D, et al. (CDF Collab.) *Phys. Rev. Lett.* 93:072001 (2004)

65. Abazov VM, et al. (DØ Collab.) *Phys. Rev. Lett.* 93:162002 (2004)

66. Aubert B, et al. (BaBar Collab.) *Phys. Rev. D* 71:071103 (2005)

67. Yao WM, et al. (Particle Data Group) *J. Phys. G* 33:1 (2007)

68. Aubert B, et al. (BaBar Collab.) *Phys. Rev. D* 74:071101 (2006)

69. Abe K, et al. (Belle Collab.) BELLE-CONF-0540, arXiv:hep-ex/0505037. Pap. LP-2005–175. *Int. Symp. Lepton-Photon Interact. High Energy, XXII, Uppsala, Swed.* (2005)

70. Abulencia D, et al. (CDF Collab.) *Phys. Rev. Lett.* 96:102002 (2006)

71. Swanson ES. *Phys. Lett. B* 588:189 (2004)

72. Close FE, Page PR. *Phys. Lett. B* 578:119 (2004)

73. Abulencia D, et al. (CDF Collab.) *Phys. Rev. Lett.* 98:132002 (2007)

74. Cawfield C, et al. (CLEO Collab.) *Phys. Rev. Lett.* 98:092002 (2007)

75. Voloshin MB. *Phys. Lett. B* 579:316 (2004)

76. Gamermann D, Oset E. *Eur. Phys. J. A* 33:119 (2007)

77. Ebert D, Faustov RN, Galkin VO. *Phys. Lett. B* 634:214 (2006)

78. Abe K, et al. (Belle Collab.) Belle-CONF-0711 (2007)

79. Aubert B, et al. (BaBar Collab.) *Phys. Rev. D* 73:011101 (2006)

80. Aubert B, et al. (BaBar Collab.) *Phys. Rev. D* 71:031501 (2007)

81. Gokhroo G, et al. (Belle Collab.) *Phys. Rev. Lett.* 97:162002 (2006)

82. Aubert B, et al. (BaBar Collab.) *Phys. Rev. D* 77:011102 (2008)

83. Dunwoodie W, Ziegler V. *Phys. Rev. Lett.* 100:062006 (2008)

84. Hanhart C, Kalashnikova YS, Kudryavtsev AE, Nefediev AV. *Phys. Rev. D* 76:014007 (2007)

85. Voloshin MB. *Phys. Rev. D* 76:014007 (2007)

86. Braaten E, Lu M. *Phys. Rev. D* 77:014029 (2008)

87. Abe K, et al. (Belle Collab.) *Phys. Rev. Lett.* 98:082001 (2007)

88. Choi S-K, et al. (Belle Collab.) *Phys. Rev. Lett.* 94:182002 (2005)

89. Uehara S, et al. (Belle Collab.) *Phys. Rev. Lett.* 96:082003 (2006)

90. Swanson E. *Int. J. Mod. Phys. A* 21:733 (2006)

91. Barnes T. *Int. Workshop Photon-Photon Collis., La Jolla, CA*, Oak Ridge Natl. Lab. Rep. ORNL-CCIP-92-05 (1992)

92. Pakhlov P, et al. (Belle Collab.) arXiv:0707.3812v2, submitted to *Phys. Rev. Lett.* (2007)

93. Aubert B, et al. (BaBar Collab.) *Phys. Rev. Lett.* Submitted (2008)

94. Barnes T. *Int. J. Mod. Phys. A* 21:5583 (2006)

95. Godfrey S, Isgur N. *Phys. Rev. D* 32:189 (1985)

96. Aubert B, et al. (BaBar Collab.) *Phys. Rev. Lett.* 95:142001 (2005)

97. Pakhlova G, et al. (Belle Collab.) *Phys. Rev. Lett.* 98:092001 (2007)

98. Bai JZ, et al. (BES Collab.) *Phys. Rev. Lett.* 88:101802 (2002)

99. Wang XL, et al. *Phys. Lett. B* 640:182 (2007)
100. He Q, et al. (CLEO Collab.) *Phys. Rev. D* 74:091104 (2006)
101. Yuan CZ, et al. (Belle Collab.) *Phys. Rev. Lett.* 99:182004 (2007)
102. Aubert B, et al. (BaBar Collab.) *Phys. Rev. Lett.* 98:212001 (2007)
103. Wang XL, et al. (Belle Collab.) *Phys. Rev. Lett.* 99:142002 (2007)
104. Ding GJ, Zhu JJ, Yan ML. *Phys. Rev. D* 77:014033 (2008)
105. Liu X. *Eur. Phys. J. C* 54:471 (2008)
106. Rosner JL. *Phys. Rev. D* 74:076006 (2006)
107. Swanson E. *Int. J. Mod. Phys. A* 21:733 (2006)
108. Rosner JL. *J. Phys. Conf. Ser.* 69:012002 (2007)
109. Maiani L, Riquer V, Piccinini F, Polosa AD. *Phys. Rev. D* 72:031502 (2005)
110. Zhu SL. *Phys. Lett. B* 6 25:212 (2005)
111. Close FE, Page PR. *Phys. Lett. B* 628:215 (2005)
112. Kou E, Pène O. *Phys. Lett. B* 631:164 (2005)
113. Ablikim M, et al. (BES Collab.) *Phys. Lett. B* 660:315 (2008)
114. Choi S-K, et al. (Belle Collab.) *Phys. Rev. Lett.* 100:142001 (2008)
115. Rosner JL. *Phys. Lev. D* 76:114002 (2007)
116. Bugg DV, arXiv:0709:1254 [hep-ph] (2007)
117. Meng C, Chao KT. arXiv:0708.4222 [hep-ph] (2007)
118. Lee SH, Mihara A, Navarra FS, Nielsen M. *Phys. Lett. B* 661:28 (2008)
119. Liu X, Liu YR, Deng WZ, Zhu SL, *Phys. Rev. D* 77:034003 (2008)
120. Maiani L, Polosa AD, Riquer V. arXiv:0708.3997 [hep-ph] (2007)
121. Ding GJ. arXiv:0711.1485 [hep-ph] (2007)
122. Cheung KM, Keung WY, Yuan TC. *Phys. Rev. D* 76:117501 (2007)
123. Aubert B, et al. (BaBar Collab.) *Phys. Rev. Lett.* 96:232001 (2006)
124. Sokolov A, et al. (Belle Collab.) *Phys. Rev. D* 75:071103 (2007)
125. Chen KF, et al. (Belle Collab.) *Phys. Rev. Lett.* 100:112001 (2008)
126. Hou W-S. *Phys. Rev. D* 74:017504 (2007)
127. Aubert B, et al. (BaBar Collab), *Phys. Rev. D* 74:091103 (2006)
128. Ablikim M, et al. (BES Collab.) *Phys. Rev. Lett.* 100:102003 (2008)
129. Ding G-J, Yan M-L. *Phys. Lett. B* 650:390 (2007)
130. Ding G-J, Yan M-L. *Phys. Lett. B* 657:49 (2007)

Nonstandard Higgs Boson Decays

Spencer Chang,[1] Radovan Dermíšek,[2] John F. Gunion,[3] and Neal Weiner[1]

[1]Center for Cosmology and Particle Physics, Department of Physics, New York University, New York, New York 10003; email: chang@physics.nyu.edu; neal.weiner.nyu@gmail.com

[2]School of Natural Sciences, Institute for Advanced Study, Princeton, New Jersey 08540; email: dermisek@ias.edu

[3]Department of Physics, University of California, Davis, California 95616; email: gunion@physics.ucdavis.edu

Annu. Rev. Nucl. Part. Sci. 2008. 58:75–98

First published online as a Review in Advance on June 18, 2008

The *Annual Review of Nuclear and Particle Science* is online at nucl.annualreviews.org

This article's doi:
10.1146/annurev.nucl.58.110707.171200

Key Words

Higgs, supersymmetry, beyond the standard model, naturalness, fine-tuning

Abstract

This review summarizes the motivations for and the phenomenological consequences of nonstandard Higgs boson decays, with an emphasis on final states containing a pair of non–standard model particles that subsequently decay to standard model particles. Typically these non–standard model particles form part of a "hidden" sector, for example a pair of neutral Higgs bosons or a pair of unstable neutralinos. We emphasize that such decays allow for a Higgs substantially below the standard model Higgs Large Electron-Positron Collider limit of 114 GeV. A Higgs with standard model WW, ZZ, and top couplings and a mass near 100 GeV eliminates the fine-tuning problems of many beyond the standard model theories, in particular supersymmetric models, and leads to excellent consistency with precision electroweak data.

Contents

1. INTRODUCTION

Understanding the origin of the electroweak symmetry breaking (EWSB) responsible for giving mass to the W and Z gauge bosons of the standard model (SM) is the next major step in constructing the ultimate theory of particles and their interactions. The Large Hadron Collider (LHC) is designed specifically to explore the mechanism behind EWSB. In particular, its 14-TeV center-of-mass energy and >100-fb^{-1} integrated luminosity is such that $WW \to WW$ scattering can be studied at energies up to about 1 TeV, where unitarity would be violated if no new physics associated with EWSB exists.

Many mechanisms for EWSB have been explored; the simplest is the introduction of one or more elementary spin-0 Higgs fields that acquire vacuum expectation values (vevs) and that couple to WW and ZZ. Then the W and Z gauge bosons acquire a contribution to their mass from each such Higgs field proportional to the strength of the Higgs-WW and Higgs-ZZ coupling times the vev of the Higgs field. The quantum fluctuation of the Higgs field relative to its vev is a spin-0 particle called a Higgs boson. If the corresponding field couples to ZZ and WW, then so will the Higgs boson.

Although the role of the Higgs vev is to give mass to the W and Z, it is the Feynman diagrams involving the Higgs bosons that prevent unitarity violation in WW scattering—provided the Higgs bosons are light enough (roughly below 1 TeV). If the Higgs bosons whose corresponding fields have significant vevs are below ~ 300 GeV, then WW scattering will remain perturbative at all energies. Furthermore, precision measurements of the properties of W and Z gauge bosons are most consistent if the vev-weighted average of the logarithms of the Higgs masses is somewhat below ln 100 (GeV units), i.e.,

$$\sum_i \frac{v_i^2}{v_{SM}^2} \ln m_{b_i} \leq \ln(100 \text{ GeV}), \qquad\qquad 1.$$

where $\langle \Phi_j \rangle \equiv v_j$ and $\sum_j v_j^2 = v_{SM}^2 \sim (175 \text{ GeV})^2$ is the square of the vev of the SM Higgs field. Thus, a very attractive possibility is that Higgs bosons with significant WW/ZZ couplings are rather light.

A 100-GeV Higgs mass is certainly acceptable within the context of the renormalized SM, but it requires an enormous cancellation between the bare Higgs mass term in the vev-shifted Lagrangian and the superficially quadratically divergent loop corrections to the mass, especially the mass arising from the top quark loop. This requirement has led to the idea that there must be new physics below the TeV scale that will regulate these quadratic divergences. Supersymmetry (SUSY) is the earliest proposal for models with elementary Higgs fields, and it remains a very attractive theory. In SUSY, the loop corrections containing superparticles (sparticles) come in with opposite sign with respect to those with particles and the quadratic divergences are canceled. If the mass of the stop and the masses of other sparticles are below ~500 GeV, this cancellation more or less automatically results in a Higgs boson mass near 100 GeV. A higher mass for the sparticles would lead to a larger Higgs mass but, as we discuss below, it would lead to the need to fine-tune the soft SUSY breaking parameters at the grand unified theory (GUT) scale in order to obtain the correct value of the Z boson mass. The equivalent problem in more general beyond the standard model (BSM) theories would be the need to choose parameters at the new physics scale and/or coupling unification scale with great precision in order to obtain the correct value of M_Z.

The fine-tuning problem is closely related to the "little hierarchy problem" that occurs in a wide variety of BSM theories, including not only supersymmetric models but also Randall-Sundrum theories (1) and Little Higgs theories (2, 3). There is a basic tension, sometimes referred to as the LEP paradox (4), that exists in BSM physics. On the one hand, precision electroweak fits show no need for BSM physics [a possible exception is the 2.2-σ discrepancy in $g-2$ of the muon (5)], nor have there been any definitive indications of new particle production at high-energy colliders. This suggests that the scale of new physics is quite high (>1 TeV). On the other hand, within the context of the SM, electroweak observables require a light Higgs which, as discussed above, is not easy to reconcile with loop corrections to the Higgs mass if the new physics resides above 1 TeV. In these models it is often difficult to introduce a large quartic coupling for the Higgs to raise its physical mass above the LEP limit while still protecting its mass term against corrections above the TeV scale.

Thus, the most attractive possibility is a BSM model in which the Higgs bosons with large vevs (and hence large ZZ and WW couplings) have mass of order 100 GeV and new physics resides at scales significantly below 1 TeV while being consistent with current high-precision observables. In appropriately constructed BSM models, the latter can be achieved. However, in many models, having Higgs bosons below 100 GeV leads to an inconsistency with the limits from LEP searches for Higgs bosons. Consider the SM, where there is only one Higgs field and one Higgs boson. LEP has placed a limit on the SM Higgs boson, h_{SM}, of $m_{h_{SM}} > 114.4$ GeV. Except in a few nongeneric corners of parameter space, this limit also applies to the lightest CP-even Higgs boson of the minimal supersymmetric standard model (MSSM) and of many other BSM theories. There are two means of escaping this limit: (a) pushing the Higgs mass to higher values where fine-tuning of parameters becomes an issue or (b) constructing models where the Higgs bosons with large ZZ coupling have mass at or below 100 GeV but were not detected at LEP by virtue of having nonstandard decays to which existing LEP analyses are not sufficiently sensitive. In this review we aim to survey the unusual decay possibilities.

In Section 2 we review the motivations for nonstandard Higgs decays with a discussion of model-dependent and model-independent motivations, with particular attention to SUSY— especially the next-to-minimal supersymmetric standard model (NMSSM). In Section 3 we discuss the broad set of existing LEP Higgs searches. There we emphasize that Higgs bosons of low mass avoid the normal LEP limits only if the primary Higgs decays are into non-SM particles, each of which, in turn, decays to SM particles. (Such decays are known as cascade decays.) In Section 4 we specialize to the motivation for nonstandard Higgses from natural EWSB in SUSY theories.

In Section 5 we discuss generally the possibilities of extended Higgs sectors; then we focus on the best-studied cases in the context of the NMSSM in Section 6. In Section 7 we discuss some implications of nonstandard Higgs physics for B factories. We review the LHC implications in Section 8 and present our conclusions in Section 9.

2. MOTIVATION FOR NONSTANDARD HIGGS BOSON DECAYS

The motivation for nonstandard Higgs boson decays comes from two sources. First, a wide variety of theories predict new, neutral states, affording the Higgs new channels into which it can decay. This common feature motivates us to consider such decays irrespective of anything else. However, naturalness can also be a significant motivation. A natural theory is one in which the correct Z boson mass is obtained without any significant fine-tuning of the fundamental parameters of the model, for example the GUT-scale soft SUSY breaking parameters in supersymmetric models.

In BSM theories there is often a tension between naturalness and achieving a Higgs boson mass above the LEP limit. This has been especially well studied within the context of SUSY. By allowing the Higgs to decay into new final states, one can have a lighter Higgs and a more natural theory. Indeed, the recent interest in nonstandard Higgs decays was spurred by the observation that the tension between natural EWSB in supersymmetric models and not seeing the Higgs boson at LEP can be completely eliminated in models in which $h \to b\bar{b}$ is not the dominant decay mode of the SM-like Higgs boson (6).

In the SM there is only one Higgs boson, and its dominant decay mode is $h_{\rm SM} \to b\bar{b}$ when $m_{h_{\rm SM}} < 140$ GeV. Although we have not yet made a definitive observation of this new state, a wide variety of tests at high-energy experiments have already constrained its properties. In particular, precision electroweak tests have continually suggested that the Higgs boson is light and accessible at LEP. The latest fits give an upper bound of 144 GeV at 95% CL with a central value of 76 GeV (7). Compared to the direct search bound of 114.4 GeV, there is some mild tension between these two Higgs bounds. However, as Chanowitz (8) points out, the story is more complicated. Notably, the measured forward-back asymmetry for b quarks (A_{FB}^b) favors a heavy Higgs, but it is also the most discrepant with the SM fit (with a pull of about 3σ). Taking into account most of the data (8), the SM electroweak fit has a poor CL of 0.01, whereas leaving out the most discrepant measurements improves the fit to a CL of 0.65. Then, however, the best-fit Higgs mass is 43 GeV, making the indirect Higgs bound disagree more strongly with the direct search limit.

New measurements within the SM, particularly the precise top and W mass measurements from Tevatron Run II, have continued to support this preference for a light Higgs. The constraint of the top and W mass on the Higgs mass is well known (see, e.g., Reference 9). As of today, the precision electroweak fit is inconsistent with the direct search limit at the 68% CL. This includes fitting A_{FB}^b, so excluding that measurement would increase the discrepancy between the two limits. Thus, even without specifying a particular theory of physics, we see there is some tension for the SM Higgs at present, and this motivates us to consider what possibilities exist for a light Higgs, in particular one lighter than the nominal SM limit from LEP.

Furthermore, there were interesting excesses in Higgs searches at LEP, which suggest that there could be nonstandard Higgs physics. The largest excess (2.3σ) of Higgs-like events at LEP was in the $b\bar{b}$ final state for a reconstructed mass $M_{b\bar{b}} \sim 98$ GeV (10). The number of excess events constitutes roughly 10% of the number of events expected from the SM with a 98-GeV Higgs boson. Thus, this excess cannot be interpreted as the Higgs of the SM or the SM-like Higgs of the MSSM.[1] However, this excess is a perfect match to the idea of nonstandard Higgs decays, as the nonstandard decay width reduces the branching ratio to SM modes.

In the SM, the Higgs has strong $O(1)$ couplings to the W, Z, and top quarks but quite weak couplings to other fermions. This means that for a Higgs mass that is below threshold for on-shell WW decays, the decay width into standard modes (in particular, $b\bar{b}$) is quite suppressed. A Higgs of mass (for instance) 100 GeV has a decay width into SM particles that is only 2.6 MeV, or about 10^{-5} of its mass. Consequently, the branching ratios to SM particles of such a light Higgs are easily altered by the presence of nonstandard decays; it doesn't take a large Higgs coupling to some new particles for the decay width to these new particles to dominate over the decay width to SM particles (the earliest studies to identify this concern, as far as we are aware, are References 13–15).

As perhaps the most relevant example, let us consider a light Higgs with SM-like $b\bar{b}$ coupling and compare the decay width $h \rightarrow b\bar{b}$ to that for $h \rightarrow aa$, where a is a light pseudoscalar Higgs boson. If we write $\mathcal{L} \ni g_{haa} h aa$ with $g_{haa} = c \frac{g m_b^2}{2 M_W}$ and ignoring phase-space suppression, we find

$$\frac{\Gamma(h \rightarrow aa)}{\Gamma(h \rightarrow b\bar{b})} \sim 310 \, c^2 \left(\frac{m_b}{100 \, \text{GeV}} \right)^2 . \qquad\qquad 2.$$

This expression includes quantum chromodynamics (QCD) corrections to the $b\bar{b}$ width as given in HDECAY (16); these corrections are evaluated for a 100-GeV Higgs and decrease the leading order $\Gamma(h \rightarrow b\bar{b})$ by about 50%. The decay widths are comparable for $c \sim 0.057$ when $m_b = 100$ GeV. Values of c at this or a substantially higher level (even $c = 1$ is possible) are generic in BSM models containing an extended Higgs sector. Further, both the $h \rightarrow aa$ and $h \rightarrow WW$ decays widths grow as m_b^3, so that, assuming SM hWW coupling, $\Gamma(h \rightarrow aa) = \frac{1}{2} c^2 \Gamma(h \rightarrow WW)$ when neither is kinematically suppressed.

From a theoretical perspective, many BSM theories have light neutral states—including nonstandard Higgs bosons, axions, neutralinos, and sneutrinos—that are difficult to detect directly at existing colliders. Typically, the main constraint on such light neutral states arises if they contribute to the invisible Z width. Thus, there are no strong constraints on their masses as long as their coupling to the Z is suppressed. As a result, many of the light states in BSM models can be light enough that a pair of them may appear in the decays of the Higgs boson. Moreover, as discussed above even a weak coupling of the Higgs boson to these light BSM particles can cause this nonstandard decay to dominate over the standard decay width.

In many cases, the LEP constraint on the mass of the Higgs boson is much weaker in the resulting final state than is the case if the Higgs boson decays to either (a) a purely invisible final state or (b) a final state containing only a pair of SM particles. For either final state, the LEP data require that the Higgs mass be greater than 114 GeV if the Higgs ZZ coupling is SM-like. This is because these two final states are avoided if the light states are unstable, which results in a high-multiplicity final-state cascade decay with some visible particles. Note that because the cascade is initiated by Higgs decay to only a pair of nonstandard particles, there is no additional phase-space suppression relative to a pair of SM particles and the nonstandard pair can easily dominate despite the ultimate final state containing many particles. Early studies of the MSSM (13, 15, 17), $E(6)$ models (18), and the NMSSM (19) highlighted the importance of cascade decays. These models (among others, including triplet Higgs models and left-right symmetric models) with cascade

---

[1]In the MSSM, this excess can be explained by the lighter CP-even Higgs, which has highly reduced coupling to ZZ (see, e.g., Reference 11). This explanation does not remove the fine-tuning problem as it is the heavy CP-even Higgs that is SM-like and that has to satisfy the 114-GeV limit. For a detailed discussion and references, see Reference 12.

decays of one Higgs boson to a pair of lighter Higgs bosons or supersymmetric particles were summarized in *The Higgs Hunter's Guide* (20, 21), which contains references to the original works.

In more extreme models, the LEP constraints are ineffective even for light Higgs bosons. One particular example is an early work of Espinosa & Gunion (22), which describes a model in which many Higgs fields mix with one another and share the SM Higgs field vev. In this model, the physical Higgs eigenstates also share the ZZ-Higgs coupling. If the Higgs eigenstates are also spread out in mass, perhaps slightly overlapping within relevant experimental resolutions (the worst case), they could easily avoid detection at LEP even if they have mass significantly below 100 GeV and decay to a pair of SM particles. In fact, however, such models typically have at least modest triple-Higgs couplings; thus, many of these multiple Higgs bosons would decay primarily to a pair of lighter Higgs bosons, each of which might then decay either to a pair of SM particles or perhaps to a pair of still-lighter Higgs bosons. There is a related model (23) in which many unmixed (and, therefore, stable) Higgs-singlet fields are present and couple strongly to the SM Higgs field. The SM Higgs then decays primarily to pairs of singlet-Higgs bosons, yielding a very large SM Higgs width for the invisible final states. Because of the large width the corresponding signal would have been missed at LEP, so long as the SM Higgs does not have mass too far below 100 GeV.

To summarize, there is a wide-open window for Higgs decays to light unstable states with small coupling to the Z. Indeed, BSM theories in which the masses of Higgs bosons that couple strongly to WW, ZZ are light compared to the WW threshold will have generically nonstandard Higgs phenomenology. Light states are ubiquitous in BSM theories and could potentially be light enough for the Higgs to decay into a pair of them. Given that the decay width to a pair of SM particles is so small for such Higgs bosons, the decay into a pair of BSM states can easily dominate even when the relevant coupling is not particularly strong. Thus, the Higgs bosons associated with the Higgs fields that give mass to the W and the Z are highly susceptible to having nonstandard Higgs phenomenology. Below we illustrate this phenomenon in greater depth as we discuss some particularly attractive model realizations of such decays.

3. LEP SEARCHES FOR THE HIGGS

It is crucial to understand whether decays of a Higgs boson to non-SM particles allow consistency with existing LEP limits when the Higgs has mass below 100 GeV. Although researchers have focused much attention on the SM Higgs search at LEP, a wide variety of searches have been performed to constrain many scenarios of nonstandard Higgs decays for light ($\leq$114.4-GeV) Higgses. Here we summarize these constraints.

The dedicated Higgs searches at LEP encompass an impressive array of possible Higgs decay topologies. As the Higgs is dominantly produced in association with a Z boson, the search topology generally involves both the Higgs and the Z decays. The searches give a constraint on the product

$$\xi^2_{b \to X} \equiv \frac{\sigma(e^+e^- \to Zb)}{\sigma(e^+e^- \to Zb)_{SM}} \, \mathrm{Br}(b \to X). \qquad 3.$$

The cross section σ for Higgs production scales as the coupling g_{ZZb} squared, so the first factor is equivalently the square of the ratio of this Higgs's coupling to the SM value. In Section 2, we argued that precision electroweak results suggest that the nonstandard Higgs has nearly standard couplings to SM particles, so this factor is close to one.[2] The second factor, $\mathrm{Br}(b \to X)$, is the

---

[2]In some cases, the SM ZZ coupling squared is shared among several Higgs bosons. This is not typically the case for generic parameter choices for BSM models. Thus, in this section when we refer to "the Higgs," we presume that the Higgs has SM-like ZZ and WW couplings, although we allow for the possibility of nonstandard decays.

branching ratio of the Higgs decay in question. Here we discuss the LEP Higgs searches that are relevant for our purposes. Most stated mass limits are the 95%-CL lower bounds, assuming that $\xi^2_{b \to X} = 1$.

1. SM Higgs. For any Higgs that is SM-like in its couplings and decays, LEP limits are strongest for the dominant Higgs decays into $b\bar{b}$, $\tau\bar{\tau}$. The LEP combined limits on the SM Higgs (10) require $m_b \geq 114.4$ GeV. This study also includes the strongest limits on $h \to b\bar{b}$, $\tau\bar{\tau}$ rates with limits of ~ 115 GeV if the decay is exclusively into just one of these decay modes.

2. Two-parton (also known as flavor-independent) hadronic states. In this analysis, the two-parton decays of a SM-like Higgs were constrained. The analyses use the two-parton final state that was least sensitive to the candidate Higgs mass and details of the Z decay. The strongest constraint is the preliminary LEP-wide analysis (24), which requires $m_b \geq 113$ GeV.

3. Gauge boson (also known as fermiphobic) decays. This analysis focuses on two gauge boson decays of the Higgs and assumes that the Higgs coupling to SM fermions is suppressed. The final states that are considered are WW^* and ZZ^*, as well as photons. Assuming SM-like coupling to ZZ^* and WW^*, which implies the SM decay width into gauge bosons, there is a limit of $m_b \geq 109.7$ GeV, whereas decays exclusively to two photons have a limit of $m_b \geq 117$ GeV (25).

4. Invisible decays. In this analysis, the Higgs is assumed to have SM-like ZZ coupling but to decay with 100% branching into stable neutral noninteracting particles. The most stringent constraints are from an older preliminary LEP-wide analysis with a limit $m_b \geq 114$ GeV (see Reference 26). Because this constraint is so strong, it implies that a nonstandard Higgs must decay primarily into a state containing at least some visible particles if it is to have mass below 114 GeV.

5. Cascade decays. These constraints are relevant for the important nonstandard Higgs decay where the Higgs decays into two secondary particles, such as a pair of scalars ϕ, and where those scalars subsequently decay into Y (i.e., $h \to 2\phi \to 2Y$). The Omni-Purpose Apparatus for LEP (OPAL) (27) and the Detector with Lepton, Photon, and Hadron Identification (DELPHI) (28) looked at b decays ($Y \equiv b\bar{b}$), and a LEP-wide analysis (29) has constrained both b and τ decays. For $h \to 2\phi \to 4b$, the limits are 110 GeV for a Higgs produced with SM strength. For other intermediate scalar decays, $\phi \to 2g$, $c\bar{c}$, and $\tau\bar{\tau}$, the best model-independent exclusions when the mass of the scalar is below $b\bar{b}$ threshold are from OPAL's analysis; these limits are given in Reference 30. It is important to note that this latter analysis is restricted to Higgs masses ranging from 45 GeV to 86 GeV.

6. Model-independent decays. This analysis provides the most conservative limit on the Higgs boson. It assumes that the Higgs is produced with a Z boson and looks for electron and muon pairs that reconstruct to a Z mass; the Higgs decay process remains unconstrained. This study was performed by OPAL and yielded a limit of $m_b \geq 82$ GeV (31).

The only possibilities not mentioned above are Higgs decays into a pair of electrons or muons. However, even though there is no dedicated search of this type such Higgs decays would give a large enhancement to charged lepton events at LEP. Because WW and Ze^+e^- production at LEP were accurately measured to be consistent with the SM (32), limits on such decays would presumably be near the kinematic limit. Therefore, it is essentially impossible for any Higgs boson (with SM-like ZZ coupling) to have mass much below 114 GeV if it decays entirely into any single mode or combination of modes, each of which contains only a pair of SM particles.

However, this constraint does not rule out Higgs decays into a higher-multiplicity state. Consider, for instance, the cascade decay of the Higgs into $4b$. This decay has a weaker constraint than the $2b$ search, although it only lowers the limit on the Higgs mass to 110 GeV. More drastically, the decay of the Higgs into 4τ allows a Higgs as light at 86 GeV,[3] which represents a substantial weakening of the limit as compared to the ditau search limit of 115 GeV. However, this does not mean that high-multiplicity decays are completely safe. The model-independent decay search requires that the Higgs be heavier than 82 GeV. Dedicated LEP searches for particular decay topologies might of course provide more stringent limits. However, absent these dedicated limits we provide plausible arguments that certain nonstandard decays allow lighter Higgses. Our arguments are based on the application of existing LEP2 analyses to these scenarios. The estimated limits on such Higgs decays obtained in this way are intended as a guideline only.

3.1. Decay Topologies Consistent with LEP Searches

Before we go into more specific details of the various BSM models, we review the possibly important topologies and decays that are consistent with the existing data. Presently there are no strong constraints on decays for Higgses above the LEP kinematical limit, and we return to these cases below. We begin this section by focusing on what topologies are allowed in light of the existing search data.

As we have already made clear, decays of the Higgs into two-body SM states are essentially as constrained as the SM Higgs. This compels us to consider decays into new states. If these states were neutral, stable, and weakly interacting, they would contribute to the invisible Higgs search. Thus, to evade the strongest LEP limits the Higgs must decay to a final state containing at least one unstable particle that does not decay invisibly.

The simplest possible decay process is $h \rightarrow 2a \rightarrow 4x$, where x is some SM state. $x = b$ is already very constrained, but $x = \tau$ is not constrained if $m_h > 86$ GeV (29); also, no explicit limits have been placed on situations where x is a light, unflavored jet for a masses above 10 GeV, although one can reasonably extrapolate limits in the range of 90 GeV from other analyses (33). It is hard to imagine that cases where $x = e$, μ, γ are not excluded up to nearly the LEP kinematical limit; however, no analyses have been explicitly performed and the LEP collaborations are not prepared to make such an explicit statement.

More complicated decay topologies can arise when there are multiple states below the Higgs mass, for instance a bino and a singlino (which appear in generalized supersymmetric models). Assuming R-parity conservation, such decays are typically characterized by two SM fermions and missing energy. For instance, a particularly plausible decay mode is $h \rightarrow (\tilde{\chi}_1)\tilde{\chi}_0 \rightarrow (\tilde{\chi}_0 f \bar{f})\tilde{\chi}_0$, where the $\tilde{\chi}_0$ is the lightest supersymmetric particle (LSP). Typically, a single $f\bar{f}$ mode does not dominate, as the decay often includes multiple off-shell sleptons or an off-shell Z boson. As a result, for plausible branching ratios, such decays are allowed for Higgs masses in the range of 90 GeV to 100 GeV (34).

Most of the above-mentioned nonstandard decays arise in the NMSSM and in its closely related variants. Moreover, the NMSSM is well studied and is the simplest supersymmetric model in which it has been explicitly shown that fine-tuning and naturalness problems can be eliminated when the Higgs boson has mass at or below $\sim$100 GeV. In the next section we present a detailed discussion of naturalness in supersymmetric models and in the MSSM in particular. In Section 6, we explain how fine-tuning can be absent in the NMSSM by virtue of nonstandard Higgs decays allowing $m_h \sim 100$ GeV, then consider the crucial new Higgs signals within the NMSSM as well as its generalizations.

---

[3]OPAL's examination of the 4τ decay cut off the analysis at 86 GeV, so it is not clear what the reach of LEP is for a Higgs decaying predominantly to 4τ. However, it could reasonably be in the range of 90–100 GeV.

4. NATURAL ELECTROWEAK SYMMETRY BREAKING IN SUPERSYMMETRY

Within SUSY, the importance of minimizing fine-tuning provides a particularly strong motivation for nonstandard Higgs decays. Consider the MSSM: It contains two Higgs-doublet fields, H_u and H_d (with coupling to up-type quarks and down-type quarks/leptons, respectively). EWSB results in five physical Higgs states: light and heavy CP-even Higgs bosons, h and H; the CP-odd Higgs boson A; and charged Higgs bosons $H^\pm$. One typically finds that the h is SM-like in its couplings to gauge bosons and fermions. Further, because the model predicts $m_h < 140$ GeV, $h \to b\bar{b}$ is then the dominant decay mode. (For a discussion of the possibility that H is SM-like or that h and H share the coupling to ZZ and WW, see Reference 12 and references therein. Fine-tuning can be ameliorated but not eliminated in such models.) As a result, the LEP limit of $m_h > 114.4$ GeV applies and (as discussed below) in turn implies a significant fine-tuning problem. It is only by turning to more general supersymmetric models that fine-tuning can be avoided. In more general models such as the NMSSM, the SM-like nature of the lightest CP-even Higgs boson remains a generic feature, but it is not necessarily the case that it dominantly decays to $b\bar{b}$. As we have discussed, due to the small size of the SM-like $hb\bar{b}$ coupling any new decay modes that are kinematically accessible tend to dominate the Higgs decays and can allow $m_h \leq 100$ GeV to be consistent with LEP limits. For such m_h values, fine-tuning problems may be absent. The phenomenological implications of such a scenario are dramatic; in particular, prospects for detecting the h at the Tevatron and the LHC are greatly modified. In particular, the sensitivities of the standard search techniques (which employ certain production processes and decay channels appropriate to a SM Higgs boson) are substantially reduced.

Consider the issues of naturalness and fine-tuning. For the triggering of EWSB by SUSY breaking to be natural, the superpartners must be near the electroweak scale. This is necessary because the mass of the Z boson, which is determined by minimizing the Higgs potential, is related to the supersymmetric Higgs mass parameter μ and the soft SUSY breaking mass squared parameter for H_u, for $\tan\beta \geq 5$, by

$$\frac{M_Z^2}{2} \simeq -\mu^2(M_Z) - m_{H_u}^2(M_Z). \qquad 4.$$

The electroweak scale value of $m_{H_u}^2$ depends on the boundary conditions of all soft SUSY breaking parameters through renormalization group (RG) evolution. For a given $\tan\beta$, we can solve the RG equations exactly and express the electroweak values of $m_{H_u}^2$, μ^2, and consequently M_Z^2 given in Equation 4 in terms of all GUT-scale parameters. Although we consider the GUT scale as an example, the conclusions do not depend on this choice. For $\tan\beta = 10$, we have

$$M_Z^2 \simeq -1.9\mu^2 + 5.9M_3^2 - 1.2m_{H_u}^2 + 1.5m_{\tilde{t}}^2 - 0.8A_tM_3 + 0.2A_t^2 + \cdots, \qquad 5.$$

where parameters appearing on the right-hand side are the GUT-scale parameters. Here, M_3 is the $SU(3)$ gaugino mass; A_t is the trilinear stop soft SUSY breaking mixing parameter; and $m_{\tilde{t}}^2 \equiv \frac{1}{2}(m_{\tilde{t}_L}^2 + m_{\tilde{t}_R}^2)$, the latter being the soft SUSY breaking stop mass squared parameters. Other scalar masses as well as the $U(1)_Y$ and $SU(2)$ gaugino masses (M_1 and M_2, respectively) appear with negligible coefficients and we omit them from our discussion. The coefficients in this expression depend weakly on $\tan\beta$ and on $\log(M_{\text{GUT}}/M_Z)$. We can express the electroweak scale values of the stop mass squared, gluino mass, and top trilinear coupling in a similar way; for $\tan\beta = 10$ we have

$$m_{\tilde{t}}^2(M_Z) \simeq 5.0M_3^2 + 0.6m_{\tilde{t}}^2 + 0.2A_tM_3, \qquad 6.$$

$$M_3(M_Z) \simeq 3M_3, \qquad 7.$$

$$A_t(M_Z) \simeq -2.3M_3 + 0.2A_t. \qquad 8.$$

From Equations 5, 6, and 7, we see the usual expectation from SUSY,

$$M_Z \simeq m_{\tilde{t}_{1,2}} \simeq m_{\tilde{g}},$$ 9.

when all the soft SUSY breaking parameters are comparable. Furthermore, neglecting terms proportional to A_t in Equations 8 and 9, we find that a typical stop mixing is $A_t(M_Z)/m_{\tilde{t}}(M_Z) \lesssim 1.0$. This result has an important implication for the Higgs mass.

The mass of the h is approximately given as

$$m_h^2 \simeq M_Z^2 \cos^2 2\beta + \frac{3 G_F m_t^4}{\sqrt{2}\pi^2} \left\{ \log \frac{m_{\tilde{t}}^2(M_Z)}{m_t^2} + \frac{A_t^2(M_Z)}{m_{\tilde{t}}^2(M_Z)} \left(1 - \frac{A_t^2(M_Z)}{12 m_{\tilde{t}}^2(M_Z)} \right) \right\},$$ 10.

where the first term is the tree-level result and the second term is the dominant one-loop correction (35–38). At tree level, $m_h \leq M_Z \simeq 91$ GeV; increasingly larger Higgs masses are obtained as the mixing in the stop sector, $A_t(M_Z)/m_{\tilde{t}}(M_Z)$, and/or the stop mass, $m_{\tilde{t}}(M_Z)$, are increased. As we have learned, the typical mixing in the stop sector achieved as a result of RG evolution from a large range of high scale-boundary conditions is $A_t(M_Z)/m_{\tilde{t}}(M_Z) \lesssim 1.0$. With this typical mixing, we obtain the typical Higgs mass, $m_h \simeq 100$ GeV. In order to push the Higgs mass above the LEP limit of 114.4 GeV, assuming the typical mixing, the stop masses have to be ≥ 1 TeV.[4,5]

The need for 1-TeV stops is in direct contradiction with the usual expectation from SUSY (Equation 9). The hierarchy between the scale where SUSY is expected and the scale to which it is pushed by the limit on the Higgs mass requires a precise cancellation, at $>1\%$ precision, between the soft SUSY breaking terms and the μ term appearing on the right-hand side of Equation 5 in order to recover the correct value of the Z mass. This is the explicit realization of the fine-tuning problem in the MSSM and, as we stated in Section 1, is closely related to the little hierarchy problem.

The solution to the fine-tuning problem in models in which the SM-like Higgs decays dominantly to non-SM particles is straightforward. If the $h \to b\bar{b}$ decay mode is not dominant, the Higgs boson does not need to be heavier than 114 GeV; it can be as light as or lighter than the typical Higgs mass, depending on the experimental limits placed on the dominant decay mode. If the strongest limit is ≤ 100 GeV, there is no need for large superpartner masses and superpartners can be as light as current experimental limits allow.

In Section 3 we reviewed the experimental limits on the mass of the SM-like Higgs boson in various decay modes. Surprisingly, the LEP limit on m_h is above 100 GeV only if the Higgs decays primarily to two or four bottom quarks, two jets, two taus, or an invisible channel (such as two stable LSPs). Most other decay topologies have not been studied directly, and applications of other searches (e.g., the sensitivity of the flavor-independent two-jet search to the general four-jet topology) typically imply weak limits.[6] Moreover, it is reasonable to take a conservative approach in which one does not extrapolate the LEP limits beyond their explicit analyzed topology.

---

[4]The Higgs mass is maximized for $|A_t(M_Z)/m_{\tilde{t}}(M_Z)| \simeq 2$, which corresponds to the maximal mixing scenario. In this case, $m_{\tilde{t}}(M_Z)$ can be as small as ~300 GeV without violating the bound on m_h from LEP. However, it is not trivial to achieve the maximal mixing scenario in models. For more details see, e.g., the discussion in References 39 and 40.

[5]In models beyond the MSSM, with extended Higgs sectors or extended gauge symmetries, the tree-level prediction for the Higgs mass can be increased (see Reference 41 and references therein). This increase is not automatic and typically requires nontrivial assumptions. In the NMSSM, for example, assuming perturbativity up to the GUT scale, the tree-level prediction for the Higgs mass can be increased only by a small amount.

[6]We assume that the Higgs is produced with standard strength. A four–bottom quark decay for a Higgs that is strongly mixed (42) may be allowed for Higgs mass below 100 GeV within the existing constraints. Even so, a state lighter than ~105 GeV that decays to four bottom quarks cannot have a coupling larger than 40% of SM strength. Such models represent a different approach from those we consider in this review.

Regardless, the LEP limits on m_h for other decay modes are generally below 90 GeV and therefore do not place a constraint on superpartner masses. Because $m_h \sim 90 - 100$ GeV is the generic prediction for supersymmetric models in which there is no fine-tuning, those supersymmetric models where these alternate decay modes are dominant automatically provide a solution to the fine-tuning problem.[7] In addition to alleviating or completely removing the fine-tuning problem, the possibility of modified Higgs decays is independently supported experimentally. As mentioned in Section 2, the largest Higgs excess suggested a nonstandard Higgs of mass 98 GeV that only decayed 10% of the time to SM decay modes. As discussed above, from natural EWSB we expect the SM-like h to have mass very near 100 GeV. This is possible in any model wherein the SM-like Higgs boson decays mainly into a mode for which the LEP limits on m_h are below 100 GeV, such as those mentioned earlier for which the LEP limits run out at 90 GeV. [Another possibility is that a weakly mixed state existed at 98 GeV but that the dominant state coupling to the Z was above the LEP bound (see, e.g., Reference 45).] The $h \to b\bar{b}$ decay mode would still be present, but with a reduced branching ratio. Any $\mathrm{Br}(h \to b\bar{b}) \sim 30\%$ is consistent with experimental limits for $m_h \sim 100$ GeV. Further, $\mathrm{Br}(h \to b\bar{b}) \sim 10\%$ with $m_h \sim 100$ GeV provides a perfect explanation of the excess. This interpretation of the excess was first applied to the NMSSM with the $h \to aa \to \tau^+\tau^-\tau^+\tau^-$ mode being dominant (46), but it applies to a wide variety of models.

Within the MSSM context, there is one scenario worth mentioning that can alleviate fine-tuning. For example, for $\tan\beta \sim 10$, $m_{\tilde{t}}(M_Z) \sim 300$ GeV and $A_t(M_Z) \sim -400$ GeV, fine-tuning is moderate ($\sim 6\%$) and $m_h \sim 95 - 100$ GeV, thus providing a contribution to the $\sim$98-GeV excess observed (10) at LEP. In this case, the LEP limits are evaded by virtue of substantial Higgs mixing, leading to greatly reduced hZZ coupling; the HZZ coupling is large but m_H is slightly above the LEP limit of 114.4 GeV. (Without such mixing, the LEP limit of $m_h > 114$ GeV applies and at least 3% fine-tuning is necessary.) In fact, for $\tan\beta \sim 20$ one can simultaneously fit the $\sim$98-GeV and $\sim$116-GeV LEP excesses (11, 12). These scenarios, however, require highly nongeneric boundary conditions at the GUT scale and are characterized by nearly maximal mixing in the stop sector.

There is another scenario in which one allows large CP violation in the Higgs sector. The physical MSSM Higgs states would then be mixtures of the CP-even h and H and the CP-odd A; let us label the three resulting eigenstates $H_{1,2,3}$. It is possible to arrange $2m_{H_1} < m_{H_2}$ with the H_2ZZ coupling near maximal and $m_{H_2} \leq 100$ GeV (47). This arrangement can be consistent with the LEP limits if the $H_2 \to H_1 H_1$ cascade decay is dominant and $m_{H_2} < 2m_b$. Whether or not this scenario is fine-tuned has not been studied, but one can speculate that the low mass of the H_2 would imply reduced fine-tuning. However, for m_{H_1} sufficiently below the Upsilon mass, the rate for $\Upsilon \to \gamma H_1$ would typically be large and inconsistent with limits (48) from B factories. This is because the H_1 is part of a doublet (unlike the NMSSM, wherein the a_1 is mainly singlet) and, because the H_2 is the SM-like Higgs, the H_1 (and H_3) will have $\tan\beta$–enhanced coupling to $b\bar{b}$.

In summary, only models with nonstandard Higgs decays can completely avoid the fine-tuning problem. They allow the Higgs boson mass to be the value of $m_h \sim 100$ GeV predicted from natural EWSB; at the same time, they allow the now-subdominant decay mode, $h \to b\bar{b}$, with $\sim 10\%$ branching ratio to explain the largest excess of Higgs-like events at LEP at $M_{b\bar{b}} \sim 98$ GeV. A SM-like h with $m_h \sim 100$ GeV is also nicely consistent with precision electroweak data.

---

[7]In specific models, avoiding the fine-tuning problem might require another tuning of parameters in order to make an alternative decay mode for the Higgs boson dominant (see, e.g., References 43 and 44 for discussion of these issues in the NMSSM).

5. HIGGS AS A LINK TO NEW SECTORS

The Higgs field plays a unique role in the SM in that $h^\dagger h$ is a complete Lorentz and gauge singlet, but is only dimension two. As a consequence, it can couple to hidden-sector scalar fields (real or complex; the latter implies the presence of both scalar and pseudoscalar mass eigenstates) through the renormalizable operator $\phi^* \phi h^\dagger h$ or through the dimension-three trilinear interaction $\phi h^\dagger h + h.c.$. The latter can be eliminated by requiring a symmetry under $\phi \to -\phi$. If we presume that the trilinear term is absent, then couplings of the type $h\phi\phi$ will still be generated for the mass eigenstates when the h field acquires a vev. Similarly, the h can couple to (vector-like) SM-singlet fermions through the dimension-five operator $\bar{n} n h^\dagger h$. Because the width of the Higgs eigenstate (also denoted h) is small for $m_h < 160$ GeV, decays to a pair of ϕs or ns can dominate the decay of the h, in the former case with a perturbative dimensionless coupling and in the latter case if the operator is suppressed by a scale near the weak scale. We review here some of the possibilities arising from these operators. Both of the above possibilities arise quite simply in the NMSSM, but first we consider them in a general context.

There are many possible final signals in the case of $h \to \phi\phi$ decays. The various cases depend upon whether ϕ acquires a vev and whether the ϕ couples to a new heavy BSM sector. If the ϕ field does not acquire a vev and does not couple to some new BSM sector, then the ϕ mass eigenstate will be absolutely stable. If the h width remains narrow for such decays, then the LEP limits on an invisible h requiring $m_h \geq 115$ GeV will apply. However, this limit can be evaded if the invisible width is very large. Models[8] in which this can happen include the case of a large number of strongly coupled scalars (23) and, for some extreme parameter choices, the recent unparticle models (which can be deconstructed as a continuum of stable invisible scalars, a subtype of the former class of models) (49).

If the purely singlet scalar couples to the mass of some heavy BSM fermions [i.e., $(\lambda\phi + M)\bar{\psi}\psi$], then h decays to four photons or four jets can dominate the Higgs width (50, 51). The four-photon channel can also be dominant in NMSSM models (52), where $h \to aa$, the a is purely singlet, and the $a\gamma\gamma$ coupling arises from virtual loops containing supersymmetric gauginos and higgsinos. The four-photon mode would have been easily discoverable at LEP were it below the kinematic bound, whereas the four-gluon decay would have been a challenge to discover (51). If there are multiple states below the Higgs mass, then very complicated decays, such as $h \to 6f$ or $h \to 8f$, can arise, where f can represent various fermions.

A purely singlet scalar can be very long lived if it decays through loop-suppressed or non-renormalizable operators (51, 53, 54). This allows decays of the Higgs with significantly displaced vertices, which may be an intriguing avenue to search for new physics like that of Hidden Valley models (54). However, such decays would likely have been noticed if they had been the dominant decay mode at LEP.

We now discuss the cases in which the singlet scalar field acquires a vev or in which there is an $h^\dagger h \phi + h.c.$ component in the Lagrangian. In these cases, the tenets of the above discussion do not apply. The light singlet state will typically mix with the nonsinglet Higgs boson(s) and will thereby acquire a significant coupling to SM particles, especially the light fermions. Thus the cascade decays can arise (as described above) and allow the Higgs mass to be light enough to reduce or eliminate the fine-tuning. For very light singlet states, most of the phenomenology is independent of the potential (55), whereas at heavier masses there is more dependence.

However, even without considering specific decays the mixing alone can influence fine-tuning in two separate ways. First, the Higgs mixing can push up the mass of the heavy mass eigenstate,

---

[8]We do not consider invisible decay modes related to graviscalars and so forth that arise in theories with extra dimensions.

but at the cost of allowing the light state to have low enough mass that it can be produced via Higgsstrahlung. At tree level such mixing does little to alleviate fine-tuning, but with loop effects included the reduction in fine-tuning can be significant (56). More common is the reduction in fine-tuning resulting from the decay of a light SM-like Higgs to a pair of still lighter Higgses in such models; such a decay allows the SM-like Higgs to have mass ≤ 100 GeV. As we discuss in Section 8, this scenario will also make Higgs discovery at the LHC quite challenging. As one increases the number of states with which the h field can mix (including both doublets and singlets in general), the primary Higgs field(s) that couples to the Z can be spread out among many mass eigenstates. This will make discovery difficult because such a model allows a multitude of Higgs to Higgs pair decays, a reduction in the production rate for any one Higgs boson, and an overlapping of the peaks for the individual states in any given detection channel. In particular, these effects can make LHC Higgs detection essentially impossible (22, 57, 58). However, detection at a future linear collider will be possible in the $e^+e^- \rightarrow Z + X$ channel provided that sufficient integrated luminosity is available (22).

If the singlet field acquires a vev and yet parameters are chosen so that there is no mixing between the singlet-ϕ particle states and the doublet-Higgs states, one must consider whether or not the four-photon and other highly suppressed decay modes of the SM-like Higgs could be dominant. The NMSSM provides one such example: Aside from the loop-induced $a\gamma\gamma$ coupling considered by Arhrib et al. (52), supersymmetric particle loops (for example, a loop containing a $\tilde{b}$ and a gluino) also induce $ab\bar{b}$ couplings (59). The latter can be up to one-half of SM strength (i.e., similar to $h_{SM}b\bar{b}$ but with an extra γ_5 in the coupling Lagrangian) for very high values of $\tan\beta \sim 50$ and moderate sparticle masses. This is more than likely to swamp the loop-induced $a\gamma\gamma$ couplings in the NMSSM. Generically, even for a purely singlet a, dominance of $a \rightarrow \gamma\gamma$ over $a \rightarrow b\bar{b}$ will only be the case if $\tan\beta$ is small. More generally, if the BSM sector (whose loops give rise to a singlet–two photon coupling) contains any non-SM-singlet fields, one can expect important singlet-$b\bar{b}$ couplings to be associated with loops of the latter fields.

If the additional scalar is charged under some new gauge symmetry, a strongly mixed Higgs can decay into new gauge bosons (60). However, in order for this to dominate the decay the mass eigenstate must be significantly mixed ($\sin^2\theta \sim 0.5$). In the case of BSM fermions dominating the Higgs decay, Higgs decays to right-handed neutrinos are an interesting possibility (61, 62). If left-handed neutrinos are involved, decays to different fermions such as $h \rightarrow \psi_1\psi_2$ are possible (34, 63). Such decays with both visible and missing energy are also capable of evading Higgs search limits, as well as other new physics searches (34). In the NMSSM, such states could be neutralinos in addition to neutrinos.

We have noted the generic possibility of coupling the doublet-Higgs structure $h^\dagger h$ to an SM-singlet operator. In fact, in SUSY such coupling has a very compelling motivation as an extension of the MSSM. The content of the MSSM in the matter and gauge sectors is fixed by requiring a superpartner for each known particle of definite helicity. In contrast, the choice of a two-doublet Higgs sector is made purely on the basis of minimality arguments (absence of anomalies and the need to give mass to both up and down quarks) and this choice gives rise to the famous μ problem. Namely, phenomenology requires a term of the form $\mu \hat{H}_u \hat{H}_d$[9] in the superpotential, where μ is a term with dimensions of mass with a value between ~ 150 GeV and 1 TeV, as opposed to the natural values of 0 or M_{GUT}. Ideally, one would have no dimensionful parameters in the superpotential, as all dimensionful parameters would be confined to the soft SUSY breaking potential.

---

[9]Hatted fields denote superfields; unhatted fields denote normal fields.

A particularly appealing extension of the MSSM that solves the μ problem is the introduction of a completely new sector of particles that are singlets under the SM gauge symmetry. This extra (E) sector would not spoil any of the virtues of the MSSM, including the possibility of gauge coupling unification and matter particles fitting into complete GUT multiplets. In addition, E sector particles that either do not mix or have small mixing with SM particles would easily escape direct detection. Of course, if this E sector is completely decoupled from the SM then it plays no role in particle physics phenomenology at accelerators. Much more interesting is the possibility that this sector couples to the MSSM through the Higgs fields. In particular, the E sector can couple to the SM-singlet $\hat{H}_u \hat{H}_d$ form that appears in the MSSM μ term in many ways, including a renormalizable term (with dimensionless coupling) of form $\lambda \hat{E} \hat{H}_u \hat{H}_d$. When the scalar component of the singlet superfield $\hat{E}$ acquires a vev, $\langle E \rangle = x$ (as a result of SUSY breaking), an effective μ value, $\mu_{\mathrm{eff}} = \lambda x$, is generated. Such couplings would have a negligible effect on the phenomenology involving SM matter particles, whereas they can dramatically alter Higgs physics. In particular, the particle couplings generated allow the lightest CP-even Higgs boson h to decay into two of the particles associated with the E fields (E particles) if the E particles are light enough, and these $h \to EE$ decays can be dominant for even a modest $\hat{E} \hat{H}_u \hat{H}_d$ coupling strength.

The implications for Higgs discovery follow some of the patterns discussed above. In particular, when h decays to two lighter E particles are dominant, the strategy for Higgs discovery depends on the way the E particles appearing in the decays of the h themselves decay. The latter might decay predominantly into other stable E particles, in which case the MSSM-like h would decay mainly invisibly. More typically, however, the E particles mix with the SM particles via the couplings between the MSSM and the E sector. In particular, couplings between E bosons and the MSSM Higgs fields are generically present, which implies that the Higgs mass eigenstates are mixed. In this case, the mostly E particle light Higgses would decay into $b\bar{b}$, $\tau^+\tau^-$, or other quarks or leptons depending on the model. Although E particles would have small direct-production cross sections, making it difficult to detect them directly, they would be manifest in the (dominant) $h \to EE$ Higgs decay modes, leading to $h \to 4f$, where $4f$ stands for four SM particles, e.g., $b\bar{b}b\bar{b}$, $b\bar{b}\tau^+\tau^-$, $\tau^+\tau^-\tau^+\tau^-$, 4γ, and so on. The situation can become even more complicated if the h decays to E particles, which themselves decay into other E particles, which in turn decay to SM particles. In such a case, the SM-like Higgs would effectively decay into $8f$.

Finally, we note that the presence of a singlet in the potential can lead to modifications in the early universe cosmology. In particular, it allows the possibility of a first-order phase transition (64–66), which can arise consistent with the LEP experiments.

6. CASCADE DECAYS TO SCALARS IN THE NMSSM

The cascade decay scenario described in Sections 2, 3, and 5 already occurs in the simplest extension of the MSSM, the NMSSM, which adds only one singlet chiral superfield, $\hat{S}$, to the MSSM. Phenomenologically similar scenarios arise naturally in theories with additional $U(1)$s (67–69). The NMSSM particle content differs from that of the MSSM by the addition of one CP-even and one CP-odd state in the neutral Higgs sector (assuming CP conservation) and one additional neutralino. Here we follow the conventions of Ellwanger et al. (70). Apart from the usual quark and lepton Yukawa couplings, the scale invariant superpotential is

$$\lambda \, \hat{S} \hat{H}_u \hat{H}_d + \frac{\kappa}{3} \, \hat{S}^3, \qquad\qquad 11.$$

depending on two dimensionless couplings λ and κ beyond the MSSM. The associated trilinear soft terms are

$$\lambda A_\lambda S H_u H_d + \frac{\kappa}{3} A_\kappa S^3. \qquad\qquad 12.$$

The final two input parameters are

$$\tan\beta = h_u/h_d, \quad \mu_{\text{eff}} = \lambda s, \qquad\qquad 13.$$

where $h_u \equiv \langle H_u \rangle$, $h_d \equiv \langle H_d \rangle$, and $s \equiv \langle S \rangle$. These, along with M_Z, can be interpreted as determining the three SUSY breaking masses squared for H_u, H_d, and S (denoted $m^2_{H_u}$, $m^2_{H_d}$, and m^2_S, respectively) through the three minimization equations of the scalar potential. Thus, as compared to the three independent parameters needed in the MSSM context (often chosen as μ, $\tan\beta$, and M_A), the Higgs sector of the NMSSM is described by the six parameters

$$\lambda, \kappa, A_\lambda, A_\kappa, \tan\beta, \mu_{\text{eff}}. \qquad\qquad 14.$$

We choose sign conventions for the fields such that λ and $\tan\beta$ are positive, whereas κ, A_λ, A_κ, and μ_{eff} are allowed to have either sign. In addition, values must be input for the gaugino masses and for the soft terms related to the (third-generation) squarks and sleptons (especially $m^2_{\tilde{t}_L}$, $m^2_{\tilde{t}_R}$, and A_t) that contribute to the radiative corrections in the Higgs sector and to the Higgs decay widths.

Of all the possible new phenomena to which the additional Higgses in the NMSSM can lead, perhaps the most intriguing is the possibility of the lightest CP-even Higgs decaying into a pair of the two lightest CP-odd Higgses, $h_1 \to a_1 a_1$, where the latter are mostly singlets (6, 40, 46, 50, 71). This exact scenario can eliminate the fine-tuning of EWSB in the NMSSM for $m_{h_1} \sim 100$ GeV (6, 40). If $\text{Br}(h_1 \to a_1 a_1) > 0.7$ and $m_{a_1} < 2m_b$, the usual LEP limit on the Higgs boson mass does not apply and the SUSY spectrum can be arbitrarily light, perhaps just above the experimental bounds and certainly light enough for natural EWSB. In addition, without any further ingredients this scenario can completely explain the excess of Higgs-like events in the $b\bar{b}$ channel at $M_{b\bar{b}} \simeq 98$ GeV (46). Finally, the above a_1 scenario is not itself fine-tuned. Starting from A_κ and A_λ values at the GUT scale that are small [and therefore close to a $U(1)_R$ symmetry limit of the potential], the RG equations yield A_κ and A_λ values at scale M_Z that generically result in $\text{Br}(h_1 \to a_1 a_1) > 0.7$ and $m_{a_1} < 2m_b$, with some preference for $m_{a_1} > 2m_\tau$ (44). In addition, M_Z-scale values for the soft SUSY breaking parameters that correspond to a lack of electroweak fine-tuning imply values of $m^2_{H_u}$, $m^2_{H_d}$, and m^2_S at the GUT scale that are all relatively small (46). That is, the preferred GUT-scale boundary conditions for the NMSSM are close to the no-scale-type boundary conditions where many of the soft SUSY breaking parameters are near zero.

Higgs signals at colliders of all types are dramatically different in the NMSSM models that have no fine-tuning. One must look for $h \to a_1 a_1 \to 4\tau$ or $4j$ (the latter being somewhat less preferred because of a need to tune A_κ and A_λ). We discuss collider implications in the following sections.

7. LIGHT HIGGSES AT B FACTORIES

We have shown that a generic way in which a SM-like Higgs with $m_h \sim 100$ GeV can escape the LEP limits on the $h \to b\bar{b}$ and $h \to b\bar{b}b\bar{b}$ channels is for the h to decay primarily to two E bosons that have mass below $2m_b$. The NMSSM scenario of $h_1 \to a_1 a_1 \to 4\tau$ is just one example of this generic possibility. However, there is an interesting requirement within the NMSSM scenario that we have not yet mentioned. Specifically, $\text{Br}(h_1 \to a_1 a_1)$ is only large enough to escape the LEP limits if the a_1 is not purely singlet (44). There must be some mixing of the CP-odd singlet with the MSSM-like CP-odd Higgs that is a residual from the two doublets. Defining

$$a_1 \equiv \cos\theta_A \, A_{\text{MSSM}} + \sin\theta_A \, A_S, \qquad\qquad 15.$$

where A_{MSSM} is the MSSM-doublet CP-odd Higgs and A_S is the CP-odd (imaginary) component of the complex S scalar field, one finds (at $\tan\beta = 10$, for example) that $|\cos\theta_A| \gtrsim 0.06$ is required for $\mathrm{Br}(b_1 \to a_1 a_1) > 0.7$. The $a_1 b\bar{b}$ coupling, given by $\cos\theta_A \tan\beta \frac{m_b}{v} \bar{b} i\gamma_5 b a_1$, then has a lower bound that is almost SM-like in strength. Further, a light a_1 with the required properties is most naturally obtained after RG evolution of the relevant parameters from GUT-scale boundary conditions when $|\cos\theta_A|$ is near its lower bound, $|\cos\theta_A| \sim 0.1$.

The lower bound on the $a_1 b\bar{b}$ coupling has crucial consequences at B factories (72, 73). In the NMSSM one finds (72) that for any given m_{a_1} below M_Υ (where Υ denotes the 1S, 2S, or 3S state), there is a lower bound on $\mathrm{Br}(\Upsilon \to \gamma a_1)$. Not surprisingly, this lower bound is quite small. For example, to probe m_{a_1} values as high as 9.2 GeV in $\Upsilon(1S)$ decays [such an m_{a_1} being within the preferred $m_{a_1} > 2m_\tau$ range but still leaving some phase space for $\Upsilon(1S) \to \gamma a_1$ decay], at B factories one must be sensitive to $\mathrm{Br}(\Upsilon \to \gamma a_1 \to \gamma \tau^+\tau^-)$ down to $\sim 10^{-7}$ (at $\tan\beta = 10$, even lower for low $\tan\beta$ and somewhat higher for high $\tan\beta$) for full coverage of the possible scenarios. Reaching this level is a challenge, but it is not necessarily impossible if we use dedicated runs on one of the Υ resonances. Search for nonuniversality (enhancement of the $\tau^+\tau^-$ final state) in Υ decays to leptons without directly tagging the photon may also be a useful approach (73).

In more general E sector scenarios, to have a SM-like h with $m_h \sim 100$ GeV requires that there be one or more E bosons with mass below $2m_b$ and that the cumulative branching ratio for h decay to these states be $\gtrsim 0.7$. It is likely that some of these states will have reasonable coupling to $b\bar{b}$ and will have mass low enough to yield a potentially measurable rate for Υ decay to photon plus E boson, with E boson decay to $\tau^+\tau^-$ more likely than decay to the much more difficult jj final state.

Such searches are of great importance given the fact that Υ decays may be the only way prior to the construction of a linear collider to obtain confirmation of the existence of E bosons that is independent of their hoped-for observation at the LHC in h decays. Indeed, generally speaking some light E bosons that do not appear in h decays might appear in Υ decays!

8. IMPLICATIONS FOR THE LHC

The nonstandard cascade Higgs decay scenario has many interesting implications for the LHC. Earlier studies have explored how to determine whether or not a scalar discovered at the LHC is, in fact, the Higgs (74). In the present situation, we are interested in cases where new, possibly unexpected decays have arisen, and their consequences for experimental searches. In this review, we attempt to summarize two aspects of this phenomenology. (For simplicity, we presume the model predicts one and only one SM-like Higgs boson and we will refer to it as the Higgs.) The first aspect is the change in Higgs phenomenology. One primary implication for the Higgs is that the SM decays are subdominant, rendering the LHC SM Higgs searches less effective. In this regard, it is useful to consider whether the nonstandard Higgs decays will lead to a viable Higgs signal. However, it is also interesting to discuss potential model-dependent effects outside of Higgs physics, as such effects combine with the Higgs as a window into new physics. The example we discuss involves changes in the decays of the supersymmetric partners of the SM. These changes suggest that a nonstandard Higgs decay could be accompanied by nonstandard superpartner decays, which would provide correlated evidence for this model.

In some regions of parameter space, the intermediate particles facilitating the Higgs cascade decay can have highly displaced vertices. In this case, the LHCb (the dedicated detector for B physics at the LHC), with its superior ability to trigger on displaced vertices, can have a greater reach for both Higgs and superpartner decays. Thus, it is possible that the LHCb will be the first LHC experiment to discover this new physics.

8.1. Higgs

The nonstandard Higgs scenario unambiguously predicts changes in the phenomenology of the SM-like Higgs boson of the model. At the LHC, the immediate impact is the weakening of Higgs searches that depend on the SM decay modes. A light Higgs near the LEP bound is already a difficult region for the LHC to probe. Instead of relying upon the dominant decay of the Higgs to b quarks, the experiments have focused on diphoton Higgs decay and the ditau decay for a Higgs produced by vector boson fusion (VBF). Both of these searches are statistics limited, so any suppression of the SM decay branching ratio increases the required integrated luminosity for discovery. Naively, the increase in required luminosity is a factor of $1/\mathrm{Br}(h \to SM)^2$ more. This factor is naive as the searches can become more efficient as the experiment runs, but the backgrounds can change as the experiment moves to design luminosity.

For a nonstandard Higgs that is 100 GeV in mass, the SM LEP search determines that the SM branching ratio is at most 25%. Thus, the required integrated luminosity increases by a factor of at least 16. Extrapolating the numbers shown in the Compact Muon Solenoid Technical Design Report (CMS TDR) (75), an integrated luminosity $\gtrsim 16 * 25$ fb^{-1} = 400 fb^{-1} is needed for discovery. In the NMSSM context, a more typical Br($h \to SM$) is $\sim$0.1, implying a need to increase the luminosity by a factor of roughly 100. This would only be achievable at the Super Large Hadron Collider (SLHC) (assuming no change in the signal-to-background ratio; in fact, this ratio would decrease because of the huge number of multiple interactions). Therefore, in order to maintain the reach for Higgs discovery it is important to consider whether the nonstandard Higgs decays can provide a viable Higgs signal.

We focus on the case where there is a SM-like Higgs of the extended model. Because this Higgs couples to SM particles with normal strength, its production cross sections are unmodified. Thus, to determine the Higgs signal topology we need only specify the nonstandard decay. Before proceeding, it is useful to consider the advantages of the LHC over LEP to motivate the LHC search strategies. As a hadron collider, the LHC has higher integrated luminosity and production cross sections than LEP and thus will produce far more of the SM-like Higgses. This allows the LHC to look for the rarer clean decay modes that are not swamped by QCD backgrounds. In the case of a SM-like Higgs, LEP looks for the dominant decays to $b\bar{b}$ and $\tau\bar{\tau}$, while the LHC searches for $\gamma\gamma$ and for $\tau\bar{\tau}$ in VBF.

8.1.1. Higgs decays to scalars. Higgs decays to a pair of scalars or pseudoscalars (we use the notation a in our discussion to indicate the latter) are the best-known nonstandard Higgs phenomenology; it has been searched for at LEP in the *CP*-violating MSSM and has been studied extensively in the NMSSM. In these SUSY scenarios, an a with $m_a > 2m_b$ decays with branching ratios similar to the SM Higgs boson and thus $a \to b\bar{b}$ decays are dominant with $a \to \tau\bar{\tau}$ being subdominant.

The dominant decay mode of $h \to aa \to 4b$ is strongly constrained by LEP data, which require the Higgs mass to be above 110 GeV. Still, it is interesting to determine whether this decay can be seen above the QCD background at the LHC for such heavier Higgses. In recent papers (76, 77), such Higgs decays were studied at the Tevatron and at the LHC. These analyses focused on Higgses produced in association with a W boson and examined the topology of $4jl\nu$, requiring three or four b-tagged jets. For a 120-GeV Higgs, Carena et al. (77) found that 5σ discovery at the LHC requires about 30 fb^{-1} but is highly reliant on b-tagging efficiencies of 50% at $p_T \sim 15$ GeV. Such a high efficiency at this transverse momentum may be difficult to achieve at the LHC; if this tagging efficiency only holds for transverse momenta greater than 30 GeV, the necessary luminosity goes to 80 fb^{-1}. As we extrapolate to lighter Higgses, these issues will become more important, further increasing the level of luminosity required. Carena et al. also studied the $2b2\tau$ mode and found that its prospects were not as promising. For older work on the $4b$ and $2b2\tau$ modes, see References 78–83.

If the a mass is below the $b\bar{b}$ threshold (~12 GeV), the dominant Higgs decay is into 4τ and is only weakly constrained by LEP data. Thus, at the LHC it is important to analyze the ideal $m_h \sim 100$ GeV scenario in the $h \rightarrow 4\tau$ final state. The two most promising production possibilities are VBF and diffractive Higgs production. In VBF, one looks for $WW \rightarrow h \rightarrow 4\tau$ tagging the forward jets that are emitting the Ws in order to isolate the signal. Studies of this mode have begun. In diffractive Higgs production, one looks for a special class of events with protons appearing in specially designed detectors and very little additional activity in the final state. In a recent paper (84), the authors claimed that by using a track-based analysis in which all events with more than six tracks in the central region are discarded, a viable signal becomes possible after accumulating 300 fb^{-1} of integrated luminosity. This type of track-based approach may also prove crucial to extracting a viable signal in the VBF channel. There is also an older analysis wherein the authors searched for $h \rightarrow 4\tau$ at the Tevatron (85).

There exists a particularly useful technique involving mass reconstruction in the 4τ case. Because $m_a \ll m_h$, the two a decays result in two highly boosted 2τ pairs, each of which decays more or less collinearly to the visible 2τ decay products and some missing momentum. In the collinear approximation, there are enough constraint equations to solve for both the h and a masses. In the $WW \rightarrow h$ fusion case, this technique requires that the h have significant transverse momentum, as measured by the recoiling jets. In the $pp \rightarrow pph$, the forward-tagged protons provide an overconstrained system even if the h has very little transverse momentum or if the transverse momentum cannot be measured accurately. For details of the latter scenario, see Reference 84.

Another class of possible decays arises when a is fermiophobic to SM fermion decays (33, 50). This possibility does not arise in the NMSSM, but it can occur in other models. If a couples to SM-singlet heavy fermions into which it cannot decay, its leading decay is through loop-induced decays into gluons or photons. Thus, the decay modes of the Higgs are into $4g$, $2g2\gamma$, and 4γ in decreasing order of dominance. The four-gluon decay suffers from too large of a QCD background to be searched for at the LHC. However, the LEP constraints on the decays with photons could allow $a \rightarrow \gamma\gamma$ branching ratios as high as 10^{-2} (51); in this case, the subdominant decays might provide a viable LHC signal. Martin (86) analyzed the $2g2\gamma$ decay and showed that, with integrated luminosity of order 300 fb^{-1}, a branching ratio for $h \rightarrow 2g2\gamma$ of a few percent was needed to discover the Higgs and the a. Chang et al. (51) analyzed the $h \rightarrow 4\gamma$ decays for 300 fb^{-1} and showed that the background was negligible and that a branching ratio of 10^{-4} for $h \rightarrow 4\gamma$ was sufficient to discover both scalars in most of the parameter space.

A crucial issue for these fermiophobic decays is efficient triggering. The photons are relatively soft, with $p_T \sim m_h/4$, so passing the diphoton trigger is one of the biggest issues for the signal efficiency. For the 4γ decay, this can be relieved by implementing a multiple photon trigger with a lower threshold than the diphoton trigger.

8.1.2. Higgs decays with displaced vertices. In some models, the Higgs decays have significantly displaced vertices, which makes the LHCb the ideal detector to search for the Higgs. Such Higgs decays have been discussed in supersymmetric models with R-parity violation (87), in Hidden Valley models (54), and in models with light right-handed neutrinos (61, 62). Displaced vertices are possible because the intermediate particle, which facilitates the Higgs cascade decay, can have a suppressed coupling that mediates its decay. Decay lengths between 100 μm and 10 m are the most interesting, as they are potentially resolvable within the detector. The LEP constraints on such a scenario are difficult to ascertain, especially for highly displaced vertices.

However, such nonstandard Higgs decays could occur and it is important to determine whether there are ways to detect a Higgs decaying in this fashion.

In the case of R-parity violation that is baryon number violating (87), the Higgs decays into a pair of neutralinos that decay into three quarks each. If the neutralino decay is highly displaced, the hadrons formed from the three quarks point back to a vertex. Therefore, it is possible to have two highly displaced vertices that are inconsistent with the SM. Such vertices are easiest to detect and trigger on at the LHCb. This detector is forward focused and thus nonhermetic, but it is possible for the Higgs to be boosted enough so that both neutralino decays occur in the detector. An analysis at the LHCb (88) showed that such double-displaced vertices have negligible background. Furthermore, such Higgs decays will produce thousands of such double-displaced events in a year (with LHCb running at integrated luminosity ~ 2 fb^{-1}), as long as the neutralino mass is not too light. This type of analysis should also apply to other Higgs decays with double-displaced vertices, as they are only distinguished by the objects related to each vertex. Those decays with right-handed neutrinos (61, 62) have dominantly two light quark jets and a charged lepton at a vertex, whereas Hidden Valley models (54) typically have $b\bar{b}$ or $\tau\bar{\tau}$ at each vertex. Thus, depending on whether or not ATLAS or CMS can trigger and isolate such events, it is quite possible that such Higgses will first be discovered at the LHCb detector.

8.1.3. Higgs decays with missing energy. Researchers have recently explored Higgs decays that have both missing energy and visible energy (34, 61–63). If the Higgs decays into two new neutral particles, one unstable and one stable, the final state will contain both missing and visible energy. There are many potential decay topologies, but the most promising topologies for searches have two charged leptons in the final state, yielding $l^{+}l^{-}\not{E}_{T}$. Depending upon whether the Higgs is produced with associated particles, the signal topologies can look very similar to standard SUSY discovery channels with leptons, for example dilepton and trilepton events with missing energy (34). The resemblance raises interesting analysis issues: If this Higgs appears in a supersymmetric theory, it will be necessary to produce cuts to isolate the Higgs component from the superpartner production component (see, e.g., Reference 89). However, a Higgs decaying in this manner can also appear in a nonsupersymmetric theory. These issues suggest that discovery of such a Higgs could require cooperation between Higgs and SUSY experimentalists—any analysis that yields an unexpected excess or that is inconsistent with an expected signal should be closely scrutinized.

In these scenarios, the Higgs can also decay invisibly into some combination of neutrinos and other stable particles. Searches for such invisible Higgs decays are already planned for the LHC, where it has been shown that relatively small values (perhaps as small as 5–10%) for Br($h \rightarrow \not{E}_{T}$) can yield a viable signal in the WW-fusion production mode, assuming SM-like hWW coupling (90, 91). The potential of using this channel alone to discover the Higgs was studied in several extended supersymmetric SMs (92). The $pp \rightarrow pph \rightarrow pp\not{E}_{T}$ forward diffractive production channel is also expected to yield a viable signal at full 300 fb^{-1} integrated luminosity for Br($h \rightarrow \not{E}_{T}$) significantly below one (93). Generically speaking, Higgs decays containing missing energy can appear in several channels. Hopefully, some combination of these searches (potentially combined with the SM searches) can facilitate the discovery of such a Higgs.

8.2. Supersymmetric Particle Searches

Aside from changes in Higgs phenomenology, nonstandard Higgs models have important implications for other sectors of the theory. For instance, in order to avoid fine-tuning, low masses for the superpartners (in particular the stop and the gluino) are required; these masses are typically just beyond current Tevatron limits. For the required masses, production rates of superpartners at the LHC will be very large. SUSY will be discovered with relatively little integrated luminosity, whereas Higgs discovery will require large integrated luminosity and will therefore take more time. Thus, the LHC experimental collaborations should look for a situation in which they have discovered SUSY but have not yet seen any of the Higgs signals in the MSSM for the expected amounts of integrated luminosity. Higgs channels with cascade decays should then become a high priority. In addition, it will be important to determine whether WW scattering is perturbative in nature. If it is perturbative, then there must be one or more relatively light (below 300 GeV) Higgs bosons with large WW coupling to be searched for.

Implications for BSM particle searches are of even greater importance in models where the Higgs decays into particles that transform under a new symmetry. In supersymmetric models, this symmetry is R-parity. Supersymmetric particles are odd under R-parity and thus have to cascade decay down into the lightest particle that is R-parity odd, namely the LSP. When the (SM-like) Higgs decays into supersymmetric particles, those particles are typically an LSP pair or an LSP plus another light supersymmetric particle that in turn decays to a final state that includes the LSP. The branching ratio for such decays often determines or at least constrains the properties of the light supersymmetric particles, which in turn constrains how the heavier supersymmetric particles cascade down to the LSP.

The simplest possibility, wherein the light ($\leq$100-GeV) Higgs decays into two LSPs, is not allowed (without R-parity violation), as the decay is invisible and is ruled out by the LEP invisible Higgs search. The next simplest possibility is for the Higgs to decay into the LSP and a heavier supersymmetric particle. Both particles are neutral and the heavier one is unstable, decaying down into the LSP. This gives a missing and visible energy component to the Higgs decay, which we discussed above in Section 8.1.3.

In supersymmetric theories, such a nonstandard decay can result in neutralinos or sneutrinos. For neutralinos, requiring the Higgs to decay into $\tilde{\chi}_1 \tilde{\chi}_0$ and imposing the constraints on charginos and neutralinos specify the neutralino spectrum. This requires an NMSSM-like supersymmetric theory where the LSP $\tilde{\chi}_0$ is mostly singlino in gauge eigenstate composition and where $\tilde{\chi}_1$ is mostly bino, as verified via a scan using NMHDECAY (70, 94). Thus, the LSP has very weak couplings mostly mediated through the superpotential interaction $\hat{S}\hat{H}_u\hat{H}_d$. This has drastic consequences for the cascade decays of supersymmetric particles. The cascades lengthen, as they dominantly cascade to $\tilde{\chi}_1$, which then decays down to $\tilde{\chi}_0$. Thus, at first order the supersymmetric cascades are as in the MSSM, followed by a final decay of the binos into a lighter neutralino. NMSSM-like models with an extra $U(1)$ and several extra Higgs fields transforming differently under the extra $U(1)$ can lead to an even more complex scenario for Higgs decays and supersymmetric cascades (67). If such a model is realized in nature, it could take decades to understand this physics.

For now, we focus on the less complex nonstandard decay cascades. Even these have important consequences for collider searches (95, 96). At the Tevatron and LEP, searches for squarks and staus will have weaker constraints due to these decays (S. Chang, D. Tucker-Smith & N. Weiner, manuscript in preparation). At the LHC, most cascades of superpartner decays will include the characteristic decay of $\tilde{\chi}_1$ to $\tilde{\chi}_0$. Furthermore, because the $\tilde{\chi}_1$ and the $\tilde{\chi}_0$ must be light in order to appear in the Higgs decay, their production cross sections (at least that for $\tilde{\chi}_1\tilde{\chi}_1$) at the LHC will be large. Most probably, other superpartner particles will also be relatively light. In this case, SUSY will be discovered with an early amount of luminosity ($\sim$30 fb^{-1}), whereas the Higgs, because of its nonstandard decays, will not be discovered. By analyzing the SUSY events, it may be possible to measure the branching ratios of the decays of $\tilde{\chi}_1$ to $\tilde{\chi}_0$ and some of the properties of the $\tilde{\chi}_1$ and $\tilde{\chi}_0$. This will help determine whether the Higgs has a large Br($b \rightarrow \tilde{\chi}_1\tilde{\chi}_0$) and will provide crucial information regarding the nonstandard decay topology of the SM-like Higgs. This information can then be used to design searches to pick out this decay in the design luminosity run of the LHC.

In the cascade decay scenario wherein the neutralino decays via R-parity violation with a displaced vertex (87), the LHCb's capabilities enable efficient searches for such vertices. Kaplan & Rehermann recently considered the production of a squark decaying into the lightest neutralino (88). Compared to the Higgs signal, it is less likely for two squarks to appear in the LHCb detector. Still, there is a reasonable region of parameter space to allow for the discovery of the squark at the LHCb detector via the appearance of one such displaced vertex within one year of running. Thus, it is possible that the LHCb detector will discover both the Higgs and SUSY before ATLAS/CMS.

9. CONCLUSION

The motivations for a light (≤ 100-GeV) Higgs boson with SM-like couplings to SM particles, but with dominant decays to non-SM particles, are very substantial. Typically (and explicitly in the NMSSM), fine-tuning can be minimized and/or eliminated if the Higgs has mass at or below 100 GeV. In addition, such mass is most consistent with precision electroweak data. Furthermore, because of the very small $h \to SM$ decay widths for a light h, the $h \to SM$ branching ratios are easily greatly suppressed by the presence of couplings to a pair of particles (with summed mass below m_b) from a nonstandard sector. Dominance of nonstandard decays typically implies that the LEP limits on m_h are reduced to below roughly 90 GeV so long as the ultimate final state is not $h \to 4b$ (for which LEP requires $m_h > 110$ GeV). In many cases, moreover, the $h \to b\bar{b}$ branching ratio is reduced to the $\sim 10\%$ level that would explain the excess in $Z + b\bar{b}$ seen at $M_{b\bar{b}} \sim 98$ GeV at LEP.

The NMSSM scenarios with no fine-tunings, where the lightest CP-even Higgs, h_1, has $m_{h_1} \sim 100$ GeV and is SM-like in its couplings to SM particles but decays via $h_1 \to a_1 a_1 \to 4\tau$ (or, less likely, $4j$) and/or $h_1 \to \tilde{\chi}_1 \tilde{\chi}_0 \to f\bar{f} + \not{E}_T$, deserve particular attention. In the NMSSM, to have low fine-tuning the stop and gluino should be just above Tevatron limits and should be easily discoverable at the LHC. If $h_1 \to \tilde{\chi}_1 \tilde{\chi}_0$, $m_{\tilde{\chi}_1} + m_{\tilde{\chi}_0} < m_{h_1}$ implies that $\tilde{\chi}_1 \tilde{\chi}_1$ detection may also be possible early on. However, Higgs discovery will be challenging in all of these cases. If supersymmetric particle decays indicate that R-parity is violated baryonically, then one should also be alert to the possibility that $h_1 \to \tilde{\chi}_0 \tilde{\chi}_0 \to 6j$ decays could be dominant. This kind of mode can be present in the MSSM as well as in the NMSSM. If one is willing to accept a significant but not outrageous fine-tuning of 6%, many more Higgs scenarios emerge. For example, in the NMSSM the $h_1 \to a_1 a_1 \to 4b$ and $2b + 2\tau$ channels with $m_{h_1} > 110$ GeV (from the LEP limits) would provide possible discovery modes.

To summarize, the allowed nonstandard Higgs decay topologies are of a few limited types. There are decays into four SM fermions, which are often mediated by a scalar ϕ to yield $h \to 2\phi \to 4f$. Heavier fermions are usually favored, although the strong limits on $4b$ decays suggest that ϕ is lighter than the $b\bar{b}$ threshold and that the dominant decay is into 4τs. If the scalar ϕ is fermiophobic, loop-induced decays can generate the decay $h \to 2\phi \to 4V$, where V is a photon or a gluon. When there is more than one new state into which the Higgs can decay, it opens up the possibility of one of these states being stable. Thus, there can be decays with both missing and visible energy, usually of the type $h \to (X_2)X_1 \to (f\bar{f}X_1)X_1 = f\bar{f} + \not{E}$. In addition, there is the potential of displaced vertices when the decaying ϕ or X_2 is long lived; these vertices could give the LHCb an inside track on finding such Higgs decays. Finally, adding additional particles can make the Higgs cascade decay longer and more complex. In some cases, input from B factories and/or non-Higgs LHC searches can pin down some properties of the intermediate states in the Higgs cascade. Thus, if no SM Higgs is found at the LHC at the expected integrated luminosity, it will be advantageous to use all available information about these new states to design efficient searches for the nonstandard Higgs decays.

In general, Higgs decays and phenomenology provide an unexpectedly fertile probe of and window to physics beyond the SM and potentially beyond the MSSM. Nonstandard decays are a double-edged sword: On the one hand, they may make Higgs detection at the LHC much more difficult, but on the other hand they may provide valuable information regarding a new sector of the theory. The additional BSM or beyond-the-MSSM particles could have very weak direct production cross sections at the LHC and might only be observed via Higgs decays. Therefore, a highly detailed understanding and delineation of all Higgs decays will be crucial to understanding BSM physics. We hope that the LHC will prove equal to the task, but we cannot rule out the possibility that a linear collider will ultimately be necessary—at the very least, it would greatly refine the LHC's observations.

DISCLOSURE STATEMENT

The authors are not aware of any biases that might be perceived as affecting the objectivity of this review.

ACKNOWLEDGMENTS

S.C. and N.W. are supported by NSF CAREER grant number PHY-0449818 and the U.S. Department of Energy under grant number DE-FG02-06ER41417. R.D. is supported by the U.S. Department of Energy under grant number DE-FG02-90ER40542. J.F.G. is supported by the U.S. Department of Energy under grant number DE-FG03-91ER40674. J.F.G. would like to acknowledge support from the Kavli Institute for Theoretical Physics, through National Science Foundation grant number NSF PHY05-51164, while preparing this manuscript.

LITERATURE CITED

1. Randall L, Sundrum R. *Phys. Rev. Lett.* 83:3370 (1999)
2. Schmaltz M, Tucker-Smith D. *Annu. Rev. Nucl. Part. Sci.* 55:229 (2005)
3. Perelstein M. *Prog. Part. Nucl. Phys.* 58:247 (2007)
4. Barbieri R, Strumia A. arXiv:hep-ph/0007265 (2000)
5. Particle Data Group, Yao WM, et al. *J. Phys. G* 33:1 (2006)
6. Dermisek R, Gunion JF. *Phys. Rev. Lett.* 95:041801 (2005)
7. LEP Electroweak Work. Group. **http://www.cern.ch/LEPEWWG**
8. Chanowitz MS. *Phys. Rev. D* 66:073002 (2002)
9. Ferroglia A, Ossola G, Sirlin A. arXiv:hep-ph/0406334 (2004)
10. Barate R, et al. (LEP Work. Group Higgs Boson Searches) *Phys. Lett. B* 565:61 (2003)
11. Drees M. *Phys. Rev. D* 71:115006 (2005)
12. Dermisek R, Gunion JF. arXiv:0709.2269 [hep-ph] (2007)
13. Gunion JF, Haber HE. *Nucl. Phys. B* 272:1 (1986)
14. Li L-F, Liu Y, Wolfenstein L. *Phys. Lett. B* 159:45 (1985)
15. Gunion JF, Haber HE. *Nucl. Phys. B* 278:449 (1986)
16. Djouadi A, Kalinowski J, Spira M. *Comput. Phys. Commun.* 108:56 (1998)
17. Gunion JF, Haber HE. *Nucl. Phys. B* 307:445 (1988)
18. Gunion JF, Roszkowski L, Haber HE. *Phys. Rev. D* 38:105 (1988)
19. Ellis JR, et al. *Phys. Rev. D* 39:844 (1989)
20. Gunion JF, Haber HE, Kane GL, Dawson S. *The Higgs Hunter's Guide*. Cambridge, MA: Perseus (1990)
21. Gunion JF, Haber HE, Kane GL, Dawson S. arXiv:hep-ph/9302272 (1992)

22. Espinosa JR, Gunion JF. *Phys. Rev. Lett.* 82:1084 (1999)
23. Binoth T, van der Bij JJ. *Z. Phys. C* 75:17 (1997)
24. Junk T, et al. (LEP Higgs Work. Group Higgs Boson Searches) arXiv:hep-ex/0107034 (2001)
25. Rosca A. (LEP Collab.) arXiv:hep-ex/0212038 (2002)
26. Junk T, et al. (LEP Higgs Work. Group Higgs Boson Searches) arXiv:hep-ex/0107032 (2001)
27. Abbiendi G, et al. (OPAL Collab.) *Eur. Phys. J. C* 37:49 (2004)
28. Abdallah J, et al. (DELPHI Collab.) *Eur. Phys. J. C* 38:1 (2004)
29. Schael S, et al. (ALEPH Collab.) *Eur. Phys. J. C* 47:547 (2006)
30. Abbiendi G, et al. (OPAL Collab.) *Eur. Phys. J. C* 27:483 (2003)
31. Abbiendi G, et al. (OPAL Collab.) *Eur. Phys. J. C* 27:311 (2003)
32. Alcaraz J, et al. (ALEPH Collab.) arXiv:hep-ex/0612034 (2006)
33. Chang S, Fox PJ, Weiner N. *JHEP* 08:068 (2006)
34. Chang S, Weiner N. arXiv:0710.4591 [hep-ph] (2007)
35. Okada Y, Yamaguchi M, Yanagida T. *Prog. Theor. Phys.* 85:1 (1991)
36. Haber HE, Hempfling R. *Phys. Rev. Lett.* 66:1815 (1991)
37. Ellis JR, Ridolfi G, Zwirner F. *Phys. Lett. B* 257:83 (1991)
38. Ellis JR, Ridolfi G, Zwirner F. *Phys. Lett. B* 262:477 (1991)
39. Dermisek R, Kim HD. *Phys. Rev. Lett.* 96:211803 (2006)
40. Dermisek R, Gunion JF. *Phys. Rev. D* 76:095006 (2007)
41. Dine M, Seiberg N, Thomas S. *Phys. Rev. D* 76:095004 (2007)
42. Barbieri R, et al. arXiv:0712.2903 [hep-ph] (2007)
43. Schuster PC, Toro N. arXiv:hep-ph/0512189 (2005)
44. Dermisek R, Gunion JF. *Phys. Rev. D* 75:075019 (2007)
45. Demir DA, Solmaz L, Solmaz S. *Phys. Rev. D* 73:016001 (2006)
46. Dermisek R, Gunion JF. *Phys. Rev. D* 73:111701 (2006)
47. Carena MS, Ellis JR, Pilaftsis A, Wagner CEM. *Phys. Lett. B* 495:155 (2000)
48. Kreinick D. arXiv:0710.5929 [hep-ex] (2007)
49. Delgado A, Espinosa JR, Quiros M. *JHEP* 10:094 (2007)
50. Dobrescu BA, Landsberg GL, Matchev KT. *Phys. Rev. D* 63:075003 (2001)
51. Chang S, Fox PJ, Weiner N. *Phys. Rev. Lett.* 98:111802 (2007)
52. Arhrib A, Cheung K, Hou T-J, Song K-W. *JHEP* 03:073 (2007)
53. Strassler MJ, Zurek KM. *Phys. Lett. B* 651:374 (2007)
54. Strassler MJ, Zurek KM. arXiv:hep-ph/0605193 (2006)
55. O'Connell D, Ramsey-Musolf MJ, Wise MB. *Phys. Rev. D* 75:037701 (2007)
56. Kim SG, et al. *Phys. Rev. D* 74:115016 (2006)
57. Patt B, Wilczek F. arXiv:hep-ph/0605188 (2006)
58. Bahat-Treidel O, Grossman Y, Rozen Y. *JHEP* 05:022 (2007)
59. Hodgkinson RN, Pilaftsis A. *Phys. Rev. D* 76:015007 (2007)
60. Gopalakrishna S, Jung S, Wells JD. arXiv:0801.3456 [hep-ph] (2008)
61. Graesser ML. arXiv:0705.2190 [hep-ph] (2007)
62. Graesser ML. *Phys. Rev. D* 76:075006 (2007)
63. de Gouvea A. arXiv:0706.1732 [hep-ph] (2007)
64. Apreda R, Maggiore M, Nicolis A, Riotto A. *Class. Quant. Grav.* 18:L155 (2001)
65. Menon A, Morrissey DE, Wagner CEM. *Phys. Rev. D* 70:035005 (2004)
66. Profumo S, Ramsey-Musolf MJ, Shaughnessy G. *JHEP* 08:010 (2007)
67. Han T, Langacker P, McElrath B. *Phys. Rev. D* 70:115006 (2004)
68. Barger V, Langacker P, Lee H-S, Shaughnessy G. *Phys. Rev. D* 73:115010 (2006)
69. Barger V, et al. arXiv:0706.4311 [hep-ph] (2007)
70. Ellwanger U, Gunion JF, Hugonie C. *JHEP* 02:066 (2005)
71. Gunion JF, Haber HE, Moroi T. arXiv:hep-ph/9610337 (1996)
72. Dermisek R, Gunion JF, McElrath B. *Phys. Rev. D* 76:051105 (2007)
73. Fullana E, Sanchis-Lozano M-A. *Phys. Lett. B* 653:67 (2007)
74. Burgess CP, Matias J, Pospelov M. *Int. J. Mod. Phys. A* 17:1841 (2002)

75. CMS Collaboration, TDR Volume II, *J. Phys. G Nucl. Phys.* 34:995 (2007)
76. Cheung K-M, Song J, Yan Q-S. arXiv:0710.1997 [hep-ph] (2007)
77. Carena M, Han T, Huang G-Y, Wagner CEM. arXiv:0712.2466 [hep-ph] (2007)
78. Ellwanger U, Gunion JF, Hugonie C. *JHEP* 07:041 (2005)
79. Ellwanger U, Gunion JF, Hugonie C, Moretti S. arXiv:hep-ph/0401228 (2004)
80. Ellwanger U, Gunion JF, Hugonie C, Moretti S. arXiv:hep-ph/0305109 (2003)
81. Moretti S, Munir S, Poulose P. *Phys. Lett. B* 644:241, arXiv:hep-ph/0608233 (2007)
82. Stelzer T, Wiesenfeldt S, Willenbrock S. *Phys. Rev. D* 75:077701 (2007)
83. Cheung K, Song J, Yan Q-S. *Phys. Rev. Lett.* 99:031801 (2007)
84. Forshaw JR, et al. arXiv:0712.3510 [hep-ph] (2007)
85. Graham PW, Pierce A, Wacker JG. arXiv:hep-ph/0605162 (2006)
86. Martin A. arXiv:hep-ph/0703247 (2007)
87. Carpenter LM, Kaplan DE, Rhee E-J. arXiv:hep-ph/0607204 (2006)
88. Kaplan DE, Rehermann K. *JHEP* 10:056 (2007)
89. Baer H, et al. *Phys. Rev. D* 47:1062 (1993)
90. Eboli OJP, Zeppenfeld D. *Phys. Lett. B* 495:147 (2000)
91. Di Girolamo B, et al. Presented at *Workshop Phys. TeV Colliders*, Les Houches, Fr. (2001)
92. Barger V, Langacker P, Shaughnessy G. *Phys. Rev. D* 75:055013 (2007)
93. Belotsky K, Khoze VA, Martin AD, Ryskin MG. *Eur. Phys. J. C* 36:503 (2004)
94. Barger V, Langacker P, Shaughnessy G. *Phys. Lett. B* 644:361 (2007)
95. Strassler MJ. arXiv:hep-ph/0607160 (2006)
96. Ellwanger U, Hugonie C. *Eur. Phys. J. C* 13:681 (2000)

Weak Gravitational Lensing and Its Cosmological Applications

Henk Hoekstra[1] and Bhuvnesh Jain[2]

[1] Department of Physics and Astronomy, University of Victoria, Victoria, British Columbia V8P 5C2, Canada; email: hoekstra@uvic.ca

[2] Department of Physics and Astronomy, University of Pennsylvania, Philadelphia, Pennsylvania 19104; email: bjain@physics.upenn.edu

Annu. Rev. Nucl. Part. Sci. 2008. 58:99–123

First published online as a Review in Advance on May 22, 2008

The *Annual Review of Nuclear and Particle Science* is online at nucl.annualreviews.org

This article's doi:
10.1146/annurev.nucl.58.110707.171151

Key Words

gravitational lensing, dark matter, dark energy, cosmology

Abstract

Weak gravitational lensing is a unique probe of the dark side of the universe: It provides a direct way to map the distribution of dark matter around galaxies and clusters of galaxies as well as on cosmological scales. Furthermore, the measurement of the weak lensing–induced distortions of the shapes of distant galaxies is a potentially powerful probe of dark energy. In this review we discuss how this challenging measurement is made and interpreted. We describe the various systematic effects that can hamper progress and how they may be overcome. We review some of the recent results in weak lensing by galaxies, galaxy clusters, and cosmic shear and discuss the prospects for dark energy measurements from planned surveys.

Contents

1. INTRODUCTION

The deflection of light rays by intervening structures, a phenomenon referred to as gravitational lensing, provides astronomers with a unique tool to study the distribution of dark matter in the universe. Unlike other observational probes, the lensing effect provides a direct measure of the mass, irrespective of the dynamical state of the lens. A well-publicized recent example is the study of the merging Bullet cluster of galaxies, in which a lensing study showed that the dark matter is displaced from the bulk of the baryonic mass (1). Such measurements can provide important insights into the properties of dark matter.

Several applications of gravitational lensing have proven important for observational cosmology. When the lens is sufficiently strong, multiple images of the same source can be observed. If the source is variable, time delays between the variation of the images can be determined. An example of the applications of strong lensing is the use of time delays to estimate the Hubble constant, provided that a good model for the lens can be derived (see, e.g., References 2 and 3). In this review, however, we focus upon applications of weak gravitational lensing that can help us understand the properties of dark energy and dark matter on cosmological scales.

Weak lensing refers to the shearing of distant galaxy images due to the differential deflection of neighboring light rays. The signal is small, typically inducing an ellipticity of order 1%. Although this signal is negligible compared to the intrinsic shape of individual galaxies, it can be measured statistically using the coherence of the lensing shear over the sky. In the past two decades it has become possible to measure these subtle changes in order to study the distribution of dark matter in the universe. The first measurements used lensing by galaxy clusters; more recently cosmic shear measurements have been made in "blank fields" without using any knowledge of foreground structures. Several topics related to galaxy and cluster lensing are discussed in Section 6, but the main focus of this review is cosmic shear, i.e., lensing by large-scale structure in the universe.

The reason for the recent popularity of cosmic shear is that the signal is a direct measure of the projected matter power spectrum over a redshift range determined by the lensed sources (see, e.g., References 4 and 5). This straightforward interpretation of the signal is rather unique in the tools available for cosmology, and it potentially enables the determination of cosmological parameters with high precision. Lensing measurements are not only an important complement to distance measures (such as type Ia supernovae or baryonic acoustic oscillations), they also provide measures of the growth of large-scale structure that test gravity on cosmological scales. These features make cosmic shear one of the most powerful probes of dark energy and modified gravity theories (6, 7), albeit an observationally challenging one.

In this review we discuss the methods and principal challenges in the cosmological applications of weak lensing. We review lensing theory but focus primarily on measurements, current surveys, and prospects for planned surveys in the coming decade. We refer the interested reader to reviews with a more detailed treatment of many other aspects of lensing (8–11).

In Section 2, we describe the key steps of the measurement; in Section 3 we discuss interpretations of cosmological weak lensing. In Section 4 we review the primary systematic errors as well as ways to deal with them. We highlight some current results in Section 5 and discuss lensing by galaxies and galaxy clusters in Section 6. We conclude in Section 7 with a discussion of prospects for the coming decade.

2. HOW TO MEASURE SHEAR

2.1. Weak Lensing Basics

Massive structures along the line of sight deflect photons originating from distant galaxies. If the source is small, the effect is a (re)mapping of f^s, the source's surface brightness distribution (see Reference 8 for more details),

$$f^{\mathrm{obs}}(\theta_i) = f^s(\mathcal{A}_{ij}\theta_j), \qquad\qquad 1.$$

where $\mathcal{A}$ is the distortion matrix (the Jacobian of the transformation) and $\boldsymbol{\theta}$ is the position on the sky.

$$\mathcal{A} = \frac{\partial(\delta\theta_i)}{\partial\theta_j} = (\delta_{ij} - \Psi_{,ij}) = \begin{pmatrix} 1 - \kappa - \gamma_1 & -\gamma_2 \\ -\gamma_2 & 1 - \kappa + \gamma_1 \end{pmatrix}, \qquad\qquad 2.$$

where we have introduced the two-dimensional lensing potential Ψ, and where $\Psi_{,ij} \equiv \partial^2\Psi/\partial\theta_i\partial\theta_j$. The lensing convergence κ is a scalar quantity and is given by a weighted projection of the mass density fluctuation field,

$$\kappa(\boldsymbol{\theta}) = \frac{1}{2}\nabla^2\Psi(\boldsymbol{\theta}) = \int d\chi\, W(\chi)\delta[\chi, \chi\boldsymbol{\theta}], \qquad\qquad 3.$$

with the Laplacian operator ∇^2 defined using the flat-sky approximation as $\nabla^2 \equiv \partial^2/\partial\boldsymbol{\theta}^2$ and with χ as the comoving distance (we have assumed a spatially flat universe). Note that χ is related to redshift z via the relation $d\chi = dz/H(z)$, where $H(z)$ is the Hubble parameter at epoch z. The lensing efficiency function W is given by

$$W(\chi) = \frac{3}{2}\Omega_{m0}H_0^2 a^{-1}(\chi)\chi \int d\chi_s\, n_s(\chi_s)\frac{\chi_s - \chi}{\chi_s}, \qquad\qquad 4.$$

where $n_s(\chi_s)$ is the redshift selection function of source galaxies and H_0 is the Hubble constant $(H_0 = 100h$ km s^{-1} Mpc^{-1}). If all source galaxies are at a single redshift z_s, then $n_s(\chi) = \delta_D(\chi - \chi_s)$.

In Equation 2 we introduce the components of the complex shear $\gamma \equiv \gamma_1 + i\gamma_2$, which can also be written as $\gamma = \gamma \exp(2i\alpha)$, where α is the orientation angle of the shear. The Cartesian components of the shear field are related to the lensing potential through

$$\gamma_1 = \frac{1}{2}(\Psi_{,11} - \Psi_{,22}) \quad \text{and} \quad \gamma_2 = \Psi_{,12}. \qquad 5.$$

In the weak lensing regime, the convergence gives the magnification of an image and the shear gives the ellipticity induced on an initially circular image. Under the assumption that galaxies are randomly oriented in the absence of lensing, the strength of the tidal gravitational field can be inferred from the measured ellipticities of an ensemble of sources (see Section 4.2 for a discussion of intrinsic alignments). In the absence of observational distortions, the observed ellipticity e^{obs} is related to its unlensed value e^{int} through (8, 12)

$$e^{\text{obs}} = \frac{e^{\text{int}} + \gamma}{1 + \gamma^* e^{\text{int}}}, \qquad 6.$$

where $e \simeq [(1 - b/a)/(1 + b/a)]\ \exp(2i\alpha)$ for an ellipse with major and minor axes a and b, respectively, and orientation angle α. The average value of $e^{\text{obs}} \approx \gamma$ in the weak lensing regime. Hence the unbiased measurement of the shapes of background galaxies (which constitute the small, faint end of the galaxy sample) lies at the heart of any weak lensing analysis.

2.2. Weak Lensing Pipeline

The unbiased measurement of galaxy shapes is not a trivial task because the observed images have been corrupted: In space-based data, the finite size of the mirror and the complicated telescope optics give rise to a nontrivial point spread function (PSF). In ground-based data the situation is worse because of turbulence in the atmosphere (an effect called seeing). Finally, the detector used to sample the image in discrete pixels may suffer from charge transfer inefficiencies.

The combination of seeing and the intrinsic size of the PSF leads to a circularization of the observed images, whereas PSF anisotropy introduces coherent alignments in the shapes of the galaxies. The former effect lowers the amplitude of the inferred lensing signal; the latter can mimic a lensing signal. Hence to infer the true lensing signal, one needs to determine the original galaxy shape; this determination requires some form of deconvolution in the presence of noise. Therefore it is not surprising that the development of methods that can undo the effects of the PSF has been a major focus of lensing research. Below we describe the schematic steps of a pipeline that starts with raw galaxy images and that ultimately delivers cosmological measurements (see Reference 13 for details and discussion of potential systematic errors at each step).

2.2.1. Object detection. Detection of the faint galaxies to be analyzed forms the first step in the lensing analysis. Detection can be done on the individual exposures (as multiple images of the same area of sky are typically obtained) or on a stacked image. In either case an algorithm to distinguish stars from galaxies is needed. Note also that the images need to be corrected for any shearing by the camera. The next step is to quantify shape parameters for these objects. The optimal way to detect galaxies and measure their shapes using multiple exposures and a set of filters is an area of ongoing research that, due to space constraints, we do not address in this review.

2.2.2. Point spread function estimation. To deal with the effects of the PSF, a sample of moderately bright stars is identified from the actual data. The sample is subsequently used to characterize the PSF in terms of its size, second moment, and possibly higher moments.

The variation of the PSF across the field of view is described with an interpolating function, which is typically a simple polynomial (14). Although this approach appears to be adequate for current results, its accuracy is reduced by the fact that only a limited number of stars is observed. One way to address this issue is to study the PSF in observations with a high number density of stars (14). However it is reasonable to assume that the PSF varies in a relatively systematic fashion from exposure to exposure. This allows one to decompose the observed patterns into their principal components, as proposed by Jarvis & Jain (15). As the accuracy of cosmic shear measurements improves, such careful modeling of the PSF will likely be required to undo the effects of the PSF.

2.2.3. Point spread function correction. After identifying the galaxies of interest, the next step is to correct the observed galaxy shapes for convolution by the PSF. This is arguably the most difficult, yet most important step in the analysis. Improving the correction methods is one of the most active areas of study and innovation, wherein researchers endeavor not only to derive reliable results from the current generation of surveys, but also to ensure that future, much more demanding, cosmic shear surveys can reach their full potential.

Numerous techniques have been developed to address this problem (see References 16 and 17 for detailed descriptions of these). One of the oldest methods (and the most widely used), the Kaiser-Squires-Broadhurst (KSB) method, was developed by Kaiser et al. (18); other researchers have suggested modifications (19, 20). The KSB method assumes that the PSF can be described as the convolution of a compact anisotropic kernel and a large isotropic kernel. Although this might be a reasonable assumption for ground-based data, it is not correct for space-based data (20). One advantage of this method is that the correction for PSF anisotropy and the circularization by the PSF are separate operations. The latter step (the closest to the actual deconvolution) is typically performed by averaging the correction for objects of similar size.

The KSB approach is limited by the assumptions that must be made about the PSF and galaxy profiles. Relaxing such assumptions and expanding the object surface brightness distribution using a suitable set of basis functions have attracted much attention in recent years (21–24). A related approach is to fit versatile models to the data and perform the deconvolution using the best fit models; for instance Kuijken (25) explored whether objects can be modeled as sums of Gaussians. An advantage of the model fitting methods is that pixelation effects are readily implemented. Although researchers have made progress, it is currently unclear which of these approaches is the best.

2.2.4. Measurement of shear correlations and cosmological parameters. Once a catalog of galaxy shapes becomes available, one can calculate cosmological statistics. The two-point correlations of the shear are calculated simply from the galaxy positions, ellipticities, and weights that characterize the signal-to-noise ratio of the shape measurement. These may be calculated as a power spectrum or as a correlation function for varying angular separations. For other applications to galaxy and cluster lensing, one can work with background shapes with reference to foreground objects.

Cosmological inferences rely on one additional property of the source galaxies, namely their redshift. The galaxies of interest are too faint to be observed spectroscopically; instead, weak lensing studies rely on photometric redshifts (henceforth photo-zs). These are based on the measured galaxy colors and other properties that provide a coarse estimate of the galaxy's redshift. Improving photo-z estimation and quantifying the effect of photo-z errors on cosmological inferences from lensing are both active areas of research.

2.3. Diagnostics of the Lensing Signal

An obvious concern is that one cannot "see" the weak lensing signal: A weakly sheared galaxy appears unchanged because of its much larger intrinsic ellipticity. How can we be sure that the recovered lensing signal is cosmological in nature and not dominated by observational distortions?

As we discuss below, we can test the weak lensing analysis pipeline on simulated data, but these simulations may lack a systematic effect present in real data. Fortunately, a number of diagnostic tools can be used to test the reliability of the recovered lensing signal. These tests cannot guarantee whether the recovered signal is free of systematics, but they do often indicate whether systematics are present. (Note, however, that the correction for the circularization by the PSF cannot be tested using the diagnostics discussed below.)

One diagnostic makes use of the fact that the corrected galaxy shapes should not correlate with the (uncorrected) shapes of stars (see, e.g., Reference 26). The measurement of this correlation is sensitive to imperfections in the model for PSF anisotropy and imperfections in the correction scheme itself. The former can be tested by correlating the corrected shapes of stars (14).

Another unique diagnostic makes use of the fact that the weak lensing shear arises from a gravitational potential. Consequently the resulting shear field is expected to be curl free (see, however, Reference 27). The observed ellipticity correlation functions can be separated into two independent components, an E mode that is curl-free and a B mode that is sensitive to the curl of the shear field (27, 28). Hence the presence of a significant B mode indicates that residual systematics remain. (Note that the B mode may also have a physical origin caused by intrinsic alignments of the sources; see Section 4.2 for more details.)

A diagnostic of the cosmological nature of the lensing signal is its variation with redshift. The distance factors in the lensing efficiency function of Equation 4 lead to a characteristic variation with source redshift. Thus, provided that the redshift estimates are accurate, this variation can be used to test the cosmological origin of the lensing signal. Another diagnostic that we discuss below is the use of different statistical measures, such as two- and three-point shear correlations, that have a distinct relationship for a signal due to gravitational lensing. Finally, one can compare different lensing observables, such as those related to shear and to magnification effects.

2.4. Tests on Simulated Images

The main hurdle in lensing measurements is a proper handling of the PSF-induced systematics, not our lack of understanding of the relevant physics. Our ability to correct for shape measurement systematics can therefore be tested using simulated data, which is an important advantage of lensing over other methods.

The shear testing programme (STEP) is a collaborative effort of the weak lensing community to improve the accuracy of weak lensing measurements in preparation for the next generation of cosmic shear surveys. The first STEP paper (16) involved the blind analysis of simulated ground-based images. The galaxies in this simulation had relatively simple morphologies; however, despite these limitations the results provided an important benchmark for the accuracy of current ground-based weak lensing analysis methods.

The results of this exercise are shown in **Figure 1**. The dominant source of error is the correction for the size of the PSF, which leads to an overestimate of the shear by a multiplicative factor $(1 + m)$. Massey et al. presented a blind analysis of more complicated galaxies (17); their paper also included an improvement in the statistical accuracy of the test. These two studies showed that pipelines that have been used to constrain cosmological parameters can recover the lensing signal with a precision better than 7%, which is within the statistical errors of current weak lensing analyses. The most successful methods have been shown to achieve 1–2% level accuracy. Although

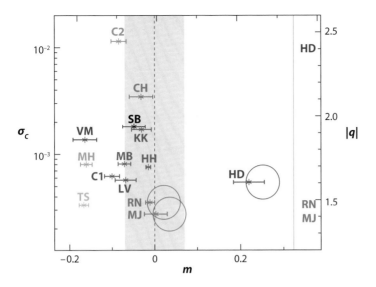

Figure 1

Measurement of the calibration bias m and point spread function residuals σ_c (from Reference 16). The ideal method has $m = 0$ and small σ_c. The shaded region indicates a bias of less than 7%. Methods used for the most recently published cosmic shear results were found to have biases on the order of a few percent. See Reference 16 for a detailed description of the symbols and methodology. The methods indicated by a circle show a strong nonlinearity and are listed on the right-hand side of the vertical line. The amount of nonlinearity is quantified by the parameter q on the right-hand scale.

they are not problematic for current work, biases as a function of object size and magnitude remain. The next phase in this work is to identify the points of failure and means for improvement. The simulations must also become more realistic, for instance through the inclusion of systematics at the detector level.

3. COSMIC SHEAR AND DARK ENERGY

3.1. Two-Point Shear Correlations and Tomography

To quantify the lensing signal, we measure the shear correlation functions from galaxy shape catalogs. The two-point correlation function of the shear, for source galaxies in the ith and jth redshift bin, is defined as

$$\xi_{\gamma_i \gamma_j}(\theta) = \langle \gamma_i(\theta_1) \cdot \gamma_j^*(\theta_2) \rangle, \qquad \qquad 7.$$

with $\theta = |\theta_1 - \theta_2|$. Note that the two-point function of the convergence is identical to that of the shear. It is useful to separate ξ_γ into two correlation functions by using the $+/\times$ decomposition: The $+$ component is defined parallel or perpendicular to the line connecting the two points taken, whereas the $\times$ component is defined along $45°$. This allows us to define the rotationally invariant two-point correlations of the shear field: $\xi_+(\theta) = \langle \gamma_{i+}(\theta_1)\gamma_{j+}(\theta_2) \rangle$ and $\xi_\times(\theta) = \langle \gamma_{i\times}(\theta_1)\gamma_{j\times}(\theta_2) \rangle$. The correlation function of Equation 7 is simply given by $\xi_{\gamma_i \gamma_j} = \xi_+ + \xi_\times$.

The E/B mode decomposition discussed in Section 2.3 is given by linear superpositions of $\xi_+(\theta)$ and $\xi_\times(\theta)$ (although it involves integrals over all θ). A more direct way to perform the E/B decomposition is through the mass aperture variance, $M_{ap}^2(\theta)$, which is a weighted second moment of the tangential shear measured in apertures. This provides a very useful test of systematics in the

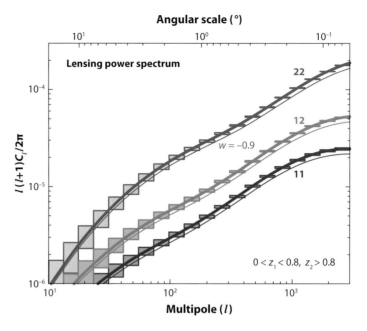

Figure 2

The lensing power spectra constructed from galaxies split into two broad redshift bins. The two auto spectra and one cross spectrum are depicted. Shown are predictions for the fiducial Λ cold dark matter (CDM) model, including nonlinear evolution (*thick curves*) (40). The boxes show the expected measurement error due to the sample variance and intrinsic ellipticity errors from a 5000-deg^2 survey with median redshift $z = 0.8$. Also shown are the predictions for a dark energy model with $w = -0.9$ (*thin curves*). Note that at least four or five redshift bins are expected to be useful from such a survey, which will lead to many more measured power spectra.

measurements; we do not use it here but instead refer the reader to Reference 27. All two-point statistics such as $M_{\mathrm{ap}}^2(\theta)$ can be expressed in terms of the shear correlation functions defined above.

The shear power spectrum at angular wavenumber ℓ is the Fourier transform of $\xi_{\gamma_i \gamma_j}(\theta)$. It is equivalent to the power spectrum of the convergence and can be expressed as a projection of the mass density power spectrum P_δ. For source galaxies in the ith and jth redshift bin it is (5, 29)

$$C_{\gamma_i \gamma_j}(\ell) = \int_0^\infty dz \, \frac{W_i(z) \, W_j(z)}{\chi(z)^2 \, H(z)} \, P_\delta \left(\frac{\ell}{\chi(z)}, z \right). \qquad 8.$$

where the indices i and j cover all the redshift bins. The redshift binning is assumed to be provided by photo-zs that can be estimated from multicolor imaging. If both source galaxy bins are taken at redshift z_s, then the integral is dominated by the mass fluctuations at a distance about halfway to the source galaxies. **Figure 2** shows the predicted auto and cross spectra for galaxies split into two redshift bins. The error bars show the contributions to the measurement error of (*a*) sample variance (which dominates at low ℓ) and (*b*) intrinsic ellipticity (which dominates at high ℓ). (Note that the measured power spectrum includes contributions from systematic errors, which we discuss in Section 4.)

Equation 8 shows the sensitivity of the observable shear-shear power spectra both to the geometric factors given by $W_i(z)$ and $W_j(z)$ and to the growth of structure contained in the mass density power spectrum P_δ. Both power spectra are sensitive to dark energy and its possible evolution, which determines the relative amplitudes of the auto and cross spectra shown in **Figure 2**. P_δ also contains information about the primordial power spectrum and other parameters such as neutrino masses. In modified gravity theories, the shape and time evolution of the density power spectrum can differ from that of a dark energy model, even one that has the same expansion history. Lensing is a powerful means of testing for modifications of gravity as well (30–34). The complementarity of lensing with other probes is critical, especially with the cosmic microwave background (CMB) and measurements of the distance-redshift relation using type Ia supernovae and baryonic acoustic oscillations in the galaxy power spectrum.

The mass power spectrum is simply related to the linear growth factor $D(z)$ on large scales (low ℓ): $P_\delta \propto D^2(z)$. However, for source galaxies at redshifts of about 1, observable scales $\ell \geq 200$ receive significant contributions from nonlinear gravitational clustering. So we must go beyond the linear regime using simulations or analytical fitting formulas to describe the nonlinear mass power spectrum (35–38). To the extent that only gravity describes structures on scales larger than the sizes of galaxy clusters, this can be done with high accuracy. There is ongoing work to determine this scale and to model the effect of baryonic gas on smaller scales (39).

3.2. Cross Correlations and Higher-Order Statistics

The cross correlation of foreground galaxy positions with background shear is also an observable. As we discuss below in Section 6, cross correlation has been measured by averaging the tangential component of the background galaxy ellipticities in circular annuli centered on the foreground galaxy. It is denoted by $\langle \gamma_T \rangle(\theta)$ and is related to the Fourier transform of the galaxy-convergence power spectrum, which in turn can be expressed analogously to the power spectrum of Equation 8:

$$C_{g_i \kappa_j}(\ell) = \int_0^\infty dz \, \frac{W_{gi}(z) \, W_j(z)}{\chi(z) \, H(z)} \, P_{g\delta} \left(\frac{\ell}{\chi(z)}, z \right),$$

9.

where W_{gi} is the normalized redshift distribution of the lens (foreground) galaxies and $P_{g\delta}$ is the three-dimensional galaxy–mass density power spectrum.

Along with the galaxy-galaxy power spectrum, $C_{g_i g_i}(\ell)$, Equations 8 and 9 represent the three sets of auto and cross spectra that can be measured from (foreground) galaxy positions and (background) galaxy shapes (41). Each of the three power spectra can be measured for multiple photo-z bins. These spectra contain all the two-point information one can extract from multicolor imaging data on both galaxy clustering and lensing. It would be an exhaustive exercise in parameter estimation to perform model fitting on a set of such measurements; only pieces of this have been carried out so far.

In addition, cosmographic information via the distance-redshift relation can be obtained using the variation of the galaxy-galaxy lensing signal with redshift. Although this approach has less constraining power than other tests of the distance-redshift relation, it would help isolate the geometric and growth of structure information that can be obtained from lensing (41–45).

The combination of $C_{g_i g_i}(\ell)$ and $C_{g_i \kappa_j}(\ell)$ can be used to determine the bias factor b that relates the three-dimensional galaxy power spectrum to that of the mass density spectrum (the ratio of these two spectra for appropriate redshift bins is proportional to b). With this empirical determination of b, cosmological parameters can be obtained more robustly from $C_{g_i g_i}(\ell)$ and its three-dimensional counterpart measured from spectroscopic surveys (46). Planned surveys with good-quality imaging and well-calibrated photo-zs will enable cosmological applications of $C_{g_i \kappa_j}(\ell)$ as well once the bias is known for the lens galaxies as a function of scale.

Thus a variety of cosmological measurements can be made from lensing and galaxy power spectra. The two main advances awaiting these applications are reliable photo-zs and lensing shapes measured over a wide-area survey. Finally, the non-Gaussian properties of the lensing mass imprints three-point and higher-order correlations in the shear field. These are valuable both for complementary cosmological information and for checks on systematic errors (47, 48). The lensing three-point function (or bispectrum in Fourier space) arises from nonlinear gravitational evolution of the lensing mass. It vanishes at lowest order in perturbation theory, as the leading-order (linear) density field is Gaussian random. The second-order contributions to the bispectrum give it special value: Its dependence on cosmological parameters differs from that of the power spectrum. In particular it is possible to combine the power spectrum and bispectrum to constrain the matter or dark energy density with little dependence on the power spectrum amplitude (35, 40, 47).

The signal-to-noise ratio for a measurement of the bispectrum is lower than for the power spectrum and is more sensitive to the number density of source galaxies. While three-point lensing correlations have been detected in current data, their measurement is expected to be useful for cosmology only in next-generation datasets. Perhaps of equal importance is the ability to test for systematic errors using three-point correlations. Huterer et al. (48) showed how the degradation due to systematics can be reduced by adding bispectrum and power spectrum measurements.

3.3. Cosmological Parameters

Given a data vector, the Fisher information matrix describes how errors propagate into the precision on cosmological parameters p_α. The Fisher matrix applied to the lensing power spectra is given by

$$F_{ij} = \sum_\ell \left(\frac{\partial \mathbf{C}}{\partial p_i} \right)^T \mathbf{Cov}^{-1} \frac{\partial C}{\partial p_j},$$ 10.

where $\mathbf{C}$ is the column matrix of the observed power spectra and $\mathbf{Cov}^{-1}$ is the inverse of the covariance matrix between the power spectra. The partial derivative with respect to a parameter p_α is evaluated around the fiducial model. The Fisher matrix quantifies the best statistical errors achievable on parameter determination for a given dataset: The variance of an unbiased estimator of a parameter p_α obeys the inequality

$$\left\langle \Delta p_\alpha^2 \right\rangle \geq (F^{-1})_{\alpha\alpha},$$ 11.

where (F^{-1}) denotes the inverse of the Fisher matrix and Δp_α represents the relative error on parameter p_α around its fiducial value, including marginalization over the other parameters.

This formalism has been used to forecast constraints on the dark energy density Ω_{de} and equation of state parameters w_0 and w_a. Lensing is also sensitive to other cosmological parameters that affect either the primordial power spectrum or the growth of structure (40, 45, 49). Because the projected power spectrum probed by lensing is a slowly varying function of wavenumber (unlike the CMB), it is not sensitive to parameters that produce localized features such as the baryon mass fraction. However its shape can help constrain neutrino masses and a running spectral index. Lensing tomography is most sensitive to variables that affect the amplitude at different redshift, which is what gives the greatest leverage on dark energy parameters. Thus utilizing all the auto and cross spectra that can be measured with redshift information is critical in extracting cosmological information from lensing.

Figure 3 shows dark energy forecasts obtained for a 5000-deg^2 stage III experiment [to use the terminology of the Dark Energy Task Force (6)], with all other relevant cosmological parameters marginalized over (40). CMB priors are used at the level of the Planck experiment. Statistical errors due to sample variance and finite intrinsic ellipticity are included, but the effect of systematic errors is not (these errors are discussed and estimated in Section 4 below). Aside from the issue of systematics, forecasts for lensing are still challenging due to the multiple observables

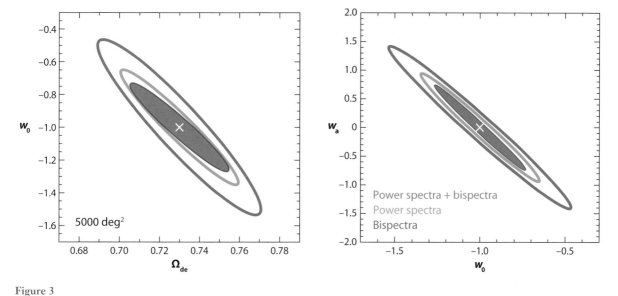

Figure 3

Dark energy contours (68% CL) from lensing power spectra and bispectra from an ambitious stage III survey (as in **Figure 2**). The estimated non-Gaussian covariances between the power spectra and bispectra are included in the joint constraints. These forecasts assume Planck priors and do not include systematic errors.

(power spectra, bispectra, cluster counts). These observables are not independent, and much of the information is in the non-Gaussian regime, which makes estimation of covariances difficult. In **Figure 3** we show the results of using power spectra and bispectra in three broad redshift bins, and include covariances based on the halo model (M. Takada & B. Jain, in preparation).

4. SYSTEMATIC ERRORS

Weak lensing measurements are prone to a number of systematic errors. One category of systematics arises from the measurement of galaxy shapes. However, there are others that enter into the estimation of cosmological parameters given a galaxy shape catalog. The primary sources of systematic error can be characterized as (*a*) knowledge of the PSF, (*b*) correction of the PSF and shear calibration, (*c*) photometric redshifts, (*d*) intrinsic alignments, and (*e*) nonlinear power spectrum/effect of baryons.

Although each of these errors is well studied and can be modeled, small residuals in the corrections of these errors may well be comparable to statistical errors in lensing measurements. The first two sources of error follow directly from our discussion in Section 2 of lensing shape measurements. The remaining systematics become important if we wish to interpret the lensing signal and compare it with a cosmological model.

Intrinsic alignments are caused by the tidal gravitational field, which can align the shape of a galaxy with another due to direct interactions. Photo-z uncertainties can contribute to systematic errors because the cosmological inferences of lensing measurements depend sensitively on the estimated photo-z. Finally, the theoretical model predictions may have uncertainties due to nonlinear gravitational clustering and baryonic gas physics that affect the lensing power spectrum. Because systematic errors due to intrinsic alignments are currently the least well known of the items listed above, we discuss them in detail in the following section.

4.1. Intrinsic Alignments

Thus far we have assumed that the galaxy ellipticities are uncorrelated in the absence of lensing. However, there are reasons to believe that this assumption is not valid and that intrinsic alignments in the galaxy shapes contaminate the lensing signal. Two kinds of intrinsic alignment effects have been identified. However, before we discuss these in more detail, we note that relatively little is known about this effect (except that the alignments are relatively small). Currently it is almost as difficult to make a robust measurement of this signal as it is to measure the cosmic shear signal itself.

The first type of intrinsic alignment results from alignments of galaxy halos with other halos that respond to tidal gravitational forces. Early work based on simulations and analytical models (28, 50) demonstrated how such alignments can compromise cosmic shear measurements. There is, however, considerable theoretical uncertainty in modeling the alignment of halos themselves, and how well the (observed) luminous matter aligns with the dark matter. Importantly, this source of systematics can be greatly reduced with photo-zs by using cross spectra of galaxies in two different redshift bins (so that galaxy pairs are separated by large distances over which the tidal effects are very weak).

The second alignment effect was identified by Hirata & Seljak (51). It arises from the fact that the shapes of galaxies may be correlated with their surrounding density field. This field is also responsible for the weak lensing shear. As a result an anticorrelation between the shapes of galaxies at different redshifts is introduced, leading to suppression of the lensing signal. Although the first intrinsic alignment effect can be minimized by using galaxies at different redshifts in shear correlation measurements, this second mechanism affects pairs of galaxies at different redshifts. Without further theoretical and observational progress, therefore, the two classes of intrinsic alignments can be a very difficult systematic to overcome and can bias cosmic shear results (see, e.g., Reference 52). Fortunately researchers are beginning to gain an understanding of these effects thanks to spectroscopic data (53, 54), and investigators are also making theoretical progress via numerical simulations (55). Nonetheless intrinsic alignments must be taken into account when designing future surveys as they affect the accuracy of photo-zs (52).

4.2. How Systematics Degrade Cosmological Constraints

A comprehensive study of lensing systematics can be made with the following general expression of the estimated shear (48):

$$\hat{\gamma}(z_s, \mathbf{n}) = \gamma_{lens}(z_s, \mathbf{n})\left[1 + \gamma_{sys}^{mult}(z_s, \mathbf{n})\right] + \gamma_{sys}^{add}(z_s, \mathbf{n}). \qquad 12.$$

Equation 12 includes two kinds of systematic error contributions that modify the lensing shear via additive and multiplicative terms. In addition, the bin redshift z_s and its width may also be in error, which can lead to biases in cosmological parameters (56).

Two key points in understanding the degradation of cosmological information due to systematics are:

1. The impact of systematics on shear correlations is of primary significance, e.g., errors that affect individual galaxy shapes but are uncorrelated between galaxy pairs simply act as additional statistical errors (and are likely to be subdominant to the intrinsic shape noise of galaxies).
2. Systematic errors typically do not share the full redshift dependence of the lensing signal. For example errors in shear calibration may depend on galaxy size and brightness, but not directly on redshift. This allows us to fit for uncertainty in the shear calibration from the data. In general, by using all available auto and cross spectra, one can attempt to marginalize over a set

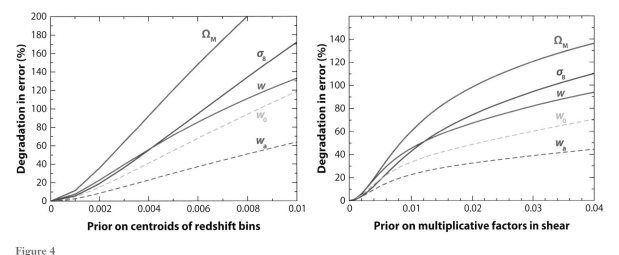

Figure 4

Degradation in cosmological parameter accuracy due to systematic errors (48). *Left*: The effect of biases in photo-zs for a stage III survey. *Right*: The effect of shear calibration errors. There is some evidence for a self-calibration regime for these, unlike for photo-z biases. Note that only the fractional degradation in parameter accuracy is shown here. The individual curves show the degradation for the labeled parameters.

of systematic error parameters. (Systematic errors due to photo-z biases, however, can mimic the cosmological signal and must be controlled with an appropriate calibration sample.)

Figure 4 shows how two of these systematic errors, shear calibration errors and photo-z biases, degrade cosmological parameter accuracy. The right panel shows the possibility of self-calibration: The degradation plateaus somewhat because the redshift dependence of the lensing signal allows for joint measurements of parameters describing both systematics (shear calibration in this case) and cosmology. The modeling and reduction of systematics are areas of active study (see, e.g., Reference 57). The degradation estimates shown in **Figure 4** are meant to be conservative in that no assumptions are made about the functional forms of these systematics and only the shear power spectra are used.

In summary, investigators are making progress in handling systematic errors (*a*) for PSF effects through the use of improved algorithms, (*b*) for photo-zs via large calibration samples, (*c*) for intrinsic alignments via new measurements as well as physical models, and (*d*) for predictions in the nonlinear regime from N-body and hydrodynamical simulations. The scientific returns of planned surveys rely on continued advances in these directions.

5. OBSERVATIONAL RESULTS

The advent of wide-field imaging cameras on 4-m-class telescopes in the late 1990s made the first cosmic shear detections possible (58–61; see 62 for an early attempt). Since then, the size of weak lensing surveys has increased significantly, and current surveys have imaged several tens of square degrees of the sky. An extensive list of early work can be found in Reference 10, but here we limit the discussion to the relatively large surveys listed in **Table 1**. We list references for only the most up-to-date analyses, which include a separation of the signal into E and B modes. The results listed in **Table 1** all find small or negligible B modes, particularly on scales larger than a few arcminutes. Furthermore, the lensing pipelines used to obtain these measurements are among the most accurate available (see Section 2.4) (16, 17). The cosmological measurements from these surveys are discussed below in Section 5.1.

Table 1 Overview of recent surveys[a]

Survey	Area (deg^2)	Reference	σ_8 ($\Omega_m = 0.3$)	w	Reference
RCS	53	63	0.65 ± 0.07		73
VIRMOS	8.5	64	0.83 ± 0.06		73
CTIO[b]	70	65	$0.81^{+0.15}_{-0.10}$	$-0.89^{+0.16}_{-0.21}$	65
GaBoDS	13	66	0.78 ± 0.08		73
CFHTLS[c,d]	57	67	0.71 ± 0.04	< -0.5	67
COSMOS	2	68	$0.87^{+0.09}_{-0.7}$		68

[a] The survey size and inferred value of σ_8 and w (where available) are shown for the large ground-based surveys and the largest space-based survey. The σ_8 values are quoted at fixed Ω_m to check the consistency of the measured lensing amplitude in different surveys. Meaningful confidence intervals on σ_8 require a joint analysis with CMB data (see Section 5.1). Further, since these studies have dealt with marginalization and systematic errors in different ways, direct comparisons are difficult.

[b] Error bars correspond to 95% CL and are joint constraints using WMAP priors.

[c] Published analyses do not include full area and are based on i' data only. The completed survey will image 140 deg^2 in 5 filters.

[d] The upper limit on w is from Reference 69.

Due to our limited knowledge of the source redshifts, constraints on cosmological parameters have not greatly improved. The ability to measure the growth of structure as a function of redshift will be the next major leap forward for cosmic shear studies. Researchers have already made some progress in that direction; three surveys listed in **Table 1**—the Garching-Bonn Deep Survey (Ga-BoDS), the Canada-France-Hawaii Telescope Legacy Survey (CFHTLS), and the Cosmological Evolution Survey (COSMOS)—are able to derive photometric redshifts for the sources thanks to their multicolor data. (A fourth survey, the Deep Lens Survey, has also collected multicolor data, but no recent results have been published.)

The first tomographic results have already been presented (68, 70); they are, however, based on small areas, leaving them susceptible to non-Gaussian contributions to the sample variance. The COSMOS survey combines the excellent image quality of the Hubble Space Telescope (HST) with an extensive campaign to map the three-dimensional large-scale structure (71) and measure the cosmic shear signal as a function of redshift (68). Expanding space-based observations beyond the COSMOS survey area would require a dedicated space-based mission (see Section 7); ground-based surveys will lead the way in the immediate future.

CFHTLS is the largest cosmic shear survey carried out to date. Once it is completed in early 2009 it will have imaged 140 deg^2 in the five Sloan filters, and it will include galaxies as faint as $i' = 24.5$ in its analysis. The availability of photometric redshifts for the sources will significantly improve the constraints on cosmological parameters. The goal of the completed survey is to constrain w with a relative accuracy of 5–10%. Its first results, which were based on a rather conservative analysis of the first-year i' data, were presented by Hoekstra et al. (69) and Semboloni et al. (72), who measured the signal from the "deep" component of the survey. More recently Fu et al. (67) measured the lensing signal out to $4°$, well into the linear regime (**Figure 5**).

5.1. Implications for Cosmology

As discussed above, our limited knowledge of source redshifts has led to much uncertainty in many lensing studies. This situation is improving rapidly, however, thanks to multicolor surveys such as COMBO-17 (Classifying Objects by Medium-Band Observations), COSMOS, and CFHTLS. This has led to new analyses of the Red-Sequence Cluster Survey (RCS) (63), Visible and In-frared Multi-Object Spectrographs (VIRMOS) (64), GaBoDS (66), and first-year CFHTLS (69)

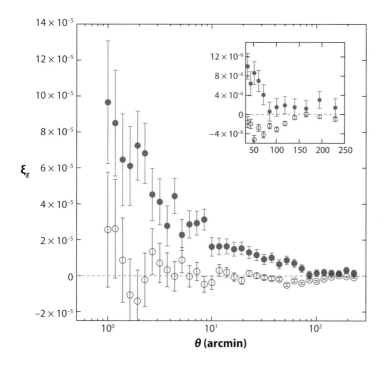

Figure 5

Ellipticity correlation function (67). These measurements, based on the analysis of 57 deg² of the Canada-France-Hawaii Telescope Legacy Survey's i' imaging data, extend out to 4°. The E modes are indicated by filled red points. The B modes, represented by open blue points, are consistent with zero on most scales. The inset shows an indication of residual systematics on a scale of 1°, which corresponds to the size of the camera.

measurements (73). Benjamin et al. (73) offer a more sophisticated treatment than did the original measurements of the sample variance errors on small scales. These new analyses also include, where necessary, corrections to the signal based on the STEP results (16, 17). Most importantly, they use up-to-date redshift distributions for the surveys based on the large photometric redshift catalog (75). Due to the lack of tomographic measurements most lensing results only constrain a combination of Ω_m and σ_8. This is demonstrated clearly in **Figure 6**, which shows in purple the weak lensing results from Reference 67. The various estimates for σ_8 are listed in **Table 1** [where we adopt a ΛCDM cosmology with $\Omega_m = 0.3$ for reference, except for Jarvis et al. (65), who have marginalized over all parameters in combination with CMB data].

The ensemble averaged value for σ_8 (adopting $\Omega_m = 0.3$) from these recent measurements is $\sigma_8 = 0.75 \pm 0.03$ with $\chi^2 = 7.4$ and with 5 degrees of freedom. The agreement between these results is therefore reasonable (the probability of a larger χ^2 is 0.19). However this statistical error ignores common systematics that might be caused (for instance) by biases in the source redshift distribution or the nonlinear power spectrum. These results are in agreement with recent studies of the number density of clusters of galaxies (see, e.g., References 76 and 77; also see Reference 66 for a compilation of recent measurements).

As shown in **Figure 6**, the combination of lensing and CMB measurements is useful in constraining Ω_m and σ_8. This joint analysis (67) with the Wilkinson Microwave Anisotropy Probe (WMAP3) results (78) yields $\Omega_m = 0.248 \pm 0.019$ and $\sigma_8 = 0.771 \pm 0.029$. These data are fully consistent with the previous lensing-based analysis from the Cerro Tololo Inter-American (CTIO)

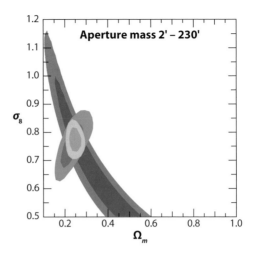

Figure 6

Joint constraints on Ω_m and σ_8 from the Canada-France-Hawaii Telescope Legacy Survey (CFHTLS) (*purple*) (67) and the Wilkinson Microwave Anisotropy Probe (WMAP3) (*green*) (78). The CFHTLS results are based on the aperture mass statistic on scales ranging from 2–230′. The combined constraints from weak lensing and cosmic microwave background are indicated by the orange region, demonstrating excellent agreement. The complementarity of lensing to cosmic microwave background observations is also shown.

survey (65). Measurements of w, the dark energy equation of state, are still limited due to the lack of tomographic results from large-area surveys (see, however, the two tentative results from analyses with constant w listed in **Table 1**).

6. LENSING BY GALAXIES AND GALAXY CLUSTERS

The study of cosmic shear has been a main driver of many recent weak lensing studies. In this section, however, we highlight galaxy and cluster lensing applications that pertain to cosmology and the study of dark matter.

6.1. Mapping the Distribution of Dark Matter

The observed weak lensing shear field provides estimates of the derivatives of the lensing potential (see Equation 5). As shown by Kaiser & Squires (79), it is possible to invert this problem to obtain a parameter-free reconstruction of the surface density distribution, that is, to create an image of the dark matter distribution. The surface density (up to an arbitrary constant κ_0) can be written as (79)

$$\kappa(\boldsymbol{\theta}) - \kappa_0 = \frac{1}{\pi} \int d^2\boldsymbol{\theta}' \frac{\zeta(\boldsymbol{\theta}' - \boldsymbol{\theta})\gamma(\boldsymbol{\theta}')}{(\boldsymbol{\theta}' - \boldsymbol{\theta})^2},$$ 13.

where the convolution kernel $\zeta(\theta)$ is given by

$$\zeta(\boldsymbol{\theta}) = \frac{\theta_2^2 - \theta_1^2 + 2i\theta_1\theta_2}{|\boldsymbol{\theta}|^4}.$$ 14.

Proper evaluation of this integral requires data out to infinity, which is impractical. This complication spurred the development of finite-field inversion methods (80–82).

The intrinsic shapes of the sources add significant noise to the reconstruction; as a result only the distribution of matter in massive clusters of galaxies can be studied in detail using weak lensing

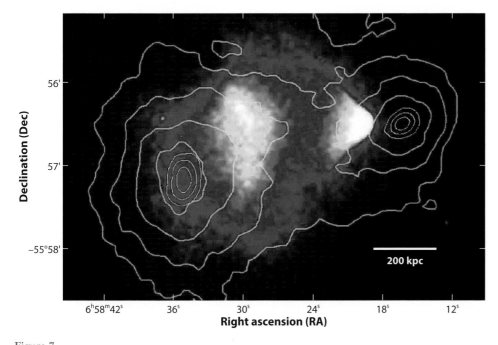

Figure 7

X-ray emission from the Bullet cluster of galaxies as observed by Chandra. The object on the right is a small galaxy cluster that has passed through a larger cluster and whose hot gas is seen in X-rays as the triangular shape on the right. The contours correspond to the mass reconstruction from Reference 1. The dark matter distribution is clearly offset from the gas, which contains the majority of baryonic matter, but it agrees well with the distribution of galaxies; this is to be expected if both the dark matter and stars in galaxies are effectively collisionless. See Reference 1 for a complete discussion of this intriguing object.

mass reconstructions. Of particular interest is the study of merging systems, where dynamical techniques cannot be used (1, 83, 84). **Figure 7** shows a reconstruction of the mass distribution of the Bullet cluster (1) based on HST observations. As shown by Clowe et al. (1), these observations provide some of the best evidence for the existence of dark matter (see also the discussion in Reference 85). This is because in alternative theories of gravity, such as Modified Newtonian Dynamics (86, 87), the hot X-ray gas is the main source of the lensing signal. In the near future we can expect improved constraints on the properties of dark matter particles based on a systematic study of merging systems.

6.2. Cosmology with Galaxy Clusters

Because clusters trace the highest peaks in the density, their number density as a function of mass and redshift depends strongly on the underlying cosmology (see, e.g., References 77 and 88), making the cluster abundance an interesting complementary probe for dark energy studies (see, e.g., Reference 89). Although conceptually straightforward, implementing this method has proven difficult. One reason is that precise measurements of the cosmological parameters require cluster catalogs with well-defined selection functions. In principle clusters can be identified in mass reconstructions from large weak lensing surveys (90–92), but projections along the line of sight lead to a relatively high false positive rate (93, 94). Hence one must work either with a statistic that includes projection effects (see, e.g., Reference 95) or with samples derived from optical, X-ray, or radio observations.

Even in the latter case, however, it is essential to have a well-determined relation between the observed cluster properties and mass. This is where weak lensing studies of large cluster samples can play an important role. The determination of the mean relation between the quantity of interest (e.g., richness, X-ray temperature) and cluster mass can be done statistically. For instance Sheldon et al. and Johnston et al. (96, 97) have measured the ensemble averaged weak lensing signal as a function of richness and luminosity using data from Sloan Digital Sky Survey (SDSS). Unfortunately the mass observable is expected to have an intrinsic scatter as well, which is the result of differences in formation history, etc. Knowledge of the precise characterization of this unknown scatter is important to ensure accurate measurements of cosmological parameters. Individual weak lensing masses can be derived for massive clusters. Ultimately, however, the accuracy of these mass measurements is limited by projections along the line of sight (93, 98–100).

Multiwavelength observations of samples that contain up to ∼50 massive clusters have only recently started (101–103). These comprehensive studies, which also combine data at other wavelengths, will not only help quantify the scatter but will also improve our understanding of cluster physics. This in turn will increase the reliability of other cluster mass estimators (such as X-ray temperature). For instance Mahdavi et al. (104) recently found evidence that the outer regions of clusters are not in hydrostatic equilibrium, suggesting that additional pressure may be provided by bulk motion of the plasma (105). Cluster cosmology is an evolving field; we hope that when large samples of clusters are observed in multiple wavelengths, their internal physics will be modeled well enough for cosmological applications.

6.3. Properties of Dark Matter Halos

Simulations of hierarchical structure formation in CDM cosmologies have shown that the density profiles of virialized halos over a wide range in mass have a nearly universal profile with radius: the Navarro-Frenk-White (NFW) profile (106, 107). The only difference between halos of galaxies and clusters of different mass is their concentration, which reflects the central density of the halo. Gravitational lensing provides us with powerful tools to test a range of predictions of the CDM paradigm via the structure of halos. For instance, the dark matter–dominated outer regions can be uniquely probed by weak lensing, whereas strong gravitational lensing can be used to study the density profile on small scales.

6.3.1. Central regions.
In the context of CDM, simulations indicate a power law density profile $\rho \propto r^{-\beta}$ as $r \to 0$. The original studies (106, 107) found a slope of $\beta = 1$, but the exact value is still subject to debate (108, 109). Without a complete treatment of the effects of baryons, observational results will be difficult to interpret. Despite these complications, much effort has been expended to determine the slope of the density profile observationally, as it can provide unique constraints on physical properties of the dark matter particle, such as its interaction cross section (see, e.g., References 110 and 111).

Dynamical studies of galaxies have proven useful, and much of the current controversy about the central slope is based on observations of the rotation curves of low–surface brightness galaxies; these observations suggest that the dark matter distribution has a central core (see, e.g., References 112–114). Strong lensing by galaxies can provide only limited information because the typical Einstein radius is large compared to the region of interest. Nevertheless the combination of strong lensing and dynamics has been extremely useful for the study of the stars and dark matter in galaxies (see, e.g., References 115 and 116) and to test general relativity (117).

Strong lensing can be used to study the inner density profiles of clusters, although results are still somewhat ambiguous (118). Of particular interest are clusters that show both tangential and radial arcs because they can help to constrain the density profile. An analysis of such systems by Sand et al. (119) suggests an average slope $\beta \sim 0.5$. However Meneghetti et al. (120) studied simulated clusters and found that too-restrictive assumptions can bias core slope estimates to lower values (also see References 121 and 122).

6.3.2. Outer regions. The value for the outer slope of the density profile is expected to be $\beta \sim 3$. A related prediction is that the mean central density of the halo decreases with virial mass, i.e., lower-mass systems are more concentrated (106, 107). The average dark matter profile of galaxy clusters has been studied by Johnston et al. (97) using SDSS. These results, along with measurements by Mandelbaum et al. (123) and Comerford & Natarajan (124), agree well with predictions from Λ CDM models, as do studies of individual clusters such as Abell 1689 (125).

The study of the outer parts of galaxies is more difficult because the signal of an individual galaxy is too small to be detected. Interpretation of the observed signal, also known as the galaxy-mass cross correlation function (see, e.g., References 46, 126, and 127), is complicated by the fact that it is the convolution of the galaxy dark matter profile and the (clustered) distribution of galaxies. Despite these limitations galaxy-galaxy lensing studies provide a number of useful tests of the CDM paradigm.

One such test is the measurement of the extent of dark matter halos. Pioneering studies (128, 129) were unable to provide constraints because of the small numbers of lens-source pairs. Large surveys such as SDSS (see, e.g., References 127, 130, and 131), RCS (126), and CFHTLS (132) have measured the lensing signal with much higher precision, enabling Hoekstra et al. (126) to determine the extent of dark matter halos around field galaxies. Note that these measurements use the small-scale end of the galaxy-shear cross correlation discussed above in Section 3.2.

Another area where galaxy-galaxy lensing studies will have a great impact is the study of the shapes of dark matter halos. CDM simulations predict that halos are tri-axial (see, e.g., Reference 133). This is supported by the findings from Hoekstra et al. (126), who found that the dark matter halos are on average aligned with the light distribution with a mean axis ratio that is in broad agreement with the CDM predictions. A similar result was obtained recently using CFHTLS data (132). Both of these studies lacked the multicolor data to separate lenses by galaxy type; however, separation was performed by Mandelbaum et al. (134) using SDSS data. The authors of this study did not detect a significant flattening, although their data do suggest a positive alignment for the brightest ellipticals.

The accuracy of these measurements is expected to improve significantly over the next few years as more data are collected as part of cosmic shear surveys. An accurate measurement of the anisotropy of the lensing signal around galaxies (i.e., the signal of flattened halos in CDM) is also a powerful way to test alternative theories of gravity (126, 135).

7. THE FUTURE

The first cosmic shear results, published less than a decade ago, were based on areas of several square degrees at most (58–61). Current leading surveys, most notably the CFHTLS, are many times larger and provide photometric redshift information for the sources. Even so, the area coverage of CFHTLS is still modest (below 200 deg^2) given that it is now technologically feasible to image more than 1000 deg^2 per year to depths of interest for cosmology. Furthermore, despite the recent success in measuring the cosmic shear signal, current data are obtained using telescopes that are not optimized for weak lensing. Finally, the use of photo-zs for cosmological inferences is still in its early stages. The CFHTLS lacks good coverage at near-IR wavelengths, which impacts the accuracy of photo-zs.

Table 2 Overview of planned surveys

Survey	Year of activation	Area (deg^2)	n_{eff} (arcmin^{-2})	Ground or space
KiDS	>2008	1500	~10	ground
PanSTARRS[a]	>2008	30,000	~4	ground
DES	>2010	5000	~10	ground
Subaru	>2012	2000	~20–30	ground
LSST	>2014	20,000	~30–40	ground
SNAP	>2015	4000	~100	space
DUNE	>2015	20,000	~40	space

[a]Here we consider PS1, the PanSTARRS project with a single telescope and the 3π survey. This survey may be expanded into a four-telescope project (called PS4) in the future.

7.1. Planned Surveys

The next generation of surveys will address some or even all of these limitations. For instance, many will make use of new telescopes specifically designed to provide a stable PSF with minimal anisotropy. Equipped with new cameras with fields of view of 1 deg^2 or larger, these surveys will deliver over 1000 deg^2 of well-calibrated images of galaxies beyond $z = 1$. **Table 2** lists basic information for a number of these projects. As many of these surveys are still in the planning stages, we stress that these numbers may change (experience shows that this is particularly true for the starting dates!). What is clear from this table is that the volume of data will increase by another order of magnitude within approximately the next five years.

Of the first four surveys listed in **Table 2**, the Kilo Degree Survey (KiDS) (**http://www.strw.leidenuniv.nl/kuijken/KIDS/**) and the Panoramic Survey Telescope and Rapid Response System (PanSTARRS) (**http://pan-starrs.ifa.hawaii.edu**) use telescopes and cameras specifically designed for the projects. The Dark Energy Survey (DES) (**http://www.darkenergysurvey.org**) will use a new camera built for the 4-m Blanco telescope at CTIO. Another new camera, the HyperSuprimeCam, has been proposed for the Subaru 8.2-m telescope. KiDS will combine its optical data with near-IR imaging using the Visible and Infrared Survey Telescope for Astronomy (VISTA); the resulting nine-band data will give it excellent photometric redshift accuracy, which is critical for the measurement of intrinsic alignments and cosmic shear tomography. DES also plans to use near-IR imaging from VISTA over a substantial part of the survey.

The accuracy with which the lensing signal can be measured depends on the area covered and the number density of distant source galaxies for which reliable shapes and photo-zs can be determined. For a fixed amount of observing time, one must therefore strike a balance between the amount of sky covered and the depth of the observations. If the survey is too shallow, most sources will be at low redshift and the induced lensing signal will be too small to be of interest.

On the other hand, increasing the number density of sources used in the analysis is useful only if systematic effects for these small, faint galaxies can be controlled or corrected for. The blurring of the images by the atmosphere is a limiting factor. If the size of the galaxy is comparable to that of the PSF, any residual systematic is amplified by the deconvolution. Compared to space-based observations, ground-based observations are more sensitive to problems with PSF correction. Furthermore, obtaining deep near-infrared (NIR) data, which is needed for accurate photometric redshifts, will be more difficult for a ground-based telescope (although it would be feasible to add imaging in these bands from space, provided that the depth and sky coverage match).

Much of the cosmological information in planned surveys is extracted from large-scale modes for which sample variance, not number density, is the limiting factor. Consequently ground-based surveys may suffer only a modest loss of accuracy if only galaxies with well-measured shapes and photo-zs are used. Further, the cost of a space-based project requires careful consideration of the benefits. It is clear that the requirements to reach percent-level accuracy in the dark energy equation of state are very challenging.

In **Table 2** we provide crude estimates for the expected effective source number densities for the various surveys. These numbers could change depending on the delivered seeing and noise levels for a given survey. We note that due to PSF degradation effects, the effective number density of sources that can be used in the lensing analysis, n_{eff}, is lower than the number density of detected objects. Studies based on simulated and actual deep ground-based images suggest that it is difficult to exceed an effective density of 30 galaxies arcmin^{-2} in typical ground-based data (this upper limit depends on the seeing and other factors). A space-based mission is required to reach significantly higher source densities.

The projects that will start in the immediate future represent a major step forward, but they will not be carried out on general-purpose facilities (with the exception of PanSTARRS). This limits the amount of time available for large multiwavelength surveys. Hence a significantly larger deep survey would require a dedicated large-aperture telescope with a very wide field of view. One proposal is the expansion of PanSTARRS to include more telescopes to increase the étendue (field of view times collecting area) of the facility. A proposal for arguably the definitive ground-based survey is the six-band imaging survey over 20,000 deg^2 proposed for the Large Synoptic Survey Telescope (LSST) (**http://www.lsst.org**), an 8.4-m telescope with a 10-deg^2 field of view whose survey capacity is an order of magnitude larger than any stage III project.

Alternatively, in an attempt to minimize PSF-related systematics, space-based missions have been proposed. Such missions have the added benefit that high-quality multiwavelength data out to NIR wavelengths can be obtained. A European project, the Dark Universe Explorer (DUNE) (**http://www.dune-mission.net**), focuses on the improved image quality and stability that can be obtained from space; however, in its current form DUNE still relies upon extensive ground-based follow up. Also the improvement in n_{eff} is relatively small compared to LSST. The Supernova/Acceleration Probe (SNAP) (**http://snap.lbl.gov**) is the most comprehensive proposal, as it combines stable optics for weak lensing shape measurements with nine-filter optical/NIR photometry for superb photometric redshifts. It will survey a smaller area of the sky than DUNE, but to a greater depth.

7.2. Prospects for Lensing Cosmology

This review has covered weak lensing by galaxies, galaxy clusters, and large-scale structure. We have discussed the measurement of cosmological parameters via lensing, with a focus on dark matter and dark energy. The use of lensing tomography for dark energy measurements can be performed using (two- and three-point) shear correlations, galaxy-shear cross correlations, and galaxy clusters. Tests of the nature of dark matter and of gravity on scales of 10 kpc to 1 Mpc are provided by galaxy and cluster lensing. Modified gravity theories that attempt to explain cosmic acceleration can also be tested using weak lensing measurements on larger (cosmological) scales. The success of particular applications of lensing will no doubt depend on how well systematic errors can be reduced, corrected from the data, or marginalized over in making cosmological inferences.

Most weak lensing studies (and therefore this review) have focused on the measurement of the shear using galaxy images. These studies will continue to provide unique insights into the dark side of the universe. In conclusion, we highlight a few other aspects of lensing that form the focus of ongoing research. For instance, the lensing signal can be inferred by measuring magnification effects, which change the number counts of source galaxies (136, 137). These effects can provide a useful complementary measure of lensing, as the systematic errors involved are quite different from shear measurements. We described three-point shear correlations as useful measures of the non-Gaussian distribution of the lensing mass. Other measures of non-Gaussianity include global characterization of the topology of lensing maps, topological charge distributions, and peak statistics in convergence maps.

We have also discussed the binning of galaxies using photo-zs for lensing tomography. It is possible to do better by treating the source galaxy distribution as three dimensional (with the position in the redshift direction having much larger uncertainty than in the transverse direction), which can lead to improved cosmological constraints (138). Another application of tomography is the actual reconstruction of the three-dimensional lensing mass distribution (139, 140); the COSMOS survey has attempted such a reconstruction using the HST (71). A relatively new area of research is the measurement of higher-order derivatives of the lensing potential, which provide additional information on small-scale variations in the mass distribution (141, 142).

Finally, we mention two high-redshift applications of lensing. First, the effect of lensing by foreground structures on the CMB (143, 144) is currently an area of active study. This represents a significant contaminant for studies of the CMB polarization (145), but it can also provide additional information about the lensing mass. Second, future radio telescopes may be able to detect galaxies at high redshift through their 21-cm emission. If lensing effects can be measured accurately with 21-cm surveys, they can provide high-accuracy power spectra over a wide range in redshift (146–148).

DISCLOSURE STATEMENT

The authors are not aware of any biases that might be perceived as affecting the objectivity of this review.

ACKNOWLEDGEMENTS

We acknowledge helpful discussions and comments on the manuscript from Gary Bernstein, Jacek Guzik, Mike Jarvis, Nick Kaiser, Steve Kahn, Eric Linder, Alexandre Refregier, Jason Rhodes, Fritz Stabenau, Masahiro Takada, Andy Taylor, and Ludo van Waerbeke. This work is supported in part by the Department of Energy, the Research Corporation, and National Science Foundation grant AST-0607667.

LITERATURE CITED

1. Clowe D, et al. *Astrophys. J.* 648:L109 (2006)
2. Refsdal S. *MNRAS* 128:307 (1964)
3. Koopmans LVE, et al. *Astrophys. J.* 599:70 (2003)
4. Blandford RD, Saust AN, Brainerd TG, Villumsen JV. *MNRAS* 251:600 (1991)
5. Kaiser N. *Astrophys. J.* 388:272 (1992)
6. Albrecht A, et al. arXiv:astro-ph/0609591 (2006)
7. Peacock JA, et al. arXiv:astro-ph/0610906 (2006)
8. Bartelmann M, Schneider P. arXiv:astro-ph/9912508 (1999)
9. Mellier Y. *Annu. Rev. Astron. Astrophys.* 37:127 (1999)
10. Refregier A. *Annu. Rev. Astron. Astrophys.* 41:645 (2003)
11. Munshi D, Valageas P, van Waerbeke L, Heavens A. arXiv:astro-ph/0612667 (2006)
12. Seitz C, Schneider P. *Astron. Astrophys.* 318:687 (1997)
13. Jain B, Jarvis M, Bernstein G. *JCAP* 2:1 (2006)

14. Hoekstra H. *MNRAS* 347:1337 (2004)

15. Jarvis M, Jain B. arXiv:astro-ph/0412234 (2004)

16. Heymans C, et al. *MNRAS* 368:1323 (2006)

17. Massey R, et al. *MNRAS* 376:13 (2007)

18. Kaiser N, Squires G, Broadhurst T. *Astrophys. J.* 449:460 (1995)

19. Luppino GA, Kaiser N. *Astrophys. J.* 475:20 (1997)

20. Hoekstra H, Franx M, Kuijken K, Squires G. *Astrophys. J.* 504:636 (1998)

21. Bernstein GM, Jarvis M. *Astron. J.* 123:583 (2002)

22. Refregier A. *MNRAS* 338:35 (2003)

23. Refregier A, Bacon D. *MNRAS* 338:48 (2003)

24. Nakajima R, Bernstein G. *Astron. J.* 133:1763 (2007)

25. Kuijken K. *Astron. Astrophys.* 352:355 (1999)

26. Bacon DJ, Massey RJ, Refregier AR, Ellis RS. *MNRAS* 344:673 (2003)

27. Schneider P, van Waerbeke L, Mellier Y. *Astron. Astrophys.* 389:729 (2002)

28. Crittenden RG, Natarajan P, Pen U-L, Theuns T. *Astrophys. J.* 559:552 (2001)

29. Hu W. *Astrophys. J.* 522:L21 (1999)

30. Knox L, Song Y-S, Tyson JA. *Phys. Rev. D* 74:023512 (2006)

31. Amendola L, Kunz M, Sapone D. arXiv:0704.2421 (2007)

32. Jain B, Zhang P. arXiv:0709.2375 (2007)

33. Heavens AF, Kitching TD, Verde L. *MNRAS* 380:1029 (2007)

34. Huterer D, Linder EV. *Phys. Rev. D* 75:023519 (2007)

35. Jain B, Seljak U. *Astrophys. J.* 484:560 (1997)

36. Jain B, Seljak U, White S. *Astrophys. J.* 530:547 (2000)

37. White M, Vale C. *Astropart. Phys.* 22:19 (2004)

38. Francis MJ, Lewis GF, Linder EV. *MNRAS* 380:1079 (2007)

39. Zentner AR, Rudd DH, Hu W. arXiv:0709.4029 (2007)

40. Takada M, Jain B. *MNRAS* 348:897 (2004)

41. Hu W, Jain B. *Phys. Rev. D* 70:043009 (2004)

42. Jain B, Taylor A. *Phys. Rev. Lett.* 91:141302 (2003)

43. Bernstein G, Jain B. *Astrophys. J.* 600:17 (2004)

44. Zhang J, Hui L, Stebbins A. *Astrophys. J.* 635:806 (2005)

45. Song YS, Knox L. *Phys. Rev. D* 70:063510 (2004)

46. Seljak U, et al. *Phys. Rev. D* 71:043511 (2005)

47. Bernardeau F, van Waerbeke L, Mellier Y. *Astron. Astrophys.* 322:1 (1997)

48. Huterer D, Takada M, Bernstein G, Jain B. *MNRAS* 366:101 (2006)

49. Hu W, Tegmark M. *Astrophys. J.* 514:L65 (1999)

50. Croft RAC, Metzler CA. *Astrophys. J.* 545:561 (2000)

51. Hirata CM, Seljak U. *Phys. Rev. D* 70:063526 (2004)

52. Bridle S, King L. *NJP* 9:444 (2007)

53. Mandelbaum R, et al. *MNRAS* 367:611 (2006a)

54. Hirata CM, Mandelbaum R, Ishak M, Seljak U. *MNRAS* 381:1197 (2007)

55. Heymans C, et al. *MNRAS* 371:750 (2006)

56. Ma Z, Hu W, Huterer D. *Astrophys. J.* 636:21 (2006)

57. Amara A, Refregier A. arXiv:0710.5171 (2007)

58. Bacon DJ, Refregier AR, Ellis RS. *MNRAS* 318:625 (2000)

59. Kaiser N, Wilson G, Luppino GA. arXiv:astro-ph/0003338 (2000)

60. van Waerbeke L, et al. *Astron. Astrophys.* 358:30 (2000)

61. Wittman DM, et al. *Nature* 405:143 (2000)

62. Mould J, et al. *MNRAS* 271:31 (1994)

63. Hoekstra H, Yee HKC, Gladders MD. *Astrophys. J.* 577:595 (2002)

64. van Waerbeke L, Mellier Y, Hoekstra H. *Astron. Astrophys.* 429:75 (2005)

65. Jarvis M, Jain B, Bernstein G, Dolney D. *Astrophys. J.* 644:71 (2006)

66. Hetterscheidt M, et al. *Astron. Astrophys.* 468:859 (2007)

67. Fu L, et al. arXiv:astro-ph/0712.0884 (2007)
68. Massey R, et al. *Astrophys. J. Supp.* 172:239 (2007)
69. Hoekstra H, et al. *Astrophys. J.* 647:116 (2006)
70. Kitching TD, et al. *MNRAS* 771:778 (2007)
71. Massey R, et al. *Nature* 445:286 (2007)
72. Semboloni E, et al. *Astron. Astrophys.* 452:51 (2006)
73. Benjamin J, et al. *MNRAS* 381:702 (2007)
74. Semboloni E, et al. *MNRAS* 375:6 (2007)
75. Ilbert O, et al. *Astron. Astrophys.* 457:841 (2006)
76. Henry JP. *Astrophys. J.* 609:603 (2004)
77. Rosati P, Borgani S, Norman C. *Annu. Rev. Astron. Astrophys.* 40:539 (2002)
78. Spergel DN, et al. *Astrophys. J. Supp.* 170:377 (2007)
79. Kaiser N, Squires G. *Astrophys. J.* 404:441 (1993)
80. Seitz S, Schneider P. *Astron. Astrophys.* 305:383 (1996)
81. Seitz S, Schneider P. *Astron. Astrophys.* 374:740 (2001)
82. Squires G, Kaiser N. *Astrophys. J.* 473:65 (1996)
83. Jee MJ, et al. *Astrophys. J.* 661:728 (2007)
84. Mahdavi A, et al. *Astrophys. J.* 668:806 (2007)
85. Angus GW, Shan H, Zhao H, Famaey B. *Astrophys. J.* 654:L13 (2007)
86. Milgrom M. *Astrophys. J.* 270:365 (1983)
87. Bekenstein J. *Phys. Rev. D* 70:3509 (2004)
88. Bahcall NA, et al. *Astrophys. J.* 585:182 (2003)
89. Levine ES, Schulz AE, White M. *Astrophys. J.* 577:569 (2002)
90. Wittman DM, et al. *Astrophys. J.* 643:128 (2006)
91. Miyazaki S, et al. *Astrophys. J.* 580:L97 (2002)
92. Miyazaki S, et al. *Astrophys. J.* 669:714 (2007)
93. White M, van Waerbeke L, Mackey J. *Astrophys. J.* 575:640 (2002)
94. Hennawi JF, Spergel DN. *Astrophys. J.* 624:59 (2005)
95. Marian L, Bernstein GM. *Phys. Rev. Lett.* 73:123525 (2006)
96. Sheldon ES, et al. arXiv:astro-ph/0709.1153 (2007)
97. Johnston DE, et al. arXiv:astro-ph/0709.1159 (2007)
98. Metzler CA, White M, Norman M, Loken C. *Astrophys. J.* 520:L9 (1999)
99. Metzler CA, White M, Loken C. *Astrophys. J.* 547:560 (2001)
100. Hoekstra H. *Astron. Astrophys.* 370:743 (2001)
101. Dahle H, et al. *Astrophys. J. Supp.* 139:313 (2002)
102. Hoekstra H. *MNRAS* 379:317 (2007)
103. Bardeau S, et al. *Astron. Astrophys.* 470:449 (2007)
104. Mahdavi A, Hoekstra H, Babul A, Henry JP. *MNRAS* 384:1567 (2008)
105. Nagai D, Vikhlinin A, Kravtsov AV. *Astrophys. J.* 655:98 (2007)
106. Navarro JF, Frenk C, White SDM. *Astrophys. J.* 462:563 (1996)
107. Navarro JF, Frenk C, White SDM. *Astrophys. J.* 490:493 (1997)
108. Moore B, et al. *MNRAS* 310:1147 (1999)
109. Navarro JF, et al. *MNRAS* 349:1039 (2004)
110. Spergel DN, Steinhardt PJ. *Phys. Rev. Lett.* 84:3760 (2000)
111. Meneghetti M, et al. *MNRAS* 325:435 (2001)
112. Flores RA, Primack JR. *Astrophys. J.* 427:L1 (1994)
113. Moore B. *Nature* 370:629 (1994)
114. McGaugh SS, de Blok WJG. *Astrophys. J.* 499:41 (1998)
115. Treu T, Koopmans LVE. *Astrophys. J.* 575:87 (2002)
116. Koopmans LVE, et al. *Astrophys. J.* 659:599 (2006)
117. Bolton AS, Rappaport S, Burles S. *Phys. Rev. D* 74:061501 (2006)
118. Comerford JM, Meneghetti M, Bartelmann M, Schirmer M. *Astrophys. J.* 642:39 (2006)
119. Sand DJ, Treu T, Smith GP, Ellis RS. *Astrophys. J.* 604:88 (2004)

120. Meneghetti M, Bartelmann M, Jenkins A, Frenk C. *MNRAS* 381:171 (2007)
121. Dalal N, Keeton CR. arXiv:astro-ph/0312072 (2003)
122. Bartelmann M, Meneghetti M. *Astron. Astrophys.* 418:413 (2004)
123. Mandelbaum R, et al. *MNRAS* 372:758 (2006d)
124. Comerford JM, Natarajan P. *MNRAS* 379:190 (2007)
125. Broadhurst T, et al. *Astrophys. J.* 619:L143 (2005)
126. Hoekstra H, Yee HKC, Gladders MD. *Astrophys. J.* 606:67 (2004)
127. Sheldon ES, et al. *Astron. J.* 127:2544 (2004)
128. Brainerd TG, Blandford RD, Smail I. *Astrophys. J.* 466:623 (1996)
129. Hudson MJ, Gwyn SDJ, Dahle H, Kaiser N. *Astrophys. J.* 503:531 (1998)
130. Fischer P, et al. *Astron. J.* 120:1198 (2000)
131. Mandelbaum R, et al. *MNRAS* 368:715 (2006b)
132. Parker LC, et al. *Astrophys. J.* 669:21 (2007)
133. Dubinski J, Carlberg RG. *Astrophys. J.* 378:496 (1991)
134. Mandelbaum R, et al. *MNRAS* 370:1008 (2006c)
135. Mortlock DJ, Turner EL. *MNRAS* 327:557 (2001)
136. Broadhurst TJ, Taylor AN, Peacock JA. *Astrophys. J.* 438:49 (1995)
137. Scranton R, Menard B, Richards GT, Nichol RC. *Astrophys. J.* 633:589 (2005)
138. Heavens A. *MNRAS* 343:1327 (2003)
139. Taylor AN. arXiv:astro-ph/0111605 (2001)
140. Hu W, Keeton CR. *Phys. Rev. D* 66:063506 (2002)
141. Irwin J, Shmakova M. arXiv:astro-ph/0308007 (2003)
142. Goldberg DM, Bacon DJ. *Astrophys. J.* 619:741 (2005)
143. Zaldarriaga M, Seljak U. *Phys. Rev. Lett.* 58:023003 (1998)
144. Hu W. *Astrophys. J.* 557:L79 (2001)
145. Seljak U, Hirata CM. *Phys. Rev. D* 69:043005 (2004)
146. Zahn O, Zaldarriaga M. *Astrophys. J.* 653:922 (2006)
147. Zhang P, Pen U-L. *MNRAS* 367:169 (2006)
148. Metcalf RB, White SDM. *MNRAS* 381:447 (2007)

Top Quark Properties
and Interactions

Regina Demina[1] and Evelyn J. Thomson[2]

[1]Department of Physics and Astronomy, University of Rochester, Rochester, New York 14627

[2]Department of Physics and Astronomy, University of Pennsylvania, Philadelphia, Pennsylvania 19104; email: thomsone@physics.upenn.edu

Annu. Rev. Nucl. Part. Sci. 2008. 58:125–46

First published online as a Review in Advance on June 3, 2008

The *Annual Review of Nuclear and Particle Science* is online at nucl.annualreviews.org

This article's doi: 10.1146/annurev.nucl.58.110707.171224

Key Words

top quark, mass, strong interaction, electroweak interaction, Tevatron

Abstract

This review describes the properties and interactions of the top quark, to date the most massive fundamental particle discovered by experiment. We describe the measurements of the rate of pair production via the strong interaction and the techniques used to elucidate evidence for single production via the electroweak interaction. We also discuss investigations of the properties of the top quark, including potential beyond the standard model production and decay mechanisms. We pay particular attention to the explanation of the recent advances in the precision measurement of the top quark mass.

Contents

1. INTRODUCTION

The top quark is the most massive fundamental particle known to mankind. It was discovered (1) in 1995 by the CDF and DØ experiments at the Fermi National Accelerator Laboratory in collisions between protons and antiprotons at a center-of-mass energy of $\sqrt{s} = 1.8$ TeV. In the run that lasted from 1991 to 1995, the experiments each accumulated about 100 pb^{-1} of collision data. The rate for quantum chromodynamics (QCD) production of a pair of top and antitop quarks, $p\bar{p} \to t\bar{t}$, at this energy is about 5 pb (2), which implies that only about 500 collisions produced top quarks during this period. This is very rare compared to the billion-times-larger total inelastic interaction rate of about 60 mb. Given the online and offline efficiencies of the experiments' event selections, only about 50 events consistent with $t\bar{t}$ production were identified. Even so, the top quark mass was measured rather precisely in this data set mainly because of its large value, 178.0 ± 4.3 GeV/c^2 (3), which allowed accurate reconstruction of the top quark decay products.

The large value of the top quark mass surprised physicists. The top quark mass is about double that of the electroweak W and Z bosons, the next most massive known particles, and approximately 35 times larger than that of the bottom quark, the next most massive fermion. Even more surprising is the fact that the corresponding top quark Yukawa coupling is very close to unity; in other words, the top quark mass is very close to the minimum of the electroweak symmetry breaking (EWSB) potential. This fact prompted the creation of models wherein the top quark plays a special role in the process of EWSB (4). To experimentalists, it meant that none of the standard model predictions for the properties of the top quark could be taken for granted and that all of them required experimental verification.

A detailed investigation of the properties of the top quark is one of the primary motivations for run II of the Tevatron, which commenced in 2001 and is expected to continue until 2009. The CDF and DØ detectors underwent extensive upgrades (5), including replacement of the charged particle tracking detectors to improve the identification efficiency for top quark decay products. The energies of the proton and antiproton beams were raised by 80 GeV for a higher center-of-mass energy, $\sqrt{s} = 1.96$ TeV, which increased the production rate for top quarks by 30%. By the end of 2007, improvements to the accelerator (6) had increased the maximum instantaneous luminosity tenfold to 2.5×10^{32} cm^{-2} s^{-1}, about 100 pb^{-1} of collision data were delivered each month, and CDF and DØ had accumulated about 3000 pb^{-1} (3 fb^{-1}) each. With this much larger sample of top quarks, CDF and DØ are carefully examining the properties of the top quark. In this review, we discuss results based on up to 2000 pb^{-1}.

Measuring the top quark pair production rate is an interesting test of QCD and a probe for new physics. A value larger than that predicted by the standard model would indicate additional production mechanisms, e.g., through an intermediate new massive Z' boson, as predicted by the topcolor models (4), or production of additional particles that decay similarly to the top quark, e.g., a supersymmetric top quark (7). We discuss the $t\bar{t}$ production cross section in Section 2. A comparison of the rates observed in the different top quark decay channels probes for nonstandard top quark decays, e.g., to a charged Higgs boson (8). Other interesting topics we discuss in Section 3 include measurement of the top quark electric charge and the helicity of the W boson from top quark decay (9). The top quark mass is a fundamental parameter of the standard model, which through radiative corrections to the W boson mass is connected to the mass of the standard model particle of EWSB, the as-yet-undiscovered Higgs boson (10). Thus, the high-precision measurement of the top quark mass, which we describe in Section 4, is of the utmost importance for the Higgs boson search and for testing the consistency of the standard model. In Section 5 we present evidence for single top quark production via the electroweak interaction. Finally, in Section 6 we present our conclusions and the outlook for future measurements of top quark properties and interactions at the Tevatron and the Large Hadron Collider (LHC).

2. TOP QUARK PAIR PRODUCTION

Top quarks are produced in pairs via the strong interaction processes $q\bar{q} \rightarrow t\bar{t}$ and $g\bar{g} \rightarrow t\bar{t}$ (illustrated in **Figure 1**). The theoretical prediction for the production rate is $6.7\pm^{0.7}_{0.9}$ pb (2) for $m_{\text{top}} = 175$ GeV/c^2 in $p\bar{p}$ collisions at $\sqrt{s} = 1.96$ TeV, including all first-order and some second-order corrections in α_s. For pp collisions at $\sqrt{s} = 14$ TeV, the predicted rate is $833\pm^{52}_{39}$ pb (2). The factor-of-100 increase in rate at the LHC can be understood from a brief description of the structure of the proton. In principle, the proton is composed of three valence quarks (two up quarks and one down quark) bound together by gluons, the carriers of the strong force. The probability of finding a gluon with a fraction x of the proton's momentum grows extremely rapidly with decreasing x. At threshold for $t\bar{t}$ production at the Tevatron, each of the two initial partons must carry a large fraction $x = 0.2$ of the proton's momentum, so $t\bar{t}$ production is mostly (80–90%) from collisions between valence quarks. At the LHC, the initial partons only need a small fraction $x = 0.02$ of the proton's momentum, so $t\bar{t}$ production is mostly (90%) from collisions between gluons. Note that although antiquarks are by definition present in the antiproton at the Tevatron, they can easily fluctuate into existence at the required x inside one of the protons at the LHC.

In the standard model, a top quark decays via the electroweak interaction to a W boson and a b quark with a branching fraction of 99%. The large phase space for the decay results in a top

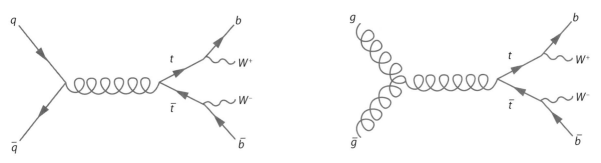

Figure 1

Feynman diagrams for top quark pair production.

quark width of 1.5 GeV, for $m_{\text{top}} = 175$ GeV/c^2, and a very short top quark lifetime on the order of 10^{-25} s. In contrast to all other quarks, this is not even enough time for hadronization into a meson or baryon. One interesting consequence of this brief lifetime is that the spin of the top quark is preserved in the angular distribution of the top quark decay products, thus any correlations between the directions of the spins of the top quark and the antitop quark are preserved as well.

There are three distinctive experimental signatures that are characterized by the number of charged leptons from the decay of the W^+ and W^- bosons: (a) dilepton for $t\bar{t} \to \ell_1^+ \nu_1 \ell_2^- \bar{\nu}_2 b\bar{b}$, (b) single lepton for $t\bar{t} \to \ell\nu q_1 \bar{q}_2 b\bar{b}$, and (c) all-hadronic for $t\bar{t} \to q_1 \bar{q}_2 q_3 \bar{q}_4 b\bar{b}$. (In this paper, lepton refers either to electron or muon unless otherwise noted.) Due to the top quark's large mass, the decay products tend to have large transverse momenta and large angular separations. For experiments at a hadron collider, the data from the millions of collisions taking place each second must be rapidly sifted through to pick out the few hundred collisions per second that can be permanently stored for later detailed analysis. Top quark pair production is relatively rare. At an instantaneous luminosity of $2 \times 10^{+32}$ cm^{-2} s^{-1} (more informatively written as 0.2 nb^{-1} s^{-1}), top quark pairs are produced on average once every 12 min at the Tevatron. At the LHC, the average rate is once every 7 s at this low luminosity (the design luminosity is 50 times higher). Fortunately, the presence of an isolated lepton with high transverse momentum is also quite rare at a hadron collider, which provides a highly efficient trigger for the dilepton and single lepton channels. The large number and high transverse momenta of the jets in the all-hadronic channel also allow a trigger with high efficiency and a rate low enough for the available bandwidth.

2.1. Dilepton

In the dilepton final state, the 11% branching fraction is sliced more finely into three channels with two like-flavor leptons, each with a 1.2% branching fraction (ee, $\mu\mu$, $\tau\tau$) and three channels with two unlike-flavor leptons, each with a 2.4% branching fraction ($e\mu$, $e\tau$, and $\mu\tau$). In order to measure the production rate from $t\bar{t}$, one must estimate the contribution to this final state from several other processes. The three most important processes are (a) $Z/\gamma \to \ell^+ \ell^-$ with associated jets, (b) $W^+ W^- \to \ell^+ \nu \ell^- \bar{\nu}$ with associated jets, and (c) $W \to \ell\nu$ with associated jets where one of the jets fakes the detector signature of a lepton. Both the CDF and DØ experiments have obtained higher selection efficiencies by relaxing the lepton identification for the second lepton at the cost of larger background from fakes.

In general, the theoretical prediction for the absolute rate of vector boson production with a specific number of associated jets from QCD has a large theoretical uncertainty from missing higher orders in the calculation. Therefore, it is best to measure the rate from data whenever possible. For instance, the number of events from $Z/\gamma \to e^+ e^-$ and $Z/\gamma \to \mu^+ \mu^-$ with associated jets can be estimated directly from the data by measuring the number of events wherein the two leptons formed an invariant mass close to the Z boson mass, then extrapolating to the whole mass range using simulation.

It is also best to estimate from data the rate for jets that fake the detector signature for leptons. With the gigantic jet production rate at a hadron collider, even one-in-a-hundred-thousand fluctuations in jet fragmentation can lead to a significant number of jets that fake the detector signature of a lepton. For instance, a jet can mimic the signature in the detector of either an isolated electron (if there is a π^0 that leaves a large electromagnetic energy deposit in the calorimeter and a charged pion to provide a reconstructed track in the detector) or an isolated muon (if there is a charged kaon that decays in flight to a muon). Although simulation is generally adequate, it is not designed to predict accurately the rate of these rare fluctuations in jet fragmentation and detector response.

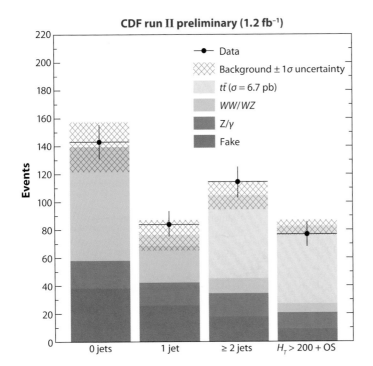

Figure 2

The number of predicted and observed events as a function of jet multiplicity in the CDF dilepton channel with 1.2 fb^{-1} (11). The rightmost bin is for events with two or more jets where the leptons also have opposite electric charges, and the total transverse energy (H_T) of the leptons, jets, and missing E_T is at least 200 GeV. The contribution from $t\bar{t}$ is normalized to the expected 6.7 pb.

A high statistics data sample collected with a jet trigger can be used to measure the rate at which jets are misidentified as leptons as functions of jet E_T and η. Applying that data-derived rate to the jets in a single lepton data sample provides an estimate of the number of events with a fake lepton. Note that the physics processes listed above produce lepton pairs with opposite electric charges, but that events with a fake lepton are expected to produce equal numbers of lepton pairs with the same and opposite electric charges. Therefore, a simple estimate of the number of events with a fake lepton can be provided by twice the number of data events with two identified leptons bearing the same sign of electric charge.

The good agreement between the background estimate and the data can be seen in the 0 and 1 jet regions of **Figure 2**, which is for a CDF data sample of 1.2 fb^{-1} with two identified electrons or muons with high p_T, and a significant imbalance in the observed transverse energy (missing E_T) from the undetected neutrinos. After requiring at least two jets, leptons with opposite electric charge, and at least 200 GeV of E_T from the jets, leptons, and missing E_T, CDF observes 77 events with an estimated background of 26 ± 6 events. With an estimated selection efficiency times branching fraction for $t\bar{t}$ of 0.8%, CDF measures $6.2 \pm 1.0_{stat} \pm 0.7_{syst} \pm 0.4_{lumi}$ pb (11), and DØ measures $6.2 \pm 0.9 \,^{+0.8}_{-0.7} \pm 0.4$ pb in 1.0 fb^{-1} (12).

2.2. Single Lepton

In the single charged lepton final state, the 44% branching fraction is sliced up into three channels with different lepton types, each with a 14.5% branching fraction (e, μ, τ). On average, the lepton, the neutrino, and the jets from $t\bar{t}$ have higher transverse energies and larger angular separations than those from W boson production with associated jets. Shown in **Figure 3** is the output of an artificial neural network that has been trained on simulation to discriminate between $t\bar{t}$ and W+jets production based on differences in event kinematics and topology for data events with

Figure 3

The distribution of a multivariate discriminant for events in the CDF single lepton channel with at least three jets and 0.8 fb^{-1} (13). Abbreviation: ANN, artificial neural network.

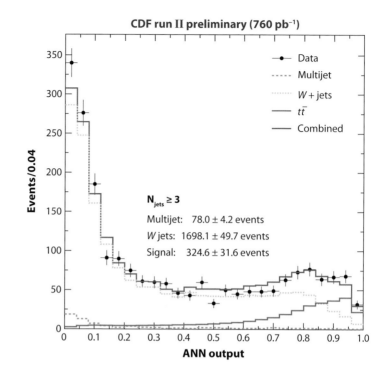

CDF run II preliminary (760 pb^{-1})

$N_{jets} \geq 3$

Multijet: 78.0 ± 4.2 events

W jets: 1698.1 ± 49.7 events

Signal: 324.6 ± 31.6 events

Events/0.04

ANN output

- Data
- Multijet
- W + jets
- $t\bar{t}$
- Combined

one identified electron or muon, significant missing E_T and at least three jets. The contribution from $t\bar{t}$ is estimated from a maximum likelihood fit to the data distribution. With an estimated selection efficiency times branching fraction for $t\bar{t}$ of 7%, CDF measures 6.6 ± 0.8 ± 0.4 ± 0.4 pb in 0.9 fb^{-1} (13), where the dominant systematic uncertainty is from the modeling of the W +jets kinematics. With a similar technique, DØ measures 6.6 ± 0.8 ± 0.4 ± 0.4 pb in 0.9 fb^{-1} (14).

Although two jets originate from B hadrons in each $t\bar{t}$ event, only a small percentage of the background events from $W+$ jets contains jets from B hadrons. Therefore, identification of jets from B hadrons (15) is key to obtaining a purer sample of events to study the properties of the top quark. Due to the long B hadron lifetime and the large boost of the high-p_T B hadrons from top quark decay, many B hadrons travel several millimeters before decaying into several particles, as shown in **Figure 4**. The precise position measurements (10 μm) of the innermost silicon detectors allow researchers to reconstruct the trajectory of the charged particles. Whereas most of the charged particles have trajectories that come close together at one point, called the primary vertex, some of the charged particles from the B hadron decay are signficantly displaced from this primary vertex and may have trajectories that come close together at a second point, called the secondary vertex, which is the reconstructed position of the B hadron decay. As about 10% of B hadron decays produce a muon, the presence of a muon inside a jet is another feature of B hadron decay. Jets with charm hadrons also produce the above signature, although charm hadrons have a shorter lifetime and lower mass. The most powerful identification (b-tag) algorithms utilize all of this information to identify jets that have a high probability of containing a B hadron. The efficiency of the best b-tag algorithm is 60% for a b jet with $E_T > 40$ GeV. Due to the finite measurement resolution, a small fraction of jets without any long-lived particles have some significantly displaced charged particles that appear to come from a secondary vertex. In principle, these resolution effects produce secondary vertices on either side of the primary vertex at equal

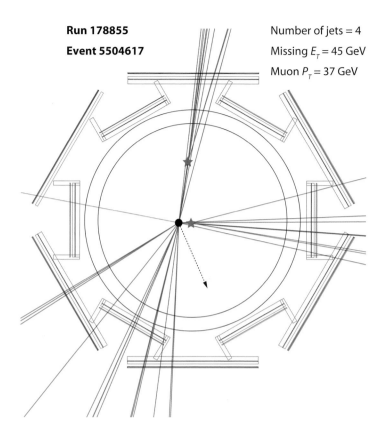

Run 178855
Event 5504617

Number of jets = 4
Missing E_T = 45 GeV
Muon P_T = 37 GeV

Tagged jet 1: E_T = 111 GeV, Phi = 79°, L2d = 7 mm

Tagged jet 2: E_T = 38 GeV, Phi = 355°, L2d = 1 mm

Figure 4

The reconstructed charged particle tracks (the circle represents the beam-pipe with radius 1.3 cm) in a CDF event in the single lepton channel with at least four jets. The locations of the secondary vertices in the two b-tagged jets are indicated by stars and their associated tracks are colored red.

rates, and that symmetry can be exploited to estimate the misidentification rate. The typical false positive (mistag) rate is 1% for light flavor jets.

With the requirement of one or two b-tagged jets, **Figure 5** shows the number of jets for a DØ data sample with a single lepton and significant missing E_T. There still remains significant background from W boson production with associated heavy flavor jets. To avoid the large uncertainty on the theoretical prediction for the absolute rate, the ratio of the rate of this process to that for W boson production with associated jets of any flavor (16) is multiplied by the observed number of W+jets events before b-tagging. The effect of missing higher-order terms on this ratio is calibrated from data. For instance, DØ found that a correction factor of 1.17 ± 0.18 is required to obtain good agreement with data in the 2-jet region of **Figure 5**.

There is also a contribution from QCD multijet production where one jet fakes a lepton and the finite-energy resolution of the calorimeter results in large missing E_T. As the QCD events tend to have lower missing E_T than W+jets and $t\bar{t}$, a fit to the data missing E_T distribution can determine the contribution from QCD. A data sample that models the QCD background can be obtained by reversing a few of the lepton identification requirements. Note that it is not recommended to reverse the isolation requirement or to assume that isolation and missing E_T are uncorrelated, as semileptonic decays of heavy flavor hadrons produce both nonisolated leptons inside jets and increased missing E_T due to undetected neutrinos.

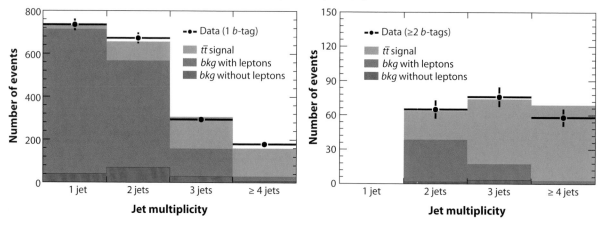

Figure 5

The number of predicted and observed events with a single *b*-tagged jet (*left*) and two or more *b*-tagged jets (*right*) as a function of jet multiplicity in the DØ single lepton channel with 0.9 fb⁻¹. The contribution from $t\bar{t}$ is normalized to the measured 8.0 pb (17).

In 0.9 fb⁻¹, DØ observes 607 events across eight categories defined by an electron or muon, three or at least four jets, and one or at least two *b*-tagged jets. DØ measures $8.0 \pm 0.5 \pm 0.7 \pm 0.5$ pb (17). With 1.1 fb⁻¹, CDF measures $8.2 \pm 0.5 \pm 0.8 \pm 0.5$ pb (18).

2.3. All-Hadronic

In the all-hadronic final state with branching fraction of 46%, the major challenge is the huge background from QCD multijet production. A kinematic selection exploits the higher transverse energy and the more spherical distribution of jets from top quark decay to increase the signal:background ratio to 1:12. For events with between six and eight jets in 1.0 fb⁻¹, CDF observes 1020 events with 1233 *b*-tagged jets with an estimated background of 846 ± 37 *b*-tagged jets. The background *b*-tag rate is parameterized from data with exactly four jets. The kinematic selection efficiency times branching fraction for $t\bar{t}$ is about 5%, and on average there are 0.95 *b* tags per $t\bar{t}$ event. With the excess ascribed to $t\bar{t}$ production, CDF measures $8.3 \pm 1.0 \pm^{2.0}_{1.5} \pm 0.5$ pb (19), where the dominant systematic uncertainty is the dependence of the selection efficiency on the jet energy scale. With 0.4 fb⁻¹, DØ measures $4.5 \pm^{2.0}_{1.9} \pm^{1.4}_{1.1} \pm 0.3$ pb (20).

2.4. Pair Production Mechanism

The fusion of initial-state gluons is predicted to produce between 10% and 20% of top quark pairs at the Tevatron, with the remainder resulting from quark annihilation. The measurement of this quantity exploits the fact that gluons tend to radiate more low-momentum gluons than quarks. Therefore, initial states with two gluons produce more final-state particles than initial states with quarks. The experimental observable is the number of low-momentum charged-particle tracks that are not close to a jet of hadrons. The observable is defined on data using W boson production with no jets as a clean data sample for the $q\bar{q}$ initial state, and W boson production with one jet as one of several data samples that have a number of gluons in the initial state. With 1.0 fb⁻¹ of data

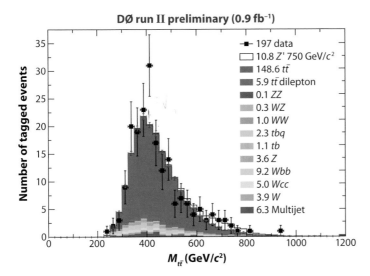

Figure 6

The distribution of invariant mass of the $t\bar{t}$ system for events in the DØ single lepton channel with at least four jets and at least one b-tagged jet in 0.9 fb^{-1}. Superimposed is the expected contribution for a Z' with mass of 750 GeV/c^2 (22).

in the single lepton channel with four or more jets and at least one b-tagged jet, CDF measures the percentage of $t\bar{t}$ production from gluons to be $7 \pm 14_{stat} \pm 7_{syst}$% (21).

Many hypotheses beyond the standard model predict new massive particles that could decay into $t\bar{t}$. This is the motivation to examine closely the reconstructed mass of the $t\bar{t}$ system for abnormal peaks over the smoothly falling standard model distribution. **Figure 6** shows an interesting though not yet statistically significant feature in the reconstructed mass of the $t\bar{t}$ system for DØ events in the single lepton channel with four or more jets (22). With 0.9 fb^{-1}, DØ excludes a Z' boson with mass below 700 GeV/c^2 at 95% confidence level (CL), where the Z' has a narrow width of 1.2% of its mass. CDF excludes a Z' boson with mass below 720 GeV/c^2 at 95% CL with 1.0 fb^{-1} (23).

Another interesting feature that is sensitive to new physics is the forward-backward charge asymmetry. The standard model predicts this asymmetry to be small (on the order of 5–10%). If there is a Z' boson that has different couplings to left- and right-handed fermions, then the charge asymmetry could be enhanced. Whereas the $t\bar{t}$ invariant mass is sensitive to narrow Z' resonances, the $t\bar{t}$ production charge asymmetry can be used to search for new massive bosons with wide widths. DØ observes an uncorrected asymmetry of $12 \pm 8_{stat} \pm 1_{syst}$% for $t\bar{t}$ events within the detector's acceptance (24). CDF observes an asymmetry of $17 \pm 7_{stat} \pm 4_{syst}$% (25).

The supersymmetric partner of the spin-1/2 top fermion is a spin-0 top boson. If this scalar top quark decays to a b quark and chargino, with subsequent chargino decay to a W boson and a neutralino, then this would produce a similar experimental signature to standard model top quark pair production. Experimental consequences would include an increase in the apparent $t\bar{t}$ rate, and distortions in the event kinematics. DØ has designed a multivariate discriminant to search for scalar top quark pair production in the single lepton channel with four or more jets and at least one b-tagged jet. With 1 fb^{-1}, the observed upper limit of 6 (12) pb at 95% CL for a scalar top quark mass of 175 (145) GeV/c^2 is a factor of 10 (7) above the theoretical prediction (26).

3. TOP QUARK DECAY

The large mass of the top quark means that its decay functions as a unique laboratory for tests of the standard model and searches for physics beyond the standard model. In this section, we discuss tests of the standard model prediction that the top quark decays to a W boson and a b quark almost 100% of the time.

Any significant fraction of light quarks (d or s) from the top quark decay would signal a new physics contribution. As discussed in Section 2.2, the identification of a jet from a b quark is possible with an efficiency ranging from 30% to 60%, depending on the jet energy, whereas the probability of misidentifying a jet from a light quark is not negligible, ranging from 0.1% to 3%. The main idea behind the measurement of the fraction of top quark decays that produce a b quark is to compare the observed numbers of events with zero or one or two identified b jets with the prediction based on the efficiency and misidentification rates measured in control data samples. Specifically, if the top quark decays into a light quark and a W boson, the number of observed events with two identified b jets in the final state will be depleted with respect to the number of events with one identified b jet or none at all. In the single lepton channel, DØ performed a simultaneous measurement of the $t\bar{t}$ rate and the ratio of the branching fractions for $t \to Wb$ to $t \to Wq$, where q is any down-type quark. The ratio was measured at 0.97 ± 0.09 and DØ set a 95%-CL lower limit of 0.79 (27).

A similar technique, extended to the number of observed leptons in $t\bar{t}$ events, has been used to probe for top quark decays that do not have a W boson in the final state. In supersymmetric models with a charged Higgs boson that is lighter than the top quark, the $t \to bH^+$ decay competes with the standard model decay $t \to bW^+$. For $\tan \beta > 1$, the most probable decay is $H^+ \to \tau^+ \nu_\tau$, so measurement of the branching fraction for $t \to \tau \nu_\tau b$ is very important (28). For $\tan \beta < 1$ and H^+ mass below 130 GeV/c^2, the most probable decay is $H^+ \to c\bar{s}$, so the dilepton channel is suppressed and the all-hadronic channel enhanced. In either case, the number of $t\bar{t}$ events with electrons and muons in the final state is suppressed. Finally, for $\tan \beta < 1$ and H^+ mass above 130 GeV/c^2, the most probable decay is via a virtual top quark, $H^+ \to t^*\bar{b} \to W^+ b\bar{b}$, so the observed number of events with one or two b jets is enhanced. No significant deviations from the standard model prediction have been observed (29).

Although it is widely believed that top quark is a member of SU(2) isospin doublet together with the b quark and thus must have an electric charge of $+\frac{2}{3}e$, there are theoretical suggestions that the observed particle has a charge of $-\frac{4}{3}e$, whereas the true top quark has higher mass and thus is still undiscovered (30). Experimentally, the electric charge of the top quark is the sum of the charges of its decay products, which are W^+b for the standard model and W^-b for this exotic model. The b jet and the W boson are considered the pair with invariant mass that is most consistent with the top quark mass. The electric charge of the reconstructed lepton track trivially defines the charge of the W boson. Determining the electric charge of the b jet is challenging: It is calculated by adding up the electric charges of the tracks reconstructed in the busy environment of the b jet, weighting each track by its momentum component along the jet axis. This so-called jet charge method is calibrated in an independent data dijet sample with high b jet content. The observed distribution in top charge favors the standard model (31), and the exotic interpretation of the data can be excluded at 87% CL.

Unlike other quarks, the top quark is so short lived that it decays before hadronization; thus the spin structure of the decay is not obscured by hadronization effects (32). An interesting way to verify the electroweak decay of the top quark to a W^+ boson and a b quark is to measure the helicity of the W^+ boson. Recall that helicity is the scalar product of a particle's spin and momentum vectors, where right-handed (left-handed) polarization means that the spin vector points in the same (opposite) direction as the momentum vector, and longitudinal polarization means that the spin vector points at right angles to the momentum vector. In the approximation of zero b quark mass, the parity-violating electroweak interaction will always produce a left-handed b quark. As a consequence of conservation of angular momentum, a right-handed W^+ boson is

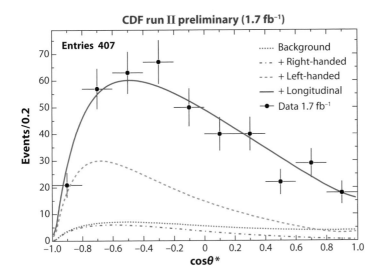

Figure 7

Observed angular distribution of the lepton from W boson decay in the W boson rest frame—with respect to the direction of W boson momentum in the top quark rest frame—for the CDF single lepton channel with at least four jets and at least one b-tagged jet, in 1.7 fb⁻¹ (34).

forbidden. A contradictory observation would signal a violation of the electroweak theory or the potential presence of other particles in top quark decay.

The large mass of the top quark dictates that 70% of W^+ bosons have a longitudinal polarization, whereas the remaining 30% must be left handed. Inclusion of b quark mass effects modifies these standard model predictions by less than 1% (33). In the approximation of zero neutrino and lepton masses, the well-tested electroweak decay of the W^+ always produces a left-handed ν and a right-handed ℓ^+. Conservation of angular momentum in the decay of a left-handed W^+ implies that the ℓ^+ will be preferentially emitted in the same direction as the W^+ spin, which is opposite to the W^+ momentum. Therefore, on average, the left-handed W^+ decays to a ℓ^+ that has lower measured momentum and is closer to the b jet than is the case for longitudinal W^+ decays. On the other hand, a right-handed W^+ decays to a ℓ^+ that has higher measured momentum and is further from the b jet than is the case for longitudinal W^+ decays. In the dilepton channel and the single lepton channel with at least three jets, several kinematic observables are sensitive to the W boson helicity, including the lepton p_T and the invariant mass of the lepton and the b jet. Shown in **Figure 7** is the angular distribution of the lepton in the W boson rest frame upon full reconstruction of the $t\bar{t}$ event by a constrained kinematic fit to the more limited statistics in the single lepton channel with at least four jets. Assuming the standard model prediction for the percentage of longitudinal W bosons, CDF found the percentage of right-handed W^+ bosons from top quark decay to be $-4\pm4_{stat}\pm3_{syst}\%$ and set a 95%-CL upper limit of 7% with 1.7 fb⁻¹. Neither CDF nor DØ found any evidence for significant deviations from the standard model electroweak interaction (34).

In the standard model, flavor changing neutral current (FCNC) decays are highly suppressed and the branching fraction for $t \rightarrow Zq$ is predicted to be $\mathcal{O}(10^{-14})$. However, much higher branching fractions, up to 1%, could occur due to physics beyond the standard model (35). CDF searches in the Z boson with four or more jets final state for $t\bar{t}$ production where one top quark decays via an FCNC, $t \rightarrow Zq \rightarrow \ell^+\ell^-q$, and the other decays in standard model fashion, $t \rightarrow Wb \rightarrow q\bar{q}'b$. With 1.9 fb⁻¹, the 95%-CL upper limit on the percentage of $t \rightarrow Zq$ is 3.7% (36).

4. TOP QUARK MASS

Thanks to the recent advances in the top quark mass measurements, the uncertainty regarding the top quark mass has decreased by a factor of three since 2004. In this section, we first explain a generic reconstruction method for the top quark mass, then discuss the two recent developments that enable the Tevatron experiments to achieve a precision significantly better than anticipated. First, the largest systematic uncertainty on the top quark mass (from the jet energy calibration) is now controlled by a calibration using the jets from the hadronic W boson decay found in these top quark events. Second, a per-event probability technique allows more information to be extracted from the measured energies and angles of the top quark decay products, and reduces systematic uncertainties from background processes. We discuss the interpretation of the measurements of the top quark mass and the W boson mass as a constraint on the mass of the Higgs boson in the standard model and beyond.

We concentrate our discussion on the single lepton channel with four or more jets, as it has the single most precise measurement of the top quark mass. In principle, the four highest E_T jets are expected to be from the four quarks from $t\bar{t}$ production and decay. However, this may not be the case due to the effects of initial- and final-state QCD radiation, limited geometric acceptance, and jet reconstruction. The simplest method to reconstruct the mass of the top quark is to calculate the invariant mass of the three jets associated with the quarks in the $t \to Wb \to q\bar{q}'b$ decay chain. If we assume that these three jets are among the four highest E_T jets, then we find that there are four ways to choose a set of three jets. Thus, there are four possible values for the reconstructed mass of the top quark in each event, although only one correctly reconstructs the decay chain and carries significant information.

The constrained-fit technique, which makes and tests the hypothesis that a given event results from top quark pair production and decay, can obtain much better resolution on the top quark mass (37). As this technique provides a complete reconstruction of the $t\bar{t}$ event, it is used in many of the measurements of top quark properties discussed in this paper. Specifically, we can infer the neutrino p_T from the missing E_T and obtain the neutrino p_z from the hypothesis that the lepton and neutrino are from a W boson decay [i.e., by finding the two solutions from the quadratic equation $M_W^2 = (p_\ell + p_\nu)^2$]. Having thus obtained estimates for the four momenta of all six partons in the final state, we observe that there are two constraints imposed on the system: (a) The two jets assigned to W boson decay form an invariant mass close to the W boson mass, so $M_W^2 = (p_{j1} + p_{j2})^2$, and (b) the reconstructed top quark masses from the $t \to Wb \to q\bar{q}'b$ and $t \to Wb \to \ell\nu b$ decay chains have nearly the same value. In order to satisfy the constraints, the momenta of the lepton and the jets must be allowed to vary from their measured values in a constrained kinematic fit. We obtain the best fitted value for the top quark mass (and for the fitted momenta of the lepton, neutrino, and jets that satisfy the constraints) by the minimization of a least-squares estimator, which is constructed from the differences between the fitted and measured momenta of the lepton and jets (normalized by the experimental resolutions) and terms representing the constraints. There are 12 permutations for assignment of jets to quarks, as there are four ways to assign one of the four highest E_T jets to the b quark from top quark decay, then three ways to assign a jet to the $\bar{b}$ quark from antitop quark decay, then one way to assign the remaining two jets to the $W \to q\bar{q}'$ decay products where the order does not change the reconstructed mass. If one of the jets is b tagged, the number of permutations decreases to six as there are only two ways to assign the b-tagged jet to a b quark and three ways to assign one of the remaining three jets to the other b quark. If two of the jets are b tagged, the number of possible values further decreases to two as there are only two ways to assign the two b-tagged jets to the two b quarks. Not forgetting the two possible values of the neutrino p_z, we observe that the least-squares estimator is also used to pick which of the 24/12/4 possible event reconstructions is most consistent with the hypothesis of top quark pair production and decay.

The top quark mass measurement requires an excellent modeling of jet fragmentation and an excellent simulation of the calorimeter response to jets. Independent data samples of photon or $Z \rightarrow \ell\ell$ against a recoiling jet and dijets provide a calibration of the jet energy to 3% (38), corresponding to an uncertainty of approximately 3 GeV/c^2 on the top quark mass. Now that there are sufficient numbers of $t\bar{t}$ events in the single lepton and all-hadronic channels, the jet energy scale is more accurately calibrated by the $W \rightarrow q\bar{q}'$ decays contained within these events (in situ). If the estimate of the jet energy scale is systematically shifted by a factor k, then the invariant mass of the jets assigned to the W boson decay, $M_{12} = k\sqrt{2E_1 E_2 (1 - \cos \psi_{12})}$, is shifted by the same factor. Comparison of M_{12} with the known value of the W boson mass allows a determination of the jet energy scale in the same data events used to determine the top quark mass. The important consequence for the top quark mass measurement is that the dominant systematic uncertainty from the jet energy scale now decreases with $1/\sqrt{N_{t\bar{t}}}$, where $N_{t\bar{t}}$ is the number of $t\bar{t}$ events analyzed. One limitation is that these calibrations are for light flavor jets—not b jets—but of course the top quark mass measurement is more sensitive to the b jet energy calibration. Both CDF and DØ estimate a systematic of approximately 0.6 GeV/c^2 that accounts for relative differences between b jets and light flavor jets due to fragmentation models, semileptonic decay branching fractions, and color flow. A direct calibration of the b jet energy from a sample of photons against a recoiling b jet, which suffers from low statistics at the Tevatron, could be a useful technique at the LHC.

Both initial- and final-state QCD radiation (ISR/FSR) can produce additional jets that can be confused with those from the top quark decay products; ISR also provides an additional boost to the $t\bar{t}$ system. ISR and FSR can systematically shift the reconstructed top quark mass. The uncertainty on the top quark mass from these effects is estimated by varying the simulation parameters that control the probability for ISR/FSR. For this purpose, CDF exploits the similar initial state of $q\bar{q} \rightarrow Z/\gamma^* \rightarrow \ell^+\ell^-$ and constrains the range of variation via the p_T distribution of the lepton pair. DØ studies the number and kinematics of the extra jets in $t\bar{t}$ events. Both experiments estimate an uncertainty of 0.6 GeV/c^2.

The best resolution on the top quark mass is obtained by assuming the predicted kinematic and angular distributions encoded in the matrix element for standard model top quark pair production and decay. This computationally intensive technique was developed by DØ in 2004 for the single lepton channel (3). Given the measured values $\mathbf{x}$ for the momenta of the lepton and the jets, this technique calculates the probability $P_s(\mathbf{x}|m_t)$ for them to have been produced by standard model top quark pair production and decay with a particular top quark mass value m_t. The calculation is repeated for several discrete values of the top quark mass. One can calculate this probability distribution for each of the 12 permutations of jet assignments to quarks. The multiplication of these 12 probability distributions produces one probability distribution for each event. Note that the correct reconstruction of the event produces a probability distribution that has a maximum around the true top quark mass, whereas the false reconstructions tend to have much flatter probability distributions. In this way, one can consider all 12 choices without the signal disappearing into a swamp of combinatoric background. Thus, this technique has additional statistical power over previous techniques as the information from the correct combination is always included (39, 40). Although the full probability distributions are used in the measurement, **Figure 8** presents the distribution of the single most probable value of the top quark mass (and also of the invariant mass of the pair of jets assigned to the W boson) for each event in the CDF single lepton channel.

The probability is calculated by integrating the leading-order matrix element over quantities that are not directly measured by the detector, namely the momentum of the neutrino, the energies of the quarks, and the momenta of the incoming partons in the initial state (including the effect of ISR potentially giving a boost to the $t\bar{t}$ system). The lepton momentum and the angular directions of the quarks are assumed to be perfectly measured. However, the broad energy resolution of the measured jet relative to the parent quark is described by a probability to measure a jet energy as a function of the parent-quark energy, which is determined from simulation. Because the numerical

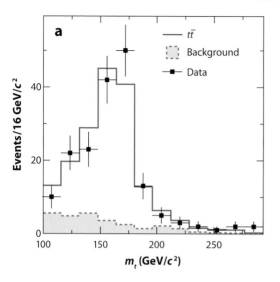
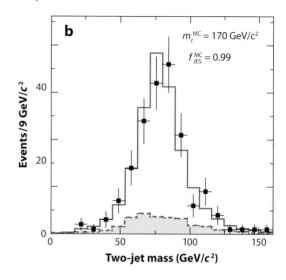

Figure 8

Comparision of two kinematic variables between data and simulation with top quark mass of 170 GeV/c^2 for the CDF single lepton channel with 0.9 fb⁻¹. (*a*) Most probable value of the top quark mass for each event and (*b*) invariant mass of the pair of jets assigned as W boson decay products calculated using the most probable permutation at the most probable value of top quark mass and jet energy scale in each event (39).

integrations required by this technique are very computationally intensive, some of the integration variables undergo transformation from quark energies into the more sharply peaked variables such as the invariant masses of the top quarks and W bosons.

Note that the probability for background can also be calculated in a similar fashion, in principle by using the leading-order matrix element for the background process. This allows the construction of a generalized event probability that includes both signal and background. Events with a large background probability thus have diminished influence on the top quark mass, and the systematic uncertainty due to background modeling is reduced.

Recently, researchers have extended this technique to the dilepton (41) and all-hadronic channels (42). In the dilepton channel, the escape of two neutrinos presents a challenge for the reconstruction of the event and top quark mass. Although 24 parameters are required to describe the momenta of the six final-state particles from $t\bar{t}$ production and decay, only 23 are determined by the measured momenta of the two leptons and two jets and the kinematic constraints in the $t\bar{t}$ hypothesis. Several other techniques make additional kinematic assumptions to solve this underconstrained system (43, 44). In the per-event probability technique, the leading-order matrix element provides a natural weight for the integration over all the unmeasured quantities, including the neutrino momenta, thus yielding an improved reconstruction of the top quark mass. Also, as the background probability reduces the systematic uncertainty due to the background model, the event selection in the low statistics dilepton channel can be relaxed to increase the number of $t\bar{t}$ events and thus reduce the statistical uncertainty.

In the all-hadronic channel with six jets, the larger number of permutations for assignments of jets to quarks (90, 30, 12 for 0, 1, 2 b-tagged jets) and the large background from multijet QCD present a rather different challenge. The recent measurement by CDF used the $t\bar{t}$

Table 1 Measurements of the top quark mass from Tevatron Run II, with 0.9 to 1.0 fb^{-1}

Channel	m_{top} (GeV/c^2)	Uncertainty (GeV/c^2)			Weight (%)	Reference
		Total	Statistical	Systematic (in situ)		
CDF dilepton	164.5	5.6	3.9	3.9	6	41
DØ dilepton	172.5	8.0	5.8	5.6	–2	43
CDF single lepton	170.9	2.5	1.6	1.9 (1.4)	39	39
DØ single lepton	170.5	2.7	1.8	2.0 (1.6)	40	40
CDF all-hadronic	171.1	4.3	2.8	3.2 (2.4)	11	42

The portion of the systematic uncertainty from the in situ jet energy scale calibration using the $W \to q\bar{q}'$ is indicated in brackets.

per-event probability both to select the events and to extract the most probable top quark mass (42). Most promisingly, CDF extracted a calibration for the jet energy from the dijet mass distribution of all pairs of non-*b*-tagged jets. This has already halved the systematic uncertainty that limited previous measurements in this channel, and the uncertainty will continue to decrease with higher statistics.

The combination of the recent best measurements from CDF and DØ in each channel, summarized in **Table 1** for run II results, yields a world average value for the top quark mass of 170.9 ± 1.8 GeV/c^2 (45). The CDF and DØ single lepton channel measurements carry a weight of about 40% each. Note that all of the run I measurements together now carry a weight below 10%.

Due to its large mass, the top quark can signficantly affect theoretical calculations in the standard model and beyond. Via quantum loops, the W boson mass is sensitive to the square of the top quark mass, the logarithm of the Higgs boson mass, and to new massive particles from beyond the standard model. A reduced experimental uncertainty on the top quark mass thus translates into a sharper theoretical prediction for the W boson mass and, therefore, a smaller range of possible values for the contributions from other undiscovered particles. The current uncertainty of 1.8 GeV/c^2 on the top quark mass corresponds to an uncertainty of about 11 MeV/c^2 on the prediction for the W boson mass. With the full two-loop electroweak corrections (46), the other theoretical uncertainties on the predicted W boson mass are on the order of 4 MeV/c^2. Only three years ago, the three-times-larger uncertainty on the top quark mass completely dominated the uncertainty on the predicted W boson mass.

The single Higgs boson of the standard model is the mechanism for breaking the electroweak symmetry and giving mass to the W and Z bosons while leaving the photon massless. The direct measurements of the top quark mass and the W boson mass, shown in **Figure 9**, clearly prefer a relatively light value for the mass of the Higgs boson. The combination of all precision electroweak measurements indicates that the Higgs boson mass is 76^{+33}_{-24} GeV/c^2 and that the 95%-CL upper limit is 144 GeV/c^2 (47). If we include the 95%-CL lower limit of 114.4 GeV/c^2 from direct searches (48), the upper limit increases to 182 GeV/c^2.

There are many other possible models of EWSB, which can have multiple Higgs bosons and many other new particles that would alter the relationship between the W boson mass and the top quark mass. In the minimal supersymmetric standard model, **Figure 10** shows that the direct measurements prefer relatively heavy supersymmetric (SUSY) particles (49). Interpretation in the constrained minimal supersymmetric model prefers a mass of 110 ± 10 GeV/c^2 for the lightest Higgs boson (51).

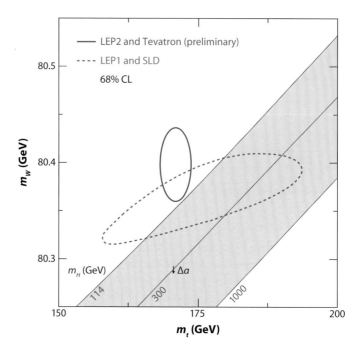

Figure 9

Direct measurements of top quark mass versus W boson mass (*blue ellipse* is 68% CL) in the standard model (47). The direct measurements are in good agreement with the inferred values from interpretation of other precision electroweak measurements (*dotted red ellipse*), demonstrating the consistency of different electroweak measurements within the standard model. Also shown is the standard model relationship between the W boson and top quark masses for three values of the Higgs boson mass of 114, 300, and 1000 GeV/c^2 (*diagonal gray lines*).

5. SINGLE TOP QUARK PRODUCTION

In contrast to top quark pair production via the strong interaction, single top quark production proceeds via the electroweak interaction and the rate is directly proportional to the Cabibbo-Kobayashi-Maskawa (CKM) element $|V_{tb}|^2$. Both experiments have reported evidence for single top quark production (50, 52). Without going into too much detail regarding the statistical methods, we review the production properties that have allowed the separation of single top quark production from the copious background processes dominated by W boson production in association with jets.

Feynman diagrams for single top quark production in $p\bar{p}$ collisions are illustrated in **Figure 11**. The theoretical prediction for the rate in the s channel is 0.88 ± 0.11 pb and in the t channel is 1.98 ± 0.25 pb (53). Because the $W \rightarrow q\bar{q}'$ boson decay results in an all-jets signature with prohibitively large backgrounds from QCD multijet production, we consider only the $W \rightarrow \ell\nu$ boson decay. The single high-p_T isolated lepton provides a trigger for the data sample, and there is also significant missing E_T from the neutrino and a high-p_T b jet, all from the top quark decay. There are also one or two more associated jets, with one in principle being from a b quark. Unfortunately, the associated b quark from t channel production is typically produced very close to the beam direction and thus is outside the geometric acceptance of the precision silicon tracking detectors, or even of the calorimeter. ISR or FSR can also add light flavor jets. Therefore the experimental signature for single top quark production is a high-p_T isolated lepton, missing E_T, and two or more jets with at least one b-tagged jet.

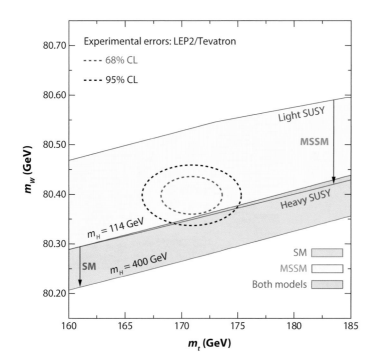

Figure 10

Direct measurements of top quark mass versus W boson mass (*blue dotted ellipse* is 68% CL, *black dotted ellipse* is 95% CL) compared to the standard model (SM) (*lower red region*) and minimal supersymmetric standard model (MSSM) (*upper yellow region*). The region of overlap between SM and MSSM is also shown (*blue region*) (49). Abbreviation: SUSY, supersymmetry.

With an expected signal:background ratio of about 1:20, a simple sequential cut-based analysis would not have enough sensitivity to establish the presence of such a small signal; we must employ more sophisticated analysis methods that combine the subtle discriminating power of many observables.

Extracting a signal for single top quark production is particularly challenging because its distribution in most discriminating variables is between that from $t\bar{t}$ and W+jets production. Jets produced in association with the W boson tend to be lower in energy and closer to each other than those from single top quark production. On the other hand, jets from $t\bar{t}$ production in the single lepton (dilepton) channel, where a jet (lepton) is not reconstructed, tend to be higher in energy and more central. A distinguishing characteristic of $t\bar{t}$ is that two of the light flavor jets are from a $W \to q\bar{q}'$ decay, and, together with one of the b jets, form a top quark whose mass is well reconstructed. Jets from QCD multijet production, where one jet fakes a lepton, are similar in topology to those from W+jets, although the missing E_T and the angle between the missing E_T and the nearest jet are typically lower.

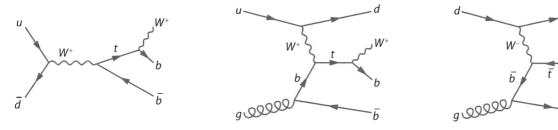

Figure 11

Feynman diagrams for single top quark production in the s channel (*left*) and in the t channel (*center and right*).

Figure 12

The distribution of the
product of the lepton
electric charge and the
η of the untagged jet in
a region enhanced in
single top quark
production (event
probability
discriminant above
0.9) from CDF with
1.5 fb^{-1} (52).

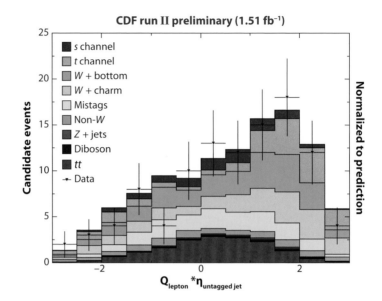

One feature of the t channel production distinguishes it from all of the background contributions. The outgoing light flavor quark shown in **Figure 11** is likely to keep moving in the direction of the original incoming particle; if this incoming particle is an up quark from the proton, then a top quark is produced; if this incoming particle is a down quark from the proton, then an antitop quark is produced. Assuming a simple model of a proton with two up quarks and one down quark, then if the incoming particle is a quark from the proton then twice as many top quarks as antitop quarks are produced. The opposite is true if the incoming particle is from the antiproton. Thus a light flavor jet with positive (negative) pseudorapidity, i.e., moving in the direction of the proton (antiproton) beam, is correlated with a positive (negative) electrically charged lepton from top (antitop) quark decay, as shown in **Figure 12**.

Both CDF and DØ use several advanced multivariate techniques to achieve the maximum discriminating power. Artificial neural networks and multivariate likelihoods are common tools in high-energy physics, and the matrix element techniques are similar to those we describe for top quark mass measurement. Decision trees, which are machine-learning techniques with the advantage of a human-readable structure, are used extensively in social sciences but have only recently begun to gain popularity in the high-energy physics community. As in a cut-based analysis, events are selected if they pass or fail a certain cut on a variable; however, the failing events are not discarded but are analyzed further with other selection variables. After each selection chain is terminated, the purity is estimated from independent simulation samples. Boosted decision trees have increased emphasis on training on signal events that were misidentified as background and vice versa. As shown in **Figure 13**, a boosted decision tree produces a continuous discriminant (purity) ranging from zero to one with background events clustered towards lower values and signal towards higher values.

We present a summary of the search results for single top quark production in **Table 2**. The probability, or p value, for the observed data to have been produced by a fluctuation in the background processes is below 0.1% or three standard deviations for several of the results. Thus, CDF and DØ can claim evidence for single top quark production and have made the first direct measurements of the CKM element V_{tb} with a 20–30% uncertainty. Because both experiments continue to accumulate more data and to refine their search techniques, a discovery claim (which

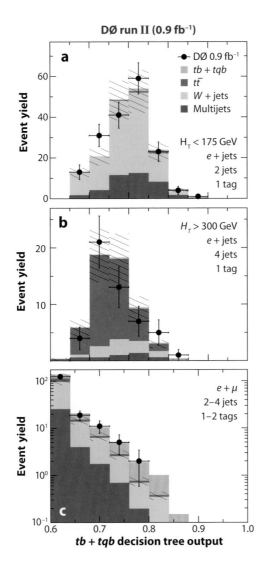

DØ run II (0.9 fb⁻¹)

(a) H$_T$ < 175 GeV
e + jets
2 jets
1 tag

Legend:
- DØ 0.9 fb⁻¹
- tb + tqb
- tt̄
- W + jets
- Multijets

(b) H$_T$ > 300 GeV
e + jets
4 jets
1 tag

(c) e + μ
2–4 jets
1–2 tags

tb + tqb decision tree output

Figure 13

The distribution in 0.9 fb⁻¹ of the DØ boosted decision tree discriminant for regions enhanced in (*a*) *W*+jets and quantum chromodynamics (QCD) multijet production, (*b*) *tt̄* production, and (*c*) single top quark production (50).

requires a signal five standard deviations above background) is expected in 2008. Looking beyond this discovery, separate measurements of the rates for *s* channel and *t* channel production can probe different models of new physics (54). The *s* channel is most sensitive to new massive resonances, like a *W′* (55), whereas the *t* channel is more sensitive to new physics in the *tWb* vertex, like FCNCs (56).

Table 2   Results of searches for single top quark production at the Tevatron

Experiment technique	Rate (pb)	*p*-value	V_{tb}	$\mathcal{L}$ (fb⁻¹)	Reference
DØ matrix element	$4.8^{+1.6}_{-1.4}$	0.08% (3.2 std)		0.9	50
DØ neural network	$4.4^{+1.6}_{-1.4}$	0.08% (3.1 std)		0.9	50
DØ boosted decision tree	4.9 ± 1.4	0.035% (3.4 std)	1.3 ± 0.2	0.9	50
CDF matrix element	$3.0^{+1.2}_{-1.1}$	0.09% (3.1 std)	1.0 ± 0.2	1.5	52
CDF likelihood	$2.7^{+1.3}_{-1.1}$	0.3% (2.7 std)		1.5	52

6. OUTLOOK AND CONCLUSIONS

Top quarks have been efficiently collected and studied in detail by the CDF and DØ experiments. This article reviews results with up to 2 fb^{-1} of $p\bar{p}$ collision data. The experiments continue to accumulate data and final results on 6–8 fb^{-1} are expected in 2010. The LHC will produce vast numbers of top quarks due to its higher energy and, in numbers of top quarks produced, even only 1 fb^{-1} is equivalent to 100 fb^{-1} at the Tevatron. These results will allow searches for even more massive new particles decaying to top quarks as well as for more subtle signs of physics beyond the standard model in top quark decay (57, 58).

The measurements of the rate for top quark pair production via the strong interaction are in good agreement with the theoretical prediction. The experimental precision of 15% for the best measurement is similar to that of the theoretical prediction. An interesting challenge is to search for mechanisms of top quark pair production and decay beyond the standard model. This requires careful interpretation and comparison of measurements from many different experimental signatures, as well as dedicated searches for beyond-the-standard-model processes.

Tests of top quark properties—including electric charge, FCNCs, and the helicity of the W boson from top quark decay—are thus far consistent with the standard model predictions. The first evidence for single top quark production via the electroweak interaction in 2007 also provides the first direct measurement of CKM element V_{tb}, with 20% precision, and promises discovery in 2008.

The precision measurement of the top quark mass continues to improve at an astonishing pace. The future is bright, as the largest systematic from the uncertainty on the jet energy scale is now controlled by a calibration from $W \rightarrow q\bar{q}\,'$ decays provided inside the $t\bar{t}$ events themselves. Most importantly, this systematic will continue to decrease as the experiments accumulate and analyze higher statistics samples of $t\bar{t}$ events. In 2009, the Tevatron experiments expect to reach a combined precision of 1 GeV/c^2 on the top quark mass with 4 fb^{-1}. An interesting phase transition in the top quark mass measurement occurs at this time for several reasons. First, further improvement at hadron colliders is limited by several other systematic effects that obscure the top quark mass, including radiation of soft gluons and calibration of the energy of jets from B hadrons. Second, the uncertainty on the top quark mass is no longer the dominant uncertainty on the standard model prediction for the W boson mass. Third, this is the time when the indirect constraint on the Higgs boson mass from precision electroweak measurements and calculations is put to the test by the results of direct searches at the Tevatron and the newly commissioned LHC.

DISCLOSURE STATEMENT

The authors are not aware of any biases that might be perceived as affecting the objectivity of this review.

LITERATURE CITED

1. Abe F, et al. (CDF Collab.) *Phys. Rev. Lett.* 74:2626 (1995); Abachi S, et al. (DØ Collab.) *Phys. Rev. Lett.* 74:2632 (1995)
2. Bonciani R, Catani S, Mangano ML, Nason P. *Nucl. Phys. B* 529:424 (1998); Cacciari M, et al. *JHEP* 0404:068 (2004); Kidonakis N, Vogt R. *Phys. Rev. D* 68:114014 (2003)
3. Abazov VM, et al. (DØ Collab.) *Nature* 429:638 (2004); Affolder T, et al. (CDF Collab.) *Phys. Rev. D* 63:032003 (2001)
4. Hill CT, Parke SJ. *Phys. Rev. D* 49:4454 (1994); Nilles HP. *Phys. Rep.* 110:1 (1984); Haber HE, Kane GL. *Phys. Rep.* 117:75 (1985)

5. Abazov VM, et al. (DØ Collab.) *Nucl. Instrum. Methods* A565:463 (2006); Blair R, et al. (CDF Collab.) FERMILAB-PUB-96-390-E (1996)

6. Shiltsev V. *Proc. 2004 Eur. Part. Accel. Conf., Lucerne, Switz.* 1:239 (2004)

7. Beenakker B, et al. *Nucl. Phys. B* 515:3 (1998); Boehm C, Djouadi A, Mambrini Y. *Phys. Rev. D* 61:095006 (2000)

8. Djouadi A, Mambrini M. *Phys. Rev. D* 63:115005 (2001)

9. Aguilar-Saavedra JA, et al. *Eur. Phys. J. C* 50:519 (2007)

10. Carena M, Haber HE. *Prog. Part. Nucl. Phys.* 50:63 (2003); Cacciari M, et al. *J. High Energy Phys.* 0404:068 (2004)

11. Abulencia A, et al. (CDF Collab.) *Phys. Rev. Lett.* 97:082004 (2006); Acosta D, et al. (CDF Collab.). *Phys. Rev. Lett.* 93:142001 (2004); CDF conf. note 8802 (2007); CDF conf. note 8770 (2007)

12. Abazov VM, et al. (DØ Collab.) *Phys. Rev. D* 76:052006 (2007); DØ conf. note 5477 (2007)

13. Acosta D, et al. (CDF Collab.) *Phys. Rev. D* 72:052003 (2005); CDF conf. note 8092 (2006)

14. Abazov VM, et al. (DØ Collab.) *Phys. Rev. Lett.* 100:192004 (2008); Abazov VM, et al. (DØ Collab.) *Phys. Rev. D* 76:092007 (2007)

15. Neu C. (CDF Collab.) In *Proc. TOP 2006: Int. Workshop Top Quark Phys., Coimbra, Portugal* (2006)

16. Campbell J, Ellis RK, Maltoni F, Willenbrock S. *Phys. Rev. D* 75:054015 (2007); Febres Cordero F, Reina L, Wackeroth D. *Phys. Rev. D* 74:034007 (2006)

17. Abazov VM, et al. (DØ Collab.) *Phys. Rev. Lett.* 100:192004 (2008); Abazov VM, et al. (DØ Collab.) *Phys. Rev. D* 74:112004 (2006); Abazov VM, et al. (DØ Collab.) *Phys. Lett. B* 626:35 (2005)

18. Abulencia A, et al. (CDF Collab.) *Phys. Rev. Lett.* 97:082004 (2006); Acosta D, et al. (CDF Collab.) *Phys. Rev. D* 71:052003 (2005); CDF conf. note 8795 (2007)

19. Aaltonen T, et al. (CDF Collab.) *Phys. Rev. D* 76:072009 (2007)

20. Abazov VM, et al. (DØ Collab.) *Phys. Rev. D* 76:072007 (2007)

21. Aaltonen T, et al. (CDF Collab.) arXiv:0712:3273

22. Abazov VM, et al. (DØ Collab.) arXiv:0804.3664 (2008)

23. Aaltonen T, et al. (CDF Collab.) *Phys. Rev. D* 77:051102 (2008)

24. Abazov VM, et al. (DØ Collab.) *Phys. Rev. Lett.* 100:142002 (2008)

25. CDF conf. note 9169 (2007)

26. DØ conf. note 5438 (2007)

27. Abazov VM, et al. (DØ Collab.) *Phys. Rev. Lett.* 100:192003 (2008); Abazov VM, et al. (DØ Collab.) *Phys. Lett. B* 639:616 (2006); Acosta D, et al. (CDF Collab.) *Phys. Rev. Lett.* 95:102002 (2005)

28. DØ conf. note 5451 (2007); Abulencia A, et al. (CDF Collab.) *Phys. Lett. B* 639:172 (2006)

29. Abulencia A, et al. (CDF Collab.) *Phys. Rev. Lett.* 96:042003 (2006); DØ conf. note 5466 (2007)

30. Chang D, Chang WFG, Ma E. *Phys. Rev. D* 61:037301 (2000); Choudhury D, Tait TM, Wagner CE. *Phys. Rev. D* 65:053002 (2002)

31. Abazov VM, et al. (DØ Collab.) *Phys. Rev. Lett.* 98:041801 (2007); CDF conf. note 8967 (2007)

32. Kane GL, Ladinsky GA, Yuan CP. *Phys. Rev. D* 45:124 (1992); Dalitz RH, Goldstein GR. *Phys. Rev. D* 45:1531 (1992)

33. Do HS, Groote S, Korner JG, Mauser MC. *Phys. Rev. D* 67:091501 (2003)

34. Abazov VM, et al. (DØ Collab.) *Phys. Rev. Lett.* 100:062004 (2008); Abazov VM, et al. (DØ Collab.) *Phys. Rev. D* 75:031102(R) (2007); CDF conf. note 8971; Abulencia A, et al. (CDF Collab.) *Phys. Rev. Lett.* 98:072001 (2007); Abulencia A, et al. (CDF Collab.) *Phys. Rev. D* 75:052001 (2007)

35. Aguilar-Saavedra JA. *Acta Phys. Polon. B* 35:2695 (2004)

36. Aaltonen T, et al. (CDF Collab.) arXiv:0805.2109 (2008)

37. Abulencia A, et al. (CDF Collab.) *Phys. Rev. D* 73:032003 (2006)

38. Bhatti A, et al. *Nucl. Instrum. Methods A* 566:375

39. Abulencia A, et al. (CDF Collab.) *Phys. Rev. Lett.* 99:182002 (2007)

40. Abazov VM, et al. (DØ Collab.) *Phys. Rev. D* 74:092005 (2006); DØ conf. note 5362 (2007)

41. Abulencia A, et al. (CDF Collab.) *Phys. Rev. D* 75:031105 (2006); Abulencia A, et al. (CDF Collab.) *Phys. Rev. Lett.* 96:152002 (2006); Abulencia A, et al. (CDF Collab.) *Phys. Rev. D* 74:032009 (2006)

42. Aaltonen A, et al. (CDF Collab.) *Phys. Rev. Lett.* 98:142001 (2007); CDF conf. note 8709 (2007)

43. Abazov VM, et al. (DØ Collab.) *Phys. Lett. B* 655:7 (2007); DØ conf. note 5347 (2007)
44. Abulencia A, et al. (CDF Collab.) *Phys. Rev. D* 73:112006 (2006)
45. Tevatron Electroweak Work. Group/(CDF/DØ Collab.) arXiv:hep-ex/0703034 (2007)
46. Awramik M, et al. *Phys. Rev. D* 69:053006 (2004)
47. LEP Collab. ALEPH, DELPHI, L3, and OPAL/LEP Electroweak Work. Group. arXiv:0712.0929 (2007)
48. LEP Collab. ALEPH, DELPHI, L3, and OPAL/LEP Higgs Work. Group.) *Phys. Lett. B* 565:61 (2003)
49. Heinemeyer S, et al. *JHEP* 0608:052 (2006); Heinemeyer S, Hollik W, Weiglein G. *Phys. Rep.* 425:265 (2006)
50. Abazov VM, et al. (DØ Collab.) arXiv:0803.0739 (2008); Abazov VM, et al. (DØ Collab.) *Phys. Rev. Lett.* 98:181802 (2007)
51. Buchmueller O, et al. *Phys. Lett. B* 657:87 (2007)
52. CDF conf. note 8968 (2007); CDF conf. note 8964 (2007)
53. Harris BW, et al. *Phys. Rev. D* 66:054024 (2002); Kidonakis N, Vogt R. *Phys. Rev. D* 68:114014 (2003); Sullivan Z. *Phys. Rev. D* 70:114012 (2004)
54. Tait TM, Yuan CP. *Phys. Rev. D* 63:014018 (2001)
55. Abazov VM, et al. (DØ Collab.) *Phys. Rev. Lett.* 100:211803 (2008); Abazov VM, et al. (DØ Collab.) *Phys. Rev. Lett.* 99:191802 (2007); CDF conf. note 9150
56. Abazov VM, et al. (DØ Collab.) *Phys. Lett. B* 641:423 (2006)
57. Gerber CE, et al. (TEV4LHC Top\Electroweak Work. Group) arXiv:0705.3251 (2007)
58. Beneke M, et al. *Proc. Workshop on Standard Model Physics (and more) at the LHC, Geneva, Switz.* arXiv:hep-ph/0003033 (2000); ATLAS Collab. *ATLAS: Detector and Physics Performance.* Tech. Des. Rep. Vol. 2. CERN-LHCC-99-15:619 (1999); Bayatian GL, et al. (CMS Collab.) *J. Phys. G* 34:995 (2007)

RELATED RESOURCES

See Supplemental references and conference notes (follow the **Supplemental Material link** from the Annual Reviews home page at **http://www.annualreviews.org**).

Measurement of the W Boson Mass at the Tevatron

Ashutosh V. Kotwal[1] and Jan Stark[2]

[1]Physics Department, Duke University, Durham, North Carolina 27708;
email: kotwal@phy.duke.edu

[2]Laboratoire de Physique Subatomique et de Cosmologie, Université Joseph Fourier
Grenoble 1, CNRS/IN2P3, Institut National Polytechnique de Grenoble, Grenoble, France;
email: stark@in2p3.fr

Annu. Rev. Nucl. Part. Sci. 2008. 58:147–75

First published online as a Review in Advance on
June 6, 2008

The *Annual Review of Nuclear and Particle Science*
is online at nucl.annualreviews.org

This article's doi:
10.1146/annurev.nucl.58.110707.171227

0163-8998/08/1123-0147$20.00

Key Words

precision, electroweak, Higgs, new physics, supersymmetry

Abstract

Over the past four decades, the standard model of electroweak interactions
has achieved tremendous success in describing the experimental data. One
of the key observables is the mass M_W of the W boson. The experimental
measurements, including M_W, have reached a level of precision that tests
the theory at the quantum loop level, providing indirect constraints on the
hypothetical Higgs boson and other new physics. Improved measurements
of M_W are driven by new data from Run II of the Fermilab Tevatron ($p\bar{p}$
collider at $\sqrt{s} = 1.96$ TeV). We discuss the techniques used for measuring
M_W at hadron colliders, summarize the measurements from Run I of the
Tevatron, and review the state of the art of the Run II analyses, which are
based on significantly larger data sets collected with upgraded detectors. We
discuss the constraints on the Higgs boson, and conclude with a discussion
of the ultimate precision in M_W that can be expected from Run II.

Contents

1. INTRODUCTION

In its four decades of existence, the standard model (SM) of the electroweak interactions has been an impressive success. The massive W and Z bosons that it predicted have since been discovered. In the SM, the mass of the W boson, M_W, is related at tree level to the mass of the Z boson, M_Z, and the electromagnetic (EM) and weak coupling constants. Given the precise measurements of the latter quantities, plus experimental determinations of the weak mixing angle from scattering data available at the time, the masses of both the W boson and the Z boson can be predicted to within a few gigaelectronvolts (GeV).[1] The agreement of these predictions with the early measurements is one of SM's successes. The precision of the direct measurements of M_W and M_Z has increased dramatically over the past 25 years, and the predictions are now being tested at the quantum loop level. In the SM, the quantum loop corrections to M_W are dominated by the top quark and Higgs boson loops, aside from the running of the electromagnetic coupling. Extensions to the SM (e.g., supersymmetry) predict additional loops that can result in sizeable corrections. Even more precise measurements of M_W are needed to test the SM at the loop level and to fully exploit this window on physics beyond the SM.

---

[1] Throughout this review we use units of $\hbar = c = 1$.

A previous review of direct experimental determinations of M_W was published in 2000 (1). At that time the most precise measurements available were from Run I of the Tevatron and from the Large Electron-Positron Collider (LEP). The analyses of the Tevatron Run I data were then being finalized and LEP was about to finish collecting data. As of now the Tevatron is operating again, and the results from Run II will drive the precision on M_W for at least the next few years. These data are the focus of this review.

1.1. Historical Overview

The electroweak $SU(2) \times U(1)$ gauge theory, which unifies the weak and EM forces, was proposed in 1967 (2). In this theory the weak force is mediated by the massive W and Z bosons. In 1983 this central prediction was confirmed by the discovery (3, 4) of the W boson (with a mass of 81 ± 5 GeV) and the discovery of the Z boson just months later (5, 6) by the UA1 and UA2 experiments at the European Organization for Nuclear Research (CERN) $Sp\bar{p}S$ collider ($p\bar{p}$ at $\sqrt{s} = 546$ GeV). More precise measurements of the W boson mass were performed by UA1 (7) and UA2 (8) with upgraded detectors and much larger data sets delivered by the upgraded $Sp\bar{p}S$ operating at $\sqrt{s} = 630$ GeV. UA2 performed the first measurement with a precision better than 1 GeV (8). Shortly thereafter the Collider Detector at Fermilab (CDF) and DØ experiments at the Fermilab Tevatron collider ($p\bar{p}$ at $\sqrt{s} = 1.8$ TeV) pushed the precision below 100 MeV (9–12) using data from Run I (1992–1995) of the Tevatron, achieving a combined precision of 59 MeV (13). At about the same time, the LEP at CERN became the first e^+e^- collider to operate above the $e^+e^- \rightarrow W^+W^-$ threshold. The combined measurements of M_W from the Apparatus for LEP Physics at CERN (ALEPH), Detector with Lepton, Photon, and Hadron Identification (DELPHI), L3, and Omni-Purpose Apparatus for LEP (OPAL) experiments at the LEP have an uncertainty of 33 MeV (14). Since 2001 the upgraded CDF and DØ experiments have been taking data at Run II of the upgraded Tevatron at $\sqrt{s} = 1.96$ TeV, and they are further improving our knowledge of M_W.

1.2. Electroweak Theory

In the "on-shell" scheme, the W boson mass can be written as

$$M_W^2 \left(1 - \frac{M_W^2}{M_Z^2} \right) = \frac{\pi \alpha}{\sqrt{2} G_F} \left(\frac{1}{1 - \Delta r} \right),$$

where α is the EM coupling at the renormalization energy scale $Q = M_Z$ and G_F is the Fermi weak coupling extracted from the muon lifetime (see Reference 15; also see Reference 1 for a concise overview). The term Δr includes all radiative corrections, i.e., $\Delta r = 0$ corresponds to the tree level result. In the SM, the corrections can be separated into three main pieces:

$$\Delta r = \Delta \alpha + \Delta \rho [(M_{\text{top}}/M_Z)^2] + \Delta \chi [\ln(M_H/M_Z)].$$

The contribution $\Delta \alpha$ represents the running of the EM coupling due to the light quarks. The contribution $\Delta \rho$, which depends on the top quark mass (M_{top}) as M_{top}^2, arises from loops containing the top and bottom quarks (**Figure 1**). The contribution $\Delta \chi$ and its logarithmic dependence on the Higgs boson mass M_H arise from the Higgs loops (shown in **Figure 2**). Additional contributions to Δr arise in extensions of the SM: For example, contributions from supersymmetric particles are dominated by squark loops (**Figure 3**). Generally, the lighter the squark masses and the larger the

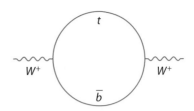

Figure 1

The one-loop contribution to the W boson mass from top and bottom quarks. Reproduced from Reference 20 with permission.

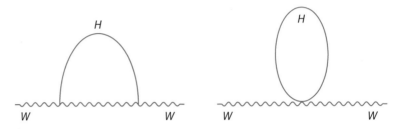

Figure 2

Higgs one-loop contributions to the W boson mass. Reproduced from Reference 20 with permission.

squark weak doublet mass splitting, the larger the contribution to M_W. Supersymmetric particles can induce a total radiative correction to M_W of several hundred megaelectronvolts (MeV) (16).

In the framework of the SM, precise measurements of M_{top} and M_W can be translated into a constraint on the mass of the as-yet-unobserved Higgs boson. The experimental uncertainties ΔM_{top} and ΔM_W contribute equally to the uncertainty ΔM_H on the predicted Higgs mass if $\Delta M_W \simeq 0.006 \cdot \Delta M_{\text{top}}$ (17). The uncertainties from experimental determinations of the other parameters (17) and from higher order corrections (17) will not be a limiting factor in the foreseeable future. The current combined Tevatron results on M_{top} have an uncertainty $\Delta M_{\text{top}} = 1.8\,\text{GeV}$ (18), which is expected to be further reduced as more data from Run II are analyzed. For this ΔM_{top}, the equivalent ΔM_W for equal contribution to ΔM_H would be $\Delta M_W \simeq 11\,\text{MeV}$ (17), which is smaller than the current experimental error on M_W by more than a factor of two; the latter is therefore the limiting factor in precision tests and must be reduced.

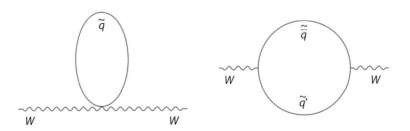

Figure 3

One-loop squark contributions to the W boson mass. Reproduced from Reference 20 with permission.

2. FINAL LEP MEASUREMENTS

Before we discuss the M_W measurements at the Tevatron in detail, we summarize the final results from LEP. From 1989 to 1995, the LEP at CERN provided e^+e^- collisions at center-of-mass energies at or near the Z boson mass. The four experiments—ALEPH, DELPHI, L3, and OPAL—have published their final results and combinations (21) based on the Z pole data set. These results are critical in the context of our review because they include a precise measurement of the Z boson mass (used to calibrate the absolute energy scale in many Tevatron measurements) and a wealth of other inputs to the SM fits discussed in Section 6.

From 1996 to 2000 LEP ran at center-of-mass energies above the W pair production threshold, $\sqrt{s} > 2M_W$. At these energies LEP produced significant samples of W bosons, predominantly in pairs: $e^+e^- \to W^+W^-$. There are two main methods of measuring M_W in these data sets, both of which have been discussed in another review (1). The first method exploits the fact that the W^+W^- production cross section is particularly sensitive to M_W in the threshold region. The final results, based on roughly 10 pb^{-1} of data at $\sqrt{s} \simeq 161$ GeV per experiment (22–25), are (14)

$$M_W = 80,400 \pm 200(\text{stat}) \pm 70(\text{syst}) \pm 30(E_{\text{beam}})\,\text{MeV}.$$

At energies significantly above the W^+W^- threshold, M_W is measured through the direct reconstruction of the invariant mass of W boson candidates from measured jets and leptons. The principle and the earlier versions of these measurements, based on subsets of the LEP data, have been discussed before (1). Since then, all four collaborations have published their final measurements (26–29) based on the full data set of about 700 pb^{-1} per experiment. The combination (14)

$$M_W = 80,375 \pm 25(\text{stat}) \pm 22(\text{syst})\,\text{MeV},$$

however, uses only a preliminary combined estimate for the effect of color reconnection (CR). This result is significantly more precise than that from the threshold analysis cited above. A breakdown of the uncertainties (14) is summarized in **Table 1**. Compared to the time of the last review (1), the statistical uncertainties have been substantially reduced. Furthermore, important reductions in the systematic uncertainties have been achieved so that they are comparable in magnitude to the statistical uncertainties. In particular, the estimates of the LEP beam energy and of the effects of fragmentation, Bose–Einstein correlations (BE), and CR have been significantly improved.

As the typical decay distance of the W boson, $\Gamma_W^{-1} \simeq 0.1$ fm, is small compared to the typical fragmentation radius, $\Lambda_{\text{QCD}}^{-1} \simeq 1$ fm, the hadronic decay products from the two different W bosons in $e^+e^- \to W^+W^- \to q\bar{q}q\bar{q}$ cannot be modeled as independent. The BE and CR mechanisms are the dominant sources of correlation. The LEP collaborations have performed extensive studies (see Reference 14 and references therein) of BE and CR to quantify the effect on the M_W measurements. Furthermore the final measurements in the $q\bar{q}q\bar{q}$ channel use selection criteria that reduce the effect of BE and CR at the expense of some statistical power. The preliminary combination (14) of the LEP results based on the two methods yields

$$
\begin{aligned}
M_W &= 80,376 \pm 25(\text{stat}) \pm 22(\text{syst})\,\text{MeV}, \\
&= 80,376 \pm 33\,\text{MeV}.
\end{aligned}
$$

At the time of this review [i.e., with one Run II result based on 200 pb^{-1} of CDF data (19, 20) available], these data are still more precise than the combined Tevatron results.

Table 1 Summary of uncertainties in the combined LEP measurement of M_W based on direct mass reconstruction in the $W^+W^- \rightarrow q\bar{q}l\bar{\nu}_l$ and $W^+W^- \rightarrow q\bar{q}q\bar{q}$ channels

Source	Systematic error on M_W (MeV)		
	$q\bar{q}l\bar{\nu}_l$	$q\bar{q}q\bar{q}$	Combined
ISR/FSR	8	5	7
Hadronization	13	19	14
Detector systematics	10	8	10
LEP beam energy	9	9	9
Color reconnection	–	35	8
Bose–Einstein correlations	–	7	2
Other	3	11	4
Total systematic	21	44	22
Statistical	30	40	25
Total	36	59	33

Abbreviations: FSR, final-state radiation; ISR, initial-state radiation.

3. MEASUREMENT TECHNIQUES AT HADRON COLLIDERS

Two hadron colliders have provided collisions at sufficient center-of-mass energies to produce on-shell W bosons: the CERN $Sp\bar{p}S$ and the Fermilab Tevatron. (See References 1 and 10 for Feynman diagrams for W and Z boson production at hadron colliders.) Z bosons provide a crucial control sample that is used in the tuning of many key aspects of the detector model for the measurement of the W boson mass. At hadron colliders measurements of the W boson mass are performed in the leptonic $W \rightarrow e\nu$ and $W \rightarrow \mu\nu$ channels.[2] Decays to quark pairs are not useful for this purpose, given the large direct $q\bar{q}'$ background from quantum chromodynamics (QCD) processes. Electrons and muons are relatively easy to identify and trigger on, and their kinematic properties can be measured precisely. Hadronic decays of the τ lepton are difficult to identify. The leptonic decays of the τ lepton are considered backgrounds to the electron and muon channels. The branching ratio $\mathcal{B}$ for each lepton decay $W \rightarrow \ell\nu$ ($Z \rightarrow \ell\ell$) is approximately 11% (3.3%). The W boson production cross sections σ at $p\bar{p}$ colliders are large: $\sigma \cdot \mathcal{B} \simeq 680$ pb at $\sqrt{s} = 630$ GeV (30), 2.3 nb at $\sqrt{s} = 1.8$ TeV (31), and 2.8 nb at $\sqrt{s} = 1.96$ TeV (32). The corresponding values for Z bosons are about ten times smaller, e.g., $\sigma \cdot \mathcal{B} \simeq 0.25$ nb at $\sqrt{s} = 1.96$ TeV (32).

The Large Hadron Collider (LHC) at CERN (pp at $\sqrt{s} = 14$ TeV) is expected to deliver its first collisions later in 2008. At the LHC, $\sigma \cdot \mathcal{B}(W \rightarrow \ell\nu) \simeq 20$ nb (33). An integrated luminosity of 10 fb^{-1} could be accumulated in one year of low-luminosity running at the LHC. Such an accumulation would lead to $W \rightarrow \ell\nu$ and $Z \rightarrow \ell\ell$ samples of unprecedented size, and the LHC experiments are expected (33–35) to contribute precision measurements of M_W once the detectors are well understood.

In this review, we use a right-handed coordinate system that has its origin at the nominal average $p\bar{p}$ collision point. The z axis points in the direction of the proton beam, the y axis points upwards, and the x axis points horizontally. With respect to the z axis, θ is the polar angle, ϕ denotes the azimuthal angle, and r denotes the distance from the z axis. Because the longitudinal momenta p_Z of the interacting partons are not known on a per-event basis, one generally works with momenta transverse to the beam line. Lepton momenta are denoted $\vec{p}$ and the corresponding transverse momenta are denoted $\vec{p}_T$, with magnitude $p_T = |\vec{p}_T|$. Energy is denoted E and the lepton masses

---

[2]Throughout this review, references to a lepton or to a W decay reaction also imply their charge conjugate.

are neglected. The rapidity $y = \frac{1}{2} \ln[(E + p_z)/(E - p_z)]$ is additive under Lorentz boosts along the z axis. For massless particles this quantity is equal to the pseudorapidity $\eta = \ln[\cot(\theta/2)]$.

The momentum $\vec{p}(\ell)$ of the charged lepton from the W boson decay is measured with good precision, whereas the neutrino escapes detection. Its presence is inferred from an apparent imbalance in the net observed transverse momentum. The hadronization of the p and $\bar{p}$ fragments and of any quarks or gluons from the hard scatter typically leads to a large number of hadrons in the final state. Some of them escape through the beam pipe and are not detected. Although these particles may carry substantial p_Z, they carry little p_T. No attempt is made to detect these particles individually in the W boson mass analysis; instead the calorimeter is used to obtain an approximate measurement of their vectorially summed transverse momentum. Specifically, one defines

$$\vec{u}_T = \sum_i E_i \, \sin\theta_i \, \hat{\imath},$$

where the sum runs over all calorimeter cells that are not included in the lepton cluster, E_i is the energy in cell i, and the unit vector $\hat{\imath}$ provides the cell's transverse direction from the beam axis. The observable $\vec{u}_T$, often referred to as hadronic recoil, is used to infer the transverse momentum of the W boson ($\vec{p}_T(W) = -\vec{u}_T$) and the neutrino ($\vec{p}_T(\nu) = -\vec{u}_T - \vec{p}_T(\ell)$). Researchers use this technique because the most reliable calculations and parameterizations of the hadronic activity are those for the fully inclusive measurement of $p_T(W)$, rather than a measurement based on (for example) reconstructed jets. To summarize, the basic observables are the measured $\vec{p}(\ell)$ and $\vec{u}_T$ and the inferred quantities are $\vec{p}_T(\nu)$ and $\vec{p}_T(W)$.

For studies of the Z boson in $Z \to \ell\ell$, the invariant mass of the lepton pair is a key observable. The invariant mass of W bosons in $W \to \ell\nu$ cannot be reconstructed because $p_z(\nu)$ is not measured. Instead, the most precise measurements of M_W are based on the transverse mass m_T:

$$m_T = \sqrt{2\, p_T(\ell) p_T(\nu)\{1 - \cos[\phi(\ell) - \phi(\nu)]\}}.$$

This variable has the advantage that its spectrum is relatively insensitive to the production dynamics of the W boson. Relative contributions to m_T due to the motion of the W boson are of $\mathcal{O}((p_T(W)/M_W)^2)$. But because m_T uses the inferred neutrino momentum, it is sensitive to the details of the recoil measurement (see Reference 10, Figure 3). Alternatively M_W can be extracted from the lepton p_T spectrum (see Reference 10, Figure 4), which is indirectly sensitive to the recoil measurement (via any u_T requirement in the event selection). Its shape, however, is sensitive to the motion of the W boson and receives corrections of $\mathcal{O}(p_T(W)/M_W)$. Examples from the CDF Run II analysis (which we discuss in detail below) are shown in **Figure 4**. The spectrum of the inferred neutrino p_T is sensitive to both effects. The $p_T(\ell)$, $p_T(\nu)$, and m_T distributions exhibit the Jacobian edge (e.g., at about half the W boson mass in the p_T spectra) that characterizes all two-body decays (36). This part of the measured distributions carries most of the sensitivity to M_W. Because the Jacobian edge is smeared out by the boson p_T, events with large $p_T(W)$ are not useful for the mass measurement. Event selection is typically based on lepton identification and simple kinematic criteria, such as $p_T(\ell) > 25$ GeV, $p_T(\nu) > 25$ GeV, and $p_T(W) < 15$ GeV, which preserve the Jacobian edge.

The radiation of quarks and gluons off the initial-state partons (known as initial-state radiation, or ISR) imparts a transverse boost to the $W \to \ell\nu$ system. Fortunately the typical ISR p_T is small, $\mathcal{O}(10$ GeV$)$, and events with large ISR activity (observed as large u_T) are rejected. Furthermore the transverse direction of $\vec{p}_T(W)$ is largely uncorrelated with the leptons' transverse directions after the W boson decay, so that the average component of $\vec{p}_T(W)$ in the lepton direction is $\mathcal{O}$ (0.2 GeV). As this average is small compared to the lepton $p_T(\ell) \sim 40$ GeV, the sensitivity of the W boson mass measurement to the hadronic response calibration is suppressed. Nevertheless a

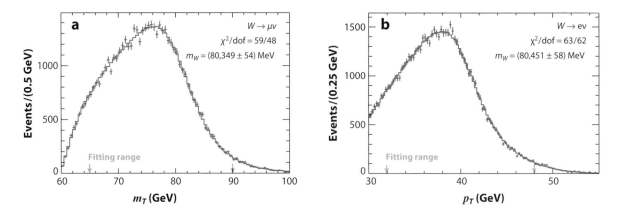

Figure 4

The distribution of the data (*points*) and the best-fit simulation template including backgrounds (*histogram*) for $m_T(\mu\nu)$ (*a*) and $p_T(e)$ (*b*) from the Collider Detector at Fermilab Run II analysis (19, 20). The orange arrows indicate the fitting range. The best-fit values of M_W and statistical uncertainty are shown, along with the χ^2 between the data and the template per degree of freedom in the fitting range.

careful measurement of the hadronic response and resolution at the $\mathcal{O}$ (1%) level is needed so that it does not dominate the mass measurement uncertainty. To first order, the fractional uncertainty in the lepton energy scale translates directly into a fractional uncertainty on M_W, i.e., lepton energy scale calibrations at the few-10^{-4} level are needed.

The convolution of the boson production and decay with the detector response results in observed $p_T(\ell)$, $p_T(\nu)$, and m_T spectra that cannot be calculated analytically. Instead one uses detailed Monte Carlo simulations (see, e.g., References 9–12, 19, 20) that incorporate the generator-level production and decay physics and a parameterized detector response. These simulations are used to generate high-statistics templates of the observed kinematic spectra, one template for each assumed value of the W boson pole mass. A maximum likelihood fitting technique is then used to select the template that best matches the data. Because templates must be generated frequently, the simulations are customized for lepton and recoil simulation at high speed. Detailed calculations using first principles are used for some aspects of lepton response, but most of the detector simulation (e.g., selection efficiencies and recoil response and resolution) is based on parameterized models. These models are tuned primarily using dilepton resonances (especially $Z \to \ell\ell$) in collider data. The analysis technique affords a large number of comparisons and cross checks between simulation and data so as to confirm that the simulation quantitatively reproduces all the features of the data.

4. TEVATRON RUN I W MASS MEASUREMENTS

CDF performed a measurement of the W mass from the 1988–1989 data (Run 0), and both CDF and DØ performed measurements from the 1992–1995 data (Run I). Although some of these measurements have been discussed before (1), it is useful to compare and contrast the Run I and Run II analyses.

4.1. CDF and DØ Run I Detectors

The CDF (9, 37) and DØ (10–12, 38) detectors used in Run I are similar in some respects and fundamentally different in others. Both detectors exploited a cylindrical geometry with the beam running along its axis, and both used tracking devices surrounded by EM and hadronic calorimeters and muon detectors. In addition to the barrel detectors, CDF and DØ exploited forward end-cap detectors to maximize the acceptance in rapidity.

The primary difference between the CDF and DØ detectors in Run I was that CDF used a magnetic spectrometer for tracking charged particles and measuring their momenta. A 1.4-T axial magnetic field was generated by a superconducting solenoid placed between the tracking detectors and the EM calorimeter. The radius of the solenoid was 1.5 m, which provided a large tracking volume occupied by a drift chamber for reconstructing the helical trajectories of charged particles. The drift chamber tracking and momentum measurement played a key role in the CDF Run I measurement of the W boson mass in the muon channel. The magnetic tracker also played a key role in calibrating the nonlinearity of the lead-scintillator EM calorimeter using the in situ sample of electrons from W boson decays. Wire and strip chambers placed at the location of the EM shower maximum provided finer transverse segmentation for particle identification using shower profile measurements. The combination of the latter with the ratio of EM energy to track momentum and with the fraction of hadronic energy provided good electron-jet discrimination. Thus CDF used both the electron and the muon channels for the W boson mass measurement.

The most important component of the DØ Run I detector from the perspective of the W boson mass measurement was the hermetic uranium/liquid argon (U/LAr) sampling calorimeter covering $|\eta| < 4$. This calorimeter enclosed a nonmagnetic tracker consisting of drift and vertex chambers that were used to measure the directions of charged particles. The choice of the U/LAr technology for calorimetry allowed for a compact device with a good sampling fraction and wide angular coverage and depth, as well as fine transverse and longitudinal segmentation. The unit-gain charge readout of the active material provided a high level of stability and uniformity and contributed strongly to the calorimeter's linear response for high-energy electrons. The fine segmentation of the readout enabled the use of sophisticated shower-shape discriminants to reject fake electron candidates from QCD jets, and the hadronic sections provided hermetic coverage without projective cracks. Together with the wide angular coverage and the relatively good response and resolution of the U/LAr technology, these attributes led to good resolution on missing E_T. These features of the DØ calorimeter, in particular the high-energy linearity of the EM calorimeter, were primarily responsible for the W boson mass measurements by DØ in Run I, which used W boson decays to electrons in both the central-rapidity and forward-rapidity regions.

4.2. CDF and DØ Analysis Methodology

Various techniques have been used to calculate the generator-level lepton momentum vectors and $\vec{p}_T(W)$. These techniques range from the use of customized matrix-element calculations augmented with ad hoc parameterizations of the $p_T(W)$ spectrum to the use of specialized programs such as The Monte Carlo for Resummed Boson Production and Decay (ResBos) (39). ResBos and similar programs (40) calculate the quintuple differential cross section $d\sigma/dm\,dq_T\,dy\,d\Omega$ for W and Z boson production, where m, q_T, and y are the boson invariant mass, transverse momentum, and rapidity, respectively, and where Ω is the solid angle of the decay leptons in the boson rest frame. The q_T spectrum includes contributions from fixed-order matrix elements at high q_T matched to a resummation calculation at intermediate q_T and a nonperturbative form factor at low q_T. As in the case of the ad hoc parameterization of the $p_T(W)$ spectrum, the parameters of the nonperturbative form factor are tuned to fit the data. In the case of the ad hoc parameterization (9), the collider $Z \to \ell\ell$ data are used, along with theoretical information on the ratio of the W and Z boson p_T spectra. In the case of the ResBos parameterization, the collider $Z \to \ell\ell$ data are also used (10, 19, 20), along with constraints from global fits to data on Drell–Yan and direct photon production.

In the Run I analysis CDF extensively studied the lepton momentum scale by (*a*) using the $J/\psi \to \mu\mu$ and $\Upsilon \to \mu\mu$ mass measurements for calibration and then (*b*) transferring the tracker momentum scale to the EM calorimeter using a fit to the distribution of the ratio of calorimeter energy to track momentum (*E/p*) for electrons from $W \to e\nu$ decays. Due to a significant discrepancy between the $Z \to ee$ mass measurement and the known value from the LEP, the lepton calibrations based on the J/ψ and $\Upsilon \to \mu\mu$ data and the *E/p* fit ultimately were not used for the W boson mass measurement (9); instead the calibrations based on the $Z \to \mu\mu$ and $Z \to ee$ mass measurements were used for the respective channels. DØ also used the EM calorimeter calibration based on the $Z \to ee$ mass measurement, along with lower energy constraints on the response nonlinearity from $\pi^0 \to \gamma\gamma$ and $J/\psi \to ee$ data. Both experiments constrained the lepton energy resolution models using the observed width of the Z boson mass peaks. The imposition of p_T balance in Z boson events was used to tune the parameterized models of the hadronic response and resolution. The latter also included a contribution from the spectator parton interactions accompanying the hard scatter, as well as from additional $p\bar{p}$ collisions.

4.3. Results and Systematics

CDF and DØ each collected $\approx$100 pb^{-1} of data at $\sqrt{s}$ = 1.8 TeV during Run I. Using both electron and muon decays in the central detector, CDF measured

$$M_W = 80,433 \pm 79\,\text{MeV}.$$

DØ used electron decays in the central- and forward-rapidity regions to measure

$$M_W = 80,483 \pm 84\,\text{MeV}.$$

The CDF result was based on the m_T fit, whereas the DØ result was based on a combination of the m_T, $p_T(e)$, and $p_T(\nu)$ fits. This combination was performed with the best linear unbiased estimator (BLUE) method (41), taking into account all correlations.

Tables 2 and **3** summarize the uncertainties that contributed to the CDF and DØ measurements from the 1994–1995 data (9–12). In addition to the statistical uncertainty from the W boson distributions, the lepton and hadronic calibrations and resolution models are uncorrelated between the two detectors for the purpose of combining their measurements (13). The lepton identification requirements have an efficiency that is mildly correlated with the hadronic activity in the vicinity of the lepton. This hadronic activity therefore induces a correlation between the lepton identification efficiency and the lepton p_T and sculpts the kinematic distributions from which the W boson mass is extracted. The measurement of this selection bias is uncorrelated between experiments. Similarly the background normalizations and shapes are measured independently and are incorporated into the simulation templates. The constraints on the $p_T(W)$ spectrum were derived largely from each experiment's own data, hence the corresponding uncertainty has also been treated as an uncorrelated uncertainty in the combination of CDF and DØ measurements (13).

The sources of uncertainties that have been taken as correlated (13) between the CDF and DØ Run I analyses are shown in **Table 3**. At hadron colliders the parton distribution functions (PDFs), i.e., the momentum densities of the partons annihilating to produce the W boson, influence the mass fit in two ways. First, the PDFs convolute to generate the mass-dependent parton luminosity that multiplies the Breit–Wigner mass distribution. Second, the PDFs govern the distribution of

Table 2 Uncorrelated uncertainties (MeV) in the W boson mass measurements from CDF and DØ data collected from 1994 to 1995

Source	CDF μ	CDF e	DØ e
W boson statistics	100	65	60
Lepton momentum scale	85	75	56
Lepton momentum resolution	20	25	19
Theoretical $p_T(W)$ spectrum	20	15	15
Detector recoil response and resolution model	35	37	35
Selection bias	18	–	12
Backgrounds	25	5	9

Electron (e) and muon (μ) decay channels are listed separately. Table reproduced from Reference 13.

the boson's longitudinal momentum. The limited lepton acceptance in rapidity causes the transverse kinematics to be correlated with the longitudinal momentum distribution. The correlation weakens as the rapidity coverage becomes more inclusive; in the limit of complete rapidity coverage the transverse kinematics and hence the W boson mass fits become independent of the boson's longitudinal momentum. As **Table 3** shows, the PDF uncertainty in the DØ measurement was smaller than that of CDF because of DØ's use of electrons up to $|y(\ell)| \approx 2.5$ (in comparison with CDF's use of leptons up to $|y(\ell)| \approx 1$). The PDFs are determined from global fits to data from many experiments.

Another source of correlated uncertainty is quantum electrodynamics (QED) radiative corrections. Photon radiation emanates from the initial-state quarks, the W boson propagator, and the final-state charged lepton. By far the dominant effect on the W boson mass fit comes from the photon radiation off the charged lepton (known as final-state radiation, or FSR), which reduces $p_T(\ell)$ and shifts the fitted mass down. Due to their smaller mass, electrons radiate substantially more than muons; however this enhancement occurs for small angular separation between the lepton and the photon. The small-angle radiation is coalesced by the calorimeter cluster, whose typical angular radius in $\eta - \phi$ space is $\mathcal{O}(0.2)$. The wide-angle radiation, which is similar for electrons and muons, causes a shift in the measured W boson mass by $\mathcal{O}(100 \text{ MeV})$. The simulation programs incorporated the calculation of radiative corrections (42, 43), which was cross-checked against other programs including PHOTOS (44) and WGRAD (45).

Because the W boson mass information is extracted from m_T or p_T distributions with one-sided Jacobian edges, the mass fit is influenced by the boson's decay width. In Run I analyses CDF and DØ used different conventions: CDF used the SM calculation of the width in the simulation with negligible uncertainty, whereas DØ used the world-average measured value and its uncertainty. For the purpose of combination (13), the correlated uncertainty was taken to be the uncertainty due to the measured world average.

Table 3 Correlated sources of systematic uncertainties (MeV) in the W boson mass measurements from CDF and DØ Run I

Source	CDF	DØ
PDF and parton luminosity	15	8
QED radiative corrections	11	12
Γ_W	10	10

Table reproduced from Reference 13. Abbreviations: PDF, parton distribution function; QED, quantum electrodynamics.

4.4. Scaling of Collider Data–Driven Systematics

In Run I the calibration of the lepton energy and the hadronic recoil was based on the boson data and was expected to scale with boson statistics. This was also true for the lepton and hadronic resolution models. However there are scenarios wherein these uncertainties scale faster or slower than boson statistics. If multiple collider data sets were to provide a self-consistent analysis model, inclusion of these data would improve the W boson mass uncertainty compared to, say, using Z boson events alone. On the other hand, reduced detector resolutions due to less-favorable running conditions can reduce the statistical power of each Z boson event. Even more importantly, at higher levels of precision the parameterizations of response and resolution may need to become more complicated in order to capture subtle effects, increasing the number of degrees of freedom to be constrained by collider data. These effects retard the scaling improvement of the W boson mass uncertainty. We discuss these two scenarios in Sections 5 and 7 below.

The selection bias is measured with Z boson events: An event can be selected with tight cuts on one lepton with the other unbiased lepton used to probe the identification efficiency. The uncertainty on the selection bias is likely to scale with statistics. Backgrounds are estimated using a combination of data-based techniques for misidentification backgrounds (such as those arising from QCD jets) and detailed simulations of SM processes that yield the $\ell\nu$ final state (such as the $W \to \tau\nu \to \ell\nu\bar{\nu}\nu$ process). The misidentification backgrounds tend to be more difficult to pin down, and their uncertainties do not automatically scale with statistics. The typical method of determining these background uncertainties is to compare the estimates obtained using different data-based techniques. More data will allow these techniques to be improved. In addition higher signal statistics allow more stringent identification requirements, and misidentification backgrounds are correspondingly suppressed.

The theoretical boson p_T spectrum can be constrained quite precisely by the measurement of the Z boson p_T using the well-measured dileptons; the measurement of $p_T(W)$ using the hadronic recoil is strongly influenced by the latter's calibration and resolution and does not provide a reliable measurement of the theoretical boson p_T spectrum, especially at low p_T. Hence the measurement of the $p_T(Z)$ spectrum will continue to improve with statistics. Given the parameterizations in use, the translation of the $p_T(Z)$ spectrum to the theoretical $p_T(W)$ spectrum has not incurred significant additional systematics. It is possible that nonperturbative effects differ between W and Z boson production; for instance effects of the charm quark mass may cause a systematic uncertainty in the $p_T(W)$ prediction and the W boson mass of a few megaelectronvolts. Initial investigations of such systematics are encouraging (46), however, and they indicate that these effects are unlikely to be an appreciable source of systematic uncertainty.

4.5. External Inputs to Systematics

The key external inputs are the PDFs and the QED radiative corrections. During the Run I analyses rigorous methods of propagating uncertainties in the PDFs were not available. The W mass uncertainty was evaluated by comparing simulated events that used different parameterizations of PDFs as inputs. The choice of PDFs to compare was heuristic and was based partly on the differences in the data sets used in the global fits. The Run II analyses use improved tools that were not available during Run I; we discuss these tools in Section 5.6.

An important input to the PDF constraints is the Tevatron measurement of the lepton charge asymmetry as a function of rapidity in W boson decay. The lepton charge asymmetry is a consequence of the W boson charge asymmetry at production, which is related to the ratio of d and u quark distributions in the proton. Continued improvement in the lepton charge asymmetry measurement, which is statistics limited in the forward-rapidity region, will provide an important constraint on the PDFs (47). A review of the measurement of the lepton charge asymmetry from the Run I data can be found elsewhere (48). Both CDF and DØ have performed measurements of the lepton charge asymmetry with early Run II data (see References 49 and 50; a more recent, preliminary analysis of 1 fb^{-1} of integrated luminosity can be found at **http://www-cdf.fnal.gov/physics/ewk/2007/WChargeAsym/PubNote/**), and measurements with greater statistics will be performed.

The uncertainty on QED radiative corrections is dominated by missing higher order corrections. Improved calculations are now available and have been used in the Run II analyses, as we discuss below.

5. TEVATRON RUN II W MASS ANALYSES

At the end of Run I, the Tevatron accelerator and the CDF and DØ detectors underwent five years of extensive upgrades. The accelerator complex was upgraded for a factor of 10–20 increase in instantaneous luminosity as well as an increase in the collision center-of-mass energy from 1.8 TeV to 1.96 TeV. The bunch crossing time was reduced from $\approx$3.5 μs in Run I to 396 ns in Run II. The detectors were upgraded for improved performance and for recording data at substantially higher rates.

5.1. CDF and DØ Run II Detector Upgrades

The replaced or upgraded components of CDF include the silicon vertex detector, the central drift chamber for tracking, the plug calorimeters for $|\eta| > 1$, the muon detector system, and the luminosity monitor (51). The front-end readout electronics, the trigger systems (52), and the data acquisition system, as well as the offline computing systems, were also upgraded. A new time-of-flight detector, a preshower detector, and an EM calorimeter timing system were installed. The CDF upgrades are described in detail in References 20, 53, 54.

From the perspective of the W boson mass measurement, the important detector upgrades are the central drift chamber (55), the muon detector system, and the plug calorimeters (56). As discussed below, the drift chamber underpins the CDF analysis in Run II. In Run I the Central Tracking Chamber (CTC) generated at most 84 hits on a fiducial track. It was replaced in Run II by the Central Outer Tracker (COT), which generates up to 96 hits, has a drift distance of $\approx$8 mm (reduced from $\approx$5 cm in the CTC) to reduce the readout time, and has more robust stereo tracking capability.

The CDF plug calorimeter was upgraded from a gas calorimeter to a scintillating-tile calorimeter, with a corresponding reduction in readout time. The calibration of the plug calorimeter is easier to perform with the upgraded detector, allowing more robust measurements of electrons, photons, and hadronic activity in the high-rapidity region. Apart from the upgrade to the CDF muon system readout electronics, the salient muon system upgrades include the installation of new muon detectors for greater azimuthal and rapidity coverage.

The DØ detector underwent even more significant changes and upgrades (57). The central tracking detector is completely new and now includes a silicon microstrip tracker and a scintillating-fiber tracker located within a 2-T solenoidal magnet (58–60). For improved electron identification, new preshower detectors were added between the magnet and the central calorimeter (CC, $|\eta| < 1$) and in front of the end-cap calorimeters (ECs). In the muon systems (61), active detectors were replaced and extended with different technologies for improved triggering. To withstand the harsh radiation environment, additional shielding has been added. The readout electronics and trigger systems (61, 62) were significantly upgraded in response to the large reduction in bunch spacing time and the higher event rates. The data acquisition systems and the offline systems were replaced.

As discussed in Section 4, the calorimeter was the centerpiece of the DØ Run I measurements of the W boson mass. The calorimeter itself has not been changed since Run I, so the drift time across the LAr gaps is still 450 ns. The readout electronics, however, were upgraded significantly. New preamplifiers and signal-shaping electronics were installed, and analog pipelining was introduced. The new shapers use only two-thirds of the charge collected by the preamplifier circuit, corresponding to the first $\simeq 260$ ns of signal from the gaps. The shaper circuit produces a unipolar signal with a peak at about 320 ns and a return to zero after $\simeq 1.2$ µs. The shaped signals are sampled every 132 ns, including samples close to the peak. Upon receiving an accept from the hardware-based stages of the trigger system, the sample at the corresponding peak and the sample taken 396 ns earlier are retrieved from analog memory and the analog difference (known as baseline subtracted signal) is digitized. Subsequently zero-suppression is applied to the data. The suppression thresholds are significantly higher than in Run I; the choice to raise them was driven by the higher noise levels.

Moreover the environment in which the calorimeter operates has changed significantly. The most important of these changes concerns the large amount of uninstrumented material (from the point of view of calorimetric energy measurements) in front of the DØ calorimeter. For example, in the CC the radiation lengths of material between the interaction region and the first active LAr gap is now about 4.0 X_0 at normal incidence (increased from ≈ 1 X_0 in Run I), which corresponds to 7.2 X_0 at the most extreme angles that are encountered for CC electrons.

Another important aspect of Run II that affects CDF and DØ is the large additional transverse energy flow from multiple $p\bar{p}$ interactions. For example the net measured transverse energy flow from additional $p\bar{p}$ interactions (from the concurrent and previous crossings) averaged over the so-called Run IIa data-taking period (2001–2006) is already comparable to the flow from the spectator partons in the $p\bar{p} \rightarrow W + X$ interaction. The relative importance of the additional $p\bar{p}$ interactions has further increased since then because of the steady increase of instantaneous luminosities delivered by the Tevatron.

5.2. Impact of Upgrades on Analysis Methodology

With regard to the CDF analysis methodology, the COT has excellent coverage, efficiency, and resolution. A tracking efficiency for isolated particles in excess of 99% and a single-hit resolution of $\mathcal{O}$ (150 µm) have been achieved. The resolution on inverse momentum (which is proportional to track curvature) is $\delta p_T^{-1} \approx 0.0015$ GeV^{-1} using only COT hits in the fit; the resolution improves to $\delta p_T^{-1} \approx 0.0005$ GeV^{-1} for prompt particles when beamline coordinates are included in the fit. The high efficiency and resolution for the lepton tracks from boson decays are major factors in the CDF Run II analysis, as they allow the momentum-scale calibration to rely upon tracking for both the muon and electron decay channels.

Because the leptons from W and Z bosons and the Υ are produced promptly and can be beam constrained, adding the hits from the silicon vertex detector does not significantly improve the track resolution. Therefore the CDF analysis does not use silicon detector hits in the lepton track reconstruction and fitting. One of the benefits of this choice is that any subtle misalignments between the silicon sensors as well as between the silicon detector and the COT do not bias the track measurement.

A side effect of the upgrade to a more powerful silicon detector is that the passive material traversed by the muons and electrons increased substantially from Run I to Run II. This effect has increased the multiple scattering for muons from J/ψ and Υ decays and has also increased the rate of electron bremsstrahlung and subsequent photon conversions. A careful accounting of the detector mass and material properties was performed and modeled. The passive material model was cross checked and tuned using collider data on converted photons from $\pi°$ decays, the p_T dependence of the measured J/ψ mass, and the measured bremsstrahlung spectrum off electrons.

The upgrade of the CDF plug calorimeter enabled researchers to make more reliable measurements of the hadronic recoil in W and Z boson events. Because the rapidity distribution of the hadrons is approximately uniform and is uncorrelated with their p_T distribution, about two-thirds of the recoil transverse energy is detected in the plug calorimeters. CDF used hadron tracks to calibrate the relative response of the central and plug calorimeters, thereby making the calorimeter response more uniform as a function of rapidity. The final calibration of the recoil transverse energy was performed using p_T balance in Z boson decays to leptons; the uniformity of the response in rapidity renders the recoil calibration largely insensitive to possible differences in the rapidity distribution of the recoiling particles between W and Z boson events.

As discussed above, DØ in Run II has magnetic central tracking, which means that measurement of the W boson mass in the $W \to \mu\nu$ channel is now possible. As the tracking system must fit inside the central calorimeter (reused from Run I; inner diameter 1.42 m), the lever arm in track fitting is short and consequently the curvature resolution is relatively poor: $\delta p_T^{-1} \simeq 0.0024\,\mathrm{GeV}^{-1}$. This translates into an experimental $Z \to \mu\mu$ mass resolution of 8 GeV, which is significantly worse than the experimental mass resolution in $Z \to ee$ (e.g., 2.8 GeV for the subsample where both electrons are in the CC). More importantly, in the muon channel the boson mass resolution is large compared to the natural width of the Z boson [$\Gamma_Z = 2.4952 \pm 0.0023$ GeV (21)], i.e., the poor experimental mass resolution significantly reduces the statistical power of each $Z \to \mu\mu$ event used in momentum-scale calibrations. The mass resolution is also a limiting factor in detailed studies of momentum-scale uniformity (in terms of different regions of the detector and in terms of p_T). The main channel for the W boson mass measurement at DØ remains the $W \to e\nu$ decay with calorimetric electron energy measurement. Confirmation of electron candidates by central tracking provides substantial reduction of fakes from QCD jets, and central tracking provides a precise measurement of the electron direction.

The changes implemented during the upgrade have had a significant impact on the DØ methodology. The change in calorimeter integration time has given rise to new nonuniformities in the calorimeter response that were not present in Run I, and it has significantly amplified some of the small nonuniformities that were already present. The underlying cause of these effects is the nonuniformities in the mechanical structure of the calorimeter modules. Variations in the thickness of the uranium absorber plates from one readout cell to another lead to variations in the response, independent of the integration time. Other types of nonuniformities lead to small response nonuniformities when essentially all charge is read out (as in Run I) but to sizeable nonuniformities when only a fraction of the charge is read out (Run II). A striking example of the latter effect in Run II that leads to $\mathcal{O}$ (2%) contribution to the constant term in the calorimeter energy resolution before corrections is the spread in position of the readout boards between two neighboring absorber plates. Another example is the effect of the ϕ cracks between the 32 azimuthal modules of the EM section of the CC. Due to the reduction in integration time, the size of the region close to the module edges that would have to be cut out to eliminate the effect of the cracks has roughly doubled from 20% of the CC acceptance in Run I (12) to 40% today.

The DØ group has developed new methods based on relatively inclusive events collected using dedicated calibration triggers during normal collider data–taking to measure and correct for variations in the energy response from one readout cell to another. Similar techniques are used for both the EM and hadronic (63) sections of the calorimeters. As in Run I (12), the regions near cracks are

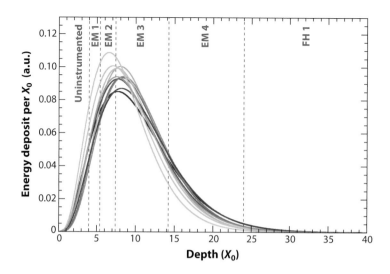

Figure 5

Illustration of partial sampling of showers in DØ Run II. The profile of the longitudinal energy depositions from ten electron showers at $E = 45$ GeV is simulated using the GFLASH (64) parameterized shower model. The ten energy profiles are superimposed in the plot (*solid lines*). The positions of the four electromagnetic (EM) layers (EM1–EM4) and the first hadronic layer (FH1) of the DØ calorimeter, assuming normal incidence, are also indicated (*dashed lines*). The energy deposition is shown in arbitrary units.

studied using subsamples of $Z \to ee$ events with electrons detected therein. In Run I the cracks were excluded from the first measurement of the W boson mass, and a refined measurement including the crack electrons was published later (12). In Run II this separation is no longer practical.

In the DØ Run I analysis, the effect of the uninstrumented material in front of the first active layer of LAr was taken into account using a small energy offset δ_{EM} in the electron energy response model (10). The mean reconstructed electron cluster energy $E(e)$ was described as $E(e) = \alpha_{\mathrm{EM}} E_0 + \delta_{\mathrm{EM}}$, where E_0 denotes the true electron energy. The value of $\delta_{\mathrm{EM}} = -0.16^{+0.03}_{-0.21}$ GeV was measured using $Z \to ee$ data and lower energy $J/\psi \to ee$ and $\pi^0 \to \gamma\gamma$ data. The impact of the uninstrumented material has increased dramatically in Run II because large parts of the typical shower are no longer sampled (shown in **Figure 5**).

The partial sampling has multiple consequences. The calorimeter energy response now has a strong dependence on the angle of impact on the CC, because the amount of material seen by a shower depends on the angle of impact. At a given angle, the response has a nontrivial energy dependence, as the average position of the shower maximum increases logarithmically (65) with energy. At a given angle and energy, the fractional energy deposited in the uninstrumented region varies strongly from one shower to another due to fluctuations in showering. These fluctuations represent a significant contribution to the energy resolution. Furthermore, in the absence of miscalibrations and noise the resolution is no longer described by a single sampling term. As with the response, the resolution is a complicated function of energy and angle of incidence. At normal incidence, and at energies close to 45 GeV, the resolution can be described by a sampling term of 0.19 GeV$^{-1/2}$, which is (as expected) worse than the Run I sampling term of 0.135 GeV$^{-1/2}$. At the same energy and at more extreme angles ($|\eta| \sim 1$), the resolution degrades by another factor of two (illustrated in **Figure 6**). For Run II, DØ developed completely new parameterizations of the calorimeter response and resolution, along with completely new techniques to determine the values of the many new parameters.

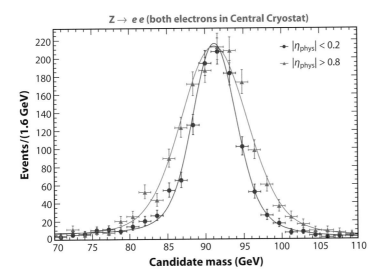

Figure 6

Reconstructed $Z \to ee$ mass distribution in 1 fb^{-1} of DØ Run II data. The red (blue) distribution corresponds to events where both electrons reach the CC at normal (highly nonnormal) incidence (66).

In Run I, DØ measured u_T with a response of 70% for boson $p_T > 1.5$ GeV and a resolution sampling term of (0.49 ± 0.14) GeV$^{-1/2}$ (10). The resolution arises from a combination of many effects, such as neutrinos in the recoil and particles escaping the angular coverage of the calorimeter, which did not change from Run I, as well as the calorimeter response and resolution for charged hadrons, which changed significantly in Run II. The hadronic energy resolution in the DØ U/LAr calorimeter depends on the ability to detect clouds of small individual energy deposits from thermalized neutrons (67). In Run II these deposits are read out less efficiently than in Run I because of the shorter integration time (thermalization is slow on the timescale of the Run II integration time) and the tight zero-suppression thresholds. In Run II the sampling term in the recoil resolution is close to 0.8 GeV$^{-1/2}$.

In Run I the simulation of the spectator parton and additional $p\bar{p}$ interactions was based on data collected using a minimum-bias trigger and an underlying event scale parameter determined from $Z \to ee$ data. The particles from these interactions and the particles recoiling against the boson were treated as independent, i.e., the measured transverse energy fluxes from the two contributions were treated as additive. In Run II the two components are correlated in DØ because of the tight zero-suppression thresholds: In the presence of a significant energy flow from the additional interactions, the response for the particles balancing the boson p_T increases because readout cells are more likely to pass the zero-suppression threshold. The corresponding increase in response can be up to 30% at low boson p_T. Similar effects must be taken into account in the precise determination of the DØ jet energy scale (68). In the latter case the corrections are taken from a detailed detector simulation based on GEANT (69). The GEANT-based simulation is not expected to predict the precise values of all parameters in the W mass parametric detector model. However, it can model the subtle detector effects discussed above at the right order of magnitude, and it can be used to check the validity of the parametric models as well as the methods that are used to extract the parameter values from Z boson data. In order to validate the W mass analysis procedure, the DØ group uses the same methods as for collider data to perform entire W boson mass measurement on Monte Carlo Z and W boson events from the detailed GEANT-based simulation. The values of all parameters in the detector model, as well as the measured W boson mass, are checked against the values obtained using Monte Carlo truth information.

5.3. Details of the CDF Run II Analysis

The first CDF Run II analysis, with the result $M_W = 80,413 \pm 48$ MeV, was recently published (19, 20). The analysis performed a momentum-scale calibration with the COT tracker, which was then transferred to the EM calorimeter using the ratio of calorimeter energy to track momentum E/p of electrons from W boson decays. The result was extracted from maximum-likelihood fits to the m_T, $p_T(\ell)$, and $p_T(\nu)$ distributions.

The W and Z bosons in both the electron and muon channels were triggered inclusively on the presence of a single high-p_T lepton. A hardware-level COT track trigger (52) was used to identify high-p_T tracks. These were matched spatially and temporally (again at the hardware level) to track-segments detected in the muon chambers, or to clusters of high-energy towers in the EM calorimeter. The resolution of the hardware-level quantities such as p_T and calorimeter transverse energy E_T was enough to substantially suppress the background rate. If an electron or a muon was detected, the event was read out and another, software-based filter was applied. At this stage full event reconstruction in real time was performed and more stringent criteria were applied for inclusive lepton selection, including the use of reconstructed quantities to provide improved resolution. Events passing the software filter were recorded on magnetic media for later analysis.

In order to minimize the biases in track reconstruction due to misalignments and deformations of the drift chamber, the CDF analysis used a large sample of cosmic rays that diametrically traversed the fiducial volume of the COT. These cosmic ray data were continuously acquired concurrently with collider data using the signal muon trigger. A specialized reconstruction procedure was used to fit the entire trajectory of the cosmic ray muon to a single helix (70). Because this fit incorporated many constraints, aligning the COT cells with respect to these fitted tracks suppressed misalignments that cause curvature and impact parameter biases. Individual cell alignment improved from $\mathcal{O}$ (50 μm) precision with the optical survey to $\mathcal{O}$ (5 μm). As a cross check, the ratio E/p was compared between positrons and electrons from W boson decays. Because the calorimeter responses for high-energy electrons and positrons are essentially identical, a difference in E/p between them indicated a track curvature bias. Although the bulk of the alignment biases were eliminated by the cosmic ray method, an empirical correction based on the E/p difference was applied to tracks to remove the residual curvature bias.

As the CDF analysis is anchored on tracking, a first-principles custom tracker simulation was developed for the first Run II analysis. The simulation encoded the equations for multiple scattering and energy loss by ionization and bremsstrahlung and for pair production $\gamma \to ee$ and Compton scattering of bremsstrahlung and radiative photons. A three-dimensional geometry describing the material properties as a function of (r, ϕ, z) was used in order to capture the details of EM energy and particle flow in the vicinity of the leptons. About 90% of the passive material traversed by the leptons in the tracking volume is presented by the beam pipe, the silicon vertex detector, and the latter's associated readout infrastructure. The average number of radiation lengths at normal incidence is $\approx 20\%$, and the average ionization energy loss per track is ≈ 9 MeV. The lepton tracks were propagated in the simulation in small radial steps, generating hits in the COT active volume according to a resolution and efficiency model that was tuned on the collider data. A helical fit was performed to these hits, where the fit included a beam constraint for leptons from W, Z, and Υ decays. Accompanying photons and conversion electrons were also propagated to the calorimeter, and their energy was combined with the primary lepton energy deposition to simulate the cluster (if they impact the same towers).

The simulation of electron and muon energy deposition in the calorimeter was based on parameterizations and distributions that were either tuned on the collider data or derived from collider data directly. For muons the distribution of the ionization energy loss in the calorimeter was measured from cosmic rays. There is also a contribution of energy flow into the leptons' towers from the underlying event accompanying the hard scatter, as well as from additional proton-antiproton collisions in the same bunch crossing. The distribution of this energy flow was measured in the W boson data from the energy detected in towers adjacent to the lepton. The electron energy deposition was parameterized with a straight-line response function and a resolution function consisting of a sampling term and a constant term. The sampling term, $\sigma_E/E = 13.5\%/\sqrt{E_T}$, was fixed at the value measured in test-beam data, leaving the constant term $\sigma_E/E = \kappa$ to be constrained from collider data. The first DØ measurement from Run II is not yet available, but it is expected to be released in the near future.

5.4. Calibrations in the CDF Analysis

In the CDF analysis (19, 20), the calibration of the tracker momentum scale was performed using mass fits to the $J/\psi \rightarrow \mu\mu$ and $\Upsilon \rightarrow \mu\mu$ decays. The muons from J/ψ decays span a range of curvature, allowing the energy-loss model to be pinned down with high precision by studying the variation of the fitted J/ψ mass with curvature. A small empirical correction was made to the energy-loss model such that the fitted J/ψ mass was independent of muon curvature, within statistical uncertainty. The Υ mass fit yielded a consistent measurement of the momentum scale, and also provided confirmation that the beam-constraining procedure did not bias the track curvature. In this calibration the dominant systematic uncertainties arose from the imperfect description of these narrow lineshapes by the simulation and from the nonuniformity of the magnetic field, which affects these tracks differently from the W bosons' decay leptons. These systematics are likely reducible with further study. Using these calibrations, the Z boson mass fit to the $Z \rightarrow \mu\mu$ sample yielded the value (see **Figure 7**) $M_Z = 91,184 \pm 43$ (stat) MeV, which is consistent with the world average (21, 71) and provides a very important cross check of the momentum scale obtained from the J/ψ and Υ mass fits.

The electron channel measurement was made using the calorimeter energy, as the track momentum is significantly affected by external bremsstrahlung. The calorimeter energy response can be calibrated using two techniques: (a) the $Z \rightarrow ee$ mass measurement and (b) the ratio E/p of the nonradiative electrons that form a peak near unity. Even though only about half of the electrons from W boson decay lie in this peak region, this method still provides the best statistical precision because the E/p peak is quite narrow (see **Figure 8**) and because the W boson sample is much larger than the Z boson sample. In addition the E/p peak fit can be performed in bins of electron E_T to constrain the nonproportionality of the EM calorimeter response. The peak position is sensitive to the bremsstrahlung spectrum and rate, which were simulated with care (see Reference 20 for details). The rate was constrained by measuring the fraction of radiative electrons (i.e., large E/p) and comparing it with the prediction of the simulation. The comparison confirmed that the bremsstrahlung model was accurate within the statistical uncertainty of the data. The energy-scale calibration from the $Z \rightarrow ee$ mass fit (see **Figure 7**) was found to be consistent with the E/p-based calibration; the latter yields $M_Z = 91,190 \pm 67$ (stat) MeV, consistent with the world average (21, 71). This is a very important consistency requirement and provides much confidence in the electron channel measurement. To achieve maximum precision the final result used the combination of both methods, in which the E/p-based calibration and the $Z \rightarrow ee$ mass calibration contributed with weights of approximately 2:1.

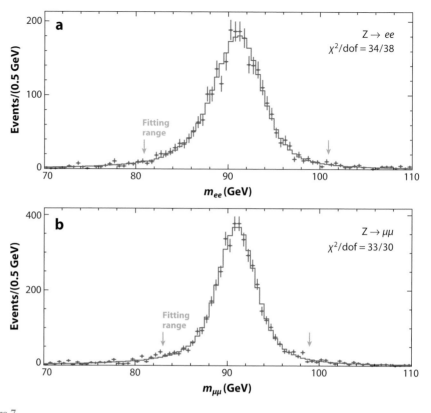

Figure 7

The $Z \to \mu\mu$ (*a*) and $Z \to ee$ (*b*) mass fits from the CDF Run II analysis (19, 20), showing the data (*points*) and the simulation (*histogram*). The orange arrows indicate the fitting range.

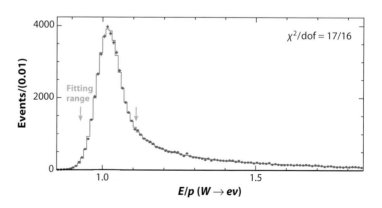

Figure 8

The distribution of E/p for the $W \to e\nu$ data (*points*) and the best-fit simulation (*histogram*), including the small jet background (*shaded*), from the CDF Run II analysis (19, 20). The orange arrows indicate the fitting range used for the electron energy calibration.

The tracking resolution model contained two parameters, the individual hit resolution and the transverse size of the beam spot. The hit resolution was tuned on the observed width of the $\Upsilon \to \mu\mu$ mass distribution without applying the beam constraint to the tracks. The width of the $Z \to \mu\mu$ mass distribution, where the resolution of the high-p_T muons is more sensitive to the beam constraint, was used to tune the size of the beam spot. With this tracking resolution model, the observed width of the E/p peak was used to tune the constant term in the calorimeter resolution model. The observed width of the $Z \to ee$ mass peak provides an independent measurement of the constant term. The CDF analysis finds that when both electrons are nonradiative (i.e., small E/p), the $Z \to ee$ mass peak and the E/p peak provide consistent measurements of the constant term. However, when a significant amount of calorimeter cluster energy is deposited by bremsstrahlung photons and conversion electrons, the corresponding $Z \to ee$ subsamples indicate that the cluster energy resolution is degraded. Additional data may be able to shed light on the reason for this effect. In the analysis, an additional resolution contribution was included in the model and applied only to the radiated energy.

5.5. Calibrations in the DØ Analysis

Thus far the DØ analysis is based on the $W \to e\nu$ channel, and the electron energy is measured using the calorimeter. The calorimeter energy scale is calibrated using mainly $Z \to ee$ events, plus $J/\psi \to ee$ events to check that the calibration obtained at the Z mass can be extrapolated to significantly smaller energies. The corrections for the energy lost in the uninstrumented regions (see Section 5.2) are based on a detailed GEANT-based simulation of the DØ detector. This simulation includes a precise accounting of the material distribution in the detector, including detailed descriptions of nonuniformities such as the windings of superconductor in the solenoid. The up-to-date cross sections for EM processes are incorporated into GEANT by DØ, and the particle tracking inside GEANT is configured to use the highest level of precision. The key experimental inputs for tuning the simulation are the distributions of energy in the longitudinal sections of the EM calorimeter. The sample of $Z \to ee$ events is split into subsamples of 15 different angular combinations (using the same approach shown in **Figure 6**), and the distributions of the $4 \times 15 = 60$ per-layer energy distributions in the four EM layers are checked between data and detailed simulation. Good agreement, within the statistical uncertainties of the collider data, is achieved after tuning five free parameters in the detailed simulation: the absolute energy scale of each of the four readout sections and a small amount of uninstrumented material missing from the material map in the full simulation. The adjusted full simulation is then used to derive energy- and η-dependent parameterizations of energy response and sampling resolution. After this adjustment, the Z boson mass, measured separately in all of the 15 subsamples, is found to be consistent between subsamples. The constant term in the energy resolution, measured from the width of the 15 mass distributions, is also found to be consistent between subsamples. As in Run I, the absolute energy scale is determined using the precise world average of the Z boson mass (21), which is utilized as an input to the simulations.

5.6. Backgrounds

The background sources can be categorized according to whether the lepton candidates are true prompt leptons from other SM processes, or whether they are hadrons misidentified as leptons due to detector effects. In general sources in the former category can be reliably calculated because the cross sections, decay rates, and angular distributions of the corresponding SM electroweak physics processes are well known, and because the detector acceptances for these final states are well understood from a full detector simulation. On the other hand, the misidentification backgrounds arise from QCD-hadronic processes, which have much larger cross sections than the electroweak signal but which are suppressed by lepton misidentification rates of $\mathcal{O}\ (10^{-3})$. Thus the hadronic background events form a small but highly sculpted subset of events in the tail of large parent distributions and are very difficult to simulate from first principles. For this latter category of backgrounds, various data-based techniques are devised to extract their rates and kinematic distributions. Because these background distributions are already sculpted by the online trigger requirements, the signal-trigger data sets are used as the base sample for these methods.

The electroweak physics processes generating backgrounds in the W boson samples are the $W \to \tau\nu$ and $Z \to \ell\ell$ processes; other electroweak processes have negligible cross sections. The τ lepton decays to leptons and hadrons with well-known branching ratios. Both sources of background can be calculated using a full detector simulation and reconstruction, including the τ decay to charged and neutral hadrons that can mimic electrons. The τ decay polarization is accounted for (72), as it impacts the momentum distribution of the decay products in the laboratory frame. The $Z \to \ell\ell$ process can mimic W boson decays if one of the leptons is undetected or misreconstructed such that its undetected transverse energy mimics a neutrino. For the electron channel, this background is small because the EM calorimeter coverage is fairly complete. For the muon channel, this background is appreciable because a muon outside the acceptance of the central barrel is difficult to track; nevertheless it is well-calculable as it is essentially a geometric effect.

The W and Z events selected by the CDF online triggers and offline selection are fairly pure, with misidentification backgrounds constituting about 0.5% of the candidate sample. The analysis requires $p_T(\ell) > 30$ GeV, $p_T(\nu) > 30$ GeV, and $u_T < 15$ GeV, which preserve W boson events containing the mass information while suppressing the QCD jet background that preferentially populates the low-$p_T(\nu)$, high-u_T region. Misidentification backgrounds could be suppressed further with tighter cuts on identification quantities, such as isolation energy in the vicinity of the lepton and the number of hits on the track. However, tighter cuts increase the correlation between lepton identification efficiency and the boson p_T, which biases the lepton p_T distributions and the mass fits. Hence identification variables that are only weakly influenced by hadronic activity are used for event selection.

5.7. Production and Decay Model

For the Run II analyses, CDF and DØ are using the ResBos generator (39), which we discussed in Section 4.2. Although the W boson decay angular distribution is specified at Born level by its $V - A$ (left-handed) coupling, it receives $p_T(W)$–dependent corrections due to kinematic boosting and QCD dynamics. These corrections have been calculated and compared to the data (73, 74). The ResBos (39) and DYRAD (75) programs incorporate these $p_T(W)$–dependent corrections to the decay angular distribution. As the precision of the W boson mass measurement continues to improve at hadron colliders, higher order calculations will likely be needed.

The full quintuple differential cross section for W and Z boson production and decay from ResBos provides a unified model for describing these events. A particle-level description of the hadronic recoil is not needed as the recoil is reconstructed inclusively using calorimetric energy flow. To the extent that the model simultaneously describes Z and W boson production, the Z boson events can be used to tune the parameters of the model. For example, in the CDF Run II analysis the dilepton p_T spectrum in the Z boson events is used to constrain the dominant parameter in the nonperturbative form factor, which is then used as an input for predicting the $p_T(W)$ spectrum. The constraints from the Z boson data have become sufficiently precise that possible differences between Z and W boson dynamics may need to be corrected for (46).

QED radiative corrections have been implemented in the CDF Run II analysis using the two-dimensional probability distribution of the radiated photon's energy and angle with respect to the charged lepton. The distribution is calculated using the WGRAD program (45), which is a complete electroweak calculation of radiative corrections at $\mathcal{O}(\alpha)$. Higher order photon radiation has been emulated by increasing the leading-order photon energy by an estimated 10% (76), but with a 5% uncertainty assigned. The higher order corrections need to be studied in more detail in order to reduce this source of uncertainty, which will become important when more data are analyzed.

The technique for estimating PDF uncertainties has improved significantly since the Run I analyses were published. The Coordinated Theoretical-Experimental Project on QCD (CTEQ) (77) and the Martin–Roberts–Stirling–Thorne (MRST) (78) sets of PDFs now provide associated ensembles of PDFs, which describe the independent variations of the PDF fit parameters that are permitted by the uncertainties in the global data sets. The corresponding uncertainty on M_W is obtained by performing a Monte Carlo pseudoexperiment for each PDF in the ensemble by fitting the simulated events using the templates generated with the default PDF and noting the resulting shift in M_W with respect to its default value. The M_W shifts due to all the PDF eigenvector pairs are summed in quadrature. This scheme provides a robust procedure for propagating uncertainties in PDFs to any observable. Nevertheless, some ambiguities in the procedure remain. First, if a PDF eigenvector variation is found to map nonlinearly to M_W (i.e., if the positive and negative variation in the PDF eigenvector does not result in equal, opposite shifts in M_W), its contribution to the M_W uncertainty is not uniquely defined. It would be useful to understand the source of these nongaussian M_W uncertainties predicted by the PDF variation sets. Second, the confidence interval represented by the PDF ensemble is not calculated analytically from the quality of the global fit. The confidence interval of the CTEQ6 ensemble is estimated to be 90%, and it is used as such in the CDF Run II analysis. As the detector-related uncertainties on M_W shrink with the analysis of more data, these issues in PDF uncertainty estimation will become more important.

6. WHAT HAVE WE LEARNED ABOUT THE HIGGS AND OTHER NEW PHYSICS?

From 200 pb^{-1} of data, the CDF Run II analysis measures

$$M_W = 80,413 \pm 34(\text{stat}) \pm 34(\text{syst})\,\text{MeV}$$

by combining the results of the electron and muon transverse mass, lepton, and neutrino p_T fits using the BLUE (41) method. The m_T fits contribute 80% of the weight to this combination. Two of the fits are shown in **Figure 4** and the m_T systematic uncertainties are shown in **Table 4**, along with the systematic uncertainties on the combined result.

Table 5 summarizes recent measurements and their averages, showing both the impact of the CDF Run II measurement (19, 20) on the Tevatron and the world averages. The Tevatron combination has been updated using the BLUE method (as discussed in Reference 13), with the uncertainties due to PDFs and QED radiative corrections assumed to be fully correlated. The combination of the LEP and Tevatron measurements assumes no correlation. Possible correlation of the QED radiative corrections between the LEP and Tevatron measurements should be explored.

Figure 9 compares the latest world-average masses of the W boson (19, 20) and the top quark (18) with the predictions (16, 79) of the SM and the minimal supersymmetric extension of the standard model (MSSM). The measurements are consistent with the SM, although the central

Table 4 Systematic and total uncertainties in MeV for the m_T and combined fits in the CDF Run II analysis

Systematic	$W \to e\nu$	$W \to \mu\nu$	Common[a]	Combined[b]
$p_T(W)$ model	3	3	3	3.9
QED radiation	11	12	11	11.6
Parton distributions	11	11	11	12.6
Lepton energy scale	30	17	17	23.1
Lepton energy resolution	9	3	0	4.4
Recoil energy scale	9	9	9	8.3
Recoil energy resolution	7	7	7	9.6
Selection bias	3	1	0	1.7
Lepton tower removal	8	5	5	6.3
Backgrounds	8	9	0	6.4
Total systematic	39	27	26	34
Total uncertainty	62	60	26	48

[a]"Common" column shows the correlated uncertainties between the electron and muon channel m_T fits.
[b]"Combined" column shows the systematic uncertainty on the combined result from both channels, including the m_T, $p_T(\ell)$ and $p_T(\nu)$ fits. Data is from Reference 20. Abbreviation: QED, quantum electrodynamics.

values show some preference (albeit not definitive) for the MSSM over the SM (16, 79). Performing an electroweak fit within the context of the SM using these latest values of M_W and M_{top} and the methods and data described in References 14 and 80 yields the inferred value of the SM Higgs mass, $M_H = 76^{+33}_{-24}$ GeV (20). The effect of the CDF Run II measurement of M_W is to reduce the inferred value of M_H by 6 GeV (20). The corresponding upper limit is $M_H < 144$ GeV at the 95% confidence level. It is interesting to compare this confidence interval, derived from precision data alone, with the result of the direct Higgs boson searches at LEP, $M_H > 114.4$ GeV (81). The combination of these two pieces of information restricts the SM Higgs boson mass to a relatively narrow, low-mass range, with interesting and significant implications for direct searches at the Tevatron and the LHC.

Table 5 Current world's best W boson mass measurements and averages

Experiment	Mass (MeV)
DELPHI	80336 ± 67
L3	80270 ± 55
OPAL	80416 ± 53
ALEPH	80440 ± 51
CDF-I	80433 ± 79
DØ-I	80483 ± 84
LEP average	80376 ± 33
Tevatron-I average	80454 ± 59
World average	80392 ± 29
CDF-II	80413 ± 48
New CDF average	80418 ± 42
New Tevatron average	80429 ± 39
New world average	80398 ± 25

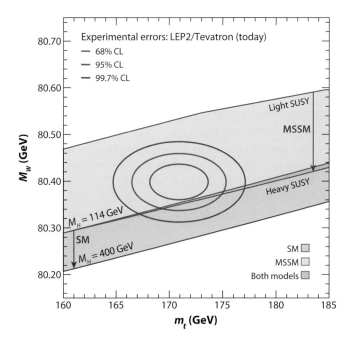

Figure 9

The $1\sigma-$, $2\sigma-$, and $3\sigma-$confidence level contours for the world-average W boson mass (19, 20) and the top quark mass (18), compared with the predictions (16, 79) of the standard model (SM) and the minimal supersymmetric extension of the standard model (MSSM). Figure from Reference 79.

7. ULTIMATE M_W PRECISION FROM THE TEVATRON RUN II

The M_W measurement depends critically on calibration of the lepton momentum, as well as a sufficiently precise and robust understanding of the hadronic recoil and the backgrounds. In addition, because the kinematic quantities to be fit are necessarily transverse kinematics rather than Lorentz-invariant kinematics the theoretical model of W boson production and decay must have a commensurate level of precision.

As discussed in this and previous reviews and the respective experiments' publications, sophisticated techniques have been developed to constrain the detector and theory models using the collider data. The measurements of M_W have been performed for the last two decades with samples of increasing statistics, and the total uncertainty has shrunk by a factor of ten, generally scaling with statistics. Over this time period, not only have the analysis techniques improved, but the calculations of W boson production and decay have been performed to higher order in QCD and QED and the global data constraints on PDFs and boson p_T have improved considerably. There is every reason to expect that improvements will continue to occur on all these fronts.

CDF and DØ will analyze larger Run II data sets with the goal of statistics scaling of as many of the systematic uncertainties as possible. There will be challenges along the way; for example if the lepton momentum resolution or the recoil resolution degrades due to multiple interactions, the precision will be worse with respect to scaling. Although some loss of resolution is inevitable, in our opinion this will not be a severe effect in itself. A greater challenge is the increase in the number of degrees of freedom needed to adequately describe the response and resolution functions of the leptons and the recoil. We have noted above that the DØ analysis is facing this issue in Run II with respect to Run I. There will likely be tension between the increasing complexity of the models and the additional data sets that can be used to constrain the new parameters. For instance, if the Z boson data alone were used to constrain an increasing number of parameters, the measurement precision would degrade with respect to scaling. However, the use of minimum-bias data, jet data, $\mathcal{J}/\psi$, and Υ data to augment the analysis and constrain new parameters has been demonstrated by the CDF Run II analysis. By continuing to add such constraints, scaling can be maintained and even improved upon.

The CDF Run II analysis provides insightful comparisons with the Run I analysis regarding the scaling of uncertainties. The Run II tracking resolution obtained with the COT is better than in CDF Run I, mostly due to the detector upgrade but also due to algorithm and alignment improvements. The electron energy resolution from calorimetry was maintained from Run I to Run II. In the early Run II data used for the publication (19, 20), the rate of multiple interactions was low and did not degrade the recoil resolution. As a result the fit statistical errors have continued to scale with event statistics. For the most important systematic uncertainty, which results from the lepton momentum calibration, the $\mathcal{J}/\psi$, Υ, $W \rightarrow e\nu$, and Z boson data have all been used in Run II; this represents an improvement in statistical scaling compared to Run I, where the momentum scale was set using primarily the Z boson data. Similarly, isolated tracks from minimum bias data were used in Run II to improve the uniformity of the hadronic calorimeter response with respect to rapidity, thereby reducing the reliance on Z boson data for recoil calibration and improving the u_T, m_T and $p_T(\nu)$ resolution. Finally, the number of ad hoc parameters in the recoil response and resolution parameterizations, as well as the $p_T(W)$ parameterization, was smaller in the CDF Run II analysis compared to Run I, but these parameters still provided a consistent description of the data. This reduction in the number of parameters was a result of using physically motivated parameterizations, and it contributed to smaller systematic uncertainties in the Run II analysis relative to scaling. If these models continue to prove adequate with higher statistics, future scaling of these uncertainties can be expected.

The detailed GEANT-based simulation of the detector is also being increasingly exploited to motivate response and resolution parameterizations. Careful first-principles calculations can eliminate ad hoc parameters in some cases and can improve the statistical power of the control data sets. Both CDF and DØ are utilizing these first-principles calculations more heavily in Run II than in Run I, a trend that is likely to continue.

As we anticipate improvements in PDFs due to new W asymmetry measurements (49, 50), higher order QED radiative corrections (76), and $p_T(W)$ parameterizations (46), we can expect Tevatron measurements to improve substantially. While the data in the CDF Run II publication were based on 200 pb^{-1}, both CDF and DØ now analyze 1–2 fb^{-1} and may ultimately analyze about 6 fb^{-1}. There is much to learn from the next round of publications from CDF and DØ; the CDF group has mentioned its goal of surpassing 25 MeV total uncertainty with its 2-fb^{-1} analysis (82). An ultimate M_W precision of 15 MeV from the Tevatron may be possible.

8. SUMMARY

The direct measurement of the W boson mass is one of the most important precision measurements at high Q^2—the others are M_Z, $\sin^2\theta_W$, and M_{top}—that constrain the mechanism of electroweak symmetry breaking. The LEP experiments have measured M_W with a combined precision of 33 MeV. Run I at the Tevatron ended with CDF and DØ publishing a combined hadron collider average with a precision of 59 MeV, based on 100 pb^{-1} each. Run II at the Tevatron is running successfully, and CDF has recently published its first Run II measurement with a precision of 48 MeV, using 200 pb^{-1}. The consistent measurements made by CDF and DØ have yielded a world average $M_W = 80,398 \pm 25$ MeV. For precision better than 15 MeV, M_W carries more weight in the SM fit for M_H than the weight of $\sin^2\theta_W$, given an M_{top} uncertainty of 1.5 GeV (M. Chanowitz, private communication). We are entering a new era of stringent electroweak tests of the SM Higgs mechanism in which M_W will play an increasingly important (even dominant) role and in which measurements of M_W (and M_{top}) will continue to improve at the Tevatron with the analysis of >1-fb^{-1} data sets. It will be interesting to see whether the precision electroweak fits will continue to support the SM, whether they will prefer an alternate theory such as its supersymmetric extension, and how the big picture will evolve with the discovery of new particles.

DISCLOSURE STATEMENT

The authors are not aware of any biases that might be perceived as affecting the objectivity of this review.

ACKNOWLEDGEMENTS

We would like to thank our colleagues with whom we have collaborated while working on the M_W measurement. We appreciate the useful comments on the manuscript from Douglas Glenzinski, Paul Grannis, Christopher Hays, Ronald Madaras, Larry Nodulman, Peter Renton, Oliver Stelzer-Chilton, and David Waters. The work of A.V.K. is partially supported by the U.S. Department of Energy under a grant to Duke University and by the Alfred P. Sloan Foundation.

LITERATURE CITED

1. Glenzinski DA, Heintz U. *Annu. Rev. Nucl. Part. Sci.* 50:207 (2000)
2. Glashow SL. *Nucl. Phys.* 22:579 (1961); Weinberg S. *Phys. Rev. Lett.* 19:1264 (1967); Salam A. In *Elementary Particle Theory*, p. 367, ed. N Svartholm. Stockholm: Almquist & Wiksell (1968)
3. Arnison G, et al. (UA1 Collab.) *Phys. Lett.* 122B:103 (1983)
4. Banner M, et al. (UA2 Collab.) *Phys. Lett.* 122B:476 (1983)
5. Arnison G, et al. (UA1 Collab.) *Phys. Lett.* 126B:398 (1983)
6. Bagnaia P, et al. (UA2 Collab.) *Phys. Lett.* 129B:130 (1983)
7. Albajar C, et al. (UA1 Collab.) *Z. Phys. C* 44:15 (1989)
8. Alitti J, et al. (UA2 Collab.) *Phys. Lett. B* 241:150 (1990)
9. Affolder T, et al. (CDF Collab.) *Phys. Rev. D* 64:052001 (2001)
10. Abazov VM, et al. (DØ Collab.) *Phys. Rev. D* 58:092003 (1998); Abbott B, et al. (DØ Collab.) *Phys. Rev. D* 58:012002 (1998)
11. Abbott B, et al. (DØ Collab.) *Phys. Rev. D* 62:092006 (2000)
12. Abazov VM, et al. (DØ Collab.) *Phys. Rev. D* 66:012001 (2002)
13. Abazov VM, et al. (CDF and DØ Collab.) *Phys. Rev. D* 70:092008 (2004)
14. Alcaraz J, et al. (ALEPH, DELPHI, L3, OPAL Collab., LEP Electroweak Working Group) arXiv:hep-ex/0612034 (2006)
15. Sirlin A. *Phys. Rev. D* 22:971 (1980)
16. Heinemeyer S, et al. *JHEP* 0608:052 (2006)
17. Awramik M, et al. *Phys. Rev. D* 69:053006 (2004)
18. Brubaker E, et al. (CDF and DØ Collab., Tevatron Electroweak Working Group) arXiv:hep-ex/0703034 (2007)
19. Aaltonen T, et al. (CDF Collab.) *Phys. Rev. Lett.* 99:151801 (2007)
20. Aaltonen T, et al. (CDF Collab.) arXiv:hep-ex/0708.3642 (2007)
21. Schael S, et al, (ALEPH Collab., DELPHI Collab., L3 Collab., OPAL Collab., SLD Collab., LEP Electroweak Working Group, SLD Electroweak and Heavy Flavor Groups) *Phys. Rep.* 427:257 (2006)
22. Barate R, et al. (ALEPH Collab.) *Phys. Lett. B* 401:347 (1997)

23. Abreu P, et al. (DELPHI Collab.) *Phys. Lett. B* 397:158 (1997)
24. Acciarri M, et al. (L3 Collab.) *Phys. Lett. B* 398:223 (1997)
25. Ackerstaff K, et al. (OPAL Collab.) *Phys. Lett. B* 389:416 (1996)
26. Schael S, et al. (ALEPH Collab.) *Eur. Phys. J. C* 47:309 (2006)
27. Abdallah J, et al, arXiv:0803.2534 (2008)
28. Acciarri M, et al. (L3 Collab.) *Eur. Phys. J. C* 45:569 (2006)
29. Abbiendi G, et al. (OPAL Collab.) *Eur. Phys. J. C* 45:307 (2006)
30. Alitti J, et al. (UA2 Collab.) *Phys. Lett. B* 276:365 (1992)
31. Abbott B, et al. (DØ Collab.) *Phys. Rev. D* 60:052003 (1999)
32. Acosta D, et al. (CDF Collab.) *Phys. Rev. Lett.* 94:091803 (2005)
33. Haywood S, et al. arXiv:hep-ph/0003275 (2000)
34. ATLAS Collab. *ATLAS TDR 15, CERN/LHCC 99/15.* (1999)
35. Buge V, et al. *J. Phys. G* 34:193 (2007)
36. Gordon AS. Ph.D. thesis, Harvard Univ. (1998); Adam IM. Ph.D. thesis, Columbia Univ. (1997); Flattum E. Ph.D. thesis, Michigan State Univ. (1996)
37. Abe F, et al. (CDF Collab.) *Nucl. Instrum. Methods A* 271:387 (1988)
38. Abachi S, et al. (DØ Collab.) *Nucl. Instrum. Methods A* 338:185 (1994)
39. Landry F, Brock R, Nadolsky PM, Yuan C-P. *Phys. Rev. D* 67:073016 (2003); Landry F, Brock R, Ladinsky G, Yuan C-P. *Phys. Rev. D* 63:013004 (2000); Balazs C, Yuan C-P. *Phys. Rev. D* 56:5558 (1997); Ladinsky GA, Yuan C-P. *Phys. Rev. D* 50:4239 (1994)
40. Ellis RK, Veseli S. *Nucl. Phys. B* 511:649 (1998)
41. Lyons L, Gibaut D, Clifford P. *Nucl. Instrum. Methods Phys. Res. A* 270:110 (1988)
42. Berends FA, Kleiss R, Revol JP, Vialle JP. *Z. Phys. C* 27:155 (1985); Berends F, Kleiss R. *Z. Phys. C* 27:365 (1985)
43. Wagner RG. *Comput. Phys. Commun.* 70:15 (1992)
44. Barberio E, Was Z. *Comput. Phys. Commun.* 79:291 (1994); Barberio E, van Eijk B, Was Z. *Comput. Phys. Commun.* 66:115 (1991)
45. Baur U, Keller S, Wackeroth D. *Phys. Rev. D* 59:013002 (1999)
46. Berge S, Nadolsky PM, Olness FI. *Phys. Rev. D* 73:013002 (2006); Konychev AV, Nadolsky PM. *Phys. Lett. B* 633:710 (2006)
47. Bodek A, et al. arXiv:0711.2859 (2007)
48. Thurman-Keup RM, Kotwal AV, Tecchio M, Byon-Wagner A. *Rev. Mod. Phys.* 73:267 (2001)
49. Acosta D, et al. (CDF Collab.) *Phys. Rev. D* 71:051104 (2005)
50. DØ Collaboration, Abazov VM, et al. arXiv:0709.4254 *Phys. Rev. D* 77:011106 (2008)
51. Elias J, et al. *Nucl. Instrum. Methods Phys. Res. A* 441:366 (2000)
52. Thomson EJ, et al. *IEEE Trans. Nucl. Sci.* 49:1063 (2002)
53. Acosta D, et al. (CDF Collab.) *Phys. Rev. D* 71:032001 (2005)
54. Abulencia A, et al. (CDF Collab.) *J. Phys. G* 34:2457 (2007)
55. Affolder T, et al. *Nucl. Instrum. Methods Phys. Res. A* 526:249 (2004)
56. Albrow M, et al. *Nucl. Instrum. Methods Phys. Res. A* 480:524 (2002); Apollinari G, et al. *Nucl. Instrum. Meth. Phys. Res. A* 412:515 (1998)
57. Abazov VM, et al. (DØ Collab.) *Nucl. Instrum. Methods A* 565:463 (2006)
58. Lincoln D. (DØ Collab.) *Nucl. Instrum. Methods A* 379:424 (1996)
59. Fast J. (DØ Collab.) *Nucl. Phys. Proc. Suppl.* 125:352 (2003)
60. Lipton R. (DØ Collab.) *Nucl. Instrum. Methods A* 566:104 (2006)
61. Abazov VM, et al. *Nucl. Instrum. Methods A* 552:372 (2005)
62. Abolins M, et al. *Nucl. Instrum. Methods A* 584:75 (2007)
63. Peters K. *AIP Conf. Proc.* 867:17 (2006)
64. Grindhammer G, Rudowicz M, Peters S. *Nucl. Instrum. Methods A* 290:469 (1990)
65. Yao W-M, et al. *J. Phys. G* 33:258 (2006)
66. Buchanan NJ. *AIP Conf. Proc.* 867:3 (2006)
67. Wigmans R. *Calorimetry.* Oxford: Clarendon, 754 pp. (2000) and references therein

68. Abazov VM, et al. (DØ Collab.) **http://www-d0.fnal.gov/phys_id/jes/public/plots_v7.1/** (2008)

69. Brun R, Carminati F. *CERN Program Libr. Long Writeup W5013* (unpublished) (1993)

70. Kotwal AV, Gerberich HK, Hays C. *Nucl. Instrum. Methods Phys. Res. A* 506:110 (2003)

71. Yao W-M, et al. *J. Phys. G* 33:1 (2006)

72. Jadach S, Kuhn JH, Was Z. *Comput. Phys. Comm.* 64:275 (1990); Jezabek M, et al. *Comput. Phys. Comm.* 70:69 (1992); Jadach S, Was Z, Decker R, Kuhn JH. *Comput. Phys. Comm.* 76:361 (1993); Was Z, Golonka P. *Nucl. Phys. Proc. Suppl.* 144:88 (2005); Was Z, et al. *Nucl. Phys. Proc. Suppl.* 98:96 (2001)

73. Acosta DE, et al. (CDF Collab.) *Phys. Rev. D* 70:032004 (2004); Acosta DE, et al. (CDF Collab.) *Phys. Rev. D* 73:052002 (2006)

74. Abbott B, et al. (DØ Collab.) *Phys. Rev. D* 63:072001 (2001)

75. Giele WT, Glover EWN, Kosower DA. *Nucl. Phys. B* 403:633 (1993)

76. Carloni Calame CM, Montagna G, Nicrosini O, Treccani M. *Phys. Rev. D* 69:037301 (2004)

77. Pumplin J, et al. *J. High Energy Phys.* 0207:012 (2002)

78. Martin AD, Roberts RG, Stirling WJ, Thorne RS. *Eur. Phys. Jour. C* 28:455 (2003); Martin AD, Roberts RG, Stirling WJ, Thorne RS. *Eur. Phys. J. C* 35:325 (2004)

79. Heinemeyer S, et al. *Pramana* 69:783 (2007)

80. Renton PB. *Rep. Prog. Phys.* 65:1271 (2002)

81. Barate R, et al. (LEP Working Group for Higgs Boson Searches, ALEPH Collab., DELPHI Collab., L3 Collab., OPAL Collab.) *Phys. Lett. B* 565:61 (2003)

82. Stelzer-Chilton O. (CDF Collab.) arXiv:0706.0284 (2007); Hays C. (CDF Collab.) *Frascati Physics Series*, p. 231, ed. M Greco, vol. XLIV (2007)

Coalescence Models for Hadron Formation from Quark-Gluon Plasma

Rainer Fries,[1,2] Vincenzo Greco,[3,4] and Paul Sorensen[5]

[1]Cyclotron Institute and Department of Physics, Texas A&M University, College Station, Texas 77843

[2]RIKEN/BNL Research Center, Brookhaven National Laboratory, Upton, New York 11973; email: rjfries@comp.tamu.edu

[3]Laboratori Nazionali del Sud, Istituto Nazionale di Fisica Nucleare, 95125 Catania, Italy

[4]Department of Physics and Astronomy, University of Catania, 95125 Catania, Italy; email: greco@lns.infn.it

[5]Physics Department, Brookhaven National Laboratory, Upton, New York 11973; email: prsorensen@bnl.gov

Annu. Rev. Nucl. Part. Sci. 2008. 58:177–205

The *Annual Review of Nuclear and Particle Science* is online at nucl.annualreviews.org

This article's doi: 10.1146/annurev.nucl.58.110707.171134

0163-8998/08/1123-0177$20.00

Key Words

quark-gluon plasma, recombination, coalescence, hadronization, elliptic flow, heavy ion collisions

Abstract

We review hadron formation from a deconfined quark-gluon plasma (QGP) via coalescence or recombination of quarks and gluons. We discuss the abundant experimental evidence for coalescence from the Relativistic Heavy Ion Collider (RHIC) and compare the various coalescence models advocated in the literature. We comment on the underlying assumptions and remaining challenges as well as the merits of the models. We conclude with a discussion of some recent developments in the field.

Contents

1. INTRODUCTION

Collisions between heavy nuclei are used to probe the properties of nuclear matter at high temperature and density. Lattice quantum chromodynamics (QCD) calculations indicate that if nuclear matter is heated above a critical temperature $T_c \approx 185$ MeV, quark and gluon degrees of freedom are liberated and a deconfined quark-gluon plasma (QGP) forms (1, 2). Unambiguous signatures of QGP formation in heavy ion collisions have been sought for decades. Recently, experiments at the Relativistic Heavy Ion Collider (RHIC) have yielded evidence that such a new state of matter has been found in collisions of Au atoms at a center-of-mass energy of $\sqrt{s} = 200$ GeV per nucleon-nucleon pair (3, 4).

The hot QGP phase formed in nuclear collisions at RHIC with a core temperature above 300 MeV only lasts for an extremely short time. The QGP quickly expands due to the high pressure and cools as it does so. Eventually, the quark and gluon constituents must combine into color-neutral objects and hadrons must form when the temperature reaches T_c. Hadronization from a QGP may be quite different from other cases, such as hadronization of hard scattered partons in elementary collisions, where no thermalization is reached and no bulk of partons is formed. In this review we discuss a model of QGP hadronization by coalescence or recombination of quarks and gluons. The models discussed herein have been successful in describing many salient features of hadron production in heavy ion collisions.

The emergence of recombination models was largely motivated by several unexpected observations (3), collectively known as the baryon puzzle. This term refers to measurements of baryon production in the intermediate transverse momentum region ($1.5 < p_T < 5$ GeV/c) (5, 6). Both the yield and the elliptic flow of baryons exhibit strange features. In nucleon-nucleon collisions at $p_T = 3$ GeV/c, only one baryon is produced for every three mesons (1:3), reflecting the larger mass and the requirement of a nonzero baryon number to form the baryon. In Au + Au collisions at RHIC, however, baryons and mesons are created in nearly equal proportions (1:1) despite those differences. In the same p_T region, the elliptic anisotropy (v_2) of baryons is also 50% larger than that of mesons. Therefore, baryon production is particularly enhanced in the direction of the impact vector between the colliding nuclei (6, 7).

The large baryon v_2 eliminates several alternative solutions that had been put forward for the baryon puzzle. The most common explanations for the baryon anomaly at RHIC were (*a*) coalescence or recombination, i.e., multiquark or -gluon processes during hadron formation (8–12); (*b*) baryon junctions, i.e. gluon configurations that carry baryon number (13); and (*c*) flow, i.e. a collective motion that populates the higher-p_T regions of phase space for the more massive baryons, as described by hydrodynamics (14–16). Only the coalescence models have survived the tests imposed by the impressive amount of data taken after the original discovery of the baryon enhancement. These models are particularly attractive because they seem to provide a natural explanation for the valence quark–number scaling that has been observed in v_2 measurements. They also relate hadronic observables to a prehadronic stage of interacting quarks and gluons. As such, they touch on issues central to the heavy ion physics program: deconfinement and chiral symmetry restoration.

This review is organized as follows. In the remainder of Section 1 we discuss the general context of hadronization and provide a brief history of recombination models. We also review the experimental evidence from RHIC. In Section 2 we review the basic theory and compare the different implementations of recombination models. In Section 3 we present a comprehensive overview of the available data that can be addressed by coalescence. In Section 4 we conclude with a discussion of open questions, recent developments, and future directions for research.

1.1. Hadronization

Hadronization has always been a challenging aspect of QCD, the fundamental theory of the strong force. QCD bound states are nonperturbative in nature and a first-principle description of their formation has yet to be obtained. Here we briefly discuss two approaches to dealing with hadronization that are routinely used in nuclear and particle physics; both of them have connections to the recombination model discussed in this review.

Light cone wave functions are used to describe the structure of hadrons relevant for exclusive processes (17). By exclusive, we mean that these wave functions involve a full set of partons with the quantum numbers of the hadron. Exclusive processes at high momentum transfer are naturally dominated by the few lowest Fock states. Formally, light cone wave functions are matrix elements of the set of parton operators between the vacuum and the hadron state in the infinite momentum frame, e.g., $\phi_p \sim \langle 0 \,|uud|\, p \rangle$, schematically, for a proton p. They describe the decomposition of the hadron in longitudinal momentum space in terms of partons with momentum fractions x_i. From theory, these wave functions are only constrained by very general arguments such as Lorentz covariance and approximate conformal symmetry. Direct measurements are difficult to obtain, but estimates have become available in recent years, in particular for the lowest Fock state of the pion (18, 19).

A complementary technique has been developed for inclusive hadron production, initial state $\to h + X$, at large momentum transfers in which a single colored parton a has to hadronize into the hadron h. For this purpose, fragmentation or parton decay functions $D_{a \to b}(z)$ have been defined (20). They give the probability of finding hadron h in parton a with a momentum fraction z,

$0 < z < 1$. The cross section for inclusive hadron production in $e^+ + e^-$, lepton-hadron, or hadron-hadron collisions can then be written as

$$\sigma_H = \sigma_a \otimes D_{a \to b},$$ 1.

which is a convolution of the production cross section σ_a for parton a with the fragmentation function $D_{a \to b}(z)$ (21, 22). Fragmentation functions are not reliably calculable from first principles in QCD. However, they are observables and can be measured experimentally. Parameterizations using data mostly from $e^+ + e^-$ collisions are available from several groups (23). Physically, the fragmentation of a single parton happens through the creation of $q\bar{q}$ pairs (through string breaking or gluon radiation and splitting), which subsequently arrange into color singlets and eventually form hadrons.

Both of the examples presented above apply to processes with a large momentum transfer, i.e., with a perturbative scale $\mu \gg \Lambda_{\text{QCD}}$. They are based on the concept of QCD factorization, which separates the long- and short-distance dynamics.[1] Such a perturbative scale is absent for the hadronizing bulk of partons in a heavy ion collision and neither technique—fragmentation or exclusive wave functions—can be readily applied in this situation.

To understand the challenge more clearly, let us compare the different initial conditions for the hadronization process. Fragmentation applies to a single parton in the vacuum, whereas exclusive wave functions are applied to a full set of valence quarks in the vacuum. On the other hand, the initial state just before hadronization in nuclear collisions is a thermal ensemble of partons just above T_c. The exact degree of thermalization is not clear a priori, but as we discuss below, complete thermalization may not be necessary.

The crucial point is that partons have a certain abundance in phase space such that there is no need for the creation of additional partons through splitting or string breaking. The most naïve expectation for such a scenario is a simple recombination of the deconfined partons into bound states. Indeed, there is experimental evidence that this is the correct description of hadronization, even long before a thermal occupation of parton phase space is reached.

1.2. Early Approaches to Recombination

Recombination models were first suggested shortly after the theory of QCD was developed in the 1970s. These models successfully described hadron production in the very forward region of hadronic collisions (24). The observed relative abundances of hadrons clearly deviate from expectations for fragmentation. This is known as the leading particle effect (25). As an example, a clear asymmetry between D^- and D^+ mesons was found in fixed target experiments with π^- beams on nuclei by the Fermi National Accelerator Laboratory (FNAL) E791 collaboration (26). The measured D^-/D^+ asymmetry goes to unity in the very forward direction, whereas fragmentation predicts that this asymmetry is very close to zero. This result can be explained by recombination of the $\bar{c}$ from a $c\bar{c}$ pair produced in the collision with a d valence quark from the π^- beam remnants. This mechanism is enhanced compared to the $c + \bar{d}$ recombination, which involves only a sea quark from the π^- (27). There is no thermalized parton phase in this example, which strongly backs the argument we set forth at the end of Section 1.1.

We arrive at the important conclusion that the presence of any reservoir of partons leads to significant changes in hadronization. Vacuum fragmentation is no longer valid in this situation. The reservoir of partons in the case of the leading particle effect is the soft debris from the broken

---

[1]We have neglected the scale dependence in the notation for wave functions and fragmentation functions for simplicity. A discussion of the scale dependence can be found in the original references given.

beam hadron. In heavy ion collisions it is the distribution of thermal partons. First applications of the coalescence picture to nuclear collisions appeared in the early 1980s (28), and they eventually led to the development of the algebraic coalescence rehadronization (ALCOR) model in the 1990s (29–31). ALCOR focuses on hadron multiplicities and was successfully applied to hadron production at RHIC and to the lower energies at the Super Proton Synchrotron (SPS) at the European Laboratory for Particle Physics (CERN).

1.3. Challenges at the Relativistic Heavy Ion Collider

Results from the first years of RHIC triggered a revival for recombination models applied to heavy ion collisions in an unexpected region. Three measurements in particular, taken in the intermediate p_T range (1.5 GeV/c < p_T < 5 GeV/c), have defied all other explanations. This region is outside of what was thought to be the "bulk" of hadron production (p_T < 1.5 GeV/c), whose features should be described by thermalization and hydrodynamic collective motion (ALCOR describes bulk hadronization). Rather, the intermediate p_T region was expected to be dominated by fragmentation of QCD jets, as it had been confirmed for pion production in $p + p$ collisions at RHIC (32). However, the results from RHIC clearly pointed towards a strong deviation from the fragmentation process at intermediate p_T in central Au + Au collisions. The three key observables were (*a*) the enhanced baryon-to-meson ratios (5, 33); (*b*) the nuclear modification factors R_{AA} and R_{CP}, i.e., the ratio of yields in central Au + Au collisions compared to those in peripheral Au + Au (R_{CP}) or $p + p$ (R_{AA}) collisions scaled by the number of binary nucleon-nucleon collisions (5, 6); and (*c*) the anisotropy of particle production in azimuthal angle relative to the reaction plane, i.e., the elliptic flow parameter v_2 (6, 7, 34, 35).

Figure 1 shows the measured antiproton-to-pion (5) and antilambda-to-kaon (33) ratios as a function of p_T for various centralities and collision systems. At intermediate p_T, a striking difference is observed between the baryon-to-meson ratios in central Au + Au collisions and those in $e^+ + e^-$ (36) or $p + p$ collisions (37). The measurements in **Figure 1** indicate that the processes by which partons are mapped onto hadrons are different in Au + Au collisions and in $p + p$ collisions. Changes only to the parton distributions prior to hadronization are not likely to lead to such drastic changes in the relative abundances.

Figure 2 shows the nuclear modification factor R_{CP} measured at RHIC for various identified hadrons. If the centrality dependence of particle yields scales with the number of binary nucleon-nucleon collisions, R_{CP} equals unity. A suppression at high p_T is taken as a signature for the quenching of jets in the bulk matter formed in central collisions. However, baryons (e.g., $\Lambda + \bar{\Lambda}$, $\Xi + \bar{\Xi}$, and $\Omega + \bar{\Omega}$) (33, 38) systematically show less suppression than mesons (e.g., kaons or ϕ) (39, 40). The same behavior was found for protons and pions (41). This key result shows that the mass of a hadron is less important for its behavior at intermediate p_T than whether it has two or three valence quarks. This finding rules out explanations blaming collective motion (i.e., flow) for the baryon enhancement, and it is a strong indication that parton degrees of freedom are important. Any remaining doubts were erased by a direct comparison of protons and ϕ mesons, which have the same mass but a different valence quark content: ϕ mesons behave like other, lighter mesons, not like protons (40, 42).

In noncentral nucleus-nucleus collisions, the overlap region of the nuclei is elliptical in shape. Secondary interactions can convert this initial coordinate space anisotropy into an azimuthal anisotropy of the final momentum-space distribution. That anisotropy is commonly expressed in terms of the coefficients from a Fourier expansion of the azimuthal dependence of the invariant yield (43); see Section 2. The second component (the elliptic flow parameter v_2) is large due to the elliptical shape of the overlap region. **Figure 3** shows the measured values for v_2 as a

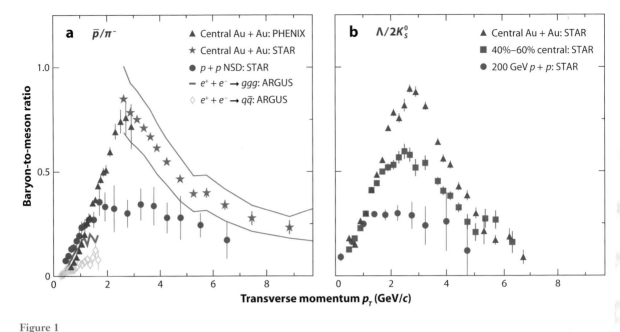

Figure 1

(*a*) $\bar{p}/\pi^-$ ratios measured in central Au + Au collisions at $\sqrt{s_{NN}} = 200$ GeV at the Relativistic Heavy Ion Collider (RHIC) compared to measurements from $e^+ + e^-$ and $p + p$ collisions. (*b*) The ratio $\bar{\Lambda}/2K_S^0$ for central and midcentral Au + Au collisions at $\sqrt{s_{NN}} = 200$ GeV measured by the Solenoidal Tracker at RHIC (STAR). The $\bar{p}/\pi^-$ ratio from $p + p$ collisions from STAR is shown for comparison. Abbreviations: NSD, nonsingle diffractive; PHENIX, Pioneering High Energy Nuclear Interaction Experiment.

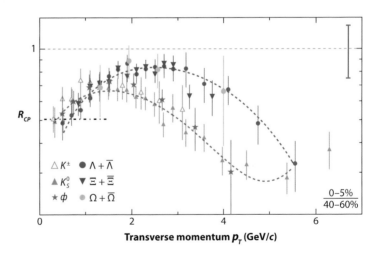

Figure 2

Nuclear modification factors (R_{CP}) for various identified particles measured in Au + Au collisions at $\sqrt{s_{NN}} = 200$ GeV by the Solenoidal Tracker at the Relativistic Heavy Ion Collider (STAR) collaboration. The K_S^0 and $\Lambda + \bar{\Lambda}$ R_{CP} values demonstrate that strange baryon yields are enhanced in central Au + Au collisions compared to strange meson yields. Later measurements of the ϕ, $\Xi + \bar{\Xi}$, and $\Omega + \bar{\Omega}$ showed that the rate of increase of the particle yields with collision centrality depended strongly on whether the particle was a baryon or meson, with the mass dependence being subdominant. The baryon and meson R_{CP} values fall into two separate bands (*lines*), with the baryon R_{CP} appearing larger than the meson R_{CP}.

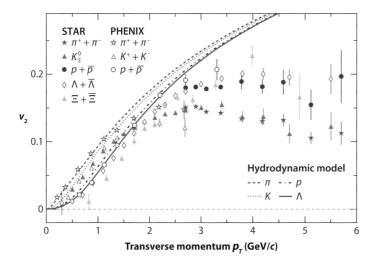

Figure 3

v_2 for several hadron species from a minimum-bias sample of Au + Au collisions at $\sqrt{s_{NN}} = 200$ GeV measured by the Solenoidal Tracker at the Relativistic Heavy Ion Collider (STAR) (6) and Pioneering High Energy Nuclear Interaction Experiment (PHENIX) (35) collaborations. The curves show the results from hydrodynamic model calculations (14). v_2 values also show that baryon production at intermediate p_T is enhanced in the in-plane direction, leading to larger baryon v_2. This observation is incompatible with the expectation of v_2 arising from parton energy loss.

function of p_T for pions, kaons, protons, and Λ hyperons (6, 35). In the bulk region ($p_T < 1.5$ GeV/c), v_2 increases with p_T (44). In this region the v_2 values for different hadrons are ordered by their mass, with more massive particles having smaller v_2 values (6, 35, 45). This mass ordering is qualitatively understood in hydrodynamic models of the expansion of the bulk of the fireball (14). Some hydrodynamic calculations are also shown in **Figure 3**. For $p_T > 1.5$ GeV/c, the data clearly deviate from hydrodynamic calculations. The measured v_2 seems to saturate, as predicted by parton cascades (46), and the particle-type dependence reverses: v_2 values for the more massive baryons are larger than those for mesons.

v_2 can also be generated if jets are quenched in the QGP (47). However, such calculations grossly underestimate the measured values of v_2, particularly when they simultaneously have to explain values of R_{CP} close to one. The data clearly show that although protons and hyperons have R_{CP} values near unity, their maximum v_2 values exceed those of pions and kaons by approximately 50%. Taken together, the particle-type dependence of v_2 and R_{CP} provides very stringent tests of various models for particle production and rule out pure jet fragmentation or simple hydrodynamics as models for hadron production at intermediate p_T.

2. FORMULATIONS OF HADRONIZATION BY RECOMBINATION

2.1. Basic Theory

Coalescence or recombination of particles is a very general process that occurs in a wide array of systems from the femtometer scale to astrophysics. In all these fields the first approach is to discard the details of the dynamical process in favor of exploiting an adiabatic approximation, in which a projection of the initial state onto the final clusterized state is considered. In the specific case of recombination of partons, most of the work described in the literature uses an instantaneous projection of parton states onto hadron states. The expected number of hadrons h from a partonic system characterized by a density matrix ρ is given by

$$N_h = \int \frac{d^3 P}{(2\pi)^3} \langle h; \mathbf{P} | \rho | h; \mathbf{P} \rangle.$$

2.

Here instantaneous means that the states are defined on a hypersurface, which is typically taken to be either at constant time, $t = $ constant, or on the light cone, $t = \pm z$. In this case information about the hadron bound state is schematically encoded in a wave function or a Wigner function. This approach leads to very simple math, but it is conceptually disadvantaged in that only three components of the four-momentum are conserved in such a $2 \to 1$ or $3 \to 1$ coalescence process. A more dynamical approach based on resonance scattering, which avoids this problem, can be realized (48). The information about the hadron bound state is then encoded in a cross section. In this section, we focus upon the instantaneous projection formalism, which has had great success explaining RHIC data. We return to the dynamic formulation in Section 4.

All available models of instantaneous coalescence can be traced back to the following basic formula, which can be derived from Equation 2. The number of mesons with a certain momentum $\mathbf{P}$ is (49)

$$\frac{dN_M}{d^3 P} = \sum_{a,b} \int \frac{d^3 R}{(2\pi)^3} \frac{d^3 q\, d^3 r}{(2\pi)^3} W_{ab} \left(\mathbf{R} - \frac{\mathbf{r}}{2}, \frac{\mathbf{P}}{2} - \mathbf{q}; \mathbf{R} + \frac{\mathbf{r}}{2}, \frac{\mathbf{P}}{2} + \mathbf{q} \right) \Phi_M(\mathbf{r}, \mathbf{q}).$$

3.

Here M denotes the meson and a, b are its coalescing valence partons. W_{ab} and Φ_M are the Wigner functions of the partons and the meson, respectively, $\mathbf{P}$ and $\mathbf{R}$ are the momentum and spatial coordinates of the meson, and $\mathbf{q}$ and $\mathbf{r}$ are related to the relative momentum and position of the quarks. The sum runs over all possible combinations of quantum numbers of the quarks in the hadron, essentially leading to a degeneracy factor C_M.

Note that coalescence, just like its counterpart in exclusive processes, is based on the assumption of valence quark dominance, i.e., the lowest Fock states are the most important ones. The corresponding formula for baryons containing three valence quarks can easily be given as well. It is also straightforward to generalize Equation 3 to include more partons, which would be gluons or pairs of sea quarks, accounting for the next terms in a Fock expansion (51).

For a meson consisting of two quarks, its Wigner function is formally defined as

$$\Phi_M(\mathbf{r}, \mathbf{q}) = \int d^3 s\, e^{-i s \cdot \mathbf{q}} \varphi_M \left(\mathbf{r} + \frac{\mathbf{s}}{2} \right) \varphi_M^* \left(\mathbf{r} - \frac{\mathbf{s}}{2} \right),$$

4.

where the two-quark meson wave function in position space φ_M can be represented as

$$\langle \mathbf{r}_1; \mathbf{r}_2 | M; \mathbf{P} \rangle = e^{-i \mathbf{P} \cdot (\mathbf{r}_1 + \mathbf{r}_2)/2} \varphi_M (\mathbf{r}_1 - \mathbf{r}_2).$$

5.

The Wigner function of the partons can be similarly defined from the density matrix ρ (49).

To evaluate Equation 3, expressions for the hadron wave functions and for the distribution of partons are used as input. We discuss the different implementations in the following subsection. Let us emphasize two common features of all implementations. First, the Wigner function for the multiparton distribution is usually approximated by its classical counterpart, the phase-space distribution of the partons on the hypersurface of hadronization. Second, Equation 3 is made explicitly Lorentz covariant to account for the relativistic kinematics.

2.2. Different Implementations of Recombination

Different manifestations of Equation 3 have been used in the literature (52). Closest to the master formula is the implementation by Greco, Ko & Lévai (GKL) (11, 53). In this approach the full overlap integral in Equation 3 over both relative position and momentum of the partons is calculated. However, several other groups [e.g., Fries, Müller, Nonaka & Bass (FMNB) (10, 49, 50); Hwa & Yang (HY) (54, 55); and Rapp & Shuryak (RS) (56)] simplify the situation by integrating out the information about position space. This leads to a formulation solely in momentum space, in which the information about the hadron is further compressed into a squared (momentum-space) wave function (also known as a recombination function).

The GKL implementation was originally motivated by a relativistic extension of the formalism for the coalescence of nucleons into deuterons and other light clusters in relativistic heavy ion collisions. Coalescence has been successfully applied to nucleons for more than two decades (57, 58). GKL use a manifestly covariant version of Equation 3 for the number of mesons coalescing,

$$N_M = C_M \int \prod_{i=a,b} (p \cdot d\sigma)_i d^4 p_i \delta \left(p_i^2 - m_i^2 \right) W_{ab}(r_a, p_b; r_b, p_b) \Phi_M(r; q), \qquad 6.$$

where the relative phase-space coordinates $r = r_b - r_a$ and $q = p_b - p_a$ are the four-vector versions of the vectors $\mathbf{r}$ and $\mathbf{q}$ in Equation 3 and where $d\sigma$ is a volume element of a space-like hypersurface. The hypersurface of coalescing partons is usually fixed by GKL through the condition of equal longitudinal proper time, $\tau = \sqrt{t^2 - z^2}$.

In the GKL formalism, the full phase-space overlap of the coalescing particles is calculated. For mesons this leads to a six-dimensional phase-space integral, which is computed using Monte Carlo techniques (53). This procedure has the advantage of avoiding some of the more restrictive approximations employed by other research groups. In addition, the numerical implementation of the six-dimensional phase-space integral can be applied directly to a quark phase that has been extracted from a realistic dynamic modeling of the phase-space evolution in the collision. Soon after the first implementation of GKL, Molnar (59) used similar techniques for hadronization in the partonic cascade approach.

The hadron Wigner function for light quarks used by GKL is a simple product of spheres in position and momentum space,

$$\Phi_M(r; q) = \frac{9\pi}{2} \Theta \left[\Delta_r^2 - r^2 \right] \times \Theta \left[\Delta_p^2 - q^2 + (m_1 - m_2)^2 \right]. \qquad 7.$$

The radii Δ_r and Δ_p in the Wigner formalism obey the relation $\Delta_p = \Delta_r^{-1}$, which is motivated by the uncertainty principle. The parameter Δ_p is taken to be different for baryons and mesons and is of the order of the Fermi momentum. Gaussian Wigner functions are used if heavy quarks are involved (60).

The Wigner functions used in the GKL approach appear to be more arbitrary than those based on light cone wave functions (e.g., the FMNB approach, discussed in detail below). However, many aspects of coalescence do not depend critically on the wave function for systems close to thermalization. Using the full information about the phase-space distribution of partons permits a direct connection to many quantitative properties of the bulk of the fireball, such as the multiplicity of partons and the energy and entropy densities just prior to hadronization. The parameters found by GKL in order to reproduce the behavior of hadron spectra at intermediate p_T also provide the bulk of the partonic fireball, which is consistent with what can be inferred from hydrodynamics and experimental data (e.g., the radial flow, parameterized as $\beta = \beta_0 r/R$, which exhibits a slope parameter $\beta_0 = 0.5$ that is consistent with hydrodynamical calculations at the end of the QGP phase) (15). Moreover, the energy density at hadronization is $\varepsilon = 0.8$ GeV fm^{-3}, which is very close to what is expected from lattice QCD calculations (1, 2). In addition, the entropy is found to be $dS/dy \approx 4800$, which agrees with the value inferred from experimental data by Pratt & Pal (61).

Compared to the rather complex full phase-space implementation, simplified momentum-space models focus on a direct exposition of some key features that then can be treated analytically. We discuss the FMNB implementation in detail here, but the HY and RS approaches are very similar.

The first assumption made by FMNB is that variations in the quark distribution across the size of a prehadronic state (which may be smaller than a free hadron) are small. The integration over the relative position of the quarks can then be carried out. For further simplification, we focus on the case where the momentum $|\mathbf{P}|$ of the hadron is much larger than the mass M. This allows us to treat the hadron as being on the light cone with a large $+ -$ momentum, $P^+ \gg P^-$ (the z axis in the lab frame is here taken to point into the direction of the hadron; this is termed the hadron light cone frame in Reference 49). The momenta of the partons inside the hadron can be parameterized by light cone fractions x_i of P^+ ($0 < x_i < 1$) and transverse momenta $\mathbf{k}_i$ orthogonal to the hadron momentum $\mathbf{P}$. The momenta $\mathbf{k}_i$ are usually also integrated out in a trivial way, leaving a single longitudinal momentum integration.

In the absence of any perturbative scale, the light cone wave functions are not known from first principles. However, again, the coalescence from partons thermally distributed in phase space is not very sensitive to the shape of the wave functions. For the lowest Fock state of a meson, the squared wave function or recombination function is usually parameterized as (49)

$$\Phi_M(x_1, x_2) = B x_1^{\alpha_1} x_2^{\alpha_2} \delta(x_1 + x_2 - 1), \qquad 8.$$

where the α_i are powers that determine the shape and where the constant B is fixed to normalize the integral over Φ_M to unity. The yield of mesons with momentum P can then be expressed as

$$\frac{dN_M}{d^3 P} = C_M \int_\Sigma \frac{d\sigma \cdot \mathbf{P}}{(2\pi)^3} \int_0^1 dx_1 \, dx_2 \, \Phi_M(x_1, x_2) W_{ab}(x_1 \mathbf{P}; x_2 \mathbf{P}), \qquad 9.$$

where $d\sigma$ is the hypersurface of hadronization. In many cases the emission integral over the hypersurface is not calculated explicitly, but rather is replaced by a normalization factor proportional to the volume of the hadronization hypersurface.

Several different values for the powers α_i can be found in the literature. Asymptotic light cone distribution amplitudes suggest $\alpha_i = 2$ for light valence quarks. For heavy-light mesons the relative size of the powers must be adjusted such that the average velocity of the quarks is approximately the same. For instance, for a charm and light quark system such as the D meson, RS (56) use the values $\alpha_c = 5, \alpha_{u,d} = 1$. It may be useful to look at the extreme case $\alpha_i \to \infty$, with the ratio of the α_i fixed. For two light quarks this implies $\Phi_M(x_1, x_2) = \delta(x_1 - 1/2)\delta(x_2 - 1/2)$. This is the limit of a very narrow wave function in momentum space and the remaining integral is trivial.

Analytic implementations of recombination applied to intermediate p_T in heavy ion collisions usually assume a thermal distribution of partons at hadronization. For such a system it seems sufficient to neglect correlations between partons and to use a factorization into single-particle phase-space distributions:

$$W_{ab}(r_a, p_a; r_b, p_b) = f_a(r_a, p_a) f_b(r_b, p_b). \qquad 10.$$

With thermal one-particle distributions f, this equation yields good results for single inclusive spectra, hadron ratios, etc. at RHIC. Observables pertaining to correlations of hadrons are more sensitive to correlations among partons. Results from RHIC seem to suggest that jetlike correlations between bulk partons exist down to intermediate p_T and have to be taken into account (62); we address this issue in more detail below. Coalescence applied to nonthermal systems, e.g., parton showers (63, 64) or hadronic collisions (56), requires more sophisticated models for multiparton distributions.

As mentioned above, recombination of partons in a thermal ensemble is largely independent of the shape of the hadron wave function. This can be most easily understood using the FMNB formalism, where the partons come from the tail of a Boltzmann distribution $e^{-p/T}$. For a meson with large momentum P, the integral in Equation 9 is

$$\sim \int_0^1 dx_a dx_b\, \Phi_M(x_a, x_b) e^{-x_a P/T} e^{-x_b P/T} \sim e^{-P/T} \int_0^1 dx_a dx_b\, \Phi_M(x_a, x_b), \qquad 11.$$

which is independent of the shape of Φ_M. Moving to lower-hadron P_T or using the full phase-space overlap, as in GKL, makes this argument less rigorous. Even in those cases, however, the results are only weakly dependent on the shape of the wave function unless very extreme choices are made. From this exercise we learn another important fact, which is tantamount to solving the baryon puzzle at RHIC: Both mesons and baryons would lead to the same Boltzmann distribution $\sim e^{-P/T}$ (for sufficiently large momentum P), which is very different from the suppression for baryons expected from fragmentation.

2.3. Competing Mechanisms of Hadron Production

In order to compute realistic hadron spectra that can be compared to data measured in heavy ion collisions, we must consider other important mechanisms of hadron production as well. QCD factorization theorems state that leading-twist hard parton scattering with fragmentation is the dominant mechanism of hadron production at asymptotically high momentum transfer (22). This is evident from the simple analytic formulas discussed in the previous subsection. Let us again consider the tail of a thermal parton distribution $f_{\mathrm{th}} \sim A e^{-p/T}$ and compare it to a power-law distribution $f_{\mathrm{jet}} \sim B p^{-\alpha}$ for large p. Power-law distributions are typical for partons coming from single hard scatterings. Both recombination and fragmentation preserve the basic shapes of the underlying parton distribution.

As argued above, recombination of n thermal partons leads to a thermal distribution for the resulting hadrons with the same slope $\sim A^n e^{-p/T}$, whereas the slope of a hadron recombining from n hard partons would steepen to $\sim B^\alpha p^{-n\alpha}$. Note that these n hard partons would come from n different jets! However, fragmentation from a single hard parton only leads to a shift in the slope of the power law $\sim B p^{-\alpha - \delta}$. Given that $\alpha \approx 6\ldots 8$, this suggests that recombination of hard partons is not an important mechanism, but that recombination is very efficient for thermal partons. Moreover, the exponential suppression of the thermal spectrum will set in at some value of p and leads to a power-law spectrum of hadrons from fragmentation off jets at very large p, in accordance with perturbative QCD.

From very basic considerations, therefore, we expect a transition from a domain dominated by recombination of thermal partons at intermediate p_T to a regime dominated by fragmentation of jets at very high p_T. This transition happens at higher values of p_T for baryons compared to mesons, as recombination produces baryons and mesons with roughly the same abundance, whereas baryons are suppressed in jet fragmentation.

This dual aspect of hadron production and the transition region is treated in different ways in the literature:

1. In publications by the FMNB group, thermal recombination is supplemented by a perturbative calculation that includes jet quenching and fragmentation. The two components of the spectrum are simply added (49). No mixing of the thermal and hard partons is included, leading to a rather sharp transition between the two regions.

2. The GKL group allows coalescence between soft and hard partons. For mesons this would correspond to a term

$$\sim f_{\text{th}}(p_a) f_{\text{jet}}(p_b) \Phi_M(p_a - p_b). \qquad 12.$$

3. Instead of fragmenting hard partons directly, the HY group (63) defines the parton contents of a jet (initiated by a hard parton), the so-called shower distributions. These distributions are given by nonperturbative splitting functions $S_{ij}(z)$, which describe the probability of finding a parton of flavor j with momentum fraction z in a jet originating from a hard parton i. The parton content of a single jet then recombines and the resulting hadron spectrum must match the result from jet fragmentation. HY (63) fit the shape of the parton shower distributions to describe the known fragmentation functions for pions, protons, and kaons. The power of this approach lies in the fact that the fragmentation part of the hadron spectrum is computed with the same formalism. Thus, it is natural to also coalesce shower partons with thermal partons (55).

The HY approach is also well suited to medium corrections to fragmentation in much more dilute systems such as $p + A$ collisions (64). Hwa and collaborators found that the hadron-dependent part of the Cronin effect in $d + Au$ collisions at RHIC can be attributed to coalescence of jet partons with soft partons from the underlying event. A more rigorous definition of parton showers and a discussion of the scale dependence can be found in work by Majumder et al. (65).

2.4. Elliptic Flow

In the momentum-space formulation we can straightforwardly predict the particle-type dependence of the elliptic flow v_2 of hadrons (43) arising from coalescence. This derivation (given below) has been criticized as being too simplistic (66, 67). However, the scaling law holds numerically to very good approximation in the GKL approach; as we show in the next section, the data from RHIC follow this law with surprising accuracy. In Section 4 we further discuss criticism of this derivation.

Let us assume that the elliptic flow of a set of partons a just before hadronization is given by an anisotropy $v_2^a(p_T)$ at midrapidity ($y = 0$). The phase-space distribution of partons a can then be written in terms of the azimuthal angle ϕ as

$$f_a(\mathbf{p}_T) = \bar{f}_a(p_T) \left(1 + 2v_2^a(p_T) \cos 2\phi\right), \qquad 13.$$

where odd harmonics vanish due to the symmetry of the system and where higher harmonics are neglected. $\bar{f}$ is the distribution averaged over the azimuthal angle ϕ. A general expression for the elliptic flow of hadrons coalescing from these partons can be derived as a function of the parton elliptic flow. For a meson with two valence partons a and b and for small elliptic flow $v_2 \ll 1$, we have

$$
\begin{aligned}
v_2^M(p_T) &= \frac{\int d\phi \cos(2\phi) d N_M/d^2 p_T}{\int d\phi d N_M/d^2 p_T} \\
&\sim \int dx_a dx_b \, \Phi_M(x_a, x_b) \left[v_2^a(x_a \, p_T) + v_2^b(x_b \, p_T)\right]. \qquad 14.
\end{aligned}
$$

The full expressions, including corrections for large elliptic flow, can be found in Reference 49. In the case of a very narrow wave function in momentum space ($\alpha \to \infty$), Equation 14 leads to the expression

$$v_2^M(p_T) = v_2^a(x_a \, p_T) + v_2^b(x_b \, p_T), \qquad 15.$$

with fixed momentum fractions x_a and x_b ($x_a + x_b = 1$).

Thus, for hadrons consisting of light quarks that exhibit the same elliptic flow before hadronization, we arrive at a simple scaling law with the number of valence quarks n:

$$v_2^h(p_T) = nv_2^a(p_T/n).$$ 16.

This scaling law was originally suggested by several authors after first indications for scaling were found in data gathered at RHIC (8, 12, 49, 68). Equation 15 has also been used to estimate the elliptic flow of heavy quarks from measurements of heavy-light systems such as D mesons (60, 69). This treatment has also been extended to harmonics beyond the second order and generalized scaling laws for the fourth- and sixth-order harmonics have been derived (70).

2.5. Comparison of Approximations and Assumptions

The main features of the coalescence models of hadronization are shared by all the approaches discussed here, each of which has been overwhelmingly successful. However, despite the agreement on the general properties and their ability to describe baryon and meson spectra, there are different approximations and assumptions involved. Some have already been mentioned in the previous paragraphs. Here we discuss additional points in more detail.

One important difference between these coalescence models is the mass of the quarks in the parton phase. GKL and FMNB use effective masses that are roughly the size of the constituent quark masses in the hadrons formed (i.e., $m_{u,d} \approx 300$ MeV, $m_s \approx 475$ MeV). This can be justified by the fact that coalescence does not explicitly include all the interactions. A part of the nonperturbative physics is encoded in the dressing of quarks, leading to a finite mass, which is also consistent with the requirement of (at least approximate) energy conservation. Furthermore, quasi-particle descriptions of the thermodynamics properties of the QGP estimate thermal masses of approximately 400 MeV (71, 72). However, the exact relation between masses in a chirally broken phase and thermal masses above T_c remains an open question. In the HY approach massless quarks are assumed. For the phenomenology at intermediate momenta, $p > m$, masses do not play a crucial role, as a good description of measured spectra can be obtained with both assumptions.

The missing position-space information is a weakness of the FMNB and HY implementations. In principle, very complex space-momentum correlations might exist in the parton phase before hadronization, and they might be needed to describe elliptic flow in an appropriate fashion (66–68). However, in the actual GKL computations, the spatial distribution is taken to be uniform, similar to the assumption used in pure momentum-space implementations. The only space-momentum correlation in GKL is that arising from radial flow; no systematic tests of more complicated space-momentum correlations are available in this formalism.

The GKL implementation can easily accommodate resonance formation and decay (53). Currently, direct observations of baryon anomaly and elliptic flow scaling are available only for stable hadrons. However, stable hadrons can contain a large feed-down contribution from resonance decays, especially pions (73–75). At intermediate p_T the role of resonance decays is somewhat reduced, which justifies neglecting resonances in the work by FMNB and HY. The violation of the v_2 scaling law is generally mild at intermediate p_T; however, GKL show that by including resonance decays both p_T spectra and v_2 exhibit better agreement with data toward lower p_T (76). A schematic study of the elliptic flow of resonances themselves has been conducted in the FMNB formalism. It was found that elliptic flow is sensitive to the amount of resonances formed in the hadronic phase versus resonances emerging directly from

Table 1 Key differences among the most popular implementations of recombination

	GKL	FMNB	HY
Instantaneous coalescence	Yes	Yes	Yes
Overlap integral	Full six-dimensional	Longitudinal momentum	Longitudinal momentum
Soft-hard coalescence	Yes	No	Soft-shower
Massive quarks	Yes	Yes	No
Resonances	Yes	No	No

Abbreviations: FMNB, Fries, Müller, Nonaka & Bass (10, 49); GKL, Greco, Ko & Lévai (11, 53); HY, Hwa & Yang (9, 54).

hadronization (77). We summarize the main differences among the approaches discussed in this section in **Table 1**.

3. DATA FROM ELEMENTARY AND HEAVY ION COLLISIONS

In this section we compare various coalescence model calculations to the available data and present predictions for future measurements. We start with single inclusive measurements, specifically spectra, hadron ratios, and nuclear modification factors. We proceed to discuss elliptic flow, particle correlations, and fluctuations. Although all of these observables naturally focus upon RHIC data taken during runs at $\sqrt{s} = 200$ we conclude with an overview of data at different energies.

3.1. Hadron Spectra and Baryon-to-Meson Ratios

In **Figure 4** we show results from a coalescence model calculation of identified particle spectra using the FMNB method (49). The spectra of neutral pions, kaons, protons, and hyperons for central Au + Au collisions at 200 GeV are compared to date from RHIC (38, 41). The salient features of the spectra are an exponential fall-off at intermediate p_T with a transition to a harder power-law shape at higher p_T, as predicted above. The transition from an exponential shape to a power-law shape occurs at a higher p_T for baryons than for mesons, again in accordance with the predictions from simple underlying principles.

Figure 5 shows two baryon-to-meson ratios: antiprotons versus pions and Λ baryons versus K_S^0 mesons. Results from the GKL model for $\bar{p}/\pi^-$ (53) and $\Lambda/2K_s^0$ (78), as well as from the FMNB model (49, 79), are compared with data from RHIC. Both calculations describe a baryon enhancement at intermediate p_T that diminishes until the spectra are dominated by fragmentation at higher p_T. The GKL model appears to provide a better description of the data, but a comprehensive analysis of the systematic uncertainties in the models has not been presented.

3.2. Elliptic Flow and Quark Number Scaling

Early identified particle measurements at RHIC showed that for $p_T < 1$ GeV/c, v_2 at a given p_T is smaller for more massive hadrons and that when plotted against m_T-m_0, the v_2 for different species fell on a single curve. With higher statistics, measurements revealed that at higher p_T the mass ordering breaks and more massive baryons exhibit larger v_2 values (80, 81). This observation led to speculation about hadron formation from coalescence and scaling of v_2 with quark number. These speculations culminated in detailed calculations, which we present in this subsection.

Figure 6 shows data on v_2 scaled by the number n of valence quarks in a given hadron as a function of p_T/n for several species of identified hadrons at $\sqrt{s_{NN}} = 200$ GeV (40, 82). A polynomial function has been fit to the scaled values of v_2. Best agreement with scaling is found for $p_T/n > 0.6$ GeV/c. Below this point, hadron v_2/n is ordered by mass.

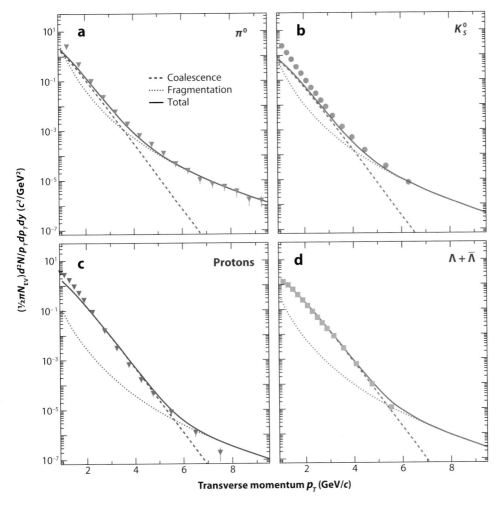

Figure 4

p_T spectra at midrapidity from 200-GeV central Au + Au collisions for (*a*) pions, (*b*) kaons, (*c*) protons, and (*d*) hyperons. The curves show the recombination and fragmentation components of the spectra obtained in the Fries, Müller, Nonaka & Bass (FMNB) (49) formalism along with the total, which accords well with the data.

By combining m_T–m_0 scaling and quark number scaling, one can achieve a better scaling across the whole momentum range (42). **Figure 7** shows v_2/n versus $(m_T - m_0)/n$ for several species of mesons and baryons. The scaling at low m_T–m_0 holds with an accuracy of 5–10%. At higher m_T–m_0, a violation of the simple scaling becomes apparent.

The breakdown of simple quark number scaling was predicted by several authors (66–69, 76). However, no clear consensus has emerged on whether kinetic energy scaling at intermediate p_T is merely a consequence of p_T scaling (as m_T–$m_0 \rightarrow p_T$ with increasing p_T) or whether it offers genuine new insights. **Figure 8** presents a comparison of data with the predictions for scaling violations.

Three possible sources of violations of quark number scaling have been studied within the GKL and FMNB implementations. Realistic wave functions with finite width (as opposed to the limit $\alpha = \infty$ needed for the derivation of scaling) represent one of these sources. Both theoretical curves shown in **Figure 8** use realistic wave functions (note, however, that in GKL the quarks need not be

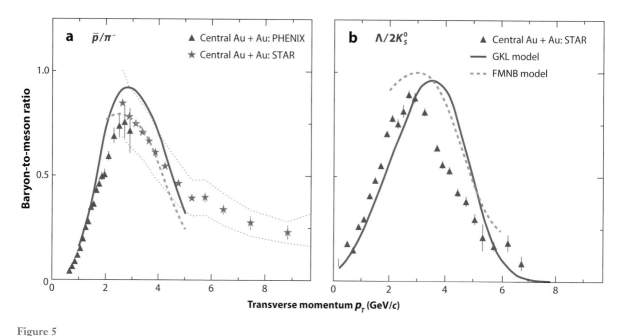

Figure 5

Ratios of baryon yields to meson yields for central Au + Au collisions at 200 GeV. The Greco, Ko & Lévai (GKL) (53, 78) and Fries, Müller, Nonaka & Bass (FMNB) (49, 79) calculations for $\bar{p}/\pi^-$ (*a*) and $\Lambda/2K_s^0$ (*b*) are compared to data from the Solenoidal Tracker at the Relativistic Heavy Ion Collider (STAR) and Pioneering High Energy Nuclear Interaction Experiment (PHENIX) collaborations.

collinear). Another correction expected from higher Fock states should scale with higher weights $n + 1, n + 2$, etc. A study within the FMNB framework showed that although thermal spectra are virtually unaltered, there are visible effects for v_2. However, those are numerically surprisingly small (51). A third breaking of scaling is expected from resonance decays studied in Reference 76.

These three effects cause the hadron v_2/n to fall below the quark v_2 values. The reduction is larger for baryons such that naive scaling is broken. The predicted violation (51, 76) is in fairly good agreement with the data (84). For $p_T > 2$–2.5 GeV, hadronization should be dominated by fragmentation; hence the ratio $(B–M)/(B+M)$ should relax to the value –0.2 if baryons and mesons from fragmentation have equal v_2 and depend only weakly on p_T. The fragmentation contribution is not included in either theoretical calculation shown in **Figure 8**. We discuss further arguments against v_2 scaling in Section 4.2.

The RHIC program has also confirmed, for the first time, the existence of nonvanishing higher azimuthal anisotropies beyond elliptic flow (85). The existence of a sizable fourth harmonic, $v_4 = \langle\cos(4\phi)\rangle$, had been anticipated in hydrodynamic calculations (86). Coalescence predictions for the relative v_4 of baryons and mesons provide further evidence for this recombination scenario. Such relations were first worked out by Kolb et al. (70). Concrete computations were later performed in the GKL model (78), where investigators found that the difference between baryon and meson v_4 is much more pronounced than for v_2. This finding may lead to valuable constraints for coalescence models in future high-statistics runs at RHIC.

3.3. Heavy Quarks

Coalescence has also been applied to the study of hadrons involving heavy quarks, particularly D and B mesons (60, 87, 88). These studies have attracted increasing interest due to the surprisingly

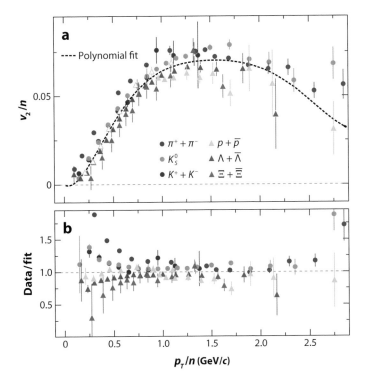

Figure 6

(*a*) The elliptic anisotropy parameter v_2 scaled by quark number n and plotted against p_T/n. (*b*) To investigate the quality of agreement between hadron species, the data from panel *a* are scaled by a fitted polynomial function and plotted here.

strong interaction between heavy quarks and the medium first seen in R_{AA} (91, 92) and v_2 of single electrons from semileptonic decays of D and B mesons. Although the primary goal of these studies is to understand the origin of this strong interaction with the medium, it is clear that the hadronization mechanism plays a significant role in the interpretation of the data (89, 90). In **Figures 9** and **10** we show R_{AA} and v_2 for single electrons from semileptonic decays, together with experimental data from PHENIX (Pioneering High Energy Nuclear Interaction Experiment) and STAR (91, 92). Comparing the coalescence-plus-fragmentation and fragmentation-only models, one notices a significant effect from coalescence that manifests in an increase in both R_{AA} and v_2 up to $p_T \sim 3$ GeV/c for single electrons (which corresponds to about $p_T \sim 7$ GeV at the meson level). The effect is crucial because coalescence reverses the usual correlation between R_{AA} and v_2 and so allows for a better agreement with the data. The nonphotonic electron spectrum can also be effected by coalescence if the Λ_c/D ratio is enhanced in Au + Au collisions compared to $p + p$ collisions (93). This is because the branching ratios to electrons are much smaller for charm baryons than for charm mesons.

An important development in the study of QCD at high temperatures is the emerging role of coalescence for quarkonia in a QGP. Even though coalescence has been applied to the J/Ψ for many years, the present implementations can be used to check not only the yield but also the spectra and elliptic flow as a function of transverse momentum. This enables investigators to perform consistency checks between the spectra observed for open charm mesons and for J/Ψs. Such studies will be of particular interest at the Large Hadron Collider (LHC), where the J/Ψ should be dominated by regeneration in the plasma (94, 95). In addition, recent studies have found that even

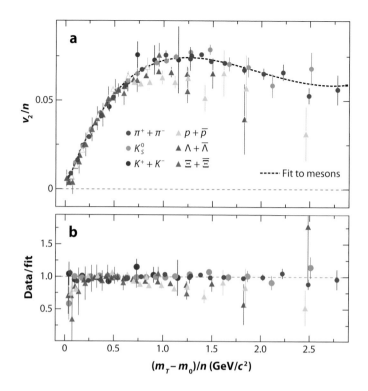

Figure 7

Quark number scaled elliptic flow versus $(m_T - m_0)/n$. (*a*) In the low $m_T - m_0$ region, the scaling is improved by plotting versus $m_T - m_0$. (*b*) v_2/n is scaled by a polynomial fit to the meson v_2/n only. The ratio of the data to the fit shows that baryon v_2/n tends to lie below the meson v_2/n.

if the binding of a J/Ψ is screened in a QGP, the spectral function still exhibits correlations above those expected for free quarks (96). These residual correlations may have important implications at hadronization that could be studied in future recombination calculations.

3.4. Particle Correlations and Fluctuations

Single-particle observables and elliptic flow–motivated coalescence models have been successfully applied throughout the history of RHIC data taking. Recently, however, measurements of hadron correlations have challenged this success. At RHIC measurements have been made of the correlation between a trigger particle with momentum p_T^{trig} and an associated particle with momentum p_T that is typically smaller than p_T^{trig}. The experimental observable is usually the associated yield, which is the yield of correlated pairs divided by the trigger yield. Associated yields are measured as a function of relative azimuthal angle $\Delta\phi$ and both trigger and associated p_T (97, 98). This observable is ideal for detecting correlations typical for jets. Jets give signals at $\Delta\phi = 0$ (near-side jet) and $\Delta\phi = \pi$ (away-side jet).

Researchers were initially surprised that such jetlike correlations were found with both trigger and associated p_T in the recombination domain below 4 to 6 GeV/c. It was quickly pointed out by several groups, however, that correlations among hadrons in this kinematic regime can come about through at least two different mechanisms. First, mixed soft-hard recombination or thermal-shower recombination naturally leads to correlated hadrons; these processes were first

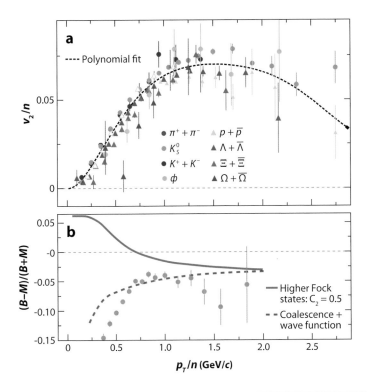

Figure 8

(*a*) Quark number–scaled v_2 showing violation of ideal scaling. A polynomial is fit to all the available data. (*b*) The difference between quark number–scaled baryon v_2 and quark number–scaled meson v_2 divided by the sum $(B-M)/(B+M)$, where B is v_2/n for baryons and M is v_2/n for mesons. The solid red curve shows model predictions in the model by Fries, Müller, Nonaka & Bass (FMNB) (51) using realistic wave functions and a 50% admixture of a higher Fock state containing an additional gluon. The dashed blue line shows calculations in the Greco, Ko & Lévai (GKL) (68) model with realistic wave functions.

explored by the HY group (99). A shower parton coalescing to become part of a hadron at intermediate p_T provides a correlation of this hadron with all of the hadrons coming from fragmentation of the same jet, or from the associated away-side jet.

A second possibility was identified in a work by Fries, Müller & Bass in an extended FMNB framework (62, 100, 101). These authors showed that any residual correlations in the tail of the bulk parton distribution automatically lead to correlations among the coalescing hadrons. To prove this point they introduced weak two-particle correlations as corrections to the usual factorization ansatz for the multiparton Wigner functions, e.g.,

$$W_{ab}(p_a, p_b) = f_{\text{th}}(p_a)f_{\text{th}}(p_b)(1 + C_{ab}(p_a, p_b))\qquad 17.$$

for two partons a, b. Under these specific assumptions, they obtained correlations for the coalescing hadrons that are amplified by the product of valence quarks numbers (i.e. 4, 6, and 9 for meson-meson, baryon-meson, and baryon-baryon pairs, respectively), similar to the enhancement of elliptic flow by the number of valence quarks. Although it is not clear that the specific assumptions (e.g. weak two-particle correlations) hold at RHIC, a reasonable result for associated yields as a function of centrality was obtained.

Figure 11 shows the associated yield of near-side hadrons for trigger baryons and trigger mesons as calculated in Reference 62, together with PHENIX results from Reference 102. Thus

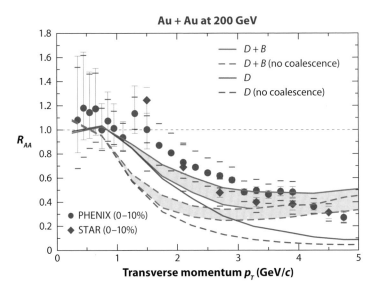

Figure 9

Nuclear modification factor R_{AA} of single electrons from semileptonic decays in Au + Au collisions at 200 GeV. The solid lines represent the predictions from a coalescence-plus-fragmentation model (89) for electrons from D and B mesons (*shaded gray band between solid red lines*) and from D mesons only (*solid blue line*). The dashed lines represent the results without coalescence. The shaded gray bands in both cases reflect the theoretical uncertainty in the heavy quark diffusion coefficients (87). Data taken from References 91 and 92. Abbreviations: PHENIX, Pioneering High Energy Nuclear Interaction Experiment; STAR, Solenoidal Tracker at the Relativistic Heavy Ion Collider.

far, a scaling law for correlations between different pairs of hadron species has not been observed in data. This is compatible with the fact that correlations from jet fragmentation are strong and must be added even at intermediate p_T, even though fragmentation is suppressed in single inclusive observables at the same p_T (62). The authors of this study (62) argue that the phase space relevant for recombination at intermediate momentum is not necessarily completely thermalized. Rather, remnants of quenched jets, so-called hot spots, could be an important component, leading to some residual jetlike correlations among partons through simple momentum conservation. Independent of the detailed modeling, recombination has been shown to be compatible with measurable correlations at intermediate p_T.

Charge fluctuations (103) have also been shown to be consistent with the recombination process and are considered to be a good probe for QGP formation. General expectations from coalescence are in fairly good agreement with data (104, 105). A recent, more specific study shows that consistency with coalescence is obtained if the number of quarks and antiquarks is approximately $dN/dy \cong 1300$ for central collisions (106). This finding agrees with the parton multiplicity estimated in the GKL implementation (53) and with the ALCOR model (107). This is a valuable consistency test for coalescence models.

3.5. Beam Energy Dependence

Most of the work published in the context of coalescence models focuses on Au + Au collisions at RHIC energies of 130 or 200 GeV. Of course, it is important to understand if the models can predict the correct behavior of observables, e.g., baryon-to-meson ratios, as a function of collision energy $\sqrt{s}$. Before the low-energy Au + Au run at RHIC with $\sqrt{s} = 62$ GeV was completed,

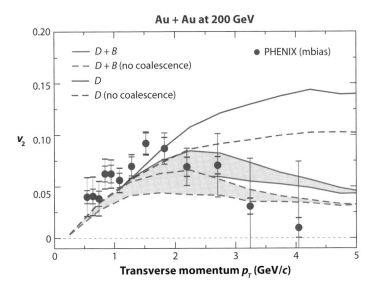

Au + Au at 200 GeV

—— $D + B$	● PHENIX (mbias)
– – $D + B$ (no coalescence)	
—— D	
– – D (no coalescence)	

v_2

Transverse momentum p_T (GeV/c)

Figure 10

Elliptic flow v_2 of single electrons from semileptonic decays in Au + Au collisions at 200 GeV. The solid lines represent the predictions from a coalescence-plus-fragmentation model (89) for electrons from D and B mesons (*shaded gray band between solid red lines*) and from D mesons only (*solid blue line*). The dashed lines represent the results without coalescence. The shaded gray bands in both cases reflect the theoretical uncertainty in the heavy quark diffusion coefficients (87). Data taken from Reference 91. Abbreviation: PHENIX, Pioneering High Energy Nuclear Interaction Experiment.

a prediction was presented within the GKL approach that utilized a simple extrapolation of the model parameters (108). It was found that the p/π ratio increases compared to $\sqrt{s} = 200$ GeV, whereas the $\bar{p}/\pi$ ratio decreases. This is exactly what was measured when the lower-energy data were analyzed (109). The predictions for scenarios with and without coalescence are shown together with the data in **Figure 12**. The data clearly favor the scenario with quark coalescence. The discrepancy found for $\bar{p}/\pi$ at $p_T > 7$ GeV may be due to the poor knowledge of the identified proton-fragmentation function (108).

Novel results from heavy ion collisions at much larger energies will soon become available. The LHC at CERN will collide Pb ions at a center-of-mass energy of $\sqrt{s} = 5.5$ TeV per nucleon-nucleon pair. This will lead to QGP fireballs with much higher temperatures. Moreover, one can also predict that the number of hard processes will increase tremendously due to the rising gluon distribution at small Bjorken x. Naïvely, one would expect the window in p_T where coalescence is dominating to increase. However, the estimates for this region depend upon the radial flow (which pushes the coalescing hadrons to higher p_T) and jet quenching (which leads to less fragmented hadrons at high p_T).

Possible scenarios have been explored in the FMNB framework using different assumptions for the radial flow (110). These estimates are shown in **Figure 13**. See also a recently published, more systematic study of elliptic flow as a function of collision energy (111).

4. CHALLENGES AND OUTLOOK

The RHIC program has provided remarkable evidence that coalescence of quarks is the dominant mechanism for hadronization from a deconfined plasma. Nonetheless, some problems remain

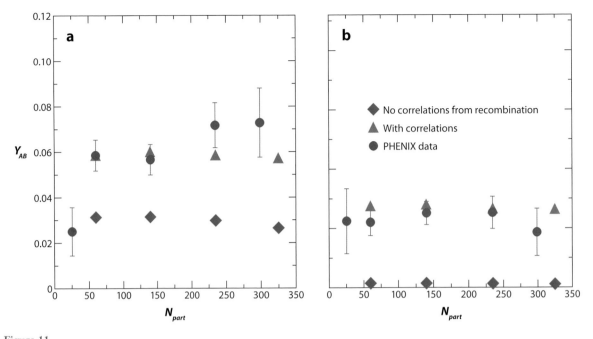

Figure 11

Associated hadron yields on the near side as a function of number of participants for meson triggers (*a*) and baryon triggers (*b*). Data taken from Reference 62. The blue diamonds represent the expected hadron correlations if fragmentation is the only source of correlations and recombination is correlation free. Red triangles indicate the same calculation with small two-particle correlations among coalescing partons. PHENIX (Pioneering High Energy Nuclear Interaction Experiment) data (*purple filled circles*) taken from Reference 102.

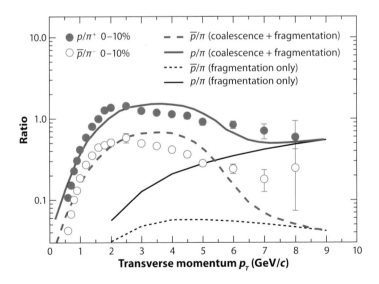

Figure 12

p/π^+ ratio and $\bar{p}/\pi^-$ ratio in central Au + Au collisions at 62.4 GeV. The predictions of the Greco, Ko & Lévai model (coalescence plus fragmentation) (see Reference 108) are shown for p/π^+ (*thick solid lines*) and for $\bar{p}/\pi^-$ (*thick dashed lines*). The predictions of fragmentation only are indicated by thin lines. Data from STAR (Solenoidal Tracker at the Relativistic Heavy Ion Collider) taken from Reference 109.

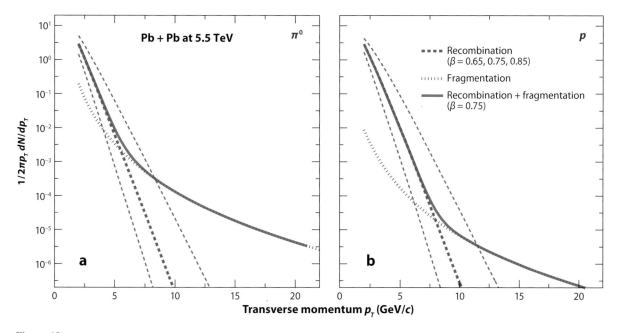

Figure 13

Predictions for π^0 (*a*) and proton (*b*) spectra in central Pb + Pb collisions at the Large Hadron Collider (LHC) using radial flow parameters β = 0.65, 0.75, and 0.85, respectively. The larger the radial flow, the more the recombination region extends to higher p_T, possibly up to 10 GeV/*c*. Data from Reference 110.

unsolved and several new questions are raised by the formalism itself (for instance, it is appealing to apply recombination at low momenta, where the phase space is more dense). Some of these problems have been touched upon briefly in previous sections. We discuss them in more detail below.

4.1. Energy and Entropy

A basic issue that involves all approaches based on instantaneous projection is that of energy conservation. The underlying kinematics of the projection is effectively $2 \rightarrow 1$ and $3 \rightarrow 1$, which makes it impossible to conserve four-momentum. This situation is somewhat mediated at intermediate transverse momenta, $p_T > m$, where the kinematics is essentially collinear, and violations of energy conservation are suppressed by factors m/p_T or k_T/p_T, where k_T is the intrinsic transverse momentum of a parton inside the hadron. This is not really satisfying because the formalism should be easily extendable to low p_T, where collinearity is missing. In fact, it should be possible to demonstrate a smooth matching with bulk coalescence models such as ALCOR that successfully describe multiplicities and related observables at low p_T (30, 112). Interestingly, a naïve extension of the GKL approach to low momenta does not lead to disagreement with the experimental data (53, 89). However, from a theoretical point of view, the issue of imperfect energy conservation needs to be addressed in more detail. Energy conservation must be achieved through interactions with the surrounding medium. Naturally, approximations to this multiparticle dynamics have to be applied to make the problem tractable. One way of solving this problem is to introduce an effective mass distribution for the quarks to incorporate some in-medium effects (113). This allows enforcement of both momentum and energy conservation, and there is fairly good agreement with data for p_T spectra.

A promising new and powerful approach has recently been developed by Ravagli & Rapp (48). They replaced the instantaneous projection of quark states onto hadron states with a procedure that solves the Boltzmann equation for an ensemble of quarks, which are allowed to scatter through hadronic states. Thus, the hadrons are introduced through cross sections with a certain width. This implementation naturally conserves four-momentum. Ravagli & Rapp found good agreement with data for p_T spectra. They also confirmed v_2 scaling (neglecting position-momentum correlations, as did the other approaches). However, they found that kinetic energy scaling (v_2 versus m_T–m_0) is in even better agreement with experimental data (cf. **Figure 7**). The Ravagli & Rapp formalism with energy conservation is the only approach that is well suited to addressing the question of kinetic energy scaling.

A related issue is entropy conservation. Coalescence through instantaneous projection seems to reduce the number of particles by approximately a factor of two, which understandably raises the question of whether the second law of thermodynamics is violated. Strictly speaking, however, this formalism should only be applied at intermediate p_T, where only a small fraction of the total particle number (<2%) is located. Furthermore, the situation is much less dire if resonance production is taken into account, as this significantly increases the number of hadrons in the final state (53, 89). Entropy depends not only on the number of particles, but also on the degeneracies in both phases as well as on the masses.

In addition, one should take into account the interaction among quarks. It has been shown, using the lattice equation of state, that for an isentropically expanding fireball the evolution of the effective number of particles reduces significantly around the crossover temperature (114). This finding, as pointed out by Nonaka and collaborators (106), could help to solve the entropy problem inherent in instantaneous quark coalescence. However, it remains a challenge to find a consistent approach to conserving energy and conserving or increasing entropy, together with a good description of single-particle spectra and elliptic flow for both low and intermediate p_T.

4.2. Space-Momentum Correlations

An important open question is the relation between space-momentum correlations and v_2 scaling. The valence quark number scaling of elliptic flow was derived in a pure momentum-space picture. This means that scaling has been explicitly proven only if the coalescence probability is homogeneous in space. GKL have gone one step further by including correlations of radial flow with the radial coordinate r. They found that scaling still holds to a good approximation with some small violations (53, 76, 89).

However, the situation could be very different if more realistic correlations of flow with the spatial azimuthal angle φ are taken into account. One would expect a strong correlation between the spatial azimuthal angle φ and the momentum azimuth ϕ. A detailed discussion of effects arising from space-momentum correlations can be found in the work by Pratt & Pal (66). These authors also map out a class of phase-space distributions that lead to approximate scaling.

Parton cascade studies that calculate the time evolution of the phase-space distributions find that approximate scaling between baryons and mesons persists even if strong deviations of v_2 are seen at the quark level (67). However, it is not clear how these distributions depend on freezeout criteria, on the width of the wave functions, and on the interplay with jet fragmentation. Another study on the effect of phase-space distributions can be found in Reference 68.

Small violations of v_2 scaling have been observed, but as discussed in Section 3, they can be explained solely by wave function effects, resonance contributions, and contributions from higher Fock states in hadrons (51, 108, 115). If the scaling feature were accidental and strongly dependent on details of the phase-space distribution, the very different dynamical evolution at LHC might lead to much stronger scaling violations there. A better understanding of Hanbury–Brown–Twiss correlation measurements could also supply fundamental information about this issue. It would also be interesting to see how realistic phase-space correlations would fare in a dynamical coalescence model such as Ravagli & Rapp's (48) formalism.

4.3. Outlook

Quark coalescence models for heavy ion collisions have reached a certain level of maturity, but it has also become clear that there are limitations. We hope that the issues described in this section will attract more attention in the future.

Within the established projection formalism, several open questions can be addressed. A huge amount of data on two- and three-hadron correlations has been collected. Although preliminary studies have shown that correlations are in principle compatible with recombination, to understand the data a comprehensive theory incorporating jets, jet quenching, and coalescing partons at intermediate p_T must be developed. Such a theory would have to include a realistic microscopic modeling of the coupling between the medium and the jets and an explanation of how jetlike correlations are conferred to the medium. A second issue concerns the role of resonance production. Little is known about the relative probabilities of coalescence into stable hadrons and unstable resonances. As we explain above, this is an important issue for multiplicities and entropy production as well as for v_2 scaling violations (particularly for pions).

Dynamical transport implementations, such as that developed by Ravagli & Rapp, are very promising candidates for investigation of more fundamental open questions. For instance, it would be straightforward to implement resonances and stable hadrons in a realistic fashion. Using these tools, researchers could make progress on the issues of kinetic energy versus transverse momentum scaling of v_2, the role of space-momentum correlations for elliptic flow scaling, and entropy production. There is also a need to explore dynamical coalescence coupled to realistic transport models for the parton and hadron phases.

There are many more profound questions that we have not yet touched upon. For example, coalescence of particles can be found in systems that do not exhibit confinement (e.g., in plasmas of electrons and protons). Confinement does not play a large role in any of the current implementations of coalescence. (In parton cascades, noncoalescing partons are usually fragmented.) Nevertheless, there should exist a fundamental difference between confining and nonconfining theories. Investigators should use transport implementations to explore this difference in the future.

Also, the nature of the role of chiral symmetry breaking during the coalescence process is not yet clear. Most implementations assign constituent-like masses to the quarks, but no direct connection to chiral or thermal masses has been made. Unfortunately, the current observables seem not to be sensitive to the nature of the quark masses. We hope that improved implementations, together with new high-statistics data, will allow us to address this question.

5. CONCLUSIONS

The first stage of the RHIC program has provided clear evidence that hadronization at transverse momenta of several GeV/c is modified when compared to $p + p$ collisions in the light quark sector. The available data are only compatible with a hadronization process through the coalescence of quarks. The baryon enhancement and the robust scaling of the elliptic flow with the number of valence quarks are signatures that rule out other explanations.

We have presented a comprehensive overview of the available coalescence models, which are mostly based on an instantaneous projection of quark states onto hadron states. The more recent dynamical coalescence approach uses scattering of quark states into hadron states in a transport implementation. We have discussed some of the weaknesses of current models and how the field might evolve in the future.

We conclude by discussing a statement that arose after coalescence models were applied to RHIC. Several research groups pointed out that coalescence might be the most convincing argument that deconfinement takes place at RHIC and that a QGP does indeed form. This argument relies on the fact that elliptic flow v_2 is a collective effect (arising from the hydrodynamic expansion due to pressure gradients), and that this collectivity seems to happen on the parton level, leading to a universal elliptic flow for quarks just above T_c. In other words, elliptic flow of hadrons at intermediate p_T did not emerge from hadronic interactions.

This is indeed a strong argument for deconfinement. All signatures for deconfinement use indirect arguments and require theoretical input to reach this conclusion. Coalescence, in particular the v_2 scaling, appears convincing because it seems that almost no additional assumptions are needed. We hope that this argument is validated with future improvements in our understanding of the data and of the mechanism of recombination.

DISCLOSURE STATEMENT

The authors are not aware of any biases that might be perceived as affecting the objectivity of this review.

ACKNOWLEDGMENTS

We would like to thank the numerous colleagues who have worked with us on the topic of quark recombination during recent years. We also thank the editors of the *Annual Review of Nuclear and Particle Science* for the pleasant collaboration. R.J.F. is supported by RIKEN/BNL, U.S. Department of Energy grant number DE-AC02-98CH10886, and the Texas A&M College of Science. P.R.S. would like to thank the Battelle Memorial Institute and Stony Brook University for support in the form of the Gertrude and Maurice Goldhaber Distinguished Fellowship.

LITERATURE CITED

1. Karsch F. *Lect. Notes Phys.* 583:209 (2002); Cheng M, et al. *Phys. Rev. D* 74:054507 (2006)
2. Fodor Z, Katz SD. *JHEP* 0203:014 (2002); Fodor Z, Katz SD. *JHEP* 0404:050 (2004)
3. Adams J, et al. (STAR Collab.) *Nucl. Phys. A* 757:102 (2005); Adcox K, et al. (PHENIX Collab.) *Nucl. Phys. A* 757:184 (2005)
4. Gyulassy M, McLerran L. *Nucl. Phys. A* 750:30 (2005)
5. Adler SS, et al. (PHENIX Collab.) *Phys. Rev. Lett.* 91:172301 (2003)
6. Adams J, et al. (STAR Collab.) *Phys. Rev. Lett.* 92:052302 (2004)
7. Adams J, et al. (STAR Collab.) *Phys. Rev. C* 72:014904 (2005)
8. Voloshin SA. *Nucl. Phys. A* 715:379 (2003)
9. Hwa RC, Yang CB. *Phys. Rev. C* 67:064902 (2003)
10. Fries RJ, Müller B, Nonaka C, Bass SA. *Phys. Rev. Lett.* 90:202303 (2003)
11. Greco V, Ko CM, Levai P. *Phys. Rev. Lett.* 90:202302 (2003)
12. Molnar D, Voloshin SA. *Phys. Rev. Lett.* 91:092301 (2003)
13. Vance SE, Gyulassy M, Wang XN. *Phys. Lett. B* 443:45 (1998); Vitev I, Gyulassy M. *Phys. Rev. C* 65:041902 (2002); Pop VT, et al. *Phys. Rev. C* 70:064906 (2004)
14. Huovinen P, et al. *Phys. Lett. B* 503:58 (2001); Kolb PF, *AIP Conf. Proc.* 698:694 (2004)
15. Kolb PF, Heinz UW. In *Quark-Gluon Plasma*, Vol. 3, ed. RC Hwa, XN Wang, p. 634. Singapore: World Scientific (2004)

16. Hirano T, Nara Y. *Phys. Rev. C* 69:034908 (2004)
17. Chernyak VL, Zhitnitsky IR. *Nucl. Phys. B* 246:52 (1984); Brodsky SJ, Lepage GP. *Adv. Ser. Direct High Energy Phys.* 5:93 (1989)
18. Aitala EM, et al. (E791 Collab.) *Phys. Rev. Lett.* 86:4768 (2001)
19. Bakulev AP, Mikhailov SV, Stefanis NG. *Phys. Lett. B* 508:279 (2001); Erratum *Phys. Lett. B* 590:309 (2004)
20. Collins JC, Soper DE. *Nucl. Phys. B* 194:445 (1982)
21. Owens JF. *Rev. Mod. Phys.* 59:465 (1987)
22. Collins JC, Soper DE, Sterman G. *Adv. Ser. Direct High Energy Phys.* 5:1 (1988)
23. Kniehl BA, Kramer G, Potter B. *Nucl. Phys. B* 582:514 (2000); Albino S, Kniehl BA, Kramer G. *Nucl. Phys. B* 725:181 (2005)
24. Das KP, Hwa RC. *Phys. Lett. B* 68:459 (1977); Erratum *Phys. Lett. B* 73:504 (1978)
25. Adamovich M, et al. (WA82 Collab.) *Phys. Lett. B* 305:402 (1993)
26. Aitala EM, et al. (E791 Collab.) *Phys. Lett. B* 371:157 (1996)
27. Braaten E, Jia Y, Mehen T. *Phys. Rev. Lett.* 89:122002 (2002)
28. Gupt C, Shivpuri RK, Verma NS, Sharma AP. *Nuovo Cim. A* 75:408 (1983); Lopez JA, Parikh JC, Siemens PJ. *Phys. Rev. Lett.* 53:1216 (1984)
29. Biro TS, Levai P, Zimanyi J. *Phys. Lett. B* 347:6 (1995)
30. Biro TS, Levai P, Zimanyi J. *J. Phys. G* 28:1561 (2002)
31. Zimanyi J, Biro TS, Csorgo T, Levai P. *Phys. Lett. B* 472:243 (2000)
32. Adler SS, et al. (PHENIX Collab.) *Phys. Rev. Lett.* 91:241803 (2003)
33. Adams J, et al. (STAR Collab.) arXiv:nucl-ex/0601042 (2006); Long H (STAR Collab.) *J. Phys. G* 30:S193 (2004)
34. Adams J, et al. (STAR Collab.) *Phys. Rev. Lett.* 95:122301 (2005)
35. Adler SS, et al. (PHENIX Collab.) *Phys. Rev. Lett.* 91:182301 (2003)
36. Abreu P, et al. (DELPHI Collab.) *Eur. Phys. J. C* 17:207 (2000)
37. Alper B, et al. (Br.-Scand. Collab.) *Nucl. Phys. B* 100:237 (1975)
38. Adams J, et al. (STAR Collab.) *Phys. Rev. Lett.* 98:062301 (2007)
39. Adams J, et al. (STAR Collab.) *Phys. Rev. C* 71:064902 (2005)
40. Abelev BI, et al. (STAR Collab.) *Phys. Rev. Lett.* 99:112301 (2007)
41. Abelev BI, et al. (STAR Collab.) *Phys. Rev. Lett.* 97:152301 (2006)
42. Afanasiev S, et al. (PHENIX Collab.) *Phys. Rev. Lett.* 99:052301 (2007)
43. Voloshin SA, Zhang Y. *Z. Phys. C* 70:665 (1996); Poskanzer AM, Voloshin SA. *Phys. Rev. C* 58:1671 (1998)
44. Ackermann KH, et al. (STAR Collab.) *Phys. Rev. Lett.* 86:402 (2001)
45. Adler C, et al. (STAR Collab.) *Phys. Rev. Lett.* 89:132301 (2002)
46. Molnar D, Gyulassy M. *Nucl. Phys. A* 697:495 (2002); Erratum *Nucl. Phys. A* 703:893 (2002)
47. Baier R, Schiff D, Zakharov BG. *Annu. Rev. Nucl. Part. Sci.* 50:37 (2000); Gyulassy M, Vitev I, Wang XN, Zhang BW. arXiv:nucl-th/0302077 (2003)
48. Ravagli L, Rapp R. *Phys. Lett. B* 655:126 (2007)
49. Fries RJ, Müller B, Nonaka C, Bass SA. *Phys. Rev. C* 68:044902 (2003)
50. Fries RJ, Müller B, Nonaka C, Bass SA. *J. Phys. G* 30:S223 (2004)
51. Müller B, Fries RJ, Bass SA. *Phys. Lett. B* 618:77 (2005)
52. Fries RJ. *J. Phys. G* 30:S853 (2004)
53. Greco V, Ko CM, Levai P. *Phys. Rev. C* 68:034904 (2003)
54. Hwa RC, Yang CB. *Phys. Rev. C* 67:034902 (2003)
55. Hwa RC, Yang CB. *Phys. Rev. C* 70:024905 (2004)
56. Rapp R, Shuryak EV. *Phys. Rev. D* 67:074036 (2003)
57. Kapusta JI. *Phys. Rev. C* 21:1301 (1980)
58. Dover C, Heinz U, Schnedermann E, Zimanyi J. *Phys. Rev. C* 44:1636 (1991); Baltz AJ, Dover C. *Phys. Rev. C* 53:362 (1996); Mattiello R, et al. *Phys. Rev. C* 55:1443 (1997)
59. Molnar D. *J. Phys. G* 30:S1239 (2004)

60. Greco V, Ko CM, Rapp R. *Phys. Lett. B* 595:202 (2004)
61. Pal S, Pratt S. *Phys. Lett. B* 578:310 (2004)
62. Fries RJ, Bass SA, Müller B. *Phys. Rev. Lett.* 94:122301 (2005)
63. Hwa RC, Yang CB. *Phys. Rev. C* 70:024904 (2004)
64. Hwa RC, Yang CB. *Phys. Rev. Lett.* 93:082302 (2004); Hwa RC, Yang CB, Fries RJ. *Phys. Rev. C* 71:024902 (2005)
65. Majumder A, Wang E, Wang XN. *Phys. Rev. C* 73:044901 (2006)
66. Pratt S, Pal S. *Nucl. Phys. A* 749:268 (2005)
67. Molnar D. arXiv:nucl-th/0408044 (2004)
68. Greco V, Ko CM. arXiv:nucl-th/0505061 (2005)
69. Lin ZW, Molnar D. *Phys. Rev. C* 68:044901 (2003)
70. Kolb PF, Chen LW, Greco V, Ko CM. *Phys. Rev. C* 69:051901 (2004)
71. Levai P, Heinz U. *Phys. Rev. C* 57:1879 (1998)
72. Castorina P, Mannarelli M. *Phys. Lett. B* 644:336 (2007)
73. Sollfrank J, Koch P, Heinz U. *Phys. Lett. B* 252:256 (1990)
74. Hirano T. *Phys. Rev. Lett.* 86:2754 (2001)
75. Dong X, et al. *Phys. Lett. B* 597:328 (2004)
76. Greco V, Ko CM. *Phys. Rev. C* 70:024901 (2004)
77. Nonaka C, et al. *Phys. Rev. C* 69:031902 (2004)
78. Greco V, Ko CM. *J. Phys. G* 31:S407 (2005)
79. Nonaka C, Fries RJ, Bass SA. *Phys. Lett. B* 583:73 (2004)
80. Sorensen P. (STAR Collab.) *J. Phys. G* 30:S217 (2004)
81. Adare A, et al. (PHENIX Collab.) *Phys. Rev. Lett.* 98:162301 (2007)
82. Abelev BI, et al. (STAR Collab.) arXiv:0801.3466 [nucl-ex] (2008)
83. Abelev BI, et al. (STAR Collab.) *Phys. Rev. C* 75:054906 (2007)
84. Sorensen PR. *Nucl. Phys. A* 774:247 (2006)
85. Adams J, et al. (STAR Collab.) *Phys. Rev. Lett.* 92:062301 (2004)
86. Kolb PF. *Phys. Rev. C* 68:031902 (2004)
87. van Hees H, Greco V, Rapp R. *Phys. Rev. C* 73:034913 (2006)
88. van Hees H, Mannarelli M, Greco V, Rapp R. arXiv:0709.2884 [hep-ph] (2007)
89. Greco V. *Eur. Phys. J. Spec. Top.* 155:45 (2008)
90. Greco V, van Hees H, Rapp R. *AIP Conf. Proc.* 964:232 (2007)
91. Adler SS, et al. (PHENIX Collab.) *Phys. Rev. Lett.* 96:032301 (2006)
92. Abelev BI, et al. (STAR Collab.) *Phys. Rev. Lett.* 98:192301 (2007)
93. Sorensen PR, Dong X. *Phys. Rev. C* 74:024902 (2006)
94. Grandchamp L, Rapp R. *Nucl. Phys. A* 709:415 (2002)
95. Andronic A, Braun-Munzinger P, Redlich K, Stachel J. *Phys. Lett. B* 652:259 (2007)
96. Mocsy A, Petreczky P. *Phys. Rev. Lett.* 99:211602 (2007); Mocsy A, Petreczky P. *Phys. Rev. D* 77:014501 (2008)
97. Adler C, et al. (STAR Collab.) *Phys. Rev. Lett.* 90:082302 (2003)
98. Adler SS, et al. (PHENIX Collab.) *Phys. Rev. C* 71:051902 (2005)
99. Hwa RC, Yang CB. *Phys. Rev. C* 70:054902 (2004)
100. Fries RJ. *J. Phys. G* 31:S379 (2005)
101. Fries RJ. *J. Phys. Conf. Ser.* 27:70 (2005)
102. Sickles A. (PHENIX Collab.) *J. Phys. G* 30:S1291 (2004)
103. Jeon S, Koch V. *Phys. Rev. Lett.* 85:2076 (2000); Asakawa M, Heinz U, Müller B. *Phys. Rev. Lett.* 85:2072 (2000)
104. Bialas A. *Phys. Lett. B* 532:249 (2001)
105. Mitchell J. *J. Phys G* 30:S819 (2004)
106. Nonaka C, Müller B, Bass SA, Asakawa M. *Phys. Rev. C* 71:051901 (2005)
107. Zimanyi J, Levai P, Biro TS. *Heavy Ion Phys.* 17:205 (2003)
108. Greco V, Ko CM, Vitev I. *Phys. Rev. C* 71:041901 (2005)
109. Abelev BI, et al. (STAR Collaboration). *Phys. Lett. B* 655:104 (2007)

110. Fries RJ, Müller B. *Eur. Phys. J. C* 34:S279 (2004)
111. Krieg D, Bleicher M. arXiv:0708.3015 [nucl-th] (2007)
112. Csizmadia P, Levai P. *Acta Phys. Hung. A* 22:371 (2005)
113. Zimanyi J, Levai P, Biro TS. *J. Phys. G* 31:711 (2005)
114. Biro TS, Zimanyi J. *Phys. Lett. B* 650:193 (2007)
115. Sorensen P. *J. Phys. G* 32:S135 (2006)

Experimental Tests
of General Relativity

Slava G. Turyshev

Jet Propulsion Laboratory, California Institute of Technology, Pasadena,
California 91109-0899; email: turyshev@jpl.nasa.gov

Annu. Rev. Nucl. Part. Sci. 2008. 58:207–48

First published online as a Review in Advance on
July 3, 2008

The *Annual Review of Nuclear and Particle Science*
is online at nucl.annualreviews.org

This article's doi:
10.1146/annurev.nucl.58.020807.111839

0163-8998/08/1123-0207$20.00

Key Words

standard model extensions, cosmology, modified gravity, string theory,
scalar-tensor theories, equivalence principle, gravitational experiments in
space

Abstract

Einstein's general theory of relativity is the standard theory of gravity, especially where the needs of astronomy, astrophysics, cosmology and fundamental physics are concerned. As such, this theory is used for many practical
purposes involving spacecraft navigation, geodesy, and time transfer. Here
I review the foundations of general relativity, discuss recent progress in the
tests of relativistic gravity in the Solar System, and present motivations for
the new generation of high-accuracy gravitational experiments. I discuss the
advances in our understanding of fundamental physics that are anticipated in
the near future and evaluate the discovery potential of the recently proposed
gravitational experiments.

Contents

1. INTRODUCTION

November 25, 2015 will mark the centennial of the general theory of relativity, which was developed by Albert Einstein between 1905 and 1915. Ever since its original publication (1, 2), the theory continues to be an active area of research, both theoretical and experimental (3).

The general theory of relativity first demonstrated empirical success in 1915 by explaining the anomalous perihelion precession of Mercury's orbit. This anomaly was known long before Einstein; it amounts to 43 arcsec per century and cannot be explained within Newton's gravity, thereby presenting a challenge for physicists and astronomers. In 1855, Urbain LeVerrier, who in 1846 had predicted the existence of Neptune, a planet on an extreme orbit, wrote that the anomalous residue of the Mercurial precession would be accounted for if yet another planet, the as-yet-undiscovered planet Vulcan, revolves inside the Mercurial orbit. Because of the proximity of the Sun, Vulcan would not be easily observed, but LeVerrier thought he had detected it.[1] However, no confirmation came in the decades that followed: It took another 60 years to solve this puzzle. In 1915, before publishing the historical paper containing the field equations of general relativity (2), Einstein computed the expected perihelion precession of Mercury's orbit. When he obtained the famous 43 arcsec per century needed to account for the anomaly, he realized that a new era in gravitational physics had just begun!

Shortly thereafter, Sir Arthur Eddington's 1919 observations of star lines of sight during a solar eclipse (4) confirmed the doubling of the deflection angles predicted by general relativity

---

[1] For more information, please consult: **http://en.wikipedia.org/wiki/Urbain_Le_Verrier**.

as compared to Newtonian and equivalence principle (EP) arguments.[2] Observations were made simultaneously in the city of Sobral in Brazil and on the island of Principe off the west coast of Africa; these observations focused on determining the change in position of stars as they passed near the Sun on the celestial sphere. The results were presented on November 6, 1919 at a special joint meeting of the Royal Astronomical Society and the Royal Society of London (7). The data from Sobral, with measurements of seven stars in good visibility, yielded deflections of 1.98 ± 0.16 arcsec. The data from Principe were less convincing. Only five stars were measured, and the conditions there led to a much larger error. Nevertheless, the obtained value was 1.61 ± 0.4 arcsec. Both were within 2σ of Einstein's value of 1.74 and were more than two standard deviations away from both zero and the Newtonian value of 0.87. These observations became the first dedicated experiment to test the general theory of relativity.[3] In Europe, which was still recovering from the World War I, this result was considered spectacular news, and it occupied the front pages of most major newspapers, making general relativity an instant success.

From these beginnings, the general theory of relativity has been verified at ever-higher accuracy; presently, it successfully accounts for all data gathered to date. The true renaissance in the tests of general relativity began in 1970s with major advances in several disciplines, including microwave spacecraft tracking, high-precision astrometric observations, and lunar laser ranging (LLR). Thus, analysis of 14 months' worth of data obtained from radio ranging to the Viking spacecraft verified, to an estimated accuracy of 0.1%, the prediction of the general theory of relativity that the round-trip times of light signals traveling between the Earth and Mars are increased by the direct effect of solar gravity (9, 10). The corresponding value for Eddington's metric parameter[4] γ was obtained at the level of 1.000 ± 0.002. (More information on Eddington's parameters γ and β may be found in Section 2.2.)

Spacecraft and planetary radar observations have reached an accuracy of $\sim$0.15% (12). Meanwhile, very long baseline interferometry (VLBI) has achieved accuracies of better than 0.1 mas (milliseconds of arc), and regular geodetic VLBI measurements have frequently been used to determine the space curvature parameter γ. Analyses of VLBI data have yielded a consistent stream of improvements resulting in $\gamma = 0.99983 \pm 0.00045$ (13) or accuracy of $< \sim$0.045% in tests of gravity. LLR, a continuing legacy of the Apollo program, provided improved constraint on the combination of parameters $4\beta - \gamma - 3 = (4.0 \pm 4.3) \times 10^{-4}$, leading to an accuracy of $\sim$0.011% in verification of general relativity via precision measurements of the lunar orbit (14–16). Finally, microwave tracking of the Cassini spacecraft on its approach to Saturn improved the measurement accuracy of the parameter γ to $\gamma - 1 = (2.1 \pm 2.3) \times 10^{-5}$ (17), thereby reaching the current best accuracy of $\sim$0.002% provided by tests of gravity in the Solar System (see **Figure 1**).

---

[2] Eddington had been aware of several alternative predictions for his experiment. In 1801 Johann Georg von Soldner (5) had pointed out that Newtonian gravity predicts that the trajectory of starlight bends in the vicinity of a massive object, but the predicted effect is only half the value predicted by general relativity as calculated by Einstein (6). Other investigators claimed that gravity did not affect light propagation. Eddington's experiment settled these claims by pronouncing general relativity a winner.

[3] The early accuracy, however, was poor. Dyson et al. (4) quoted an optimistically low uncertainty in their measurement, which was argued by some to have been plagued with systematic error and possibly confirmation bias, although modern reanalysis of the data set suggests that Eddington's analysis was accurate (8). However, considerable uncertainty remained in these measurements for almost 50 years, until interplanetary spacecraft and microwave tracking techniques became available. It was not until the late 1960s that it was definitively shown that the angle of deflection was in fact the full value predicted by general relativity.

[4] To describe the accuracy achieved in the Solar System experiments, it is useful to refer to the parameterized post-Newtonian (PPN) formalism (11) (see Section 2.2). Two parameters are of interest here, the PPN parameters γ and β, whose values in general relativity are $\gamma = \beta = 1$. The introduction of γ and β is useful with regard to measurement accuracies.

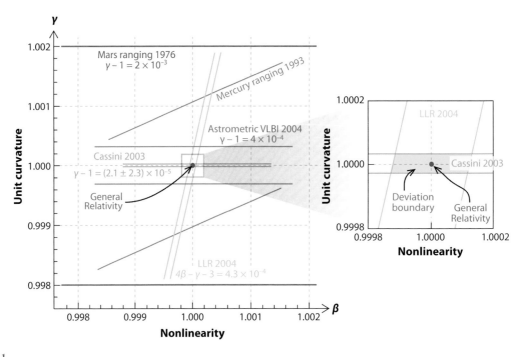

Figure 1

The progress in improving the knowledge of the parameterized post-Newtonian parameters γ and β via experiments conducted in the Solar System over the past three decades. So far, the general theory of relativity has survived every test (3), yielding $\gamma - 1 = (2.1 \pm 2.3) \times 10^{-5}$ (17) and $\beta - 1 = (1.2 \pm 1.1) \times 10^{-4}$ (15). Abbreviations: LLR, lunar laser ranging; VLBI, very long baseline interferometry.

To date, general relativity is also in agreement with data from the binary and double pulsars. Recently, investigators have shown considerable interest in the physical processes occurring in the strong-gravitational-field regime, with relativistic pulsars providing a promising possibility to test gravity in this qualitatively different dynamical environment. Although, strictly speaking, the binary pulsars move in the weak gravitational field of a companion, they do provide precision tests of the strong-field regime (18). This becomes clear when considering strong self-field effects, which are predicted by the majority of alternative theories. Such effects would clearly affect the pulsars' orbital motion, allowing us to search for these effects and hence providing us with a unique precision strong-field test of gravity. An analysis of strong-field gravitational tests and their theoretical justification is presented in Reference 19. By measuring relativistic corrections to the Keplerian description of the orbital motion, a recent analysis of the data collected from the double pulsar system PSR J0737-3039A/B found agreement with the general relativity within an uncertainty of $\sim$0.05% in measuring post-Keplerian orbital parameters of the pulsar at a 3-σ confidence level (20), to date the most precise pulsar test of gravity obtained. As a result, both in the weak-field limit (as in our Solar System) and with the stronger fields present in systems of binary pulsars, the predictions of general relativity have been extremely well tested locally.

It is remarkable that more than 90 years after general relativity was conceived, Einstein's theory has survived every test (21). Such longevity and success make general relativity the de facto standard theory of gravitation for all practical purposes involving spacecraft navigation and astrometry, astronomy, astrophysics, cosmology, and fundamental physics (3). However, despite its remarkable success there are many important reasons to question the validity of general relativity and to determine the level of accuracy at which it is violated.

On the theoretical front, problems arise from several directions, most concerning the strong-gravitational-field regime. These challenges include the appearance of spacetime singularities and the inability of classical description to describe the physics of very strong gravitational fields. A way out of this difficulty may be through gravity quantization. However, despite the success of modern gauge-field theories in describing the electromagnetic, weak, and strong interactions, we do not yet understand how gravity should be described at the quantum level.

The continued inability to merge gravity with quantum mechanics, along with recent cosmological observations, indicates that the pure tensor gravity of general relativity needs modification. In theories that attempt to include gravity, new long-range forces arise as an addition to the Newtonian inverse-square law. Regardless of whether the cosmological constant should be included, there are also important reasons to consider additional fields, especially scalar fields. Although the latter naturally appear in these modern theories, their inclusion predicts a non-Einsteinian behavior of gravitating systems. These deviations from general relativity lead to violation of the EP and to modification of large-scale gravitational phenomena, and they cast doubt upon the constancy of the fundamental constants. These predictions motivate new searches for very small deviations of relativistic gravity from the behavior prescribed by general relativity; they also provide a new theoretical paradigm and guidance for future space-based gravity experiments (3).

Note that on the largest spatial scales, such as the galactic and cosmological scales, general relativity has not yet been subject to precision tests. Some researchers have interpreted observations supporting the presence of dark matter and dark energy as a failure of general relativity at large distances, at small accelerations, or at small curvatures. **Figure 2** shows our present knowledge of gravity at various distance scales; it also indicates the theories that have been proposed to explain various observed phenomena and the techniques that have been used to conduct experimental studies of gravity at various regimes. The very strong gravitational fields that must be present close to black holes, especially those supermassive black holes that are thought to power quasars and less-active active galactic nuclei, belong to a field of intensely active research. Observations of these quasars and active galactic nuclei are difficult to obtain, and the interpretation of the observations is heavily dependent upon astrophysical models other than general relativity and competing fundamental theories of gravitation; however, such interpretations are qualitatively consistent with the black-hole concept as modeled in general relativity.

In this paper I discuss recent Solar System gravitational experiments that have contributed to the progress in relativistic gravity research by providing important guidance in the search for the next theory of gravity. I also present theoretical motivation for new generation of high-precision gravitational experiments and discuss a number of recently proposed space-based tests of relativistic gravity.

The paper is organized as follows. Section 2 discusses the foundations of the general theory of relativity, presents a phenomenological framework that is used to facilitate experimental research, and reviews the results of recent experiments designed to test the foundations of this theory. Section 3 presents motivations for extending the theoretical model of gravity provided by general relativity; it presents models arising from string theory, discusses the scalar-tensor theories of gravity, and highlights the phenomenological implications of these proposals. I briefly review recent proposals to modify gravity on large scales and review their experimental implications. Section 4 discusses future space-based experiments that aim to expand our knowledge of gravity. I focus on the space-based tests of the general theory of relativity and discuss the experiments aiming to test the EP, local Lorentz and position invariances, the search for variability of the fundamental constants, tests of the gravitational inverse-square law, and tests of alternative- and modified-gravity theories. I conclude in Section 5.

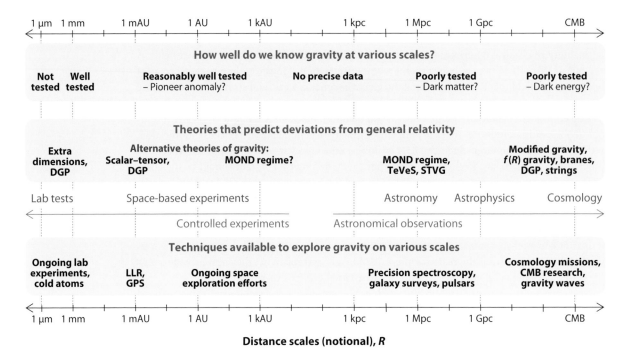

Figure 2

Present knowledge of gravity at various distance scales. Abbreviations: CMB, cosmic microwave background; DGP, Dvali–Gabadadze–Porrati; GPS, Global Positioning System; LLR, lunar laser ranging; MOND, modified Newtonian dynamics; STVG, scalar–tensor–vector–gravity; TeVeS, tensor–vector–scalar gravity. DGP data from Reference 59. MOND data from Reference 22. STVG data from Reference 23. TeVeS data from Reference 24.

2. TESTING THE FOUNDATIONS OF GENERAL RELATIVITY

General relativity is a tensor-field theory of gravitation with universal coupling to the particles and fields of the standard model. It describes gravity as a universal deformation of the flat spacetime Minkowski metric, γ_{mn}:

$$g_{mn}(x^k) = \gamma_{mn} + h_{mn}(x^k). \qquad 1.$$

Alternatively, it can also be defined as the unique, consistent, local theory of a massless spin-2 field h_{mn}, whose source is the total conserved energy-momentum tensor (see Reference 25 and references therein).

Classically (2), the general theory of relativity is defined by two postulates. One of the postulates states that the action describing the propagation and self-interaction of the gravitational field is given by

$$S_G[g_{mn}] = \frac{c^4}{16\pi\, G_N} \int d^4x \sqrt{-g}\, R, \qquad 2.$$

where G_N is Newton's universal gravitational constant, g^{mn} is the matrix inverse of g_{mn} and $g = \det g_{mn}$, R is the Ricci scalar given as $R = g^{mn} R_{mn}$ with the quantity $R_{mn} = \partial_k \Gamma^k_{mn} - \partial_m \Gamma^k_{nk} + \Gamma^k_{mn} \Gamma^l_{kl} - \Gamma^k_{ml} \Gamma^l_{nk}$ being the Ricci tensor, and $\Gamma^k_{mn} = \frac{1}{2} g^{kp}(\partial_m g_{pn} + \partial_n g_{pm} - \partial_p g_{mn})$ are the Christoffel symbols.

The second postulate states that g_{mn} couples universally, and minimally, to all the fields of the standard model by replacing the Minkowski metric everywhere. Schematically (suppressing matrix indices and labels for the various gauge fields and fermions, ψ, and for the Higgs doublet, H), this postulate can be given by

$$S_{SM}[\psi, A_m, H; g_{mm}] = \int d^4x \left[-\frac{1}{4} \sum \sqrt{-g} g^{mk} g^{nl} F^a_{mn} F^a_{kl} - \sum \sqrt{-g} \bar{\psi} \gamma^m D_m \psi \right.$$

$$- \frac{1}{2} \sqrt{-g} g^{mn} \overline{D_m H} D_n H - \sqrt{g} V(H)$$

$$\left. - \sum \lambda \sqrt{-g} \bar{\psi} H \psi - \sqrt{-g} \rho_{vac} \right], \qquad 3.$$

where $\gamma^m \gamma^n + \gamma^n \gamma^m = 2g^{mn}$; the covariant derivative D_m contains, besides the usual gauge-field terms, a (spin-dependent) gravitational contribution $\Gamma_m(x)$ (26); and ρ_{vac} is the vacuum energy density. Applying the variational principle with regard to g_{mn} to the total action that reads

$$S_{tot}[\psi, A_m, H; g_{mn}] = S_G[g_{mn}] + S_{SM}[\psi, A_m, H; g_{mn}], \qquad 4.$$

one obtains the well-known field equations of the general theory of relativity,

$$R_{mn} - \frac{1}{2} g_{mn} R + \Lambda g_{mn} = \frac{8\pi G_N}{c^4} T_{mn}, \qquad 5.$$

where $T_{mn} = g_{mk} g_{nl} T^{kl}$ with $T^{mn} = 2/\sqrt{-g} \delta L_{SM}/\delta g_{mn}$ being the (symmetric) energy-momentum tensor of matter, as described by the standard model with the Lagrangian density L_{SM}. With the value for the vacuum energy density $\rho_{vac} \approx (2.3 \times 10^{-3} \text{ eV})^4$, as measured by recent cosmological observations, the cosmological constant $\Lambda = 8\pi G_N \rho_{vac}/c^4$ (26) is too small to be observed by Solar System experiments, but it is clearly important for greater scales.

Einstein's equation (Equation 5) links the geometry of a four-dimensional, Riemannian manifold representing spacetime with the energy-momentum contained in that spacetime. Phenomena that in classical mechanics are ascribed to the action of the force of gravity (such as free fall, orbital motion, and spacecraft trajectories) correspond to inertial motion within a curved geometry of spacetime in general relativity.

2.1. Scalar-Tensor Extensions to General Relativity

Metric theories have a special place among alternative theories of gravity. The reason for this is that, independently of the different principles at their foundations, the gravitational field in these theories affects the matter directly through the metric tensor g_{mn}, which is determined from the particular theory's field equations. As a result, in contrast to Newtonian gravity, this tensor expresses the properties of a particular gravitational theory and carries information about the gravitational field of the bodies.

In many alternative theories of gravity, the gravitational coupling strength exhibits a dependence on a field of some sort; in scalar-tensor theories, this is a scalar field φ. A general action for these theories can be written as

$$S = \frac{c^3}{4\pi G} \int d^4x \sqrt{-g} \left[\frac{1}{4} f(\varphi) R - \frac{1}{2} g(\varphi) \partial_\mu \varphi \partial^\mu \varphi + V(\varphi) \right] + \sum_i q_i(\varphi) \mathcal{L}_i, \qquad 6.$$

where $f(\varphi)$, $g(\varphi)$, and $V(\varphi)$ are generic functions, $q_i(\varphi)$ are coupling functions, and $\mathcal{L}_i$ is the Lagrangian density of the matter fields.

The Brans–Dicke theory (27) is the best known alternative theory of gravity. It corresponds to the choice

$$f(\varphi) = \varphi, \qquad g(\varphi) = \frac{\omega}{\varphi}, \qquad V(\varphi) = 0. \qquad 7.$$

Note that in the Brans–Dicke theory the kinetic energy term of the field φ is noncanonical and that the latter has a dimension of energy squared. In this theory, the constant ω marks observational deviations from general relativity, which is recovered in the limit $\omega \to \infty$. In the context of the Brans–Dicke theory, one can operationally introduce Mach's Principle, which states that the inertia of bodies is due to their interaction with the matter distribution in the Universe. Indeed, in this theory the gravitational coupling is proportional to φ^{-1}, which depends on the energy-momentum tensor of matter through the field equations. The stringent observational bounds resulting from the 2002 experiment with the Cassini spacecraft (17) require that $|\omega| \gtrsim 40,000$. There exist additional alternative theories that provide guidance for gravitational experiments (see Reference 21).

2.2. Parameterized Post-Newtonian Formalism

Generalizing on a phenomenological parameterization of the gravitational metric tensor field, which Eddington originally developed for a special case, a method called the parameterized post-Newtonian (PPN) formalism has been developed (11 and 21 and references therein, 28). This method represents the gravity tensor's potentials for slowly moving bodies and weak interbody gravity and is valid for a broad class of metric theories, including general relativity as a unique case. The several parameters in the PPN metric expansion vary from theory to theory, and they are individually associated with various symmetries and the invariance properties of the underlying theory (see Reference 11 for details).

If (for the sake of simplicity) one assumes that Lorentz invariance, local position invariance, and total momentum conservation hold, the metric tensor for a system of N pointlike gravitational sources in four dimensions may be written as

$$g_{00} = 1 - \frac{2}{c^2} \sum_{j \neq i} \frac{\mu_j}{r_{ij}} + \frac{2\beta}{c^4} \left[\sum_{j \neq i} \frac{\mu_j}{r_{ij}} \right]^2 - \frac{1 + 2\gamma}{c^4} \sum_{j \neq i} \frac{\mu_j \dot{r}_j^2}{r_{ij}}$$

$$+ \frac{2(2\beta - 1)}{c^4} \sum_{i \neq j} \frac{\mu_j}{r_{ij}} \sum_{k \neq j} \frac{\mu_k}{r_{jk}} - \frac{1}{c^4} \sum_{j \neq i} \mu_j \frac{\partial^2 r_{ij}}{\partial t^2} + \mathcal{O}(c^{-5}),$$

$$g_{0a} = \frac{2(\gamma + 1)}{c^3} \sum_{j \neq i} \frac{\mu_j \dot{\mathbf{r}}_j^\alpha}{r_{ij}} \mathcal{O}(c^{-5}),$$

$$g_{\alpha\beta} = -\delta_{\alpha\beta} \left(1 + \frac{2\gamma}{c^2} \sum_{j \neq i} \frac{\mu_j}{r_{ij}} + \frac{3\delta}{2c^4} \left[\sum_{j \neq i} \frac{\mu_j}{r_{ij}} \right]^2 \right) + \mathcal{O}(c^{-5}), \qquad \qquad 8.$$

where the indices j and k refer to the N bodies and where k includes body i, whose motion is being investigated. μ_j is the gravitational constant for body j given as $\mu_j = Gm_j$, where G is the universal Newtonian gravitational constant and m_j is the isolated rest mass of a body j. In addition, the vector $\mathbf{r}_i$ is the barycentric radius vector of this body, the vector $\mathbf{r}_{ij} = \mathbf{r}_j - \mathbf{r}_i$ is the vector directed from body i to body j, $r_{ij} = |\mathbf{r}_j - \mathbf{r}_i|$, and the vector $\mathbf{n}_{ij} = \mathbf{r}_{ij}/r_{ij}$ is the unit vector along this direction.

Although general relativity replaces the scalar gravitational potential of classical physics by a symmetric rank-two tensor, the latter reduces to the former in certain limiting cases: For weak gravitational fields and slow speed relative to the speed of light, the theory's predictions converge on those of Newton's law of gravity. The $1/c^2$ term in g_{00} is the Newtonian limit; the $1/c^4$ terms multiplied by the parameters β and γ are post-Newtonian terms. The term multiplied by the post-post-Newtonian parameter δ also enters the calculation of the relativistic light propagation for some modern-day experiments (3).

In this special case, where only two PPN parameters (γ, β) are considered, these parameters have a clear physical meaning. The parameter γ represents the measure of the curvature of the spacetime created by a unit rest mass; parameter β represents a measure of the nonlinearity of the law of superposition of the gravitational fields in the theory of gravity. General relativity, when analyzed in standard PPN gauge, gives $\gamma = \beta = 1$, and the other eight parameters vanish; the theory is thus embedded in a two-dimensional space of theories.

The Brans–Dicke theory (27), in addition to the metric tensor, contains a scalar field and an arbitrary coupling constant ω, which yield the two PPN parameter values $\beta = 1$ and $\gamma = (1 + \omega)/(2 + \omega)$, where ω is an unknown dimensionless parameter of this theory. Other general scalar-tensor theories yield different values of β (29, 31).

A particular metric theory of gravity in the PPN formalism with a specific coordinate gauge is fully characterized by means of 10 PPN parameters (11, 31). Thus, in addition to γ and β, there are eight other parameters: α_1, α_2, α_3, ζ, ζ_1, ζ_2, ζ_3, and ζ_4. The formalism uniquely prescribes the values of these parameters for the particular theory under study. Gravity experiments can be analyzed in terms of the PPN metric, and an ensemble of experiments determine the unique value for these parameters (and hence the metric field itself).

To analyze the motion of an N-body system, one derives the Lagrangian function L_N (11, 31). Within the accuracy sufficient for most of the gravitational experiments in the Solar System, this function for the motion of an N-body system can be presented in the following form:

$$L_N = \sum_i m_i c^2 \left(1 - \frac{\dot{r}_i^2}{2c^2} - \frac{\dot{r}_i^4}{8c^4}\right) - \frac{1}{2}\sum_{i \neq j} \frac{Gm_i m_j}{r_{ij}}\left(1 + \frac{1+2\gamma}{2c^2}(\dot{r}_i^2 + \dot{r}_j^2)\right.$$

$$+ \frac{3+4\gamma}{2c^2}(\dot{\mathbf{r}}_i \dot{\mathbf{r}}_j) - \frac{1}{2c^2}(\mathbf{n}_{ij}\dot{\mathbf{r}}_i)(\mathbf{n}_{ij}\dot{\mathbf{r}}_j)\bigg)$$

$$+ \left(\beta - \frac{1}{2}\right)\sum_{i \neq j \neq k}\frac{G^2 m_i m_j m_k}{r_{ij}r_{ik}c^2} + \mathcal{O}(c^{-4}). \qquad 9.$$

The Lagrangian in Equation 9 leads to the point-mass Newtonian and relativistic perturbative accelerations in the Solar System's barycentric frame[5] (31, 32):

$$\ddot{\mathbf{r}}_i = \sum_{j \neq i}\frac{\mu_j(\mathbf{r}_j - \mathbf{r}_i)}{r_{ij}^3}\left\{1 - \frac{2(\beta + \gamma)}{c^2}\sum_{l \neq i}\frac{\mu_l}{r_{il}} - \frac{2\beta - 1}{c^2}\sum_{k \neq j}\frac{\mu_k}{r_{jk}}\right.$$

$$+ \gamma\left(\frac{\dot{r}_i}{c}\right)^2 + (1+\gamma)\left(\frac{\dot{r}_j}{c}\right)^2 - \frac{2(1+\gamma)}{c^2}\dot{\mathbf{r}}_i \dot{\mathbf{r}}_j$$

$$- \frac{3}{2c^2}\left[\frac{(\mathbf{r}_i - \mathbf{r}_j)\dot{\mathbf{r}}_j}{r_{ij}}\right]^2 + \frac{1}{2c^2}(\mathbf{r}_j - \mathbf{r}_i)\ddot{\mathbf{r}}_j\bigg\}$$

$$+ \frac{1}{c^2}\sum_{j \neq i}\frac{\mu_j}{r_{ij}^3}\left\{[\mathbf{r}_i - \mathbf{r}_j]\cdot[(2+2\gamma)\dot{\mathbf{r}}_i - (1+2\gamma)\dot{\mathbf{r}}_j]\right\}(\dot{\mathbf{r}}_i - \dot{\mathbf{r}}_j)$$

$$+ \frac{3+4\gamma}{2c^2}\sum_{j \neq i}\frac{\mu_j \ddot{\mathbf{r}}_j}{r_{ij}} + \mathcal{O}(c^{-4}). \qquad 10.$$

To determine the orbits of the planets and spacecraft one must also describe propagation of electromagnetic signals between any of the two points in space. The corresponding light-time

---

[5] When describing the motion of spacecraft in the Solar System, the models also include forces from asteroids and planetary satellites (30).

equation can be derived from the metric tensor (Equation 8), as below:

$$t_2 - t_1 = \frac{r_{12}}{c} + (1+\gamma) \sum_i \frac{\mu_i}{c^3} \ln \left[\frac{r_1^i + r_2^i + r_{12}^i + \frac{(1+\gamma)\mu_i}{c^2}}{r_1^i + r_2^i - r_{12}^i + \frac{(1+\gamma)\mu_i}{c^2}} \right] + \mathcal{O}(c^{-5}),$$ 11.

where t_1 refers to the signal transmission time and t_2 refers to the reception time. $r_{1,2}$ are the barycentric positions of the transmitter and receiver and r_{12} is their spatial separation (see Reference 32 for details). The terms proportional to $\propto$, μ_i^2 are important only for the Sun and are negligible for all other bodies in the Solar System.

This PPN expansion serves as a useful framework to test relativistic gravitation in the context of the gravitational experiments. The main properties of the PPN metric tensor given by Equation 8 are well established and are widely used in modern astronomical practice (see References 11, 31, and 33 and references therein). The equations of motion from Equation 10 are used to produce numerical codes used in construction of the Solar System's ephemerides, spacecraft orbit determination (31, 32, 34), and analysis of the gravitational experiments in the Solar System (3, 11, 35).

2.3. Parameterized Post-Newtonian–Renormalized Extension of General Relativity

Given the phenomenological success of general relativity, it is convenient to use this theory to describe experiments. In this sense, any possible deviation from general relativity would appear as a small perturbation to this general relativistic background. Such perturbations are proportional to the renormalized PPN parameters (i.e., $\bar{\gamma} \equiv \gamma - 1$, $\bar{\beta} \equiv \beta - 1$, etc.), which are zero in general relativity but which may have nonzero values for some gravitational theories. In terms of the metric tensor, this PPN-perturbative procedure may be conceptually presented as

$$g_{mn} = g_{mn}^{\mathrm{GR}} + \delta g_{mn}^{\mathrm{PPN}},$$ 12.

where metric g_{mn}^{GR} is derived from Equation 8 by taking the general relativistic values of the PPN parameters ($\gamma = \beta = 1$), and where $\delta g_{mn}^{\mathrm{PPN}}$ is the PPN-renormalized metric perturbation. If one assumes that Lorentz invariance, local position invariance, and total momentum conservation hold, the perturbation $\delta g_{mn}^{\mathrm{PPN}}$ may be given as

$$\delta g_{00}^{\mathrm{PPN}} = -\frac{2\bar{\gamma}}{c^4} \sum_{j \neq i} \frac{\mu_j \dot{r}_j^2}{r_{ij}} + \frac{2\bar{\beta}}{c^4} \left(\left[\sum_{j \neq i} \frac{\mu_j}{r_{ij}} \right]^2 + 2 \sum_{j \neq i} \frac{\mu_j}{r_{ij}} \sum_{k \neq j} \frac{\mu_k}{r_{jk}} \right) + \mathcal{O}(c^{-5}),$$

$$\delta g_{0\alpha}^{\mathrm{PPN}} = \frac{2\bar{\gamma}}{c^3} \sum_{j \neq i} \frac{\mu_j r_j^\alpha}{r_{ij}} + \mathcal{O}(c^{-5}),$$

$$\delta g_{\alpha\beta}^{\mathrm{PPN}} = -\delta_{\alpha\beta} \frac{2\bar{\gamma}}{c^2} \sum_{j \neq i} \frac{\mu_j}{r_{ij}} + \mathcal{O}(c^{-5}).$$ 13.

Given the smallness of the PPN-renormalized parameters $\bar{\gamma}$ and $\bar{\beta}$, the PPN metric perturbation $\delta g_{mn}^{\mathrm{PPN}}$ represents a very small deformation of the general relativistic background g_{mn}^{GR}. The expressions in Equation 13 embody the "spirit" of many tests, assuming that general relativity provides the correct description of the experimental situation and searches for small deviations.

Similarly, one can derive the PPN-renormalized version of the Lagrangian in Equation 9:

$$L_{\mathrm{N}} = L_{\mathrm{N}}^{\mathrm{GR}} + \delta L_{\mathrm{N}}^{\mathrm{PPN}},$$ 14.

where L_N^{GR} is the general relativistic Lagrangian and δL_N^{PPN} is given as

$$\delta L_N^{PPN} = -\frac{1}{2}\frac{\bar{\gamma}}{c^2}\sum_{i\neq j}\frac{Gm_im_j}{r_{ij}}(\dot{\mathbf{r}}_i+\dot{\mathbf{r}}_j)^2 + \frac{\bar{\beta}}{c^2}\sum_{i\neq j\neq k}\frac{G^2m_im_jm_k}{r_{ij}r_{ik}} + \mathcal{O}(c^{-4}).$$

15.

The equations of motion from Equation 10 may also be presented in the PPN-renormalized form with explicit dependence on the PPN-perturbative acceleration terms:

$$\ddot{\mathbf{r}}_i = \ddot{\mathbf{r}}_i^{GR} + \delta\ddot{\mathbf{r}}_i^{PPN},$$

16.

where $\ddot{\mathbf{r}}_i^{GR}$ are the equations of motion from Equation 10 with the values of the PPN parameters set to their general relativistic values. The PPN-perturbative acceleration term $\delta\ddot{\mathbf{r}}_i^{PPN}$ is given as

$$\begin{aligned}
\delta\ddot{\mathbf{r}}_i^{PPN} = \sum_{j\neq i}\frac{\mu_j(\mathbf{r}_j-\mathbf{r}_i)}{r_{ij}^3}&\left\{\left(\left[\frac{m_G}{m_I}\right]_i - 1\right) + \frac{\dot{G}}{G}\cdot(t-t_0)\right.\\
&\left.-\frac{2(\bar{\beta}+\bar{\gamma})}{c^2}\sum_{l\neq i}\frac{\mu_l}{r_{il}} - \frac{2\bar{\beta}}{c^2}\sum_{k\neq j}\frac{\mu_k}{r_{jk}} + \frac{\bar{\gamma}}{c^2}(\dot{\mathbf{r}}_i-\dot{\mathbf{r}}_j)^2\right\}\\
&+\frac{2\bar{\gamma}}{c^2}\sum_{j\neq i}\frac{\mu_j}{r_{ij}^3}\left\{(\mathbf{r}_i-\mathbf{r}_j)\cdot(\dot{\mathbf{r}}_i-\dot{\mathbf{r}}_j)\right\}(\dot{\mathbf{r}}_i-\dot{\mathbf{r}}_j)\\
&+\frac{2\bar{\gamma}}{c^2}\sum_{j\neq i}\frac{\mu_j\ddot{\mathbf{r}}_j}{r_{ij}} + \mathcal{O}(c^{-4}).
\end{aligned}$$

17.

Equation 17 provides a useful framework for gravitational research. Thus, besides the terms with PPN-renormalized parameters $\bar{\gamma}$ and $\bar{\beta}$, it also contains $[m_G/m_I]_i - 1$, the parameter that signifies a possible inequality between the gravitational and inertial masses and that is needed to facilitate investigation of a possible violation of the EP (see Section 4.1.2). In addition, Equation 17 also includes parameter $\dot{G}/G$, which is needed to investigate possible temporal variation in the gravitational constant (see Section 4.4.2). Note that in general relativity $\delta\ddot{\mathbf{r}}_i^{PPN} \equiv 0$.

Equations 16 and 17 are used to focus the science objectives and to describe gravitational experiments in the Solar System (discussed in detail below). So far, the general theory of relativity has survived every test (3), yielding ever-improving values for the PPN parameters γ and β, namely (a) $\bar{\gamma} = (2.1\pm2.3)\times10^{-5}$, using Cassini spacecraft data taken during the solar conjunction experiment (17) and (b) $\bar{\beta} = (1.2\pm1.1)\times10^{-4}$, which resulted from analysis of the LLR data (15) (see **Figure 1**).

3. SEARCH FOR NEW PHYSICS BEYOND GENERAL RELATIVITY

The fundamental physical laws of nature are described by the standard model of particles and fields and the general theory of relativity. The standard model specifies the families of fermions (i.e., leptons and quarks) and their interactions by vector fields that transmit the strong, electromagnetic, and weak forces. General relativity is a tensor-field theory of gravity with universal coupling to the particles and fields of the standard model.

However, despite the beauty and simplicity of general relativity and the success of the standard model, our present understanding of the fundamental laws of physics has several shortcomings. Although recent progress in string theory (36) is very encouraging, the search for a realistic theory of quantum gravity remains a challenge. This continued inability to merge gravity with quantum mechanics indicates that the pure tensor gravity of general relativity needs modification or augmentation. The recent remarkable progress in observational cosmology has subjected the general theory of relativity to increased scrutiny by suggesting a non-Einsteinian model of the Universe's evolution. Researchers now believe that new physics is needed to resolve these issues.

Theoretical models of the kinds of new physics that can solve the problems described above typically involve new interactions, some of which could manifest themselves as violations of the EP, variation of fundamental constants, modification of the inverse-square law of gravity at short distances, Lorenz symmetry breaking, or large-scale gravitational phenomena. Each of these manifestations offers an opportunity for space-based experimentation and, hopefully, a major discovery. Below I discuss motivations for the new generation of gravitational experiments that are expected to advance the relativistic gravity research up to five orders of magnitude below the level currently tested by experiments (3).

3.1. String/M-Theory and Tensor-Scalar Extensions of General Relativity

An understanding of gravity at the quantum level will allow us to ascertain whether the gravitational constant is a running coupling constant like those of other fundamental interactions of nature. String/M-theory (37) hints at a negative answer to this question, given the nonrenormalization theorems of supersymmetry, a symmetry at the core of the underlying principle of string/M-theory and brane models. One-loop higher-derivative quantum gravity models may permit a running gravitational coupling, as these models are asymptotically free—a striking property (38). In the absence of a screening mechanism for gravity, asymptotic freedom may imply that quantum gravitational corrections take effect on macroscopic and even cosmological scales, which has some bearing on the dark matter problem (39) and, in particular, on the subject of the large-scale structure of the Universe. Either way, it seems plausible to assume that quantum gravity effects manifest themselves only on cosmological scales.

Both consistency between a quantum description of matter and a geometric description of spacetime and the appearance of singularities involving minute curvature length scales indicate that a full theory of quantum gravity is needed for an adequate description of the interior of black holes and time evolution close to the Big Bang: a theory in which gravity and the associated geometry of spacetime are described in the language of quantum theory. Despite major efforts in this direction, no complete and consistent theory of quantum gravity is currently available; there are, however, a number of promising candidates.

String theory is viewed as the most promising means of making general relativity compatible with quantum mechanics (37). The closed-string theory has a spectrum that contains as zero-mass eigenstates the graviton g_{MN}, the dilaton Φ, and the antisymmetric second-order tensor B_{MN}. There are various ways to extract the physics of our four-dimensional world, and a major difficulty lies in finding a natural mechanism that fixes the value of the dilaton field, as it does not acquire a potential at any order in string-perturbation theory. However, although the usual quantum-field theories used in elementary particle physics to describe interactions do lead to an acceptable effective (quantum)-field theory of gravity at low energies, they result in models devoid of all predictive power at very high energies.

Damour & Polyakov (40) have studied a possible a mechanism to circumvent the above-mentioned difficulty by suggesting string-loop contributions, which are counted by dilaton interactions instead of by a potential. They proposed the least coupling principle (LCP), realized via a cosmological attractor mechanism (see, e.g., 40, 41), which can reconcile the existence of a massless scalar field in the low-energy world with existing tests of general relativity (and with cosmological inflation). It is not yet known whether this mechanism can be realized in string theory. The authors assumed the existence of a massless scalar field Ψ (i.e., of a flat direction in the potential), with gravitational strength coupling to matter. A priori, this appears phenomenologically forbidden;

however, the cosmological attractor mechanism tends to drive Ψ toward a value where its coupling to matter becomes naturally $\ll 1$. After dropping the antisymmetric second-order tensor and introducing fermions $\hat{\psi}$ and Yang–Mills fields $\hat{A}^\mu$ with field strength $\hat{F}_{\mu\nu}$, in a spacetime described by the metric $\hat{g}_{\mu\nu}$ the relevant effective low-energy four-dimensional action in the string frame can be written in the generic form as

$$S_{\text{eff}} = \int d^4x \sqrt{-\hat{g}} \left\{ B(\Phi) \left[\frac{1}{\alpha'} \left(\hat{R} + 4\hat{\nabla}_m \hat{\nabla}^m \Phi - 4(\hat{\nabla}\Phi)^2 \right) \right. \right.$$
$$\left. \left. - \frac{k}{4} \hat{F}_{mn} \hat{F}^{mn} - \bar{\hat{\psi}} \gamma^m \hat{D}_m \hat{\psi} - \frac{1}{2}(\hat{\nabla}\hat{\chi})^2 \right] - \frac{m_\psi}{2} \chi^2 \right\}, \qquad 18.$$

where[6] $B(\Phi) = e^{-2\Phi} + c_0 + c_1 e^{2\Phi} + c_2 e^{4\Phi} + \dots$, α' is the inverse of the string tension, k is a gauge-group constant, and the constants $c_0, c_1, \dots$, can, in principle, be determined via computation.

To recover Einsteinian gravity, one performs a conformal transformation with $g_{mn} = B(\Phi)\hat{g}_{mn}$ that leads to an effective action where the coupling constants and masses are functions of the rescaled dilaton φ:

$$S_{\text{eff}} = \int d^4x \sqrt{-g} \left[\frac{\tilde{m}_p^2}{4} R - \frac{\tilde{m}_p^2}{2}(\nabla\varphi)^2 - \frac{\tilde{m}_p^2}{2} F(\varphi)(\nabla\psi)^2 - \frac{1}{2}\tilde{m}_\varphi^2(\chi)\chi^2 \right.$$
$$\left. + \frac{k}{4} B_F(\varphi) F_{\mu\nu} F^{\mu\nu} + V_{\text{vac}} + \dots \right]. \qquad 19.$$

It follows that $\tilde{m}_p^{-2} = 4\pi G = \frac{1}{4}\alpha'$ and that the coupling constants and masses are now dilaton dependent through $g^{-2} = k B_F(\varphi)$ and $m_A = m_A[B_F(\varphi)]$.

The cosmological attractor mechanism leads to some generic predictions even without the knowledge of the specific structure of the various coupling functions, namely $m_\psi(\varphi)$, $m_A[B_F(\varphi)]$, ... The basic assumption is that the string-loop corrections are such that there exists a minimum in (some of) the functions $m(\varphi)$ at some (finite or infinite) value φ_m. During inflation, the dynamics is governed by a set of coupled differential equations for the scale factors ψ and φ. In particular, the equation of motion for φ contains a term $\propto -\frac{\partial}{\partial\varphi}m_\chi^2(\varphi)\chi^2$. During inflation (i.e., when ψ has a large vacuum expectation value), this coupling drives φ towards the special point φ_m, where $m_\psi(\varphi)$ reaches a minimum. Once φ has been attracted near φ_m, φ essentially (classically) decouples from ψ so that inflation proceeds as if φ were not there. A similar attractor mechanism exists during the other phases of cosmological evolution and tends to decouple φ from the dominant cosmological matter. For this mechanism to efficiently decouple φ from all types of matter, there must be a special point φ_m to approximately minimize all the important coupling functions. A way of having such a special point in field space is to assume that $\varphi_m = +\infty$ is a limiting point where all coupling functions have finite limits. This leads to the so-called runaway dilaton scenario (40), in which the mere assumption that $B_i(\Phi) \simeq c^i + \mathcal{O}(e^{-2\Phi})$ as $\Phi \to +\infty$ implies that $\varphi_m = +\infty$ is an attractor where all couplings vanish.

This mechanism also predicts (approximately composition-independent) values for the post-Einstein parameters $\bar{\gamma}$ and $\bar{\beta}$, which parameterize deviations from general relativity. For simplicity, I discuss only the theories for which $g(\varphi) = q_i(\varphi) = 1$. Hence, for a theory for which the $V(\varphi)$ can be locally neglected, given that its mass is small enough that it acts cosmologically, it has been

---

[6]In the general case, one expects that each matter field would have a different coupling function, e.g., $B_i \to B_\Phi \ne B_F \ne B_\psi \ne B_\chi$, etc.

shown that in the PPN limit, one can write

$$\ln A(\varphi) = \alpha_0(\varphi - \varphi_0) + \frac{1}{2}\beta_0(\varphi - \varphi_0)^2 + \mathcal{O}(\varphi - \varphi_0)^3,$$ 20.

where $A(\varphi)$ is the coupling function to matter and the factor that allows one to write the theory in the Einstein frame in this model is $g_{mn} = A^2(\varphi)\hat{g}_{mn}$. Then, the two post-Einstein parameters are of the form

$$\bar{\gamma} = -\frac{2\alpha_{\text{had}}^2}{1 + \alpha_{\text{had}}^2} \simeq 2\alpha_{\text{had}}^2 \quad \text{and} \quad \bar{\beta} = \frac{2\alpha_{\text{had}}^2 \frac{\partial \alpha_{\text{had}}}{\partial \varphi}}{(1 + \alpha_{\text{had}}^2)^2} \simeq \frac{1}{2}\alpha_{\text{had}}^2 \frac{\partial \alpha_{\text{had}}}{\partial \varphi},$$ 21.

where α_{had} is the dilaton coupling to hadronic matter. In this model, all tests of general relativity are violated. However, all these violations are correlated. For instance, a link between EP violations and Solar System deviations is established:

$$\frac{\Delta a}{a} \simeq 2.6 \times 10^{-5}\bar{\gamma}.$$ 22.

Given that present tests of the EP place a limit on the ratio $\Delta a/a$ of the order of 10^{-12}, one finds $\bar{\gamma} \leq 4 \times 10^{-8}$. Note that the upper limit given on $\bar{\gamma}$ by the Cassini experiment was 10^{-5}, so in this case the necessary sensitivity has not yet been reached to test the cosmological attractor mechanism.

It is also possible that the dynamics of the quintessence field evolves to a point of minimal coupling to matter. In Reference 40, the authors showed that φ could be attracted toward a value $\varphi_m(x)$ during the matter-dominated era that decoupled the dilaton from matter. For universal coupling, $f(\varphi) = g(\varphi) = q_i(\varphi)$ (see Equation 6), this would motivate improvements in the accuracy of the EP and other tests of general relativity. The authors of Reference 41 suggested that with a large number of non-self-interacting matter species, the coupling constants are determined by the quantum corrections of the matter species and φ would evolve as a runaway dilaton with asymptotic value $\varphi_m \to \infty$. Due to the LCP, the dependence of the masses on the dilaton implies that particles fall differently in a gravitational field and hence are in violation of the weak form of the EP (WEP). Although the effect (on the order of $\Delta a/a \simeq 10^{-18}$) is rather small in Solar System conditions, application of already-available technology can potentially test predictions that represent a distinct experimental signature of string/M-theory.

These recent theoretical findings suggest that the present agreement between general relativity and experiment may be naturally compatible with the existence of a scalar contribution to gravity. In particular, Damour & Nordtvedt (29; see also Reference 40 for nonmetric versions of this mechanism and Reference 41 for a recent summary of the runaway-dilaton scenario) found that a scalar-tensor theory of gravity may contain a built-in cosmological attractor mechanism toward general relativity. Scenarios considered by these authors assume that the scalar-coupling parameter $\frac{1}{2}\bar{\gamma}$ was of order one in the early Universe (i.e., before inflation) and show that this parameter then evolves to be close to (but not exactly equal to) zero at the present time. **Figure 3** illustrates this mechanism in greater detail.

The Eddington parameter γ, whose value in general relativity is unity, is perhaps the most fundamental PPN parameter in that $\frac{1}{2}\bar{\gamma}$ is a measure of the fractional strength of the scalar-gravity interaction in scalar-tensor theories of gravity (19). Within perturbation theory for such theories, all other PPN parameters to all relativistic orders collapse to their general relativistic values in proportion to $\frac{1}{2}\bar{\gamma}$. Under some assumptions (see, e.g., Reference 29), one can estimate the likely order of magnitude of the leftover coupling strength at the present time; this value, depending on the total mass density of the Universe, can be given as $\bar{\gamma} \sim 7.3 \times 10^{-7}(H_0/\Omega_0^3)^{1/2}$, where Ω_0 is the ratio of the current density to the closure density and where H_0 is the Hubble

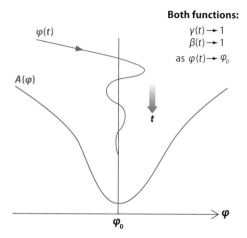

Both functions:
$$\gamma(t) \to 1$$
$$\beta(t) \to 1$$
as $\varphi(t) \to \varphi_0$

$\varphi(t)$

$A(\varphi)$

t

φ_0

φ

Figure 3

Typical cosmological dynamics of a background scalar field is shown in the case where that field's coupling function to matter, $V(\phi)$, has an attracting point, ϕ_0. The strength of the scalar interaction's coupling to matter is proportional to the derivative (*slope*) of the coupling function, so it weakens as the attracting point is approached. The Eddington parameters γ and β (and all higher-structure parameters as well) approach their pure tensor gravity values in this limit. However, a small residual scalar gravity should remain because this dynamical process is not complete (19, 29, 41).

constant in units of 100 km/sec/Mpc. Compared to the cosmological constant, these scalar-field models are consistent with the supernovae observations for a lower matter density, $\Omega_0 \sim 0.2$, and a higher age, $(H_0 t_0) \approx 1$. If this is indeed the case, the level $\bar{\gamma} \sim 10^{-6} - 10^{-7}$ would be the lower bound for the present value of the PPN parameter $\bar{\gamma}$ (29).

Recently, Damour et al. (41) estimated $\frac{1}{2}\bar{\gamma}$ within the framework compatible with string theory and modern cosmology, confirming the results presented in Reference 29. This recent analysis discusses a scenario wherein a composition-independent coupling of a dilaton to hadronic matter produces detectable deviations from general relativity in high-accuracy light-deflection experiments in the Solar System. This work assumes only some general property of the coupling functions (for large values of the field, i.e., for an "attractor at infinity") and then assumes that $\bar{\gamma}$ is on the order of one at the beginning of the controllably classical part of inflation. Damour et al. (41) showed that that one can relate the present value of $\frac{1}{2}\bar{\gamma}$ to the cosmological density fluctuations. For the simplest inflationary potentials [favored by the Wilkinson Microwave Anisotropy Probe (WMAP) mission, i.e., $m^2 \chi^2$ (42)], the authors found that the present value of $\bar{\gamma}$ could be just below 10^{-7}. In particular, within this framework $\frac{1}{2}(1 - \gamma) \simeq \alpha_{\text{had}}^2$, where α_{had} is the dilaton coupling to hadronic matter. Its value depends on the model taken for the inflation potential $V(\chi) \propto \chi^n$, with χ being the inflation field; the level of the expected deviations from general relativity is $\sim 0.5 \times 10^{-7}$ for $n = 2$ (41). These predictions are based on the work in scalar-tensor extensions of gravity that are consistent with, and indeed often part of, present cosmological models.

For the runaway-dilaton scenario, comparison with the minimally coupled scalar-field action,

$$S_\phi = \frac{c^3}{4\pi G} \int d^4 x \sqrt{-g} \left[\frac{1}{4} R + \frac{1}{2} \partial_\mu \phi \partial^\mu \phi - V(\phi) \right], \qquad 23.$$

reveals that the negative scalar kinetic term leads to an action equivalent to a "ghost" in quantum-field theory that is referred to as phantom energy in the cosmological context (43). Such a scalar-field model could in theory generate acceleration by the field evolving up the potential toward the maximum. Phantom fields are plagued by catastrophic ultraviolet instabilities, as particle excitations have a negative mass (44); the fact that their energy is unbounded from below allows vacuum decay through the production of high-energy real particles as well as negative-energy ghosts that are in contradiction with the constraints on ultrahigh-energy cosmic rays (45).

Such runaway behavior can potentially be avoided by the introduction of higher-order kinetic terms in the action. One implementation of this idea is known as ghost condensation (46). In this scenario, the scalar field has a negative kinetic energy near $\dot{\phi} = 0$, but the quantum instabilities are stabilized by the addition of higher-order corrections to the scalar-field Lagrangian of the form $(\partial_\mu \phi \partial^\mu \phi)^2$. The ghost energy is then bounded from below, and stable evolution of the dilaton occurs with $w \geq -1$ (47). The gradient $\partial_\mu \phi$ is nonvanishing in the vacuum, violating Lorentz invariance; this may have important consequences in cosmology and in laboratory experiments.

The analyses discussed above predict very small (ranging from 10^{-5} to 5×10^{-8} for $\frac{1}{2}\bar{\gamma}$) observable post-Newtonian deviations from general relativity in the Solar System, thereby motivating a new generation of advanced-gravity experiments. In many cases, such tests would require reaching the accuracy needed to measure effects of the next post-Newtonian order ($\propto G^2$) (3, 48), promising important outcomes for twenty-first-century fundamental physics.

3.2. Observational Motivations for Advanced Tests of Gravity

Recent astrophysical measurements of the angular structure of the cosmic microwave background (CMB) (49), the masses of large-scale structures (50), and the luminosity distances of type Ia supernovae (51) have placed stringent constraints on the cosmological constant Λ and have also led to a revolutionary conclusion: The expansion of the Universe is accelerating. The implication of these observations for cosmological models is that a classically evolving scalar field currently dominates the energy density of the Universe. Such models have been shown to share the advantages of Λ, namely (a) compatibility with the spatial flatness–predicted inflation, (b) a Universe older than the standard Einstein–de Sitter model predicted, and (c) combined with cold dark matter (CDM), predictions for large-scale structure formation in good agreement with data from galaxy surveys. As well as imprinting their distinctive signature on the CMB anisotropy, scalar-field models remain viable and should be testable in the near future. This completely unexpected discovery demonstrates the importance of testing important ideas about the nature of gravity. We are presently in the discovery phase of this new physics, and although there are many theoretical conjectures as to the origin of a nonzero Λ, it is essential that we exploit every available opportunity to elucidate the physics at the root of the observed phenomena.

Description of quantum matter in a classical gravitational background poses interesting challenges, notably the possibility that the zero-point fluctuations of the matter fields generate a non-vanishing vacuum energy density ρ_{vac} that corresponds to the term $-\sqrt{-g}\rho_{vac}$ in $\mathcal{S}_{SM}$ (Equation 3) (26). This is equivalent to adding a cosmological constant term $+\Lambda g_{mn}$ on the left-hand side of Einstein's equations (Equation 5), with $\Lambda = 8\pi G_M \rho_{vac}/c^4$. Recent cosmological observations suggest a positive value of Λ corresponding to $\rho_{vac} \approx (2.3 \times 10^{-3} \text{ eV})^4$. Such a small value has a negligible effect on the planetary dynamics and is irrelevant for the present-day gravitational experiments in the Solar System. Quantizing the gravitational field itself poses a challenge because of the perturbative nonrenormalizability of Einstein's Lagrangian. Superstring theory offers a promising avenue toward solving this challenge.

There is now a great deal of evidence indicating that over 70% of the critical density of the Universe is in the form of a negative-pressure dark energy component; we have no understanding of its origin or nature. The fact that the expansion of the Universe is currently undergoing a period of acceleration has been well tested: The expansion has been directly measured from the light curves of several hundred type Ia supernovae (51) and has been independently inferred from observations of CMB by the WMAP satellite (42) and other CMB experiments (52). Cosmic speed-up can be accommodated within general relativity by invoking a mysterious cosmic fluid with large negative pressure, dubbed dark energy. The simplest possibility for dark energy is a cosmological constant; unfortunately, the smallest estimates for its value are 55 orders of magnitude too large (for reviews see References 53 and 54). Most of the theoretical studies operate in the shadow of the cosmological constant problem, the most embarrassing hierarchy problem in physics. This fact has motivated a host of other possibilities, most of which assume $\Lambda = 0$, with the dynamical dark energy being associated with a new scalar field. However, none of these suggestions is compelling, and most have serious drawbacks. Given the magnitude of this problem, a number of authors have considered the possibility that cosmic acceleration is not due to a particular substance, but rather that it arises from new gravitational physics (see discussion in References 53 and 54). In particular, certain extensions to general relativity in a low-energy regime (55) were shown to predict an experimentally consistent universe evolution without the need for dark energy (56). These dynamical models are expected to explain the observed acceleration of the Universe without dark energy, but these models may also produce measurable gravitational effects on the scales of the Solar System.

3.3. Modified Gravity as an Alternative to Dark Energy

Certain modifications of the Einstein–Hilbert action (Equation 2), by introducing terms that diverge as the scalar curvature goes to zero, could mimic dark energy (55). Recently, models involving inverse powers of the curvature have been proposed as an alternative to dark energy. In these models there are more propagating degrees of freedom in the gravitational sector than in the two contained in the massless graviton in general relativity. The simplest models of this kind add inverse powers of the scalar curvature to the action ($\Delta \mathcal{L} \propto 1/R^n$), thereby introducing a new scalar excitation in the spectrum. For the values of the parameters required to explain the acceleration of the Universe, this scalar field is almost massless in vacuum; this could lead to a possible conflict with the Solar System experiments.

However, models that involve inverse powers of other invariants, in particular those that diverge for $r \to 0$ in the Schwarzschild solution, generically recover an acceptable weak-field limit at short distances from sources by means of a screening or shielding of the extra degrees of freedom at short distances (57). Such theories can lead to late-time acceleration, but they typically result in one of two problems: either they are in conflict with tests of general relativity in the Solar System, due to the existence of additional dynamical degrees of freedom (58), or they contain ghostlike degrees of freedom that seem difficult to reconcile with fundamental theories.

The idea that the cosmic acceleration of the Universe may be caused by modification of gravity at very large distances, and not by a dark energy source, has recently received a great deal of attention. Such a modification could be triggered by extra space dimensions to which gravity spreads over cosmic distances. In addition to being testable by cosmological surveys, modified gravity predicts testable deviations in planetary motions, providing new motivations for a new generation of advanced gravitational experiments in space (3). An example of recent theoretical progress is the Dvali–Gabadadze–Porrati (DGP) brane-world model, which explores the possibility that we live on a brane embedded in a large extra dimension, and where the strength of gravity in the bulk is substantially less than that on the brane (59).

Although such a theory can lead to perfectly conventional gravity on large scales, it is also possible to choose the dynamics in such a way that new effects show up exclusively in the far infrared, thereby providing a mechanism to explain the acceleration of the Universe (51). Interestingly,

DGP gravity and other modifications of general relativity hold out the possibility of having interesting and testable predictions that distinguish them from models of dynamical dark energy. One outcome of this work is that the physics of the accelerating Universe may be deeply tied to the properties of gravity on relatively short scales, from millimeters to astronomical units (59, 60).

Although many effects predicted by gravity modification models are suppressed within the Solar System, there are measurable effects induced by some long-distance modifications of gravity (59). For instance, in the case of the precession of the planetary perihelion in the Solar System, the anomalous perihelion advance $\Delta\phi$, induced by a small correction δU_N to Newton's potential U_N, is given in radians per revolution (60) by $\Delta\phi \simeq \pi r \frac{d}{dr}[r^2 \frac{d}{dr}(\frac{\delta U_N}{r U_N})]$. The most reliable data regarding the planetary perihelion advances come from the inner planets of the Solar System, where a majority of the corrections are negligible. However, LLR offers an interesting possibility to test for these new effects (15). Evaluating the expected magnitude of the effect to the Earth–Moon system, one predicts an anomalous shift of $\Delta\phi \sim 10^{-12}$ (60), compared with the achieved accuracy of 2.4×10^{-11}. Therefore, the theories of gravity modification raise an intriguing possibility of discovering new physics that could be addressed with the new generation of astrometric measurements.

3.4. Scalar-Field Models as Candidates for Dark Energy

One of the simplest candidates for dynamical dark energy is a scalar field φ with an extremely low mass and an effective potential $V(\varphi)$. If the field is rolling slowly, its persistent potential energy is responsible for creating the late epoch of inflation we observe today. For the models that include only inverse powers of the curvature, other than the Einstein–Hilbert term, it is possible that in regions where the curvature is large the scalar has a large mass that could make the dynamics similar to those of general relativity (61). At the same time, the scalar curvature—although larger than its mean cosmological value—is very small in the Solar System, thereby satisfying constraints set by the gravitational tests performed to date (62, 63). Nevertheless, it is not clear whether these models may be regarded as a viable alternative to dark energy.

Effective scalar fields are prevalent in supersymmetric field theories and string/M-theory. For example, string theory predicts that the vacuum expectation value of a scalar field, the dilaton, determines the relationship between the gauge and gravitational couplings. A general, low-energy effective action for the massless modes of the dilaton can be cast as a scalar-tensor theory (as in Equation 6) with a vanishing potential, where $f(\varphi)$, $g(\varphi)$, and $q_i(\varphi)$ are the dilatonic couplings to gravity, the scalar kinetic term, and the gauge and matter fields, respectively, which encode the effects of loop effects and potentially nonperturbative corrections.

A string-scale cosmological constant or exponential dilaton potential in the string frame translates into an exponential potential in the Einstein frame. Such quintessence potentials (54, 64, 65) can have scaling (66) and tracking (67) properties that allow the scalar-field energy density to evolve alongside the other matter constituents. A problematic feature of scaling potentials (66) is that they do not lead to accelerative expansion, as the energy density simply scales with that of matter. Alternatively, certain potentials can predict a dark energy density that alternately dominates the Universe and decays away; in such models, the acceleration of the Universe is transient (68). Collectively, quintessence potentials predict that the density of the dark energy dynamically evolves over time, in contrast to the cosmological constant. Similar to a cosmological constant, however, the scalar field is expected to have no significant density perturbations within the causal horizon, so they contribute little to the evolution of the clustering of matter in a large-scale structure (69).

In addition to couplings to ordinary matter, the quintessence field may have nontrivial couplings to dark matter (56, 70). Nonperturbative string-loop effects do not lead to universal couplings, although it is possible that the dilaton decouples more slowly from dark matter than it does from gravity and fermions. This coupling can provide a mechanism to generate acceleration with a scaling potential while also being consistent with EP tests. It can also explain why acceleration began to occur only relatively recently by being triggered by the nonminimal coupling to the CDM, rather than by a feature in the effective potential (71). Such couplings can not only generate acceleration but can also modify structure formation through the coupling to CDM density fluctuations and adiabatic instabilities (72), in contrast to minimally coupled quintessence models. Dynamical observables that are sensitive to the evolution in matter perturbations as well as to the expansion of the Universe, such as (*a*) the matter power spectrum as measured by large-scale surveys and (*b*) weak lensing convergence spectra, could distinguish nonminimal couplings from theories with minimal effect on clustering.

4. SEARCH FOR A NEW THEORY OF GRAVITY WITH EXPERIMENTS IN SPACE

It is well known that work on the general theory of relativity began with the EP, in which gravitational acceleration was a priori held indistinguishable from acceleration caused by mechanical forces; as a consequence, gravitational mass was therefore identical to inertial mass. Since Newton's time, the question about the equality of inertial and passive gravitational masses has risen in almost every theory of gravitation. Einstein elevated this identity, which was implicit in Newton's gravity, to a guiding principle in his attempts to explain both electromagnetic and gravitational acceleration according to the same set of physical laws. Thus, almost 100 years ago Einstein postulated that not only mechanical laws of motion but also all nongravitational laws should behave in freely falling frames as if gravity were absent. It is this principle that predicts identical accelerations of compositionally different objects in the same gravitational field, and it also allows gravity to be viewed as a geometrical property of spacetime—leading to the general relativistic interpretation of gravitation (**Figure 4**).

Remarkably, the EP has been (and still is) a focus of gravitational research for more than 400 years (16). Since the time of Galileo we have known that objects of different mass and

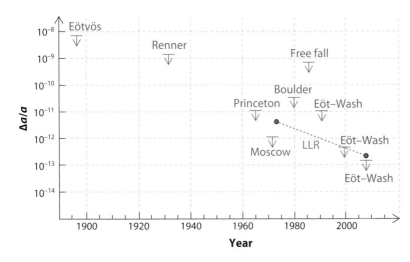

Figure 4

Progress in tests of the equivalence principle (EP) since the early twentieth century (3, 21). Abbreviation: LLR, lunar laser ranging.

composition accelerate at identical rates in the same gravitational field. From 1602 to 1604, through his study of inclined planes and pendulums, Galileo formulated a law of falling bodies that led to an early empirical version of the EP. However, these famous results were not published for another 35 years. It took an additional 50 years before a theory of gravity describing these and other early gravitational experiments was published by Newton in his *Principia* in 1687. On the basis of his second law, Newton concluded that the gravitational force is proportional to the mass of the body on which it acted; from his third law, he postulated that the gravitational force is proportional to the mass of its source.

Newton was aware that the inertial mass m_I in his second law, $\mathbf{F} = m_I \mathbf{a}$, might not be the same as the gravitational mass m_G relating force to gravitational field $\mathbf{F} = m_G \mathbf{g}$. Indeed, after rearranging these two equations, we find $\mathbf{a} = (m_G/m_I)\mathbf{g}$, and thus, in principle, materials with different values of the ratio m_G/m_I could accelerate at different rates in the same gravitational field. Newton tested this possibility with simple pendulums of the same length but with different masses and compositions, but he found no difference in their periods. On this basis Newton concluded that m_G/m_I was constant for all matter and that, by a suitable choice of units, the ratio could always be set to one (i.e., $m_G/m_I = 1$). Friedrich Bessel[7] subsequently tested this ratio more accurately, and then in a definitive 1889 experiment Eötvös (73) was able to experimentally verify this equality of the inertial and gravitational masses to an accuracy of one part in 10^9.

Today, more than 320 years after Newton proposed a comprehensive approach to studying the relation between the two masses of a body, this relation remains the subject of numerous theoretical and experimental investigations. The question regarding the equality of inertial and passive gravitational masses has arisen in almost every theory of gravitation. In 1915 the EP became a part of the foundation of Einstein's general theory of relativity; subsequently, many experimental efforts focused on testing the EP in the search for limits of general relativity. Thus, the early tests of the EP were further improved by Dicke and colleagues (74) to one part in 10^{11}. Most recently, a University of Washington group (75, 76) improved upon Dicke's verification of the EP by several orders of magnitude, reporting $(m_G/m_I - 1) = 1.4 \times 10^{-13}$, thereby confirming Einstein's intuition.

In a 1907 paper, using the early version of the EP (1), Einstein made important preliminary predictions regarding the influence of gravity on light propagation; these predictions represented the next important step in the development of his theory. He realized that a ray of light coming from a distant star would appear to be attracted by solar mass while passing close to the Sun. As a result, the ray's trajectory is bent twice as much in the direction towards the Sun, compared to the same trajectory analyzed with Newton's theory. In addition, light radiated by a star would interact with the star's gravitational potential, resulting in the radiation shifting slightly toward the infrared end of the spectrum.

In about 1912, Einstein (with the help of mathematician Marcel Grossmann) began a new phase of his gravitational research by phrasing his work in terms of the tensor calculus of Tullio Levi-Civita and Gregorio Ricci-Curbastro. The tensor calculus greatly facilitated calculations in four-dimensional spacetime, a notion that Einstein had obtained from Hermann Minkowski's 1907 mathematical elaboration of Einstein's own special theory of relativity.[8] Einstein called his new theory the general theory of relativity. After a number of false starts, he published the definitive field equations of his theory in late 1915 (2). Since that time, physicists have endeavored to understand and verify various predictions of the general theory of relativity with ever-increasing accuracy.

---

[7]For further information, please consult: **http://en.wikipedia.org/wiki/Friedrich_Bessel**.

[8]For further information, see: **http://en.wikipedia.org/wiki/Hermann_Minkowski**.

4.1. Tests of the Equivalence Principle

The EP (15, 16, 29) is at the foundation of the general theory of relativity; therefore, testing the principle is very important. The EP includes three hypotheses:

1. Universality of free fall (UFF), which states that freely falling bodies have the same acceleration in the same gravitational field independent of their compositions (see Section 4.1);

2. Local Lorentz invariance (LLI), which suggests that clocks' rates are independent of the clocks' velocities (see Section 4.2); and

3. Local position invariance (LPI), which postulates that clocks' rates are also independent of their spacetime positions (see Section 4.3).

Using these three hypotheses, Einstein deduced that gravity is a geometric property of space-time (21). One can test the validity of both the EP and the field equations that determine the geometric structure created by a mass distribution. There are two different "flavors" of the EP, the weak and the strong forms (WEP and SEP, respectively), which are being tested in various experiments performed with laboratory test masses and with bodies of astronomical sizes (16).

4.1.1. The weak equivalence principle. The WEP holds that the gravitational properties of strong and electroweak interactions obey the EP. In this case the relevant test-body differences are their fractional nuclear-binding differences, their neutron-to-proton ratios, their atomic charges, etc. Furthermore, the equality of gravitational and inertial masses implies that different neutral massive test bodies have the same free-fall acceleration in an external gravitational field, and therefore in freely falling inertial frames the external gravitational field appears only in the form of a tidal interaction. Apart from these tidal corrections, freely falling bodies behave as though external gravity were absent (77).

General relativity and other metric theories of gravity assume that the WEP is exact. However, many extensions of the standard model that contain new macroscopic-range quantum fields predict quantum exchange forces that generically violate the WEP because they couple to generalized charges rather than to mass/energy, as does gravity (29, 40, 41).

In a laboratory, precise tests of the EP can be made by comparing the free-fall accelerations, a_1 and a_2, of different test bodies. When the bodies are at the same distance from the source of the gravity, the expression for the EP takes the elegant form

$$\frac{\Delta a}{a} = \frac{2(a_1 - a_2)}{a_1 + a_2} = \left[\frac{m_G}{m_I}\right]_1 - \left[\frac{m_G}{m_I}\right]_2 = \Delta\left[\frac{m_G}{m_I}\right], \qquad 24.$$

where m_G and m_I are the gravitational and inertial masses of each body, respectively. The sensitivity of the EP test is determined by the precision of the differential acceleration measurement divided by the degree to which the test bodies differ (e.g., composition).

Various experiments have been performed to measure the ratios of gravitational to inertial masses of bodies. Recent experiments on bodies of laboratory dimensions have verified the WEP to a fractional precision of $\Delta(m_G/m_I) \lesssim 10^{-11}$ (74), to $\lesssim 10^{-12}$ (78), and finally to $\lesssim 1.4 \times 10^{-13}$ (76). The accuracy of these experiments is high enough to confirm that the strong, weak, and electromagnetic interactions contribute equally to the passive gravitational and inertial masses of the laboratory bodies.

Currently, the most accurate results in testing the WEP have been reported by ground-based laboratories (16, 75). The most recent result (76, 79) for the fractional differential acceleration

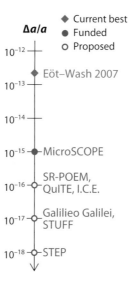

Figure 5

Anticipated progress in tests of the weak equivalence principle (WEP) (3). Abbreviations: I.C.E., Interférométrie à Source Cohérente pour Applications dans l'Espace; MicroSCOPE, Micro-Satellite à traînée Compensée pour l'Observation du Principe d'Equivalence; QuITE, Quantum Interferometer Test of the Equivalence Principle; SR-POEM, Principle of Equivalence Measurement on a Sounding Rocket; STEP, Satellite Test of Equivalence Principle; STUFF, Space Test of Universality of Free Fall.

between beryllium and titanium test bodies was given by the Eöt–Wash group[9] as $\Delta a/a = (1.0 \pm 1.4) \times 10^{-13}$. A review of the most recent laboratory tests of gravity can be found in Reference 80. Significant improvements in tests of the EP are expected from dedicated space-based experiments (3) (**Figure 5**).

The composition independence of acceleration rates of various masses toward the Earth can be tested in space-based laboratories to a precision of many additional orders of magnitude—down to levels at which some models of the unified theory of quantum gravity, matter, and energy suggest a possible violation of the EP (29, 40, 41). In some scalar-tensor theories, the strength of EP violations and the magnitude of the fifth force mediated by the scalar can be drastically larger in space than on the ground (81), providing further justification for space deployment. Importantly, many of these theories predict observable violations of the EP at various levels of accuracy ranging from 10^{-13} to 10^{-16}. Therefore, even a confirmation of no EP violation will be exceptionally valuable as it will place useful constraints on the range of possibilities in the development of a unified physical theory.

Compared with Earth-based laboratories, experiments in space can benefit from a range of conditions, including free fall and significantly reduced contributions due to seismic, thermal, and other nongravitational noise (3). As a result, many experiments have been proposed to test the EP in space. Below I present only a partial list of these missions. Furthermore, to illustrate the use of different technologies, I discuss only the most representative concepts.

---

[9]The Eöt–Wash group at the University of Washington in Seattle has developed new techniques in high-precision studies of weak-field gravity and searches for possible new interactions weaker than gravity. For details, see: **http://www.npl.washington.edu/eotwash/**.

The Micro-Satellite à traînée Compensée pour l'Observation du Principe d'Equivalence (MicroSCOPE) mission[10] is a room-temperature EP experiment in space that utilizes electrostatic differential accelerometers (82). The mission is currently under development by the Centre National d'Etudes Spatiales (CNES)[11] and the European Space Agency (ESA) and is scheduled for launch in 2010. The design goal is to achieve a differential acceleration accuracy of 10^{-15}. MicroSCOPE's electrostatic differential accelerometers are based on flight heritage designs from the CHAMP, GRACE, and GOCE missions.[12]

The Principle of Equivalence Measurement (POEM) experiment (83) is a ground-based test of the WEP and is now under development. It will be able to detect a violation of the EP with a fractional acceleration accuracy of 5 parts in 10^{14} in a short experiment (i.e., a few days long) and with a three- to tenfold better accuracy in a longer experiment. The experiment makes use of optical distance measurement [by tracking frequency gauge (84)] and will be advantageously sensitive to short-range forces with a characteristic length scale of $\lambda < 10$ km. SR-POEM, a POEM-based proposed room-temperature test of the WEP during a suborbital flight on a sounding rocket (SR), was also proposed recently (3). It is anticipated to be able to search for a violation of the EP with a single-flight accuracy of 1 part in 10^{16}. Extension to higher accuracy in an orbital mission is under study. Additionally, the Space Test of Universality of Free Fall (STUFF) (3) is a recent study of a space-based experiment that relies on optical metrology and proposes to reach an accuracy of 1 part in 10^{17} in testing the EP in space.

The Quantum Interferometer Test of the Equivalence Principle (QuITE) (85) is a proposed cold atom–based test of the EP in space. QuITE intends to measure the absolute single-axis differential acceleration, with an accuracy of 1 part in 10^{16}, by utilizing two colocated-matter wave interferometers with different atomic species.[13] QuITE will improve the current EP limits set in similar experiments conducted in ground-based laboratory conditions (86). Similarly, the Interférométrie à Source Cohérente pour Applications dans l'Espace (ICE) project[14] supported by CNES in France aims to develop a high-precision accelerometer based on coherent atomic sources in space (87), with an accurate test of the EP as one of its main objectives.

The Galileo Galilei (GG) mission (88) is an Italian space experiment[15] proposed to test the EP at room temperature with an accuracy of 1 part in 10^{17}. The key instrument of GG is a differential accelerometer made of weakly coupled coaxial, concentric test cylinders than spin rapidly around the symmetry axis and are sensitive in the plane perpendicular to it. GG is included in the National Aerospace Plan of the Italian Space Agency for implementation in the near future.

The Satellite Test of Equivalence Principle (STEP) mission (89) is a proposed test of the EP to be conducted from a free-falling platform in space provided by a drag-free spacecraft orbiting the Earth. STEP will test the composition independence of gravitational acceleration

---

[10] For details, see: **http://microscope.onera.fr/**.

[11] See: **http://www.cnes.fr/**.

[12] Several gravity missions were recently developed by the German National Research Center for Geosciences (GFZ). Among them are CHAMP (Gravity and Magnetic Field Mission); GRACE (Gravity Recovery and Climate Experiment Mission), together with NASA; and GOCE (Global Ocean Circulation Experiment), together with the ESA and other European countries. See: **http://www.gfz-potsdam.de/pb1/op/index_GRAM.html**.

[13] QuITE's ground-based analog, the Atomic Equivalence Principle Test (AEPT), is currently under construction at Stanford University. AEPT is designed to reach a sensitivity of 1 part in 10^{15}. Compared to conditions on the ground, space offers a factor of nearly 10^3 improvement in the integration times in observation of the free-falling atoms (i.e., progressing from milliseconds to seconds). The longer integration times translate into accuracy improvements (3).

[14] See: **http://www.ice-space.fr**.

[15] See: **http://eotvos.dm.unipi.it/nobili**.

for cryogenically controlled test masses by searching for a violation of the EP with a fractional acceleration accuracy of 1 part in 10^{18}. As such, this ambitious experiment will be able to test very precisely for the presence of any new nonmetric, long-range physical interactions.

This impressive evidence and the future prospects of testing the WEP for laboratory bodies is incomplete for astronomical-body scales. The experiments searching for WEP violations are conducted in laboratory environments that utilize test masses with negligible amounts of gravitational self-energy; therefore, a large-scale experiment is needed to test the postulated equality of gravitational self-energy contributions to the inertial and passive gravitational masses of the bodies (28). Once the self-gravity of the test bodies is nonnegligible (which is currently true only for bodies of astronomical sizes), the corresponding experiment will test the ultimate version of the EP—the SEP.

4.1.2. The strong equivalence principle. The SEP is extended to cover the gravitational properties resulting from gravitational energy itself (16). It is an assumption about the way that gravity begets gravity, i.e., about the nonlinear property of gravitation. Although general relativity assumes that the SEP is exact, alternate metric theories of gravity—such as those involving scalar fields and other extensions of gravity theory—typically violate the SEP. For the SEP case, the relevant test-body differences are the fractional contributions to their masses by gravitational self-energy. Because of the extreme weakness of gravity, SEP test bodies must have astronomical sizes.

The PPN formalism (28; see References 11 and 21 for reviews) describes the motion of celestial bodies in a theoretical framework common to a wide class of metric theories of gravity. To facilitate investigation of a possible violation of the SEP, Equation 10 allows for a possible inequality of the gravitational and inertial masses, given by the parameter $[m_G/m_I]_i$, which in the PPN formalism is expressed as

$$\left[\frac{m_G}{m_I}\right]_{SEP} = 1 + \eta \left(\frac{E}{mc^2}\right), \qquad 25.$$

where m is the mass of a body, E is the body's (negative) gravitational self-energy, mc^2 is its total mass-energy, and η is a dimensionless constant for SEP violation (28). Any SEP violation is quantified by the parameter η: In fully conservative, Lorentz-invariant theories of gravity (11, 21), the SEP parameter is related to the PPN parameters by $\eta = 4\beta - \gamma - 3 \equiv 4\bar{\beta} - \bar{\gamma}$. In general relativity $\gamma = \beta = 1$, so that $\eta = 0$ (11, 16, 21).

The quantity E is the body's gravitational self-energy ($E < 0$), which for a body i is given by

$$\left[\frac{E}{mc^2}\right]_i = -\frac{G}{2m_i c^2} \int_i d^3 x \rho_i U_i = -\frac{G}{2m_i c^2} \int_i d^3 x d^3 x' \frac{\rho_i(r)\rho_i(r')}{|r - r'|}. \qquad 26.$$

For a sphere with a radius R and uniform density, $E/mc^2 = -3Gm/5Rc^2 = -0.3v_E^2/c^2$, where v_E is the escape velocity. Accurate evaluation for Solar System bodies requires numerical integration of the expression of Equation 26. Evaluating the standard solar model results in $(E/mc^2)_\odot \sim -3.52 \times 10^{-6}$ (90, 77). Because gravitational self-energy is proportional to m_i^2, and also because of the extreme weakness of gravity, the typical values for the ratio E/mc^2 are $\sim 10^{-25}$ for bodies of laboratory sizes. Therefore, the experimental accuracy of 1 part in 10^{13} (76), which is so useful for the WEP, is not sufficient to test how gravitational self-energy contributes to the inertial and gravitational masses of small bodies. To test the SEP one must consider planet-sized extended bodies, where the ratio in Equation 26 is considerably higher.

Currently, the Earth–Moon–Sun system provides the best Solar System arena for testing the SEP. LLR experiments involve reflecting laser beams off retroreflector arrays placed on the Moon by the Apollo astronauts and by an unmanned Soviet lander (15, 16). Recent solutions using LLR data give $(-0.8 \pm 1.3) \times 10^{-13}$ for any possible inequality in the ratios of the gravitational and

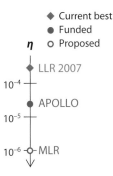

η

◆ Current best
● Funded
○ Proposed

◆ LLR 2007
10^{-4}

● APOLLO
10^{-5}

10^{-6} ○ MLR

Figure 6

Anticipated progress in the tests of the strong equivalence principle (SEP) (3). Abbreviations: APOLLO, Apache Point Observatory Lunar Laser-Ranging Operations; LLR, lunar laser ranging; MLR, Mars laser ranging.

inertial masses for the Earth and Moon. This result, in combination with laboratory experiments on the WEP, yields a SEP test of $(-1.8 \pm 1.9) \times 10^{-13}$ that corresponds to the value of the SEP violation parameter of $\eta = (4.0 \pm 4.3) \times 10^{-4}$. In addition, using the recent Cassini result for the PPN parameter γ, PPN parameter β is determined at the level of $\bar{\beta} = (1.2 \pm 1.1) \times 10^{-4}$ (see Reference 15 for details) (**Figure 6**).

With the new Apache Point Observatory Lunar Laser-Ranging Operations (APOLLO)[16] facility (14, 91), LLR science has begun a renaissance. APOLLO's 1-mm-range precision will translate into order-of-magnitude accuracy improvements in tests of the WEP and the SEP (leading to accuracy at levels of $\Delta a/a \lesssim 1 \times 10^{-14}$ and $\eta \lesssim 2 \times 10^{-5}$ respectively) in the search for variability of Newton's gravitational constant (see Section 4.4.2) and in the test of the gravitational inverse-square law (see Section 4.5) on scales of the Earth-to-Moon distance (anticipated accuracy of 3×10^{-11}) (14).

The next step in this direction is interplanetary laser ranging (92) to, for example, a lander on Mars (or, even better, on Mercury). Technology is available to conduct such measurements with a few-picosecond timing precision, which could translate into millimeter-class accuracies in ranging between the Earth and Mars. The resulting Mars laser ranging (MLR) experiment could (a) test the weak and strong forms of the EP with an accuracy at the 3×10^{-15} and the 2×10^{-6} levels, respectively; (b) measure the PPN parameter γ (see Section 4.6) with accuracy below the 10^{-6} level; and (c) test the gravitational inverse-square law at ~2-AU distances with an accuracy of 1×10^{-14}, thereby greatly improving the accuracy of the current tests (92). MLR could also advance research in several areas of science, including remote-sensing geodesic and geophysical studies of Mars.

Furthermore, with the recently demonstrated capabilities of reliable laser links over large distances (e.g., tens of millions of kilometers) in space, there is a strong possibility of improving the accuracy of gravity experiments with precision laser ranging over interplanetary scales (see discussion in References 3 and 92). The justification for such experiments is strong, the required technology is space qualified, and some components have already flown in space. With MLR, the very best venue for gravitational physics will be expanded to interplanetary distances, representing an upgrade in both the scale and the precision of this promising technique.

The experiments described above are examples of the rich opportunities offered by the fundamental physics community to explore the validity of the EP. These experiments could potentially offer an improvement of up to five orders of magnitude over the accuracy of the current tests of

---

[16]APOLLO is the new LLR station that was recently built in New Mexico; it initiated operations in 2006.

the EP. Such experiments would dramatically enhance the range of validity for one of the most important physical principles—or they could lead to a spectacular discovery.

4.2. Tests of Local Lorentz Invariance

Recently there has been an increase in activity in experimental tests of LLI, in particular light-speed isotropy tests. This increase is largely due to (*a*) advances in technology, which have allowed more precise measurements, and (*b*) the emergence of the standard model extension (SME) as a framework for the analysis of experiments, which has provided new interpretations of LLI tests. None of the experiments performed to date has yet reported a violation of LLI, although the constraints on a putative violation have improved significantly.

LLI is an underlying principle of relativity; it postulates that the outcome of a local experiment is independent of the velocity and orientation of the apparatus. To identify a violation it is necessary to have an alternative theory to interpret the experiment, and many have been developed. The Robertson–Mansouri–Sexl (RMS) framework (21, 93, 94) is a well-known kinematic test theory for parameterizing deviations from Lorentz invariance. In the RMS framework, there is assumed to be a preferred frame Σ where the speed of light is isotropic. One usually analyzes the change in a resonator frequency as a function of the Poynting vector direction with respect to the velocity of the lab in some preferred frame, which is typically chosen to be the CMB.

The ordinary Lorentz transformations to other frames are generalized to

$$t' = a^{-1}\left(t - \frac{\mathbf{v}\cdot\mathbf{x}}{c^2}\right), \quad \mathbf{x}' = d^{-1}\mathbf{x} - (d^{-1} - b^{-1})\frac{\mathbf{v}(\mathbf{v}\cdot\mathbf{x})}{v^2} + a^{-1}\mathbf{v}t, \qquad 27.$$

where the coefficients a, b, d are functions of the magnitude v of the relative velocity between frames. This transformation is the most general one-to-one transformation that preserves rectilinear motion in the absence of forces. In the case of special relativity, with Einstein clock synchronization these coefficients reduce to $a = b^{-1} = \sqrt{1 - (v/c)^2}, d = 1$. Many experiments, such as those that measure the isotropy of the one-way speed of light (11) or the propagation of light around closed loops, have observables that depend on a, b, d but not on the synchronization procedure. Due to its simplicity, RMS has been widely used to interpret many experiments (94). Most often, the RMS framework is used in situations where the velocity v is small compared to c. We therefore expand a, b, d in a power series in v/c:

$$a = 1 + \alpha\frac{v^2}{c^2} + \mathcal{O}(c^{-4}), \quad b = 1 + \beta\frac{v^2}{c^2} + \mathcal{O}(c^{-4}), \quad d = 1 + \delta\frac{v^2}{c^2} + \mathcal{O}(c^{-4}). \qquad 28.$$

The RMS parameterizes a possible Lorentz violation by a deviation of the parameters α, β, δ from their special relativistic values $\alpha = -\frac{1}{2}, \beta = \frac{1}{2}, \delta = 0$. These are typically grouped into three linear combinations that represent a measurement of (*a*) the isotropy of the speed of light or the orientation dependence ($P_{\mathrm{MM}} = \frac{1}{2} - \beta + \delta$), measured in a Michelson–Morley experiment (95) and constrained (96–98) to $(0.4 \pm 8.1) \times 10^{-11}$, (*b*) the boost dependence of the speed of light ($P_{\mathrm{KT}} = \beta - \alpha - 1$), measured in a Kennedy–Thorndike experiment (99) and constrained (97, 100) to $(3.1 \pm 6.9) \times 10^{-7}$, and (*c*) the time dilation parameter ($P_{\mathrm{IS}} = |\alpha + \frac{1}{2}|$), measured in an Ives–Stillwell experiment (101) and constrained (102) to $\leq 2.2 \times 10^{-7}$. A test of Lorentz invariance was performed by comparing the resonance frequencies of two orthogonal cryogenic optical resonators subject to Earth's rotation over ~1 year. For a possible anisotropy of the speed of light c, the authors of Reference 96 reported a constraint of $\Delta c/c = (2.6 \pm 1.7) \times 10^{-15}$, which has since been further improved (103) by an additional order of magnitude.

The RMS framework, however, is incomplete, as it says nothing about dynamics or about how given clocks and rods relate to fundamental particles. In particular, the coordinate transformation of Equation 27 only has meaning if we identify the coordinates with the measurements made by a particular set of clocks and rods. If we choose a different set of clocks and rods, the transformation laws may be different. Thus, it is not possible to compare the RMS parameters of two experiments that use physically different clocks and rods. However, for experiments involving a single type of clock/rod and light, the RMS formalism is applicable and can be used to search for violations of Lorentz invariance in that experiment.[17]

Limits on the violation of Lorentz symmetry are available from laser interferometric versions of the Michelson–Morley experiment, which compare the velocity of light c and the maximum attainable velocity of massive particles c_i up to $\delta \equiv |c^2/c_i^2 - 1| < 10^{-9}$ (105). More accurate tests can be performed via the Hughes–Drever experiment (106) by searching for a time dependence of the quadrupole splitting of nuclear Zeeman levels along the Earth's orbit. This technique achieves an impressive limit of $\delta < 3 \times 10^{-22}$ (107).

Since the discovery of the cosmological origin of gamma-ray bursts, there has been growing interest in using these transient events to probe the quantum gravity–energy scale ranging from 10^{16} to 10^{19} GeV up to the Planck-mass scale. This energy scale can manifest itself through a measurable modification in the electromagnetic radiation dispersion relation for high-energy photons originating from cosmological distances. The Gamma-Ray Large Area Space Telescope (GLAST)[18] (108) is expected to improve the LLI tests by several orders of magnitude, potentially reaching an accuracy at the level of $\delta \simeq 10^{-26}$ (see **Figure 7**) (94, 108). GLAST will measure the cosmic gamma-ray flux ranging from 20 MeV to >300 GeV, with supporting measurements for gamma-ray bursts ranging from 8 keV to 30 MeV. Upon its launch (June 11, 2008), GLAST will open a new and important window on a wide variety of phenomena, including black holes and active galactic nuclei, the optical-ultraviolet extragalactic background light, gamma-ray bursts, the origin of cosmic rays and supernova remnants, and searches for hypothetical new phenomena such as supersymmetric dark matter annihilations and Lorentz-invariance violation.

The standard model coupled to general relativity is thought to be the effective low-energy limit of an underlying fundamental theory that unifies gravity and particle physics at the Planck scale. This underlying theory may well include Lorentz violation (109), which could be detectable in space-based experiments (3). Lorentz symmetry breaking due to nontrivial solutions of string-field theory that was first discussed in Reference 110. These solutions arise from the string-field theory of open strings and may have implications for low-energy physics. Violations of Lorentz invariance may imply a breaking of the fundamental charge-parity-time (CPT) symmetry of local quantum-field theories (110). This spontaneous breaking of CPT symmetry allows for an explanation of the baryon asymmetry of the Universe: In the early Universe, after the breaking of the Lorentz and CPT symmetries, tensor-fermion interactions in the low-energy limit of string-field theories gave rise to a chemical potential that created in equilibrium a baryon-antibaryon asymmetry in the presence of baryon number–violating interactions (111, 112). The development of the SME has inspired a new wave of experiments designed to explore the uncharted regions of the Lorentz-violating parameter space.

If one adds to the standard model the appropriate terms involving operators for Lorentz-invariance violation (113), the result is the SME, which has provided a phenomenological framework for testing Lorentz invariance (110, 114), and which has also suggested a number of new tests of relativistic gravity in the Solar System (115). Compared with their ground-based analogs,

---

[17]The RMS formalism can be made less ambiguous by placing it into a complete dynamical framework, such as the SME. It has in fact been shown (104) that the RMS framework can be incorporated into the SME.

[18]See: **http://glast.gsfc.nasa.gov/**.

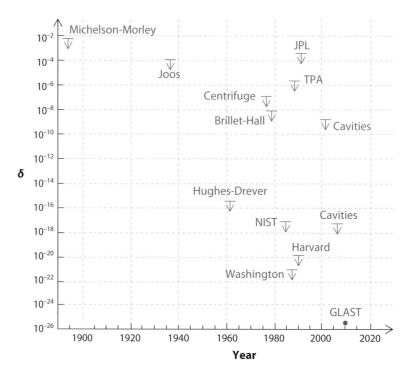

Figure 7

Progress in tests of the local Lorentz invariance (LLI) since the early twentieth century (3, 21) and the anticipated performance of the Gamma-Ray Large Area Space Telescope (GLAST) mission (funded jointly by the National Aeronautics and Space Administration and the Department of Energy). Abbreviations: JPL, Jet Propulsion Laboratory; NIST, The National Institute of Standards and Technology; TPA, two-photon absorption.

space-based experiments in this area can provide improvements by as much as six orders of magnitude. Recent studies of the "aether theories" (116) have shown that these models are naturally compatible with general relativity (21) but that they predict several nonvanishing Lorentz-violation parameters that could be measured in experiment. Kostelecky & Russell (117) tabulate experimental results for coefficients for Lorentz and CPT violation in the minimal SME formalism and report the attained sensitivities in the matter and photon sectors.

Searches for extensions of special relativity on space-based platforms are known as clock-comparison tests. Such tests involve operating two or more high-precision clocks simultaneously and comparing their rates correlated with orbit parameters, such as velocity, relative to the CMB and to position in a gravitational environment. The SME allows for the possibility that comparisons of the signals from different clocks will yield very small differences that can be detected in experiment. For present-day results see Reference 117, which provides a summary of experimental results for the coefficients for Lorentz and CPT violation within the minimal SME formalism.

An experiment known as the Atomic Clock Ensemble in Space (ACES) is aiming to perform important tests of special relativity and the SME. ACES is a European mission (118) in fundamental physics that will operate atomic clocks in the microgravity environment of the International Space Station (ISS) with fractional frequency stability and an accuracy of a few parts in 10^{16}. ACES is jointly funded by the ESA and the CNES and is being prepared for a 2013 flight to the ISS for a planned mission duration of 18 months (see discussion in Reference 3).

Optical clocks offer an improved possibility of testing the time variations of fundamental constants at a high level of accuracy (119, 120; also see 3 and references therein). Interestingly, such measurements complement tests of the LLI (121) and of the UFF to experimentally establish the validity of the EP. The universality of the gravitational redshift can be tested at the same accuracy level by two optical clocks in free flight in a varying gravitational potential. The constancy and isotropy of the speed of light can be tested by continuously comparing a space clock with a ground clock. Optical clocks orbiting the Earth, combined with a sufficiently accurate time and frequency transfer link, can improve present results by more than three orders of magnitude.

There is a profound connection between cosmology and possible Lorentz symmetry violation (122). Spontaneous breaking of the Lorentz symmetry implies that there exists an order parameter with a nonzero expectation value that is responsible for the effect. For spontaneous Lorentz symmetry breaking one usually assumes that sources other than the familiar matter density are responsible for such a violation. However, if Lorentz symmetry is broken by an extra source, the latter must also affect the cosmological background. Therefore, in order to identify the mechanism of such a violation, one must look for traces of similar symmetry breaking in cosmology, for instance, in the CMB data (see Reference 3 and references therein). In other words, were a violation of the Lorentz symmetry discovered in experiments but not supported by observational cosmology data, such a discrepancy would indicate the existence of a novel source of symmetry breaking. This source would affect the dispersion relation of particles and the performance of the local clocks, but it would leave no imprint on the cosmological metric. Such a possibility emphasizes the importance of a comprehensive program to investigate all possible mechanisms of breaking of the Lorentz symmetry, including those effects accessible by experiments conducted in space-based laboratories.

4.3. Tests of the Local Position Invariance

Einstein predicted the gravitational redshift of light from the EP in 1907 (1), but the redshift is very difficult to measure astrophysically. Given that both the WEP and the LLI postulates have been tested with great accuracy, experiments concerning the universality of the gravitational redshift measure the level to which the LPI holds. Therefore, violations of the LPI would imply that the rate of a free-falling clock would be different when compared with a standard one, for instance on the Earth's surface. The accuracy to which the LPI holds as an invariance of nature can be parameterized through $\Delta \nu / \nu = (1 + \mu) U / c^2$.

The first observation of the gravitational redshift was the measurement of the shift in the spectral lines from the white dwarf star Sirius B by Adams in 1925.[19] Although this measurement, as well as later measurements of the spectral shifts on other white dwarf stars, agreed with the prediction of relativity, the shift might stem from some other cause; hence, experimental verification using a known terrestrial source is preferable. The effect was conclusively tested by Pound & Rebka's 1959 experiment (123).

The Pound–Rebka experiment was one of the first precision experiments testing general relativity; it further verified the effects of gravity on light by testing the universality of the gravity-induced frequency shift $\Delta \nu$ that follows from the WEP: $\Delta \nu / \nu = g h / c^2 = (2.57 \pm 0.26) \times 10^{-15}$, where g is the acceleration of gravity and h is the height of fall (123). This test of LPI resulted in a limit of $\mu \simeq 10^{-2}$. The experiment was based on Mössbauer-effect measurements between sources and detectors spanning the 22.5-m tower in the Jefferson Physical Laboratory at Harvard University.

---

[19] Please consult: **http://en.wikipedia.org/wiki/Walter_Sydney_Adams**.

In 1976, an accurate verification of the LPI was performed by Vessot and collaborators (124), who compared the frequencies of two Hydrogen masers, one on Earth and another on a suborbital rocket. The resulting Gravity Probe A experiment exploited the much higher "tower" enabled by space: A suborbital Scout rocket carried a Hydrogen maser to an altitude of 10,273 km, and a novel telemetry scheme allowed comparison with Hydrogen masers on the ground. Gravity Probe A verified that the fractional change in the measured frequencies is consistent with general relativity to the 10^{-4} level, confirming Einstein's prediction to 70 ppm and thereby establishing a limit of $|\mu| < 2 \times 10^{-4}$. More than 30 years later, this remains the most precise measurement of the gravitational redshift (21).

The universality of this redshift has also been verified by measurements involving other types of clocks. Currently the most stringent bound on possible violation of the LPI is $|\mu| < 2.1 \times 10^{-5}$ (125). The ESA's ACES mission is expected to improve the results of the LPI tests (see **Figure 8**). With the full accuracy of ground and space clocks at the 10^{-16} level or better, Einstein's effect can be tested with a relative uncertainty of $\mu < 2 \times 10^{-6}$, yielding an improvement of up to a factor of 35 with respect to the previous experiment (118).

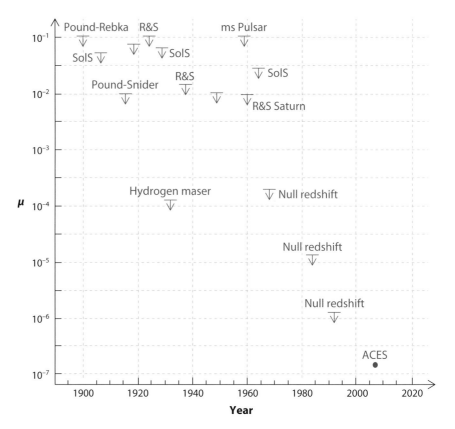

Figure 8

The progress in the tests of the local position invariance (LPI) since the early 1950s (3) and the anticipated performance of the European Space Agency's Atomic Clock Ensemble in Space (ACES) mission. SolS stands for tests with solar spectra, R&S for those using rockets and spacecraft, and Null redshift for the comparison of different atomic clocks (21).

As mentioned above, gravitational redshift has been measured both in the laboratory and by using astronomical observations. Gravitational time dilation in the Earth's gravitational field has been measured numerous times using atomic clocks, and ongoing validation is provided as a side effect of the operation of the Global Positioning System. Tests in stronger gravitational fields are provided by the observation of binary pulsars. All results are in agreement with general relativity (21); however, at the current level of accuracy these observations cannot distinguish between general relativity and other metric theories that preserve the EP.

4.4. Search for Variability of the Fundamental Constants

Dirac's 70-year-old idea of cosmic variation[20] (126) of physical constants has been revisited with the advent of models unifying the forces of nature based on the symmetry properties of possible extra dimensions, such as the Kaluza-Klein-inspired theories, Brans–Dicke theory, and supersymmetry models. Alternative theories of gravity (21) and theories of modified gravity (56) include cosmologically evolving scalar fields that lead to variability of the fundamental constants. It has been hypothesized that a variation of the cosmological-scale factor with epoch could lead to temporal or spatial variation of the physical constants, specifically the gravitational constant G, the fine-structure constant $\alpha = e^2/\hbar c \simeq 1/137.037$, and the electron-proton mass ratio m_e/m_p.

In general, constraints on the variation of fundamental constants can be derived from a number of gravitational measurements such as the test of the UFF, the motion of the planets in the Solar System, and stellar and galactic evolutions. The constraints are based on the comparison of two timescales, the first (gravitational time) dictated by gravity (e.g., ephemeris, stellar ages, etc.) and the second (atomic time) determined by a nongravitational system (e.g., atomic clocks, etc.). For instance, planetary and spacecraft ranging, neutron-star binary observations, and paleontological and primordial nucleosynthesis data allow one to constrain the relative variation of G (127). Many of the corresponding experiments could reach a much higher precision if performed in space.

4.4.1. Fine-structure constant. The current limits on the evolution of α are established by laboratory measurements, studies of the abundances of radioactive isotopes and those of fluctuations in the CMB, and other cosmological constraints (for a review see Reference 127). There exist several types of tests that are based, for instance, on geological data (e.g., measurements made on the nuclear decay products of old meteorites) and on measurements (of astronomical origin) of the fine structure of absorption and emission spectra of distant atoms (e.g., the absorption lines of atoms on the line of sight of quasars at high redshift). Laboratory experiments are based on the comparison either of different atomic clocks or of atomic clocks with ultrastable oscillators. They also have the advantage of being more reliable and reproducible, thus allowing better control of the systematics and better statistics compared with other methods. Their evident drawbacks are their short timescales, which are fixed by the fractional stability of the least-precise standards. These timescales are usually of order of a month to a year, so the obtained constraints are restricted to the instantaneous variation observed today. However, the shortness of the timescales is compensated by a much higher experimental sensitivity. All of these kinds of tests depend on the value of α.

The best measurement of the constancy of α to date is that provided by the Oklo phenomenon; it sets the following (conservative) limits on the variation of α over a period of two billion years (128 and references therein): $-0.9 \times 10^{-7} < \alpha^{\text{Oklo}}/\alpha^{\text{today}} - 1 < 1.2 \times 10^{-7}$. Converting this result

---

[20]Please consult: **http://en.wikipedia.org/wiki/Dirac_large_numbers_hypothesis**.

into an average time variation, one finds

$$-6.7 \times 10^{-17} \text{ yr}^{-1} < \frac{\dot{\alpha}}{\alpha} < 5 \times 10^{-17} \text{ yr}^{-1}. \qquad 29.$$

Note that this variation is a factor of $\sim 10^7$ smaller than the Hubble scale, which is itself $\sim 10^{-10}$ years^{-1}. Comparably stringent limits were obtained using the Rhenium 187–to–Osmium 187 ratio in meteorites (129), which yielded an upper bound of $\dot{\alpha}/\alpha = (8 \pm 8) \times 10^{-7}$ over 4.6×10^9 years. Laboratory limits were also obtained from the comparison, over time, of stable atomic clocks. More precisely, given that $v/c \sim \alpha$ for electrons in the first Bohr orbit, direct measurements of the variation of α over time can be made by comparing the frequencies of atomic clocks that rely on different atomic transitions. The upper bound on the variation of α using such methods is $\dot{\alpha}/\alpha = (-0.9 \pm 2.9) \times 10^{-15}$ year^{-1} (119). With the full accuracy of ground and space clocks at the 10^{-16} level or better, the ESA's ACES mission will be able to measure time variations of the fine-structure constant at the level of $\simeq 10^{-16}$ year^{-1} (118).

There is a connection between the variation of the fundamental constants and a violation of the EP; in fact, the former almost always implies the latter. For example, should there be an ultralight scalar particle, its existence would lead to variability of fundamental constants such as α and m_e/m_p. Because masses of nucleons are α dependent, by coupling to nucleons this particle would mediate an isotope-dependent long-range force (40, 127, 130). The strength of the coupling is within a few of orders of magnitude of the existing experimental bounds for such forces; thus, the new force could potentially be measured in precision tests of the EP. Therefore, the existence of a new interaction mediated by a massless (or very low mass) time-varying scalar field would lead both to the variation of the fundamental constants and to violation of the WEP, ultimately resulting in observable deviations from general relativity.

Following the arguments above for macroscopic bodies, one would expect that their masses depend on all the coupling constants of the four known fundamental interactions, which have profound consequences concerning the motion of a body. In particular, because the α dependence is a priori composition dependent, any variation of the fundamental constants entails a violation of the UFF (127). This allows comparison of the ability of two classes of experiments—namely clock-based and EP-testing experiments—to search for variation of the parameter α in a model-independent way (131). EP experiments have been superior performers. Thus, analysis of the frequency ratio of the 282-nm ^{199}Hg$^+$ optical clock transition to the ground-state hyperfine splitting in ^{133}Cs was recently used to place a limit on its fractional variation of $\dot{\alpha}/\alpha \leq 1.3 \times 10^{-16}$ year^{-1} (120). At the same time, the current accuracy of the EP tests (16) already constrains the variation as $\Delta\alpha/\alpha \leq 10^{-10} \Delta U/c^2$, where ΔU is the change in the gravity potential. Therefore, for ground-based experiments (for which the variability in the gravitational potential is due to the orbital motion of the Earth), the quantity U_{sun}/c^2 varies by 1.66×10^{-10} over one year, so a ground-based clock experiment must therefore be able to measure fractional frequency shifts between clocks to a precision of 1 part in 10^{20} in order to compete with EP experiments on the ground (131).

However, sending atomic clocks on a spacecraft to within a few solar radii of the Sun, where the gravitational potential grows to 10^{-6} c^2, could be a competitive experiment if the relative frequencies of different onboard clocks could be measured to a precision better than 1 part in 10^{16}. Such an experiment would allow for a direct measurement of any α variation, thus further motivating the development of space-qualified clocks. With their accuracy poised to surpass the 10^{-17} level in the near future, optical clocks may be able to provide the needed capabilities to directly test the variability of the fine-structure constant (3).

Clearly a solar fly-by on a highly eccentric trajectory with very accurate clocks and inertial sensors makes for a compelling relativity test. A potential use of highly accurate optical clocks in such an experiment would likely lead to additional accuracy improvement in the tests of α and m_e/m_p, thereby providing a good justification for space deployment (3, 132). The resulting space-based laboratory experiment could lead to an important discovery.

4.4.2. Gravitational constant. A possible variation of Newton's gravitational constant G could be related to the expansion of the Universe, depending on the cosmological model considered. Variability in G can be tested in space with a much greater precision than on Earth (15, 127). For example, a decreasing gravitational constant G, coupled with angular momentum conservation, is expected to increase a planet's semimajor axis a as $\dot{a}/a = -\dot{G}/G$. The corresponding change in orbital phase grows quadratically with time, providing for a strong sensitivity to the effect of $\dot{G}$.

Currently, space-based experiments using lunar and planetary ranging measurements are the best means of searching for very small spatial or temporal gradients in the values of G (15, 16). Thus, recent analysis of LLR data strongly limits such variations and constrains a local-scale ($\sim$1-AU) expansion of the Solar System as $\dot{a}/a = -\dot{G}/G = -(5 \pm 6) \times 10^{-13}$ year^{-1}, including the expansion resulting from cosmological effects (133). Interestingly, the achieved accuracy in $\dot{G}/G$ implies that if this rate is representative of our cosmic history, then G has changed by less than 1% over the 13.4-Gyr age of the Universe.

The ever-extending LLR data set and the increase in the accuracy of lunar ranging (i.e., APOLLO) could lead to significant improvements in the search for variability of Newton's gravitational constant; an accuracy at the level of $\dot{G}/G \sim 1 \times 10^{-14}$ year^{-1} is feasible with LLR (92). High-accuracy timing measurements of binary and double pulsars could also provide a good test of the variability of the gravitational constant (20, 131). **Figure 9** shows the anticipated progress in the tests of possible variability in the gravitational constant.

4.5. Tests of the Gravitational Inverse-Square Law

Many modern theories of gravity, including the string, supersymmetry, and brane-world theories, suggest that new physical interactions will appear at short ranges. This may happen because at submillimeter distances new dimensions can exist, thereby changing the gravitational inverse-square law (134; for a review of experiments see Reference 135). Similar forces that act at short distances are predicted in supersymmetric theories with weak-scale compactifications (136), in

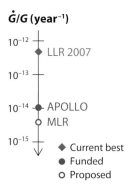

Figure 9

Anticipated progress in the tests of possible variability in the gravitational constant (3). Abbreviations: APOLLO, Apache Point Observatory Lunar Laser-Ranging Operations; LLR, lunar laser ranging; MLR, Mars laser ranging.

some theories with very low energy supersymmetry breaking (137), and also in theories of very low quantum gravity scale (138). These multiple predictions provide strong motivation for experiments that would test for possible deviations from Newton's gravitational inverse-square law at very short distances, notably on millimeter-to-micrometer ranges.

An experimental confirmation of new fundamental forces would provide important insights into the physics beyond the standard model. A great deal of interest in the subject was sparked after the 1986 claim of evidence for an intermediate-range interaction with subgravitational strength (139), leading to a wave of new experiments.

Recent ground-based torsion-balance experiments (140) tested the gravitational inverse-square law at separations between 9.53 mm and 55 µm, probing distances less than the dark energy length scale $\lambda_d = \sqrt[4]{\hbar c / u_d} \approx 85$ µm, and with an energy density $u_d \approx 3.8$ keV cm^{-3}. It was found that the inverse-square law holds down to a length scale of 56 µm and that an extra dimension must measure less than 44 µm. These results are important in that they signify the fact that modern experiments reached the level at which dark energy physics can be tested in a laboratory setting; they also provide a new set of constraints on new forces (141), making these experiments relevant and competitive with particle physics research. Also, recent laboratory experiments testing Newton's second law for small accelerations (79, 80) provided useful constraints relevant to understanding several current astrophysical puzzles. New experiments are being designed to explore length scales below 5 µm (142).

Sensitive experiments searching for weak forces invariably require soft suspension for the measurement degree of freedom. A promising soft suspension with low dissipation is superconducting magnetic levitation. Levitation in Earth's gravity (i.e., 1-g), however, requires a large magnetic field, which tends to couple to the measurement degree of freedom through metrology errors and coil nonlinearity as well as to stiffen the mode. The high magnetic field will also make suspension more dissipative. The situation improves dramatically in space: The g level is reduced by five to six orders of magnitude, so the test masses can be supported with weaker magnetic springs, which permits the realization of both the lowest resonance frequency and the lowest dissipation. The microgravity conditions also allow for an improved design of the null experiment, free from the geometric constraints of the torsion balance.

The Inverse-Square Law Experiment in Space (ISLES) is a proposed experiment whose objective is to perform a highly accurate test of Newton's gravitational law in space (143). ISLES combines the advantages of the microgravity environment with superconducting accelerometer technology to improve the current ground-based limits in the strength of violation (144) by four to six orders of magnitude in the range below 100 µm. The experiment will be sensitive enough to probe large extra dimensions down to 5 µm and also to probe the existence of the axion (145), which—if it exists—is expected to violate the inverse-square law in the range accessible by ISLES.

The recent theoretical ideas concerning new particles and new dimensions have reshaped the way we think about the Universe. Thus, should the next generation of experiments detect a force violating the inverse-square law, such a discovery would imply the existence of (*a*) an extra spatial dimension, (*b*) a massive graviton, or (*c*) the presence of a new fundamental interaction (135, 141). Although investigators have devoted much attention to the behavior of gravity at short distances, it is possible that tiny deviations from the inverse-square law occur at much larger distances. In fact, there is a possibility that noncompact extra dimensions could produce such deviations at astronomical distances (60) (for discussion see Section 4.6).

By far the most stringent constraints on a test of the inverse-square law to date come from very precise measurements of the Moon's orbit about the Earth. Even though the Moon's orbit has a mean radius of 384,000 km, the models agree with the data at the level of 4 mm! As a result, analysis of the LLR data tests the gravitational inverse-square law to 3×10^{-11} of the gravitational-field strength on scales of the Earth–Moon distance (14).

Additionally, interplanetary laser ranging could provide the conditions needed to improve the tests of the inverse-square law on interplanetary scales (92). MLR could be used to perform an experiment that could reach the accuracy of 1×10^{-14} at 2-AU distances, thereby improving the current tests by several orders of magnitude.

Although most modern experiments do not show disagreement with Newton's law, there are puzzles that require further investigation. The radiometric tracking data received from the Pioneer 10 and -11 spacecraft at heliocentric distances between 20 and 70 AU has consistently indicated the presence of a small, anomalous Doppler drift in the spacecraft carrier frequency. The drift can be interpreted as arising from a constant sunward acceleration of $a_\mathrm{P} = (8.74 \pm 1.33) \times 10^{-10}$ m s^{-2} for each particular craft (146) This apparent violation of the inverse-square law has become known as the Pioneer anomaly. The possibility that the anomalous behavior will continue to defy attempts at conventional explanation has resulted in a growing number of discussions about the origin of the discovered effect. A recently initiated investigation of the anomalous signal using the entire record of the Pioneer spacecraft telemetry files, in conjunction with the analysis of much-extended Pioneer Doppler data, may soon reveal the origin of the anomaly (147).

4.6. Tests of Alternative- and Modified-Gravity Theories

Given the immense challenge posed by the unexpected discovery of the accelerated expansion of the Universe, it is important to explore every option to explain and probe the underlying physics. Theoretical efforts in this area offer a rich spectrum of new ideas, some discussed below, that can be tested by experiment.

Motivated by the dark energy and dark matter problems, long-distance gravity modification is one of the radical proposals that have recently gained attention (148). Theories that modify gravity at cosmological distances exhibit a strong-coupling phenomenon of extra graviton polarizations (149). This phenomenon plays an important role in this class of theories in allowing them to agree with Solar System constraints. In particular, the brane-induced gravity model (59) provides a new and interesting way of modifying gravity at large distances to produce an accelerated expansion of the Universe without the need for a nonvanishing cosmological constant (148). One of the peculiarities of this model is the means of recovering the usual gravitational interaction at small (i.e., noncosmological) distances, motivating precision tests of gravity on Solar System scales (3).

The Eddington parameter γ, whose value in general relativity is unity, is perhaps the most fundamental PPN parameter (11, 21) in that $\frac{1}{2}\bar{\gamma}$ is a measure, for example, of the fractional strength of the scalar-gravity interaction in scalar-tensor theories of gravity (29). Currently, the most precise value for this parameter, $\bar{\gamma} = (2.1 \pm 2.3) \times 10^{-5}$, was obtained using radiometric tracking data received from the Cassini spacecraft (17) during a solar conjunction experiment.[21] This accuracy approaches the region where multiple tensor-scalar gravity models, consistent with the recent cosmological observations (151), predict a lower bound for the present value of this parameter at the level of $\bar{\gamma} \sim 10^{-6} - 10^{-7}$ (19, 29, 40, 41). Therefore, improving the measurement of this parameter[22] would provide crucial information to separate modern scalar-tensor theories

---

[21] A similar experiment is planned for the ESA's BepiColombo mission to Mercury (150).

[22] In addition, any experiment pushing the present upper bound on another Eddington parameter, β, i.e., $\beta - 1 = (0.9 \pm 1.1) \times 10^{-4}$ (15, 16), will also be of interest.

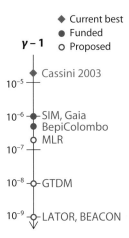

Figure 10

Anticipated progress in the tests of the parameterized post-Newtonian (PPN) parameter γ. Abbreviations: BEACON, Beyond Einstein Advanced Coherent Optical Network; GDTM, Gravitational Time Delay Mission; LATOR, Laser Astrometric Test of Relativity; MLR, Mars laser ranging; SIM, Space Interferometry Mission.

of gravity from general relativity, probe possible ways for gravity quantization, and test modern theories of cosmological evolution.

Interplanetary laser ranging could lead to a significant improvement in the accuracy of the parameter γ. Thus, precision ranging between the Earth and a lander on Mars during Solar conjunctions may offer a suitable opportunity. If the lander were equipped with a laser transponder capable of reaching a precision of 1 mm, a measurement of γ with accuracy of a few parts in 10^7 would be possible.[23] To reach accuracies beyond this level one must rely on a dedicated space experiment (3, 92) (**Figure 10**).

The Gravitational Time Delay Mission (GTDM) (152) proposes to use laser ranging between two drag-free spacecraft (with spurious acceleration levels below 1.3×10^{-13} m/s^2/$\sqrt{\text{Hz}}$ at 0.4 μHz) to accurately measure the Shapiro time delay (153) for laser beams passing near the Sun. One spacecraft will be kept at the L1 Lagrange point of the Earth–Sun system; the other will be placed on a 3:2 Earth-resonant, LATOR (Laser Astrometric Test of Relativity)-type orbit (see Reference 154 for details). A high-stability frequency standard ($\delta f/f \lesssim 1 \times 10^{-13}$ 1/$\sqrt{\text{Hz}}$ at 0.4 μHz) located on the L1 spacecraft will permit accurate measurement of the time delay. If requirements on the performance of the disturbance-compensation system, the timing-transfer process, and the high-accuracy orbit determination are successfully addressed (152), then determination of the time delay of interplanetary signals to a 0.5-ps precision in terms of the instantaneous clock frequency could lead to an accuracy of 2 parts in 10^8 in measuring parameter γ.

LATOR (154) proposes to measure parameter γ with an accuracy of 1 part in 10^9, which is a factor of 30,000 beyond the best result currently available, Cassini's 2003 result (17). The key element of LATOR is a geometric redundancy provided by the long-baseline optical interferometry and interplanetary laser ranging. By using a combination of independent time series of gravitational deflection of light in immediate proximity to the Sun, along with measurements of the Shapiro time delay on interplanetary scales (to a precision better than 0.01 picoradians and

---

[23] Future optical astrometry missions, such as the Space Interferometry Mission (SIM) and Gaia, are expected to provide the accuracy of determinations of γ at the level of 10^{-6} to 5×10^{-7}.

3 mm, respectively), LATOR will significantly improve our knowledge of relativistic gravity and cosmology. LATOR's primary measurement, the precise observation of the non-Euclidean geometry of a light triangle that surrounds the Sun, pushes to unprecedented accuracy the search for cosmologically relevant scalar-tensor theories of gravity by looking for a remnant scalar field in today's Solar System. LATOR could lead to very robust advances in the tests of fundamental physics: It could discover a violation or extension of general relativity or reveal the presence of an additional long-range interaction.

Similar to LATOR, the Beyond Einstein Advanced Coherent Optical Network (BEACON) (155) is an experiment designed to reach a sensitivity of 1 part in 10^9 in measuring the PPN parameter γ. The mission will place four small spacecraft in 80,000-km circular orbits around the Earth with all spacecraft in the same plane. Each spacecraft will be equipped with three sets of identical laser ranging transceivers, which will send laser metrology beams between the spacecraft to form a flexible light-trapezoid formation. In Euclidean geometry this system is redundant: By measuring only five of the six distances one can compute the sixth. To enable its primary science objective, BEACON will precisely measure and monitor all six interspacecraft distances within the trapezoid using transceivers capable of reaching an accuracy of ~0.1 nm in measuring these distances. The resulting geometric redundancy is what will enable BEACON's superior sensitivity in measuring a departure from Euclidean geometry. In the Earth's vicinity, this departure is primarily due to the curvature of the relativistic spacetime. It amounts to ~10 cm for laser beams just grazing the surface of the Earth, then falls off inversely proportional to the impact parameter. Simultaneous analysis of the resulting time series of these distance measurements will allow BEACON to measure the curvature of the spacetime around the Earth with an accuracy of better than 1 part in 10^9.

5. CONCLUSIONS

Today physics stands at the threshold of major discoveries. Growing observational evidence points to the need for new physics. As a result, efforts to discover new fundamental symmetries, investigations of the limits of established symmetries, tests of the general theory of relativity, searches for gravitational waves, and attempts to understand the nature of dark matter and dark energy are among the main research topics in fundamental physics today (3).

The remarkable recent progress in observational cosmology has subjected the general theory of relativity to increased scrutiny by suggesting a non-Einsteinian model of the Universe's evolution. From a theoretical standpoint, the challenge is even stronger—if gravity is to be quantized, general relativity must be modified. Furthermore, recent advances in the scalar-tensor extensions of gravity and brane-world gravitational models, along with efforts to modify gravity on large scales, are motivating new searches for experimental signatures of very small deviations from general relativity on various scales, including on the spacecraft-accessible distances in the Solar System. These theoretical advances are motivating searches for very small deviations from Einstein's theory, at the level of three to five orders of magnitude below the level currently tested by experiment.

This progress was matched by the major improvements in measurement technologies. Today, a new generation of high-performance quantum sensors (e.g., ultrastable atomic clocks, accelerometers, gyroscopes, gravimeters, gravity gradiometers) is surpassing previous state-of-the-art instruments, demonstrating the high potential of these techniques based on the engineering and manipulation of atomic systems. Atomic clocks and inertial quantum sensors represent a key technology for accurate frequency measurements and ultraprecise monitoring of accelerations and rotations (see discussion in Reference 3). New quantum devices based on ultracold atoms will enable fundamental physics experiments testing quantum physics, physics beyond the standard model of fundamental particles and interactions, special relativity, gravitation, and general relativity.

The experiments presented here are just few examples of the rich opportunities available to explore the nature of the physical laws. These experiments could potentially offer an improvement of up to several orders of magnitude over the accuracy of current tests. If implemented, the missions discussed above could significantly advance research in fundamental physics. This progress promises very important new results in gravitational research over the next decade.

DISCLOSURE STATEMENT

The author is not aware of any biases that might be perceived as affecting the objectivity of this review.

ACKNOWLEDGMENTS

The work described herein was carried out at the Jet Propulsion Laboratory of the California Institute of Technology under a contract with the National Aeronautics and Space Administration.

LITERATURE CITED

1. Einstein A. *Jarb. Radioakt. Elektron.* 4:411 (1907)
2. Einstein A. *Sitzungsber. Preuss. Akad. Wiss. Berlin* 844 (1915); Einstein A. *Ann. Phys.* 49:146 (1916)
3. Turyshev SG, et al. *Int. J. Mod. Phys. D* 16:1879 (2007)
4. Dyson FW, Eddington AS, Davidson C. *Philos. Trans. R. Soc. London* 220A:291 (1920)
5. Lenard P. *Phys. Z.* 19:156 (1921)
6. Einstein A. *Ann. Phys.* 35:898 (1911)
7. Coles P. In *Astron. Soc. Pac. Conf. Ser.*, ed. VJ Martínez, V Trimble, MJ Pons-Bordería, 252:21. San Francisco: ASP (2001)
8. Kennefick D. phys.hist-ph/0709.0685 (2007)
9. Shapiro II, et al. *J. Geophys. Res.* 82:4329 (1977)
10. Reasenberg RD, et al. *Astrophys. J. Lett.* 234:L219 (1979)
11. Will CM. *Theory and Experiment in Gravitational Physics*. Cambridge, UK: Cambridge Univ. Press (1993)
12. Anderson JD, et al. *BAAS* 34:833 (2002)
13. Shapiro SS, Davis JL, Lebach DE, Gregory JS. *Phys. Rev. Lett.* 92:121101 (2004)
14. Williams JG, Turyshev SG, Murphy TW. *Int. J. Mod. Phys. D* 13:567 (2004)
15. Williams JG, Turyshev SG, Boggs DH. *Phys. Rev. Lett.* 93:261101 (2004)
16. Williams JG, Turyshev SG, Boggs DH. In *Proc. Test. Equiv. Princ. Ground Space, Pescara, Italy, Sep. 20–23, 2004*, ed. C Lämmerzahl, CWF Everitt, R Ruffini. Berlin: Springer-Verlag. gr-qc/0507083 (2008)
17. Bertotti B, Iess L, Tortora P. *Nature* 425:374 (2003)
18. Lange C, et al. *MNRAS* 326:274 (2001)
19. Damour T, Esposito-Farese G. *Phys. Rev. D* 53:5541 (1996); Damour T, Esposito-Farese G. *Phys. Rev. D* 54:1474 (1996); Damour T, Esposito-Farese G. *Phys. Rev. D* 58:042001 (1998)
20. Stairs IH. *Living Rev. Relativ.* 6:5 (2003); Kramer M. *Lect. Notes Phys.* 648:33 (2004); Kramer M, et al. *Science* 314:97 (2006)
21. Will CM. *Living Rev. Relativ.* 9:3 (2006)
22. Milgrom M. *Acta Phys. Polon.* B32:3613 (2001)
23. Moffat JW. *JCAP* 0603:004 (2006)
24. Bekenstein JD. *Phys. Rev. D* 70:083509 (2004)
25. Yao WM, et al. (Part. Data Group) *J. Phys. G* 33:205 (2006)
26. Weinberg S. *Gravitation and Cosmology*. New York: Wiley (1972); Weinberg S. *Rev. Mod. Phys.* 61:1 (1989)
27. Brans C, Dicke RH. *Phys. Rev.* 124:925 (1961)

28. Nordtvedt K. *Phys. Rev.* 169:1014, 1017 (1968); Nordtvedt K Jr. *Phys. Rev.* 170:1186 (1968); Nordtvedt K. *Phys. Rev.* 180:1293 (1969); Thorne KS, Will CM. *Astrophys. J.* 163:595 (1971); Will CM. *Astrophys. J.* 163:611 (1971); Will CM. *Astrophys. J.* 169:125, 141 (1971); Will CM. *Astrophys. J.* 165:409 (1971); Will CM, Nordtvedt KJ. *Astrophys. J.* 177:757 (1972); Nordtvedt KJ, Will CM. *Astrophys. J.* 177:775 (1972)

29. Damour T, Nordtvedt K. *Phys. Rev. Lett.* 70:2217 (1993); Damour T, Nordtvedt K. *Phys. Rev. D* 48:3436 (1993)

30. Standish EM, Williams JG. Explan. Suppl., In *American Ephemeris and Nautical Almanac*, ed. PK Seidelmann. Mill Valley, CA: Univ. Sci. Books. In press (2008)

31. Moyer TD. *Celestial Mech.* 23:33, 57 (1981); Turyshev SG. gr-qc/9606063 (1996); *NASA JPL* Publ. 96-13 (1996)

32. Moyer TD. *Formulation for Observed and Computed Values of Deep Space Network Data Types for Navigation.* Hoboken, NJ: Wiley (2003)

33. Brumberg VA. *Relativistic Celestial Mechanics.* Moscow: Nauka. In Russian (1972); Brumberg VA. *Essential Relativistic Celestial Mechanics.* Bristol, UK: Hilger (1991)

34. Standish EM, Newhall XX, Williams JG, Yeomans DK. Explan. Suppl., In *Astronomical Almanac*, ed. PK Seidelmann, pp. 279–323. Mill Valley, CA: Univ. Sci. Books (1992)

35. Turyshev SG, et al. *Lect. Notes Phys.* 648:311 (2004)

36. Witten E. In *Proc. APS/DPF/DPB Summer Study Future Part. Phys.*, (*Snowmass 2001*), ed. N Graf. Snowmass, CO: SLAC-R-599 (2002); Witten E. In *The Future of Theoretical Physics and Cosmology*, ed. GW Gibbons, EPS Shellard, SJ Rankin, pp. 455–62. Cambridge, UK: Cambridge Univ. Press (2003)

37. Green M, Schwarz J, Witten E. *Superstring Theory.* Cambridge, UK: Cambridge Univ. Press (1987); Polchinski J. *Phys. Rev. Lett.* 75:4724 (1995); Horava P, Witten E. *Nucl. Phys. B* 475:94 (1996); Horava P, Witten E. *Nucl. Phys. B* 460:506 (1996); Lukas A, Ovrut BA, Waldram D. *Phys. Rev. D* 60:086001 (1999); Randall L, Sundrum R. *Phys. Rev. Lett.* 83:3370 (1999)

38. Julve J, Tonin M. *Nuovo Cimento* 46:137 (1978); Fradkin ES, Tseytlin AA. *Nucl. Phys. B* 201:469 (1982); Avramidi G, Barvinsky AO. *Phys. Lett. B* 159:269 (1985)

39. Goldman T, Pérez-Mercader J, Cooper F, Nieto MM. *Phys. Lett.* 281:219 (1992)

40. Damour T, Polyakov AM. *Gen. Relativ. Gravity* 26:1171 (1994); Damour T, Polyakov AM. *Nucl. Phys. B* 423:532 (1994)

41. Damour T, Piazza F, Veneziano G. *Phys. Rev. Lett.* 89:081601 (2002); Damour T, Piazza F, Veneziano G. *Phys. Rev. D* 66:046007 (2002); Veneziano G. *JHEP* 06:051 (2002)

42. Bennett CL, et al. (WMAP Sci. Team) *Astrophys. J. Suppl.* 148:1 (2003)

43. Caldwell RR. *Phys. Lett. B* 545:23 (2002)

44. Cline JM, Jeon S, Moore GD. *Phys. Rev. D* 70:043543 (2004); Rubakov VA, Tinyakov PG. hep-th/0802.4379 (2008); Sergienko S, Rubakov V. hep-th/0803.3163 (2008)

45. Sreekumar P, et al. *Astrophys. J.* 494:523 (1998)

46. Arkani-Hamed N, Creminelli P, Mukohyama S, Zaldarriaga M. *JCAP* 0404:001 (2004)

47. Piazza F, Tsujikawa S. *JCAP* 0407:004 (2004)

48. Turyshev SG, Shao M, Nordtvedt K. *Class. Quantum Gravity* 21:2773 (2004)

49. de Bernardis P, et al. *Nature* 404:955 (2000)

50. Peacock JA, et al. *Nature* 410:169 (2001)

51. Perlmutter S, et al. (Supernova Cosmol. Proj.) *Astrophys. J.* 517:565 (1999); Riess AG, et al. (Supernova Search Team Collab.) *Astron. J.* 116:1009 (1998); Tonry JL, et al. (Supernova Search Team Collab.) *Astrophys. J.* 594:1 (2003)

52. Halverson NW, et al. *Astrophys. J.* 568:38 (2002); Netterfield CB, et al. (Boomerang Collab.) *Astrophys. J.* 571:604 (2002)

53. Carroll SM. *Living Rev. Relativ.* 4:1 (2001)

54. Peebles PJE, Ratra B. *Rev. Mod. Phys.* 75:559 (2003)

55. Carroll SM, Duvvuri V, Trodden M, Turner MS. *Phys. Rev. D* 70:043528 (2004); Carroll SM, et al. *Phys. Rev. D* 71:063513 (2005); Capozziello S, Troisi A. *Phys. Rev. D* 72:044022 (2005)

56. Bertolami O, Paramos J, Turyshev SG. In *Lasers, Clocks and Drag-Free Control: Exploration of Relativistic Gravity in Space*, ed. H Dittus, C Laemmerzahl, S Turyshev, pp. 27–67. Berlin: Springer-Verlag (2007)

57. Navarro I, Van Acoleyen K. *JCAP* 0603:008 (2006)
58. Chiba T. *Phys. Lett. B* 575:1 (2003)
59. Dvali G, Gabadadze G, Porrati M. *Phys. Lett. B* 485:208 (2000)
60. Dvali G, Gruzinov A, Zaldarriaga M. *Phys. Rev. D* 68:024012 (2003)
61. Cembranos JAR. *Phys. Rev. D* 73:064029 (2006)
62. Erickcek AL, Smith TL, Kamionkowski M. *Phys. Rev. D* 74:121501 (2006)
63. Nojiri S, Odintsov SD. *Phys. Rev. D* 74:086005 (2006)
64. Wetterich C. *Nucl. Phys. B* 302:645 (1988); Wetterich C. *Phys. Rev. Lett.* 90:231302 (2003); Wetterich C. *Phys. Lett. B* 594:17 (2004)
65. Ratra B, Peebles PJE. *Phys. Rev. D* 37:3406 (1988)
66. Ferreira PG, Joyce M. *Phys. Rev. Lett.* 79:4740 (1997)
67. Zlatev I, Wang L, Steinhardt PJ. *Phys. Rev. Lett.* 82:896 (1999)
68. Albrecht A, Skordis C. *Phys. Rev. Lett.* 84:2076 (2000); Dodelson S, Kaplinghat M, Stewart E. *Phys. Rev. Lett.* 85:5276 (2000); Bento MC, Bertolami O, Santos NC. *Phys. Rev. D* 65:067301 (2002)
69. Ferreira PG, Joyce M. *Phys. Rev. D* 58:023503 (1998)
70. Farrar GR, Peebles PJE. *Astrophys. J.* 604:1 (2004)
71. Bean R, Magueijo J. *Phys. Lett. B* 517:177 (2001); Gasperini M, Piazza F, Veneziano G. *Phys. Rev. D* 65:023508 (2002)
72. Bean R. *Phys. Rev. D* 64:123516 (2001); Bean R, Flanagan EE, Trodden M. *New J. Phys.* 10:033006 (2008); Bean R, Flanagan EE, Trodden M. astro-ph/0709.1128 (2007)
73. Eötvös Rv. *Math. Naturwiss. Ber. Ung.* 8:65 (1890); Eötvös Rv, Pekár D, Fekete E. *Ann. Phys.* 68:11 (1922); Bod L, Fischbach E, Marx G, Náray-Ziegler M. *Acta Phys. Hung.* 69:335 (1991)
74. Roll PG, Krotkov R, Dicke RH. *Ann. Phys.* 26:442 (1964)
75. Baeßler S, et al. *Phys. Rev. Lett.* 83:3585 (1999)
76. Adelberger E. *Class. Quantum Gravity* 18:2397 (2001)
77. Anderson JD, Gross M, Nordtvedt KL, Turyshev SG. *Astrophys. J.* 459:365 (1996)
78. Su Y, et al. *Phys. Rev. D* 50:3614 (1994)
79. Schlamminger S, et al. *Phys. Rev. Lett.* 100:041101 (2008)
80. Gundlach JH, et al. *Phys. Rev. Lett.* 98:150801 (2007)
81. Mota DF, Barrow JD. *MNRAS* 349:291 (2004)
82. Touboul P, Rodrigues M. *Class. Quantum Gravity* 18:2487 (2001)
83. Reasenberg RD, Phillips JD. *Int. J. Mod. Phys. D* 16:2245 (2007)
84. Phillips JD, Reasenberg RD. *Rev. Sci. Instrum.* 76:064501 (2005)
85. Kasevich MA, Maleki L. **http://horology.jpl.nasa.gov/quantum/pub/QuITE singleposter2.pdf** (2003)
86. Peters A, Chung KY, Chu S. *Metrologia* 38:25 (2001); Fray S, Diez CA, Hansch TW, Weitz M. *Phys. Rev. Lett.* 93:240404 (2004)
87. Nyman R, et al. *Appl. Phys. B* 84:673 (2006)
88. Nobili AM, et al. *Int. J. Mod. Phys. D* 16:2259 (2007)
89. Mester J, et al. *Class. Quantum Gravity* 18:2475 (2001); Worden P, Mester J, Torii R. *Class. Quantum Gravity* 18:2543 (2001)
90. Ulrich RK. *Astrophys. J.* 258:404 (1982)
91. Murphy TW, et al. *Int. J. Mod. Phys. D* 16:2127 (2007)
92. Turyshev SG, Williams JG. *Int. J. Mod. Phys. D* 16:2165 (2007)
93. Robertson HP. *Rev. Mod. Phys.* 21:378 (1949); Mansouri R, Sexl UR. *Gen. Relativ. Gravity* 8:497 (1977)
94. Mattingly D. *Living Rev. Relativ.* 8:5 (2005)
95. Michelson AA, Morley EW. *Am. J. Sci.* 34:333 (1887)
96. Müller H, et al. *Phys. Rev. Lett.* 91:020401 (2003)
97. Wolf P, et al. *Gen. Relativ. Gravity* 36:2351 (2004)
98. Stanwix PL, et al. *Phys. Rev. D* 74:081101 (2006)
99. Kennedy RJ, Thorndike EM. *Phys. Rev.* 42:400 (1932)
100. Wolf P, et al. *Phys. Rev. Lett.* 90:060402 (2003)

101. Ives HE, Stilwell GR. *J. Opt. Soc. Am.* 28:215 (1938)

102. Saathoff G, et al. *Phys. Rev. Lett.* 91:190403 (2003)

103. Müller H, et al. *Phys. Rev. Lett.* 99:050401 (2007)

104. Kostelecky VA, Mewes M. *Phys. Rev. D* 66:056005 (2002)

105. Brillet A, Hall JL. *Phys. Rev. Lett.* 42:549 (1979)

106. Hughes VW, Robinson HG, Beltran-Lopez V. *Phys. Rev. Lett.* 4:342 (1960); Drever RWP. *Philos. Mag.* 6:683 (1961)

107. Lamoreaux SK, et al. *Phys. Rev. Lett.* 57:3125 (1986)

108. Ritz SM, Michelson PF, Meegan C, Grindlay J. (GLAST Mission Team). In *Am. Astron. Soc. Meet. Abstr.* 211:98.01. (2007)

109. Colladay D, Kostelecky VA. *Phys. Rev. D* 55:6760 (1997); Colladay D, Kostelecky VA. *Phys. Rev. D* 58:116002 (1998); Coleman SR, Glashow SL. *Phys. Lett. B* 405:249 (1997); Coleman SR, Glashow SL. *Phys. Rev. D* 59:116008 (1999)

110. Kostelecký VA, Samuel S. *Phys. Rev. D* 39:683 (1989); Kostelecký VA, Samuel S. *Phys. Rev. Lett.* 63:224 (1989); Kostelecký VA, Samuel S. *Phys. Rev. Lett.* 66:1811 (1991); Kostelecký VA, Potting R. *Phys. Rev. D* 51:3923 (1995)

111. Bluhm R, Kostelecky VA, Russell N. *Phys. Rev. Lett.* 82:2254 (1999); Russell N. *J. Mod. Opt.* 54:2481 (2007)

112. Bertolami O, Colladay D, Kostelecky VA, Potting R. *Phys. Lett. B* 395:178 (1997)

113. Stecker FW, Glashow SL. *Astropart. Phys.* 16:97 (2001)

114. Kostelecký VA, Potting R. *Phys. Lett. B* 381:89 (1996); Kostelecky VA, Potting R. *Phys. Rev. D* 63:046007 (2001); Kostelecký VA, Perry M, Potting R. *Phys. Rev. Lett.* 84:4541 (2000)

115. Bailey QG, Kostelecky VA. *Phys. Rev. D* 74:045001 (2006)

116. Jacobson T, Mattingly D. *Phys. Rev. D* 64:024028 (2001); Foster BZ, Jacobson T. *Phys. Rev. D* 73:064015 (2006); Jacobson T, Mattingly D. *Phys. Rev. D* 70:024003 (2004)

117. Kostelecky VA, Russell N. hep-ph/0801.0287 (2008)

118. Salomon C, Cacciapuoti L, Dimarcq N. *Int. J. Mod. Phys. D* 16:2511 (2007)

119. Marion H, et al. *Phys. Rev. Lett.* 90:150801 (2003); Bize S, et al. *Phys. Rev. Lett.* 90:150802 (2003); Fischer M, et al. *Phys. Rev. Lett.* 92:230802 (2004); Peik E, et al. *Phys. Rev. Lett.* 93:170801 (2004)

120. Fortier TM, et al. *Phys. Rev. Lett.* 98:070801 (2007)

121. Wolf P, Petit G. *Phys. Rev. A* 56:4405 (1997)

122. Kostelecky VA. *Phys. Rev. D* 69:105009 (2004); Dvali G, Pujolas O, Redi M. *Phys. Rev. D* 76:044028 (2007)

123. Pound RV, Rebka GA. *Phys. Rev. Lett.* 3:439 (1959); Pound RV, Rebka GA. *Phys. Rev. Lett.* 4:337 (1960); Pound RV, Snider JL. *Phys. Rev. Lett.* 13:539 (1964)

124. Vessot RFC, Levine MW. *Gen. Relativ. Gravity* 10:181 (1979); Vessot RFC, et al. *Phys. Rev. Lett.* 45:2081 (1980)

125. Bauch A, Weyers S. *Phys. Rev. D* 65:081101 (2002)

126. Dirac PAM. *Nature* 139:323 (1937)

127. Uzan J-P. *Rev. Mod. Phys.* 75:403 (2003)

128. Damour T, Lilley M. arXiv:0802.4169 (2008)

129. Olive KA, et al. *Phys. Rev. D* 69:027701 (2004)

130. Dvali G, Zaldarriaga M. *Phys. Rev. Lett.* 88:091303 (2002)

131. Nordtvedt K. *Int. J. Mod. Phys. A* 17:2711 (2002)

132. Schiller S, et al. *Nucl. Phys. B (Proc. Suppl.)* 166:300 (2007)

133. Williams JG, Turyshev SG, Boggs DH. *Phys. Rev. Lett.* 98:059002 (2007)

134. Arkani-Hamed N, Dimopoulos S, Dvali GR. *Phys. Lett. B* 429:263 (1998); Arkani-Hamed N, Dimopoulos S, Dvali GR. *Phys. Rev. D* 59:086004 (1999)

135. Adelberger EG, Heckel BR, Nelson AE. *Annu. Rev. Nucl. Part. Sci.* 53:77 (2003)

136. Antoniadis I, Dimopoulos S, Dvali GR. *Nucl. Phys. B* 516:70 (1998)

137. Dimopoulos S, Giudice GF. *Phys. Lett. B* 379:105 (1996)

138. Sundrum R. *JHEP* 07:001 (1999); Dvali G, Gabadadze G, Kolanovic M, Nitti F. *Phys. Rev. D* 65:024031 (2002)

139. Fischbach E, Talmadge CL. *The Search for Non-Newtonian Gravity*. New York: Springer-Verlag (1998)

140. Kapner DJ, et al. *Phys. Rev. Lett.* 98:021101 (2007)

141. Adelberger EG, et al. *Phys. Rev. Lett.* 98:131104 (2007)

142. Weld DM, Xia J, Cabrera B, Kapitulnik A. *Phys. Rev. D* 77:062006 (2008)

143. Paik H-J, Prieto VA, Moody MV. *Int. J. Mod. Phys. D* 16:2181 (2007)

144. Chiaverini J, et al. *Phys. Rev. Lett.* 90:151101 (2003)

145. Peccei RD, Quinn HR. *Phys. Rev. D* 16:1791 (1977); Peccei RD, Quinn HR. *Phys. Rev. Lett.* 38:1440 (1977); Weinberg S. *Phys. Rev. Lett.* 40:223 (1978); Wilczek F. *Phys. Rev. Lett.* 40:279 (1978)

146. Anderson JD, et al. *Phys. Rev. Lett.* 81:2858 (1998); Anderson JD, et al. *Phys. Rev. D* 65:082004 (2002); Turyshev SG, et al. In *Gravitational Waves and Experimental Gravity*, ed. J Dumarchez, J Tran Thanh Van. *Proc. 38th Workshop Rencontres de Moriond, Les Arcs, Savoi, Fr., Jan. 23–30, 1999*, pp. 481–86. Hanoi-Vietnam: World (2000); Turyshev SG, Nieto MM, Anderson JD. *Am. J. Phys.* 73:1033 (2005)

147. Turyshev SG, et al. *Int. J. Mod. Phys. D* 15:1 (2006); Toth VT, Turyshev SG. *Can. J. Phys.* 84:1063 (2006); Toth VT, Turyshev SG. *AIP Conf. Proc.* 977:264 (2008)

148. Deffayet C. *Phys. Lett. B* 502:199 (2001); Deffayet C, Dvali GR, Gabadadze G. *Phys. Rev. D* 65:044023 (2002)

149. Deffayet C, Dvali GR, Gabadadze G, Vainshtein AI. *Phys. Rev. D* 65:044026 (2002); Dvali G. *New J. Phys.* 8:326 (2006)

150. Iess L, Asmar S. *Int. J. Mod. Phys. D* 16:2117 (2007)

151. Spergel DN, et al. (WMAP Collab.) *Astrophys. J. Suppl.* 170:377 (2007)

152. Ashby N, Bender P. In *Lasers, Clocks, and Drag-Free: Technologies for Future Exploration in Space and Tests of Gravity*, ed. H Dittus, C Laemmerzahl, SG Turyshev, p. 219. Berlin: Springer-Verlag (2006); Bender PL, et al. In *Proc. Adv. Precis. Tests Exp. Gravit. Space, Firenze, Italy, Sept. 28–30*. **http://www.fi.infn.it/GGI-grav-space/EGS_w/pdf/bender.pdf** (2006)

153. Shapiro II. Phys. Rev. Lett. 13:789 (1964)

154. Turyshev SG, Shao M, Nordtvedt K. *Int. J. Mod. Phys. D* 13:2035 (2004); Turyshev SG, Shao M, Nordtvedt K. In *Lasers, Clocks, and Drag-Free: Technologies for Future Exploration in Space and Tests of Gravity*, ed. H Dittus, C Laemmerzahl, SG Turyshev, pp. 429–93. Berlin: Springer-Verlag (2006)

155. Turyshev SG, Lane BF, Shao M, Girerd AR. gr-qc/0805.4033 (2008)

Charm Meson Decays

Marina Artuso,[1] Brian Meadows,[2]
and Alexey A. Petrov[3,4]

[1]Department of Physics, Syracuse University, Syracuse, New York 13244;
email: artuso@physics.syr.edu

[2]Department of Physics, University of Cincinnati, Cincinnati, Ohio 45221;
email: meadowbt@ucmail.uc.edu

[3]Department of Physics and Astronomy, Wayne State University, Detroit, Michigan 48201

[4]Michigan Center for Theoretical Physics, University of Michigan, Ann Arbor, Michigan 48109;
email: apetrov@wayne.edu

Annu. Rev. Nucl. Part. Sci. 2008. 58:249–91

First published online as a Review in Advance on
July 21, 2008

The *Annual Review of Nuclear and Particle Science*
is online at nucl.annualreviews.org

This article's doi:
10.1146/annurev.nucl.58.110707.171131

Key Words

charmed quark, charmed meson, weak decays, CP violation, mixing

Abstract

We review some recent developments in charm meson physics. In particular,
we discuss the theoretical predictions and experimental measurements of
charmed meson decays to leptonic, semileptonic, and hadronic final states
and the implications of such measurements to searches for new physics.
We discuss $D^0 - \bar{D}^0$ mixing and CP violation in charm, as well as future
experimental prospects and theoretical challenges in this area.

Contents

1. INTRODUCTION

The charm quark has played a unique role in particle physics for more than three decades. Its discovery was an important validation of the standard model (SM), as its existence and mass scale were predicted (1) on the basis of low-energy kaon experiments before any direct experimental signature for charm was available.

Several features distinguish charmed hadrons from those with other flavors. Although their mass of $\mathcal{O}(2 \text{ GeV})$ places them in the region where nonperturbative hadronic physics is operative, theoretical methods developed for heavy quarks can, in principle, still be applied, albeit with larger uncertainties. Recent advances in unquenched lattice quantum chromodynamics (QCD) simulations have paved the way for charm data to probe the Yukawa sector of the SM. The charm quark is the only up-type quark that can have flavor oscillations. Finally, charm decays provide a unique window on new physics (NP) affecting the up-type quark dynamics. In some cases, charm transitions provide almost background-free low-energy signals of NP. For example, many popular NP models predict signals for CP violation (CPV) that are much larger than what is generally predicted within the SM (2). One hopes that, just as the manifestation of charm quark existence came from low-energy kaon-oscillation experiments, oscillations of charmed hadrons can provide hints of what is happening at the teraelectronvolt (TeV) scale.

Experiments operating at the $\psi(3770)$ resonance near threshold for $D\bar{D}$ production, such as Mark III at SPEAR (Stanford Positron Electron Accelerating Ring), performed the initial exploration of charm phenomenology (3). Later, higher-energy machines, fixed-target experiments operating either at hadron machines or higher-energy e^+e^- colliders, entered this arena and yielded much bigger data samples. In recent years we have seen a renewed interest in studying open charm in e^+e^- colliders with a center-of-mass energy close to $D\bar{D}$ threshold. After years of charm studies at a center-of-mass energy near the $\Upsilon(4S)$, the CLEO experiment (4) at CESR (Cornell Electron Storage Ring) has collected a sample exceeding 800 pb^{-1} at the $\psi(3770)$ center-of-mass energy as well as a sample of approximately 600 pb^{-1} at a center-of-mass energy close to 4170 MeV, which is optimal for D_s studies. The Beijing Spectrometer II (BES-II) experiment, at BEPC (Beijing Electron Positron Collider), has published results based on a 33-pb^{-1} sample accumulated around the $\psi(3770)$. It has an upgrade program both for the detector (BES-III) and for the machine (BEPC-II), which has been designed as a charm factory with 10^{33} cm^{-2} s^{-1} peak luminosity and which should be completed in 2008 (5). In parallel, BaBar and Belle have provided important contributions to our knowledge of charm decays, exploiting their impressive data sets. Both B factory facilities have achieved luminosities almost ten times their original design and have yielded over 1.8×10^9 $c\bar{c}$ pairs at the $\Upsilon(4S)$ resonance. A KEKB (High Energy Accelerator Research Organization B factory, Tsukuba, Japan) upgrade will attain luminosities about one order of magnitude greater than those already achieved. An alternative approach, with luminosity goals almost an order of magnitude larger and with the added capability to run at both the $\Upsilon(4S)$ and the $\psi(3770)$, is being considered but has not yet been approved. Finally, CDF (Collider Detector at Fermilab) and DØ have entered the arena of charm physics, applying to this study some of the tools developed to pursue beauty physics.

Experiments operating at the $\psi(3770)$ resonance have several advantages: (a) The final state is extremely simple, as it is dominated by a $D\bar{D}$ pair; (b) the cross section for charm production is relatively high, $\sigma(D^0\bar{D}^0) = 3.66 \pm 0.03 \pm 0.06$ nb and $\sigma(D^+D^-) = 2.91 \pm 0.03 \pm 0.05$ nb (6); and (c) the relatively high branching fractions to low-multiplicity final states allow the use of tagged samples, where one D is fully reconstructed (tag) and the rest of the event recoiling against the tag is used to study specific signals. This technique is particularly useful for the study of leptonic and semileptonic events, as it allows a precise reconstruction of the neutrino four-momentum, and for the invariant mass squared of the lepton-neutrino pair (q^2). In addition, the $D\bar{D}$ pairs are produced in a $C = -1$ state, and this quantum coherence allows unique probes of mixing and CPV. However, the B factory experiments Belle and BaBar can also be considered charm factories. At the $\Upsilon(4S)$ center-of-mass energy, $\sigma(b\bar{b}) \sim 1.1$ nb, whereas $\sigma(c\bar{c}) \sim 1.3$ nb. The background to be tackled is higher than at the lower energy, and neutrino and q^2 reconstructions in general are not as precise. Significant improvements are achieved, however, through the use of tagged samples (7), which is made possible by the impressive size of the data set accumulated: In January 2008 the samples were 484 fb^{-1} at BaBar and 763 fb^{-1} at Belle. Also, the energy at which these experiments operate enables the production of charmed baryons and boosts the charm particles sufficiently to enable time-dependent measurements.

Experiments at hadron machines have the advantage of much higher cross sections for charm and beauty production, at the expense of significant backgrounds. Luckily the relatively long lifetime ($\sim$1 ps) of charm hadrons, combined with the development of silicon micropattern detectors, provides a unique and powerful signature of charm meson decays: the identification of detached secondary vertices. Approximately 30 years after its inception (8), this technique is still being perfected with the introduction of more and more sophisticated vertex algorithms that provide charm and beauty event tagging almost in real time. This development has allowed both fixed-target experiments and the two Tevatron experiments, CDF and DØ, to provide significant contributions to our knowledge of charm decays, with competitive limits on some rare decays and on recent results in $D^0 - \bar{D}^0$ mixing, confirming the observations at the B factories. This work will be continued by LHCb, the first dedicated charm and beauty experiment at the Large Hadron Collider (LHC), which relies heavily on detached vertex criteria in the early stages of its triggering process and is considering an upgrade that would include detached vertex criteria in the lowest trigger level (9).

2. LEPTONIC AND SEMILEPTONIC DECAYS

Charm leptonic and semileptonic decays are ideal laboratories in which to study nonperturbative QCD and to determine important quark-mixing parameters. In addition, they may provide additional constraints on physics beyond the SM.

In the SM, semileptonic decays are described by an effective Hamiltonian,

$$\mathcal{H} = \frac{G_F}{\sqrt{2}} V_{cq} L^{\mu} \bar{q} \Gamma_{\mu} c, \qquad\qquad 1.$$

where L^{μ} is a leptonic current, G_F is the Fermi constant, and $\Gamma_{\mu} = \gamma_{\mu}(1 - \gamma_5)$. Theoretically, leptonic decays are the simplest to describe, as they depend only on a single nonperturbative parameter, the decay constant f_{D_q},

$$\langle 0|\bar{q}\gamma^{\mu}\gamma_5 c|D_q\rangle = -i\, f_{D_q}\, p_D^{\mu}, \qquad\qquad 2.$$

which parameterizes the amplitude of probability for a heavy quark and a light quark to "find" each other in a meson. Semileptonic decays are traditionally described in terms of form factors cast as a function of q^2, the invariant mass of the electron–neutrino pair. Experimental determinations of these form factors are performed through the study of the differential decay width $d\Gamma/dq^2$. In both cases, decay constants and form factors are QCD parameters that can only be computed using nonperturbative techniques.

Accurate calculations of nonperturbative QCD parameters are very challenging. Lattice QCD represents an appealing approach: In principle, it is the only method that can be improved in a systematic way. A significant challenge has been the inclusion of dynamical quark effects (unquenched lattice QCD). Recently, technical developments such as highly improved actions of QCD and the availability of "2+1 flavor" Multiple Input/Multiple Data Lattice Computation (MILC) configurations with three flavors of improved staggered quarks have led to results with much higher accuracy and have allowed for consistent estimates of both statistical and systematic errors involved in the simulations. Two groups have reported charm decay constant calculations with three dynamical quark flavors: the Fermilab/MILC Lattice collaboration (10) and the HPQCD (High-Precision Quantum Chromodynamics) collaboration (11). Both groups use the 2+1 MILC configurations, including three flavors of staggered quarks: one heavier with a mass close to the strange quark mass m_s and two degenerated light quarks with masses between $m_s/10$ and m_s; however, the groups differ with regard to how they treat heavy quarks in their formulations of lattice QCD. The Fermilab group has also calculated the shape and normalization of the form factors in semileptonic $D \to \pi e \nu_e$ and $D \to K e \nu_e$ decays (12).

The QCD sum rules (13, 14) provide a method for calculating hadronic matrix elements, including nonperturbative effects, which was designed to make maximum use of the known manifestations of nonperturbative QCD. A few parameters describe the nonperturbative dynamics and are fixed from well-known hadronic processes, then applied to heavy meson decays. Finally, quark models that are generally QCD inspired and based on a variety of assumptions have been used to predict form-factor normalizations and decay constants (17).

In principle, charm meson semileptonic decays provide the simplest way to determine the magnitude of quark-mixing parameters: The charm sector allows direct access to $|V_{cs}|$ and $|V_{cd}|$.

Semileptonic decay rates are related to $|V_{cq}|^2$ via matrix elements that describe strong interaction effects.

The study of charm semileptonic decays may also contribute to a precise determination of the Cabibbo–Kobayashi–Maskawa (CKM) matrix element $|V_{ub}|$. A variety of theoretical approaches have been proposed to use constraints provided by charm decays to reduce the model dependence in the extraction of $|V_{ub}|$ from exclusive charmless B semileptonic decays. In particular, if heavy quark effective theory (18) is applicable both to the c and b quarks, then there is an SU(2) flavor symmetry that relates the form factors in D and B semileptonic decays (19). For example, a flavor symmetry relates the form factors in $D \to \pi \ell \nu$ to those in $B \to \pi \ell \bar{\nu}$ at the same $E \equiv v \cdot p_\pi$, where E is the energy of the light meson in the center-of-mass D frame, v is the four-velocity of the D meson, and p_π is the four-momentum of the light hadron. The original method has been further refined (20); the large statistics needed to implement these methods may become available in the near future.

2.1. Experimental Determination of the Decay Constant

To lowest order, the leptonic decay width is given by

$$\Gamma(D_q \to \ell \nu) = \frac{G_F^2}{8\pi} f_{D_q}^2 m_\ell^2 M_{D_q} \left(1 - \frac{m_\ell^2}{M_{D_q}^2}\right)^2 |V_{cq}|^2, \qquad \qquad 3.$$

where $q = d$, s for D^+ and D_s states, respectively, M_{D_q} is the D_q mass, m_ℓ is the mass of the final-state lepton, and $|V_{cq}|$ is the CKM matrix element associated with the $c \to q$ transition. Due to helicity suppression, the rate goes as m_ℓ^2; consequently, the electron mode $D^+ \to e^+ \nu_e$ has a very small rate in the SM. The relative widths scale as $2.65 : 1 : 2.3 \times 10^{-5}$ for the $\tau^+ \nu_\tau$, $\mu^+ \nu_\mu$, and $e^+ \nu_e$ final states, respectively. The decay constant, defined in Equation 2, is the only nonperturbative parameter in Equation 3. The leptonic widths can be measured for both D^+ and D_s. Similarly, rather precise theoretical predictions for f_D exist, thus allowing a direct measurement of SU(3) breaking and a comparison with the theory.

The CLEO collaboration (28) has measured $f_{D^+} = (222.6 \pm 16.7^{+2.8}_{-3.4})$ MeV using a tagged sample of $D^+ D^-$ decays collected at a center-of-mass energy close to 3.77 GeV. Recently, they have reported an update on this measurement based on the full CLEO-c data set. They perform a simultaneous analysis of $D^+ \to \mu^+ \nu_\mu$ and $D^+ \to \tau^+ \nu_\tau$ (28). They obtain $f_{D^+} = (207.6 \pm 9.3 \pm 2.5)$ MeV, if they analyze their data allowing the $D^+ \to \tau^+ \nu_\tau$ contribution to float, and $f_{D^+} = (205.8 \pm 8.5 \pm 2.5)$ MeV, if they assume the SM ratio for $D^+ \to \tau^+ \nu_\tau / D^+ \to \mu^+ \nu_\mu$. The latter results are all corrected for radiative decay. The presence of the neutrino is inferred by requiring the missing mass squared (MM^2) to be consistent with zero:

$$MM^2 = (E_{beam} - E_{\mu^+})^2 - (\vec{p}_{D^-} - \vec{p}_{\mu^+})^2.$$

Figure 1 shows the distribution of measured MM^2 with a 50-event peak in the interval $(-0.050 \text{ GeV}^2, +0.050 \text{ GeV}^2)$, approximately $\pm 2\sigma$ wide. The background was evaluated as $2.81 \pm 0.30 \pm 0.27$ events. The same tag sample was used to search for $D^+ \to e^+ \nu_e$. No signal was found, corresponding to a 90%-CL upper limit $\mathcal{B}(D^+ \to e^+ \nu_e) < 2.4 \times 10^{-5}$. More data is available on $f_{D_s^+}$. Early measurements and a recent BaBar result of $f_{D_s^+}$ determined the ratio $\mathcal{B}(D_s \to \mu \nu)/\mathcal{B}(D_s \to \phi \pi)$ (29). These measurements include an additional source of error, as the denominator is not well known (16, 34). These measurements are not included in the new world average (15). In this category the BaBar measurement (29), with a large $\mu \nu$ signal of almost 500 events, is the most precise, and it is unique in using its own measurement of the absolute $\phi \pi$

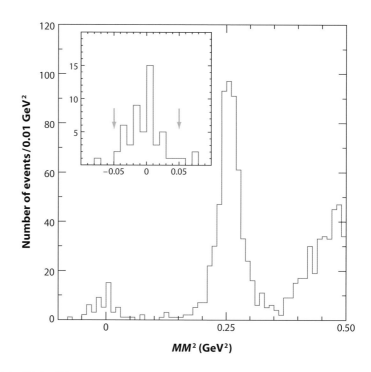

Figure 1

The CLEO-c distribution of missing mass squared (MM^2) using D^- tags and one opposite charged track with no extra energetic clusters. The inset shows the signal region for $D^+ \to \mu \nu_\mu$; the two orange arrows show the MM^2 interval chosen as signal. The figure is taken from Reference 27.

branching fraction from $B \to D^* D_s$ decays (16), rather than a world average from results using different assumptions about the backgrounds and line shapes. The absolute branching fraction for the $\mu\nu$ decay used in Reference 29 to compute $f_{D_s^+}$ therefore depends on the ratio between the $\phi\pi$ signals observed in References 29 and 16. The CLEO result (38) used the PDG average for the $D_s \to \phi\pi$ branching fraction, although this was dominated by its own measurement. As we discuss in Section 4.3.3 below (also see Reference 84), signal shapes and resolutions can affect the measured yield in $D_s \to \phi\pi$, and these effects need to be assessed.

CLEO-c used a sample of $D_s D_s^*$ collected near the center-of-mass energy of 4.17 GeV to study D_s leptonic decays (35). The CLEO group measured the absolute branching fractions for the decays $D_s \to \mu\nu_\mu$, $D_s \to \tau\nu_\tau$, $\tau \to \pi\nu_\tau$, and $\tau \to e\nu_\tau\nu_e$ (36). Recently, Belle reported an absolute value for the branching fraction $\mathcal{B}(D_s \to \mu\nu_\mu)$ based on fully reconstructed samples of events of the type $e^+e^- \to D_s^* D K X$, $D_s^* \to D_s\gamma$, where X is any number of π and at most one γ from fragmentation (37).

2.2. Summary of Theoretical Predictions for f_D

We summarize the theoretical predictions in **Table 1** and present measurements in **Table 2** (taken from Reference 15). The average of the absolute measurements is $f_{D_s^+} = 275 \pm 10$ MeV, assuming that $|V_{cs}| = |V_{cd}| = 0.9737$. Typically, the experimental value is above theoretical predictions. In general, the errors are such that the discrepancy is not yet meaningful, with the exception of the most recent United Kingdom Quantum Chromodynamics (UKQCD)–MILC calculation

Table 1 Theoretical predictions for f_{D^+}, $f_{D_s^+}$, $f_{D_s^+}/f_{D^+}$

Source	f_{D^+} (MeV)	$f_{D_s^+}$ (MeV)	$f_{D_s^+}/f_{D^+}$	Reference
Unquenched lattice calculations				
HPQCD, UKQCD	208 ± 4	241 ± 3	1.162 ± 0.009	11
FNAL, MILC, HPQCD	$201 \pm 3 \pm 17$	$249 \pm 3 \pm 16$	$1.24 \pm 0.01 \pm 0.07$	10
Quenched lattice QCD calculations				
Taiwan	$235 \pm 8 \pm 14$	$266 \pm 10 \pm 18$	$1.13 \pm 0.03 \pm 0.05$	21
UKQCD	$210 \pm 10^{+17}_{-16}$	$236 \pm 8^{+17}_{-14}$	$1.13 \pm 0.02^{+0.04}_{-0.02}$	22
Becirevic et al.	$211 \pm 14^{+2}_{-12}$	$231 \pm 12^{+6}_{-1}$	1.10 ± 0.02	23
QCD sum rules and other approximations				
J. Bordes et al.	177 ± 21	205 ± 22	$1.16 \pm 0.02 \pm 0.03$	24
S. Narison	203 ± 10	235 ± 24	1.15 ± 0.04	25
Field correlators	210 ± 10	260 ± 10	1.24 ± 0.03	26
Isospin splitting		262 ± 29		27

Abbreviations: FNAL, Fermi National Accelerator Laboratory; HPQCD, High-Precision Quantum Chromodynamics; MILC, Multiple Input/Multiple Data Lattice Computation; UKQCD, United Kingdom Quantum Chromodynamics.

(11). In this case, the discrepancy between theory and experiment exceeds the stated errors by approximately 3σ.

2.3. Constraints on New Physics from f_D

Leptonic decays are sensitive probes of NP interactions mediated by charged particles. Models with an extended Higgs sector, which include new charged scalar states, and models with broken left-right symmetry, which include massive vector $W_R^\pm$ states, are primary examples of such interactions. Recent evidence of observation of $B \to \tau \nu_\tau$ decay has brought renewed attention to such models.

Table 2 Results for decay branching fractions $\mathcal{B}_{\phi\pi} \equiv \mathcal{B}(D_s \to \phi\pi^+)$, $\mathcal{B}(D_s \to \mu^+\nu_\mu)$, $\mathcal{B}(D_s \to \tau^+\nu_\tau)$, and $f_{D_s^+}$

Name of experiment	Mode	$\mathcal{B}(\times 10^3)$	$\mathcal{B}_{\phi\pi}$(%)	$f_{D_s^+}$ (MeV)	Reference(s)
CLEO-c	$\mu^+\nu_\mu$	$5.94 \pm 0.66 \pm 0.31$		$264 \pm 15 \pm 7$	35
CLEO-c	$\tau^+\nu_\tau$	$80.0 \pm 13.0 \pm 4.0$		$310 \pm 25 \pm 8$	35
CLEO-c	$\tau^+\nu_\tau$	$61.7 \pm 7.1 \pm 3.6$		$273 \pm 16 \pm 8$	36
CLEO-c	combined			$274 \pm 10 \pm 5$	36
Belle	$\mu^+\nu_\mu$	$6.44 \pm 0.76 \pm 0.52$		$275 \pm 16 \pm 12$	37
Average				275 ± 10	15
CLEO	$\mu^+\nu_\mu$	$6.2 \pm 0.8 \pm 1.3 \pm 1.6$	3.6 ± 0.9	$273 \pm 19 \pm 27 \pm 33$	38
BEATRICE	$\mu^+\nu_\mu$	$8.3 \pm 2.3 \pm 0.6 \pm 2.1$	3.6 ± 0.9	$312 \pm 43 \pm 12 \pm 39$	39
ALEPH	$\mu^+\nu_\mu$	$6.8 \pm 1.1 \pm 1.8$	3.6 ± 0.9	$282 \pm 19 \pm 40$	40
ALEPH	$\tau^+\nu_\tau$	$58 \pm 8 \pm 18$			40
L3	$\tau^+\nu_\tau$	$74 \pm 28 \pm 16 \pm 18$		$299 \pm 57 \pm 32 \pm 37$	41
OPAL	$\tau^+\nu_\tau$	$70 \pm 21 \pm 20$		$283 \pm 44 \pm 41$	42
BaBar	$\mu^+\nu_\mu$	$6.74 \pm 0.83 \pm 0.26 \pm 0.66$	4.71 ± 0.46	$283 \pm 17 \pm 7 \pm 14$	16, 29

Numbers have been updated using D_s lifetime of 0.50 ps. Results below the line have not been used in the quoted average. The assumed value of $\mathcal{B}_{\phi\pi}$ is listed whenever available. ALEPH average their two results to obtain a value for $f_{D_s^+}$.
Abbreviations: ALEPH, Apparatus for LEP Physics; OPAL, Omnipurpose Apparatus for Large Electron-Positron Collider.

In particular, two Higgs doublet models, including the minimal supersymmetric SM (MSSM), could contribute to such transitions. Different implementations of the MSSM can be formulated (30). For example, the first doublet (Φ_1) could give mass to the up-type fermions and the second (Φ_2) to the down-type fermions. In this case,

$$\mathcal{B}(D^+ \to \ell^+ \nu_\ell) = \mathcal{B}_{SM} \left(1 + \frac{m_D^2}{m_{H^\pm}^2} \right)^2$$

$$\mathcal{B}(D_s^+ \to \ell^+ \nu_\ell) = \mathcal{B}_{SM} \left[1 + \frac{m_{D_s}^2}{m_{H^\pm}^2} \left(1 - \tan^2 \beta \frac{m_s}{m_c} \right) \right]^2. \qquad 4.$$

Note that the latter model introduces a correction to the SM expectations that may be considerable and negative at large $\tan^2 \beta$. A limit can also be set on the mass of a charged Higgs, $m_{H^+} > 2.2 \tan \beta$. This limit is similar to that obtained from the measurement $\mathcal{B}(B \to \tau \nu)$ decay (31).

2.4. Absolute Branching Fractions for Semileptonic D Decays

Determination of absolute branching fractions for D semileptonic decays constitutes important measurements. Assuming that $|V_{cx}|$ is known, these measurements determine form-factor normalization. Conversely, if the form factors are known independently from, say, the lattice QCD calculations, these branching fractions determine the relevant CKM matrix elements. By comparing the inclusive branching fractions of the D^+ and D^0 mesons with the sum of the measured exclusive branching fractions, one can determine whether there are semileptonic decay modes that have yet to be observed. BES-II (33) and CLEO-c (32) have recently presented data on exclusive semileptonic branching fractions. The BES-II results are based on 33 pb^{-1}; the CLEO-c results are based on the first 57-pb^{-1} data set. Both experiments used tagged samples and selected a specific final state through the kinematic variable,

$$U \equiv E_{miss} - |\vec{p}_{miss}|,$$

where E_{miss} represents the missing energy and $\vec{p}$ represents the missing momentum of the D meson decaying semileptonically. For signal events, U is expected to be 0, whereas other semileptonic decays peak in different regions. **Figure 2** shows the U distribution for five exclusive D^+ decay modes reported by CLEO-c, which demonstrate that U resolution was excellent, thus allowing a full separation between Cabibbo-suppressed (CS) and Cabibbo-favored (CF) modes. **Table 3** summarizes the recent measurements from CLEO-c and BES-II as well as the world averages reported in the *Review of Particle Physics* (34).

Absolute branching fractions for $D^0 \to K\ell\nu$ were recently published by Belle (7), obtaining values $\mathcal{B}(D^0 \to K\ell\nu) = (3.45 \pm 0.07 \pm 0.20)\%$ and $\mathcal{B}(D^0 \to \pi\ell\nu) = (0.255 \pm 0.019 \pm 0.016)\%$. CLEO-c used the two tagging modes with the lowest background ($\bar{D}^0 \to K^+\pi^-$ and $D^- \to K^+\pi^-\pi^-$) to measure the inclusive D^0 and D^+ semileptonic branching fractions (43). They obtained

$$\mathcal{B}(D^+ \to Xe^+\nu_e) = (16.13 \pm 0.20_{\text{stat}} \pm 0.33_{\text{sys}})\%$$
$$\mathcal{B}(D^0 \to Xe^+\nu_e) = (6.46 \pm 0.17_{\text{stat}} \pm 0.13_{\text{sys}})\%.$$

The sum of the exclusive semileptonic absolute branching fraction are $\mathcal{B}(D^+ \to Xe^+\nu_e)_{\text{excl}} = (15.2 \pm 0.5 \pm 0.5)\%$ and $\mathcal{B}(D^0 \to Xe^+\nu_e)_{\text{excl}} = (6.1 \pm 0.2 \pm 0.2)\%$. The measured exclusive modes are consistent with saturating the inclusive widths, although there remains some room for higher-multiplicity modes. The CLEO-c data have been used in this comparison, as they

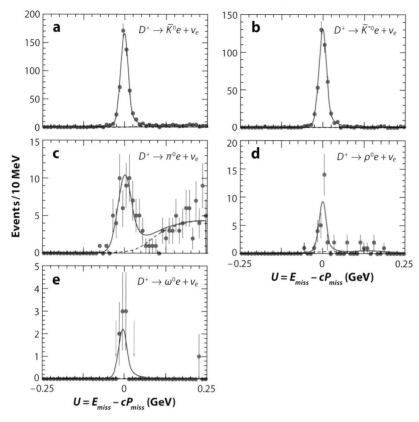

Figure 2

Fits (*solid blue lines*) to the U distributions in CLEO-c data (*red dots with error bars*) for the five D^+ semileptonic modes: (*a*) $D^+ \rightarrow \bar{K}^0 e^+ \nu_e$, (*b*) $D^+ \rightarrow \bar{K}^{*0} e^+ \nu_e$, (*c*) $D^+ \rightarrow \pi^0 e^+ \nu_e$, (*d*) $D^+ \rightarrow \rho^0 e^+ \nu_e$, and (*e*) $D^+ \rightarrow \omega e^+ \nu_e$. The orange arrows in panel (*e*) show the chosen signal region. The background (*dashed blue lines*) is visible only in panels *c* and *d*. Figure taken from Reference 31.

Table 3 Summary of recent absolute branching fraction measurements of exclusive D^+ and D^0 semileptonic decays

Decay mode	B (%) (32)	B (%) (33)	B (%) (PDG06 average)
$D^0 \rightarrow K^- e^+ \nu_e$	$3.44 \pm 0.10 \pm 0.10$	$3.82 \pm 0.40 \pm 0.27$	3.47 ± 0.13
$D^0 \rightarrow \pi^- e^+ \nu_e$	$0.262 \pm 0.025 \pm 0.008$	$0.33 \pm 0.13 \pm 0.03$	
$D^0 \rightarrow K^{*-} e^+ \nu_e$	$2.16 \pm 0.15 \pm 0.08$		
$D^0 \rightarrow \rho^- e^+ \nu_e$	$0.194 \pm 0.039 \pm 0.013$		
$D^+ \rightarrow \bar{K}^0 e^+ \nu_e$	$8.71 \pm 0.38 \pm 0.37$	$8.95 \pm 1.59 \pm 0.67$	8.7 ± 0.5
$D^+ \rightarrow \pi^0 e^+ \nu_e$	$0.44 \pm 0.06 \pm 0.0.03$		
$D^+ \rightarrow \bar{K}^{*0} e^+ \nu_e$	$5.56 \pm 0.27 \pm 0.23$		
$D^+ \rightarrow \rho^0 e^+ \nu_e$	$0.21 \pm 0.04 \pm 0.01$		
$D^+ \rightarrow \omega e^+ \nu_e$	$0.16^{+0.07}_{-0.06} \pm 0.01$		

When only the CLEO-c (second column) absolute number is available, no average number is provided.

dominate the present world average: The exclusive modes are consistent with saturating the inclusive semileptonic branching fraction at 41% CL in the case of D^+ and 18% CL in the case of D^0.

2.5. Form Factors for the Decays $D \rightarrow K(\pi)\ell\nu$

Theoretical parameterizations of semileptonic decays involve two nonperturbative quantities parameterizing the matrix element of a single hadronic current. Traditionally, the hadronic matrix elements for transitions to pseudoscalar hadrons are described in terms of two form factors, $f_+(q^2)$ and $f_-(q^2)$,

$$\langle K(\pi)|\bar{q}\,\Gamma^\mu c\,|D\rangle = f_+(q^2)P^\mu + f_-(q^2)q^\mu, \qquad 5.$$

where $P = p_D + p_{K(\pi)}$ and $q = p_D - p_{K(\pi)}$. An often-used alternative parameterization is

$$\langle K(\pi)|\bar{q}\,\Gamma^\mu c\,|D\rangle = \left(P^\mu - \frac{m_D^2 - m_{K(\pi)}^2}{q^2}q^\mu\right)f_+(q^2) + \frac{m_D^2 - m_{K(\pi)}^2}{q^2}q^\mu\,f_0(q^2), \qquad 6.$$

where $f_0(q^2) = f_+(q^2) + f_-(q^2)q^2/(m_D^2 - m_{K(\pi)}^2)$. Experimental determinations of these form factors are performed through the study of the differential decay width $d\Gamma/dq^2$. For cases where the lepton in the final state is an electron and has a negligible mass with respect to the parent D, only a single form factor, $f_+(q^2)$, contributes. The partial decay width is given by

$$\frac{d\Gamma(D \rightarrow K(\pi)e\nu_e)}{dq^2} = \frac{G_F^2|V_{cq}|^2}{24\pi^3}p_{K(\pi)}^3|f_+(q^2)|^2, \qquad 7.$$

where $p_{K(\pi)}$ is the hadron momentum in the D rest frame. Form factors have been evaluated at specific q^2 points in a variety of phenomenological models (44), where the shape is typically assumed from some model arguments. In order to restrict the function space studied, a dispersive representation (45) allows us to place rather general constraints on the shapes of the form factors from their analytic properties. Particular parameterizations of the form factors are nevertheless useful. The most common parameterization has been a single-pole form factor, where the pole is the lowest mass resonance formed by the initial- and final-state hadron. For example, in the decay $D \rightarrow \pi e\nu_e$ the dominant pole is the D^*. Now that more precise data are available, more complex representations are being investigated. One class of parameterizations includes the dominant-pole form factor and approximates the dispersion integral by a number of effective poles,

$$f_+(q^2) = \frac{f_+(0)}{(1-\alpha)}\frac{1}{1-(q^2/m_V^2)} + \sum_{k=1}^{N}\frac{\rho_k}{1-\frac{1}{\gamma_k}\frac{q^2}{m_V^2}}, \qquad 8.$$

where α determines the strength of the dominant pole, ρ_k gives the strength of the kth term in the expansion, and $\gamma_k = m_{V_k}^2/m_V^2$, with m_{V_k} representing masses of the higher-order poles. The true form factor can be approximated to any desired accuracy by introducing a large number of finely spaced effective poles. In effect, it is desirable to keep the number of terms in this expansion manageable. The popular Becirevic–Kaidalov (BK) parameterization (46) is a simplified version of the $N = 1$ truncation of this expansion. In general, both the $N = 0$ case (simple pole) and the $N = 1$ case can provide good representation of the data if the pole masses are allowed to be nonphysical. An alternative approach (51) utilizes a series expansion around an arbitrary q^2 value, t_0. To achieve a convergent series, the expansion is formulated as an analytic continuation of the form factors in the complex $t = q^2$ plane. There is a branch cut on the real axis for $t > (M_D + M_{K,\pi})^2$, which corresponds to a region associated with production of states with appropriate quantum numbers. The convergence is accelerated by mapping the whole cut region onto the unit disk $z < 1$, where

z is defined as

$$z(q^2, t_0) = \frac{\sqrt{t_+ - q^2} - \sqrt{t_+ - t_0}}{\sqrt{t_+ - q^2} + \sqrt{t_+ - t_0}}. \tag{9}$$

Here $t_\pm = (M_D \pm M_{K,\pi})^2$ and t_0 is the arbitrary q^2 value that maps onto $z = 0$. The form factors are then expressed as (51)

$$f_+(q^2) = \frac{1}{P(q^2)\Phi(q^2, t_0)} \sum_{k=0}^{\infty} \alpha_k(t_0)[z(q^2, t_0)]^k, \tag{10}$$

where $P(q^2) = z(q^2, m_V^2)$, which accounts for the pole in the form factor at $q^2 = m_V^2$. The physical observables are not expected to depend on $\Phi(q^2, t_0)$ (which can be any analytical function) or on t_0.

Unquenched lattice QCD calculations for $D \to K\ell\bar{\nu}$ and $D \to \pi\ell\nu$ have recently been reported (12). In these calculations the chiral extrapolation was performed at fixed $E = v \cdot p_{K(\pi)}$, where v represents the D four-velocity and $p_{K(\pi)}$ represents the four-momentum of the daughter hadron. The lattice "data points" were fitted to the BK parameterization (46),

$$f_+(q^2) = \frac{f_+(0)}{(1 - \tilde{q}^2)(1 - \alpha\tilde{q}^2)},$$
$$f_0(q^2) = \frac{f_+(0)}{1 - \tilde{q}^2/\beta}, \tag{11}$$

where $\tilde{q}^2 = q^2/m_{D_s^*}^2$ and α and β are fit parameters. The fitted parameters are shown in **Table 4**. The FOCUS (<u>P</u>hotoproduction of <u>C</u>harm: <u>U</u>pgraded <u>S</u>pectrometer) experiment (47) was the first to perform a nonparametric measurement of the shape of the form factor in $D \to K\mu\nu_\mu$ (52). CLEO-c (53), Belle (7), and BaBar (54) reported similar analyses. **Figure 3** shows the lattice QCD predictions for $D \to K\ell\nu$ and $D \to \pi\ell\nu$ with the Belle data points superimposed. **Table 5** summarizes the experimental form-factor fits compared to the lattice QCD predictions. By combining the information of the measured leptonic and semileptonic widths, a ratio independent of $|V_{cd}|$ can be evaluated; this ratio can serve as a check of the theoretical calculations. For instance, assuming isospin symmetry, i.e., $\Gamma(D \to \pi e^+\nu_e) = \Gamma(D^0 \to \pi^- e^+\nu_e) = 2\Gamma(D^+ \to \pi^0 e^+\nu_e)$, a ratio

$$R \equiv \sqrt{\Gamma(D^+ \to \mu\nu_\mu)/\Gamma(D \to \pi e^+\nu_e)}$$

can be formed. Using the recent unquenched lattice QCD calculations (10, 12), this ratio can be computed to be

$$R_{sl}^{th} = \sqrt{\frac{\Gamma^{th}(D^+ \to \mu\nu_\mu)}{\Gamma^{th}(D \to \pi e\nu_e)}} = 0.212 \pm 0.028.$$

The quoted error is evaluated through a careful study of the theory's statistical and systematic uncertainties, assuming Gaussian errors. The corresponding experimental ratio can be calculated

Table 4   Fit parameters from Equation 11, decay rates, and
Cabibbo–Kobayashi–Maskawa matrix elements

P	$|f_+(0)|$	α	β
π	0.64(3)(6)	0.44(4)(7)	1.41(6)(13)
K	0.73(3)(7)	0.50(4)(7)	1.31(7)(13)

The first errors are statistical, the second systematic.

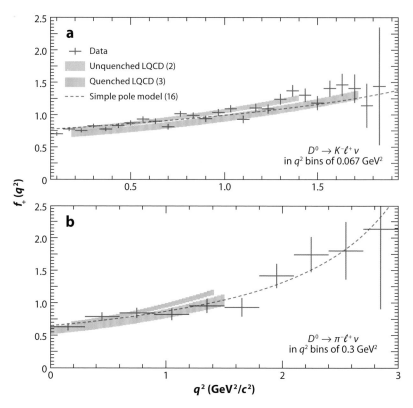

Figure 3

Belle data form factors for (*a*) $D^0 \to K^- \ell^+ \nu$ in q^2 bins of 0.067 GeV^2 and (*b*) $D^0 \to \pi^- \ell^+ \nu$ in q^2 bins of 0.3 GeV^2. Overlaid are the predictions of the simple-pole model using the physical pole masses (*dashed red line*) and quenched (*yellow*) and unquenched (*purple*) lattice quantum chromodynamics (LQCD) calculations. The shaded bands reflect the theoretical uncertainties and are shown in the q^2 ranges for which calculations are reported. The figure is taken from Reference 7.

Table 5 Measured shape parameter α compared to lattice QCD predictions

$\alpha(D^0 \to K\ell\nu)$		Reference
Lattice QCD	$0.5 \pm 0.04 \pm 0.07$	12
FOCUS	$0.28 \pm 0.08 \pm 0.07$	52
CLEO-III	$0.36 \pm 0.10^{+0.03}_{-0.07}$	55
Belle	$0.52 \pm 0.08 \pm 0.06$	7
BaBar	$0.38 \pm 0.02 \pm 0.03$	54
$\alpha(D^0 \to \pi\ell\nu)$		
Lattice QCD	$0.44 \pm 0.04 \pm 0.07$	12
CLEO-III	$0.37^{+0.20}_{-0.31} \pm 0.15$	55
Belle	$0.10 \pm 0.21 \pm 0.10$	7

Abbreviations: FOCUS, Photoprediction of Charm: Upgraded Spectrometer; QCD, quantum chromodynamics.

using the CLEO-c f_D and isospin-averaged $\Gamma(D \to \pi e^+\nu_e)$:

$$R_{sl}^{\exp} = \sqrt{\frac{\Gamma^{\exp}(D^+ \to \mu\nu)}{\Gamma^{\exp}(D \to \pi e\nu_e)}} = 0.236 \pm 0.015.$$

The theoretical calculations and data are consistent at 68% CL.

2.6. The Cabibbo–Kobayashi–Maskawa Matrix

In the framework of the SM the gauge bosons, $W^\pm$, γ, and Z°, couple to mixtures of the physical d, s, and b states. This mixing is described by the CKM matrix:

$$V_{CKM} = \begin{bmatrix} V_{ud} & V_{us} & V_{ub} \\ V_{cd} & V_{cs} & V_{cb} \\ V_{td} & V_{ts} & V_{tb} \end{bmatrix}.$$

Because the CKM matrix must be unitary, it can be expressed as a function of only four parameters. This matrix already has several experimental constraints (34), which are so far consistent with the SM picture. Eventually, experimental data and theoretical tools may reach the level of precision to uncover subtle new physics effects. In particular, an important goal of the next generation of precision experiments will be to perform direct measurements of each individual parameter. This will enable us to perform additional unitarity checks with a precision similar to that currently achieved with the first row (48). With the help of the unitarity constraints, charm quark–related V_{cd} and V_{cs} are now determined with high precision (34). The most recent result from LEP II (Large Electron-Positron Collider II), using the $W \to \ell\nu$ branching fraction and additional inputs from other CKM parameter measurements, is $V_{cs} = 0.976 \pm 0.014$ (49). The unitarity constraint implies $V_{cd} \sim V_{us} = 0.2227 \pm 0.0017$ (48).

CLEO-c (50) has extracted $|V_{cd}|$ and $|V_{cs}|$ by combining the $|V_{cq}|f_+(0)$ results from the three-parameter series expansion fit (51) with the unquenched lattice QCD predictions for $f_+(0)$ (12) to obtain

$$|V_{cs}| = 1.015 \pm 0.010 \pm 0.011 \pm 0.106$$
$$|V_{cd}| = 0.217 \pm 0.009 \pm 0.004 \pm 0.023.$$

The first two errors are experimental, statistical, and systematic, whereas the fourth errors are theoretical and dominated by the discretization uncertainties in the lattice QCD charm quark action, which should be improved in the near future. It will be interesting to see a unitarity check performed on the second row of the CKM matrix element once these errors are further reduced.

2.7. Form Factors in Semileptonic Decays Involving Vector Mesons $D \to V\ell\nu$

The structure of the hadronic current in semileptonic decays including vector mesons in the final state is more complex. It involves four independent form factors, V, A_0, A_1, and A_2:

$$\langle K^*(\rho)|\bar{q}\gamma_\mu c|D\rangle = 2\frac{V(q^2)}{m_D + m_{K^*(\rho)}}\varepsilon_{\mu\nu\alpha\beta}p_D^\nu p_{K^*(\rho)}^\alpha \varepsilon^{*\beta},$$

$$\langle K^*(\rho)|\bar{q}\gamma_\mu\gamma_5 c|D\rangle = i(m_D + m_{K^*(\rho)})\left(\varepsilon_\mu^* - \frac{\varepsilon^* \cdot q}{q^2}q_\mu\right)A_1(q^2)$$

$$-i\frac{\varepsilon^* \cdot q}{m_D + m_{K^*(\rho)}}\left(P^\mu - \frac{m_D^2 - m_{K(\pi)}^2}{q^2}q^\mu\right)A_2(q^2)$$

$$+2im_D\frac{\varepsilon^* \cdot q}{q^2}q_\mu A_0(q^2),\qquad\qquad 12.$$

where ε^* is a polarization of the final-state meson. The vector form factor V is dominated by vector meson resonance exchanges, A_0 is dominated by pseudoscalar meson resonance exchanges, and A_1 and A_2 are dominated by axial meson resonance exchanges. Generally a single-pole form factor is assumed in both experimental studies and theoretical calculations of the normalization of the form factors. The FOCUS experiment has developed an interesting technique that extends its nonparametric determination of the form factors in $D^0 \to K^- \mu^+ \nu_\mu$ to $D^+ \to K^- \pi^+ e^+ \nu_e$ (56); this technique was later adopted by the CLEO-c experiment (57). This method allows model-independent determinations of the form factors and thus provides a better check for theoretical calculations. For example, Fajfer & Kamenic (58) have studied these decays by including contributions of charm meson resonances beyond the simple pole and have found that including two poles in the vector form factor improves the agreement between their predictions and experimental results.

The FOCUS experiment (59) has reported evidence for the presence of a small scalar $K^- \pi^+$ amplitude interfering with the dominant $\bar{K}^{*0}$ component in the decay $D^+ \to K^- \pi^+ \mu^+ \nu_\mu$. CLEO-c (57) has observed the same effect in $D^+ \to K^- \pi^+ e^+ \nu_e$. This observation opens up new areas of investigation in exclusive charm semileptonic decays, namely the study of light quark spectroscopy. For example, it would be useful to verify whether this S wave resonance can be identified with the κ seen in D^+ Dalitz plot analyses (60). It will be interesting to search for similar interference phenomena in D_s semileptonic decays.

3. RARE AND RADIATIVE DECAYS

3.1. Theoretical Motivation

Rare charm decays hold great potential to be a sensitive probe of NP. Among all rare charm transitions, the most interesting are the decays that are associated with $\Delta C = 1$ flavor changing neutral currents (FCNCs), i.e., transitions that change the charm quark quantum number by one unit while conserving the electrical charge of participating quarks. Examples of such transitions include (*a*) rare radiative decays mediated by $c \to u\gamma$ or $c \to u\gamma\gamma$ quark currents and (*b*) rare leptonic and semileptonic decays mediated by $c \to u\ell\bar{\ell}$ quark currents. Here ℓ could be either a charged lepton such as e or μ or a neutrino ν. In addition, fully nonleptonic FCNC processes such as $c \to ug$ or $c \to uq\bar{q}$ are possible. We discuss these decays in Section 4.

In the SM, where FCNCs cannot occur at tree level, these processes are usually associated with the large contribution of the top quark to one-loop electroweak diagrams due to the Glashow–Iliopoulos–Maiani mechanism (61). This ensures that the bottom-type FCNC decay is dominated by the short-distance contributions; therefore, the decay is reliably computable. It has become evident that this situation is not realized in charm decays due to the relatively small mass of the charm quark and the significant hadronic dynamical effects in the region of charmed hadron mass. This leads to overwhelming long-distance contributions and decreased reliability of theoretical predictions. Indeed, model-dependent evaluations of long-distance effects are possible (62, 63) and can be used to judge the relative importance of long- and short-distance physics.

These facts can constitute a problem for the proper interpretation of NP effects in FCNC processes. In addition, constraints on the strength of new interactions can be placed unambiguously only if the SM contributions are significantly smaller than the experimentally placed bound on a branching ratio.

3.1.1. Inclusive and exclusive radiative decays $c \to u\gamma$. Because rare radiative decays are to two-body final states, a branching ratio for exclusive or inclusive transitions is the primary

observable. Thus, one must evaluate the relative NP/SM contribution for each model of NP. Only if the SM contribution (even dominated by the long-distance contributions) is seen to be much smaller than current experimental bounds and possible NP contributions can such measurements be useful in constraining NP models. Current theoretical estimates put decay rates of $D^0 \to \rho\gamma$ at the level of $(0.1 \div 0.5) \times 10^{-5}$ and rates of $D^0 \to \phi\gamma$ at $(0.1 \div 3.4) \times 10^{-5}$. Currently, the decay $D^0 \to \phi\gamma$ has been measured to be $(2.6^{+0.70\ +0.15}_{-0.61\ -0.17}) \times 10^{-5}$ (66), and experimental constraints on other radiative decays are of the order of 10^{-4} (34). As the experimental bounds for radiative decays are pushed toward the SM theoretical estimates, these decays become less and less suitable to providing unambiguous constraints on NP models (63).

In the SM, the radiative charm decays occur via the operators of the type $O_7 = (e/16\pi^2)m_c(\bar{u}\sigma_{\mu\nu}P_Rc)F^{\mu\nu}$. Renormalization group (RG) running of perturbative QCD requires a complete set of ten operators to describe this transition (62). Note that, due to the chiral structure of the SM, the contribution of a similar operator $O_7' = (e/16\pi^2)m_u(\bar{u}\sigma_{\mu\nu}P_Lc)F^{\mu\nu}$ is suppressed by a small factor m_u/m_c. Such suppression is not universal and is in fact absent in some models of NP, including supersymmetry (SUSY). Thus, measurement of polarization of the final-state photon can in principle be an effective probe of NP.

3.1.2. Rare decays $D \to X_u\ell^+\ell^-$.

Decays of the type $c \to u\ell^+\ell^-$ may allow a better separation of SM and NP effects. The simplest possible decay that can be generated by this current is $D^0 \to \ell^+\ell^-$. Decays of this type are helicity suppressed, with decay rates proportional to the masses squared of the final-state leptons. This makes decays $D^0 \to e^+e^-$ prohibitively small—even the decay $D^0 \to \mu^+\mu^-$ is quite small. A calculation of short-distance SM effects predicts a branching fraction of about 10^{-18} (63). Long-distance contributions bring the predicted branching fraction to an excess of 10^{-13}, specifically $2.6 \times 10^{-5}\mathcal{B}(D^0 \to \gamma\gamma)$ (63). Thus, decays of this type provide almost background-free constraints on NP models. For example, R-parity-violating SUSY contributions are predicted at the level of 3×10^{-6} for some regions of SUSY parameter space.

In this sense, three-body decays are more suitable for experimental studies, as they do not receive the above-mentioned helicity suppression. The two modes that have been studied the most extensively are $D \to \pi\ell^+\ell^-$ and $D \to \rho\ell^+\ell^-$. These complex final states provide additional tools to disentangle SM short- and long-distance effects and NP phenomena. **Figure 4** illustrates this point with reference to the decay $D^+ \to \pi^+e^+e^-$. It shows the predicted dilepton mass distribution normalized to Γ_{D^+}. It is clear that for dilepton masses close to vector meson resonances such as ρ or ϕ there is no sensitivity to NP contributions; however, there are regions where NP effects are unambiguous. In particular, the region of low $M_{e^+e^-}$ is of great interest. Similar considerations apply to $D \to \rho\ell^+\ell^-$, where additional information is provided by the lepton forward-backward asymmetry

$$A_{FB}(q^2) \equiv \frac{\int_0^1 d\Gamma/(dq^2dx)\,dx - \int_{-1}^0 d\Gamma/(dq^2dx)\,dx}{d\Gamma/dq^2}, \qquad 13.$$

where $x = \cos\theta$. Here θ is the angle between the ℓ^+ and the D meson in the D rest frame. In the SM, $A_{FB}(q^2)$ is negligibly small for all values of q^2.

3.2. Experimental Information

A rare D radiative decay recently observed by Belle (66) has the reported branching ratio $\mathcal{B}(D^0 \to \phi\gamma) = (2.6^{+0.70\ +0.15}_{-0.61\ -0.17}) \times 10^{-5}$. This branching fraction is measured by simultaneously studying the decays $D^0 \to \phi\gamma$, $D^0 \to \phi\pi^0$, and $D^0 \to \phi\eta$, as the last two modes, with higher branching

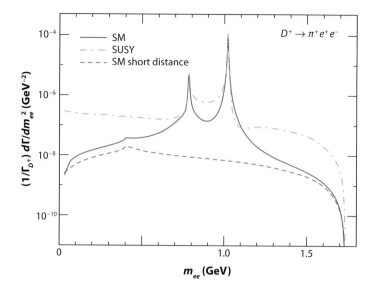

Figure 4

The dilepton mass distribution for $D^+ \to \pi^+ e^+ e^-$ (normalized to Γ_{D^+}) in the minimal supersymmetric standard model (MSSM) with non-universal soft breaking effects. The solid blue line represents the total SM prediction. The dashed line represents the short distance contribution only. The dotted-dashed line includes the contribution of R-parity-violating terms in SUSY. Figure taken from Reference 61.

fractions, induce some peaking background. $D^0 \to \phi\gamma$ is dominated by long-distance effects, and the branching fraction is at the level expected from theoretical estimates.

The most stringent limits on the dilepton channels were recently obtained by the CDF group (67), which studies $D^0 \to \mu^+\mu^-$, and by the BaBar group (68), which studies both $D^0 \to \mu^+\mu^-$ and $D^0 \to e^+e^-$. Both experiments used a D^*-tagged sample and normalized their results with respect to $D^0 \to \pi^+\pi^-$.

The channel $c \to u\ell^+\ell^-$ has been studied by CLEO-c (65), BaBar (68), and DØ (69). The CLEO-c study focuses on $D^+ \to \pi^+ e^+ e^-$ because of its excellent sensitivity to dielectron final states, whereas BaBar studies both dimuon and dielectron final states of D^+, D_s^+, and Λ_c^+. DØ recently reported results on the $D^+ \to \pi^+\mu^+\mu^-$ final state. All three experiments began by measuring $D^+ \to \pi^+\phi \to \ell^+\ell^-\pi^+$ to establish the order of magnitude of long-distance effects. CLEO-c found 2 events with an expected background of 0.02 events, BaBar found 19 events over a background of 40 events, and DØ found 115 events over a background of 850 events. They found the branching fractions

$$\mathcal{B}(D^+ \to \phi\pi^+ \to e^+e^-\pi^+) = (2.8 \pm 1.9 \pm 0.2) \times 10^{-6} \; (65),$$
$$= \left(2.7^{+3.6}_{-1.8}\right) \times 10^{-6} \; (68), \qquad 14.$$

$$\mathcal{B}(D^+ \to \phi\pi^+ \to \mu^+\mu^-\pi^+) = (1.8 \pm 0.5 \pm 0.6) \times 10^{-6} \; (69). \qquad 15.$$

These experiments also established 90%-CL upper limits on the short-distance components of these branching fractions. Their results, compared with a representative sample of theoretical expectations based on NP scenarios, are summarized in **Table 6**. These data show that experiments are reaching a sufficient sensitivity to limit the NP parameter space. The availability of higher statistics data samples from e^+e^- experiments and collider experiments, such as LHCb, will allow more stringent tests in the near future.

Table 6 Representative predictions for flavor changing neutral current charm decays and experimental upper limits

Decay mode	LD ($\times 10^6$)	MSSM ($\times 10^6$)	Experiment (90%-CL ul $\times 10^6$)	Reference[c]
$D^+ \to \pi^+ e^+ e^-$	2.0^a	0.21^a–2.0^b	7.4	65
			11.2	68
$D^+ \to \pi^+ \mu^+ \mu^-$	1.9	6.5^a–15^b	24.4	68
			3.9	69
$D^+ \to \pi^+ \mu^+ e^+$	0	30^b	10.8	68
$D^0 \to e^+ e^-$	1.0×10^{-17}	1.0×10^{-4}	1.2	70
$D^0 \to \mu^+ \mu^-$	3.0×10^{-7}	3.5	1.3	70
			2.5	71
$D^0 \to \rho^0 e^+ e^-$	1.8	5.1	100.0	72

[a]Data from Reference 64.
[b]Data from Reference 63.
[c]References are for data presented in the fourth column.
Abbreviations: LD, long-distance effects; MSSM, minimal supersymmetric standard model.

4. HADRONIC DECAYS

Hadronic decays are interesting for several reasons. Absolute measurements of D meson branching fractions affect our knowledge of several D and B meson decays, from which CKM parameters are extracted. Multibody final states provide information on light quark spectroscopy. Nonleptonic decays of charmed hadrons provide information (73) that can help in determinations of CKM angles β (74) and γ (75) in B decays as well as in the determination of $D^0 - \bar{D}^0$ mixing parameters without explicit knowledge of hadronic strong phases (76).

4.1. Theoretical Considerations

The theoretical description of fully hadronic decays is significantly more complicated than that of leptonic or semileptonic decays, even though relevant effective Hamiltonians appear quite similar to Equation 1. Charmed nonleptonic decays are usually classified by their degree of CKM suppression. The least suppressed of these decays (CF decays), where the quark level transitions are $c \to s u \bar{d}$, are governed by

$$\mathcal{H}_{CF} = \frac{G_F}{\sqrt{2}} V_{ud} V_{cs}^* \left[C_1(\mu)\mathcal{O}_1 + C_2(\mu)\mathcal{O}_2 \right] + \text{h.c},$$
$$\mathcal{O}_1 = (\bar{s}_i \Gamma_\mu c_i)(\bar{u}_k \Gamma^\mu d_k), \quad \mathcal{O}_2 = (\bar{s}_i \Gamma_\mu c_k)(\bar{u}_k \Gamma^\mu d_i), \qquad 16.$$

where $C_n(\mu)$ are the Wilson coefficients obtained by perturbative QCD running from the M_W scale to the μ scale relevant for hadronic decay and where the Latin indices denote quark color.

The CS transitions are driven by $c \to d u \bar{d}$ or $c \to s u \bar{s}$ quark processes. Due to the presence of the quark–antiquark pair of the same flavor in the final state, the effective Hamiltonian takes a much more elaborate form,

$$\mathcal{H}_{CS} = \frac{G_F}{\sqrt{2}} \sum_{q=s,d} V_{uq} V_{cq}^* \left[C_1(\mu)\mathcal{O}_1^q + C_2(\mu)\mathcal{O}_2^q \right]$$

$$- \frac{G_F}{\sqrt{2}} V_{ub} V_{cb}^* \sum_{n=3}^{6} C_n(\mu)\mathcal{O} + \text{h.c},$$

$$\mathcal{O}_1 = (\bar{q}_i \Gamma_\mu c_i)(\bar{u}_k \Gamma^\mu q_k), \quad \mathcal{O}_2 = (\bar{q}_i \Gamma_\mu c_k)(\bar{u}_k \Gamma^\mu q_i),$$

where $q = d, s$, and $\mathcal{O}_{3-6}$ are the so-called penguin operators of the type $(\bar{u}c)_{V-A} \sum_q (\bar{q}q)_{V\pm A}$ (see, e.g., Reference 77). The doubly Cabibbo-suppressed (DCS) decay is one in which the $c \to du\bar{s}$ quark transition drives the decay. The effective Hamiltonian for the DCS decay can be obtained from Equation 16 by interchanging s and d.

Calculations of hadronic decay rates governed by these transitions are quite complicated and model dependent. Most often, simplified assumptions such as factorization (78, 79) are used to estimate the needed branching ratios. Some dynamical approaches, such as QCD sum rules, have been used to justify those assumptions (80). Charmed mesons populate the energy range in which nonperturbative quark dynamics is active, leading to resonance effects that affect the phases of nonleptonic decay amplitudes (81). Finally, standard methods of flavor $SU(3)$ can be used in studies of nonleptonic D meson decays (82).

4.2. Branching Fraction Measurements

CLEO-c uses tagged samples to obtain precise values for absolute hadronic branching fractions for D^0 and D^+ (83), as well as for D_s (84). Their "double-tag" technique is similar to the one developed by Mark III (85). From data at the $\psi(3770)$, CLEO-c uses three D^0 decay modes ($D^0 \to K^-\pi^+$, $D^0 \to K^-\pi^+\pi^0$, $D^0 \to K^-\pi^+\pi^-\pi^+$), and six D^+ modes ($D^+ \to K^-\pi^+\pi^+$, $D^+ \to K^-\pi^+\pi^+\pi^0$, $D^+ \to K_S\pi^+$, $D^+ \to K_S\pi^+\pi^0$, $D^+ \to K_S\pi^+\pi^-\pi^+$, $D^+ \to K^+K^-\pi^+$). Single- and double-tag events are used to extract the branching fractions and $D\bar{D}$ yields from a combined fit (86) to all the measured modes. This powerful technique, combined with careful efficiency studies based on the data, dominates the present world averages in many cases (34). Corrections for final-state radiation are included in these branching fractions. The large numbers of $D\bar{D}$ pairs, $N_{D^0\bar{D}^0} = (1.031 \pm 0.017) \times 10^6$ and $N_{D^+D^-} = (0.819 \pm 0.012) \times 10^6$, assure measurements at the 3% level, limited by systematic uncertainties. CLEO-c applies a similar technique to derive absolute D_s branching fractions from data at a center-of-mass energy of $\sim$4170 MeV (84). Here the dominant final state is $D_s D_s^*$; thus the analysis is more complex because of the presence of γ in the D_s^* decay.

B factories use either D samples produced inclusively in B meson decays or partially reconstructed samples of D or D_s recoiling against a fully reconstructed charmed meson as normalization. Absolute branching fraction measurements for hadronic decays of D^0, D^+, and D_s are summarized in **Table 7**, which includes new absolute results for $D^0 \to K^-\pi^+$ reported by BaBar (87), with approximately a 2% uncertainty, and by Belle (88), who measured the corresponding quantity for $D_s \to K^+K^-\pi^+$ with a precision of $\sim$14%.

In the BaBar measurement (87), $\bar{B}^0 \to D^{*+}X\ell^-\bar{\nu}_\ell$ with $D^{*+} \to D^0\pi_s^+$ are identified by partial reconstruction. Events with a lepton ℓ^- and a "slow" pion π_s^+, which could come from a D^{*+}, are selected by studying the reconstructed ν invariant mass squared $M^2_{\nu,\text{meas}}$ inferred from conservation of energy and momentum in the center-of-mass system using the D^* four-momentum inferred from π_s and the measured charged lepton's four-momentum. The B normalization is determined from the peak in $M^2_{\nu,\text{meas}}$ (centered near zero for real D^0 events). Backgrounds under this peak coming from D^{**}, other $B\bar{B}$ combinations, and continuum are estimated from a wrong-sign (WS) lepton sample. Uncertainties in these backgrounds and in charged-track reconstruction and particle-identification efficiencies dominate the systematic errors.

Belle (88) used partially reconstructed $e^+e^- \to D_s^{*+}D_{s1}^-(2536)$ events where $D_s^{*+} \to D_s\gamma$. The Belle group studied two partially reconstructed samples: In the first, the D_s was not reconstructed, but the $D_{s1}^-(2536)$ was fully reconstructed in its decay to $\bar{D}^{*0}K^-$ and $\bar{D}^{*-}K_S$. The soft γ from the recoiling D_s^{*+} was also required. In the second normalization sample, the D_s was fully reconstructed in its $K^+K^-\pi^+$ decay mode and was combined with the γ to form a D_s^{*+}. A recoil K from the D_{s1} decay was also required, but the $D_{s1}^-(2536)$ was not reconstructed. The result, obtained from

Table 7 Recent absolute branching fraction (BF) data[a]

Mode	Absolute BF (%)	PDG (%)[b]	Reference[c]
$D^0 \to K^-\pi^+$	$4.007 \pm 0.037 \pm 0.070$	3.82 ± 0.07	87
	$3.891 \pm 0.035 \pm 0.069$		83
$D^0 \to K^-\pi^+\pi^0$	$14.57 \pm 01.2 \pm 0.069$		83
$D^0 \to K^-\pi^+\pi^+\pi^-$	$8.30 \pm 0.07 \pm 0.38$		83
$D^+ \to K^+\pi^+\pi^+$	$9.14 \pm 0.10 \pm 0.17$	9.51 ± 0.34	83
$D^+ \to K^+\pi^+\pi^+\pi^0$	$5.98 \pm 0.08 \pm 0.01$	6.00 ± 0.28	83
$D^+ \to K_S\pi^+$	$1.539 \pm 0.022 \pm 0.038$	1.47 ± 0.06	83
$D^+ \to K_S\pi^+\pi^0$	$7.05 \pm 0.09 \pm 0.25$	7.0 ± 0.5	83
$D^+ \to K_S\pi^+\pi^+\pi^-$	$3.149 \pm 0.046 \pm 0.096$	3.11 ± 0.21	83
$D^+ \to K^+K^-\pi^+$	$0.935 \pm 0.017 \pm 0.024$	1.0 ± 0.04	83
$D_s \to K^+K^-\pi^+$	$5.50 \pm 0.23 \pm 0.16$	5.3 ± 0.8	84
	$4.0 \pm 0.4 \pm 0.4$		88
$D_s \to K_S K^+$	$1.49 \pm 0.07 \pm 0.05$	2.2 ± 0.45	84
$D_s \to K^+K^-\pi^+\pi^0$	$5.62 \pm 0.33 \pm 0.51$	-	84
$D_s \to \pi^+\pi^-\pi^+$	$1.11 \pm 0.07 \pm 0.04$	1.22 ± 0.23	84
$D_s \to \pi^+\eta$	$1.47 \pm 0.12 \pm 0.14$	2.11 ± 0.35	84
$D_s \to \pi^+\eta'$	$4.02 \pm 0.27 \pm 0.30$	4.7 ± 0.7	84

[a]For CLEO-c results, the uncertainty due to radiative corrections has been absorbed into the systematic uncertainty.
[b]Data from Reference 34.
[c]References are for data presented in the second column.

the ratio of the $K^+K^-\pi^+$ signal in the first mode to the D_{s1} signal in the second, together with the (well-known) $D^{*+} \to D^0\pi^+$ and $D_s^{*+} \to D_s\gamma$ branching fractions, provided the required branching fraction for $D_s \to K^+K^-\pi^+$.

Of special interest are the decays to K^0. CLEO-c (89) recently studied both the $K_L\pi$ and the $K_S\pi$ final states. The K_L were identified as a peak in the missing mass. Effects of quantum correlations from the coherent D pairs from $\psi(3770)$ decay were carefully taken into account. The CLEO-c collaboration measured the asymmetries

$$R(D) = \frac{\mathcal{B}(D \to K_S\pi) - \mathcal{B}(D \to K_L\pi)}{\mathcal{B}(D \to K_S\pi) + \mathcal{B}(D \to K_L\pi)}$$

for $D = D^0$ and $D = D^+$. As pointed out in Reference 90, $D^0 \to K^0\pi^0$ involves interference between the CF and DCS modes, and as we observe K^0 without knowing its strangeness, the K_S and K_L are related to give an asymmetry $R(D) = 2\tan\theta_C$, where θ_C is the Cabibbo angle. Rosner (91) has observed that SU(3) flavor symmetry, specifically U spin symmetry, predicts that the ratio of amplitudes for $D^0 \to K^0\pi^0$ to $D^0 \to \bar{K}^0\pi^0$ is $\tan^2\theta_C \sim 0.054$. This leads to the prediction that the value for $R(D^0)$ should be $2\tan^2\theta_C \sim 0.109 \pm 0.001$. White & He (89) found $R(D^0) = 0.108 \pm 0.025 \pm 0.024$, which is significantly different from zero and is in good agreement with this prediction. There are no predictions for $R(D^+)$, measured to be $0.022 \pm 0.016 \pm 0.018$, that are compatible with zero.

4.2.1. Cabibbo-suppressed hadronic decays. Due to CKM suppression, these rates are expected to be lower by a factor $r_{CS} = |(V_{cs}V_{us})/(|V_{cs}V_{ud})|^2 \approx 0.05$ relative to CF rates. Using its 281-pb^{-1} $\psi(3770)$ sample, the CLEO-c group (92) measured branching fractions for many multipion, η, and ω decay modes of D^0 and D^+ mesons. CLEO-c used single tags and extracted absolute branching fractions using the corresponding well-measured CF modes for normalization. These branching fractions ranged from $(1-4) \times 10^{-3}$ and were measured with a precision of approximately 5% to 10%. The largest rates obtained were $(a) D^0 \to \pi^-\pi^+\pi^0$ $(13.2 \pm 0.6 \times 10^{-3})$ for D^0 and (b) $D^+ \to \pi^-\pi^+\pi^+$ $(3.35 \pm 0.22 \times 10^{-3})$ and $D^+ \to \eta\pi^+$ $(3.61 \pm 0.36 \times 10^{-3})$ for D^+. These measurements represent a significant improvement on our previous knowledge. The results are generally consistent with simple CKM suppression. However, only an upper limit was extracted for $D^0 \to 3\pi^0$ in spite of the large rate observed for $D^0 \to \pi^-\pi^+\pi^0$. A possible explanation is that the three pions from this decay were produced predominantly in an isospin $I = 0$ state (93) inaccessible to this mode after a $\Delta I = 1/2$ transition.

The dipion modes are described by the decay amplitudes $A^{+0}(D^+ \to \pi^+\pi^0)$, $A^{+-}(D^0 \to \pi^+\pi^-)$, and A^{00} $(D^0 \to \pi^0\pi^0)$, which are related to the two isospin amplitudes A_0 and A_2, which correspond to the S wave dipion isospin $I = 0$ and $I = 2$ states, respectively. These amplitudes are related by

$$A^{+0} = \sqrt{\frac{3}{2}} A_2 \quad A^{+-} = \sqrt{\frac{2}{3}} A_0 + \sqrt{\frac{1}{3}} A_2$$

$$A^{00} = \sqrt{\frac{1}{3}} A_0 - \sqrt{\frac{2}{3}} A_2. \qquad\qquad 17.$$

Following the procedure outlined in Reference 94, CLEO (92) obtained, from these new results, the ratio $|A_2/A_0| = 0.420 \pm 0.014 \pm 0.01$ and $\arg(A_2/A_0) = (86.4 \pm 2.8 \pm 3.3)°$. Naïvely, tree-level decay mechanisms would lead to suppression of the $I = 2$ final state relative to $I = 0$. This result demonstrates, therefore, the importance of final-state interactions in D hadronic decays.

A long-standing puzzle is found in the ratio $\mathcal{R}(D^0 \to K^+K^-)/\mathcal{R}(D^0 \to \pi^+\pi^-) = 3.53 \pm 0.12$, where $\mathcal{R}$ are branching fractions corrected for the two-body phase-space factor. BaBar (95) has measured the branching fractions

$$\mathcal{B}(D^0 \to \pi^+\pi^-\pi^0) = (1.493 \pm 0.008 \pm 0.055) \times 10^{-2}$$

$$\mathcal{B}(D^0 \to K^+K^-\pi^0) = (0.334 \pm 0.004 \pm 0.015) \times 10^{-2}.$$

The corresponding ratio for decays where an extra π^0 is produced gives $\mathcal{M}(D^0 \to K^+K^-\pi^0)/\mathcal{M}(D^0 \to \pi^+\pi^-\pi^0) = 0.678 \pm 0.027$, in clear contrast to the two-body ratio above. This result has recently been confirmed by Belle (96).

CLEO-c also studied $D_s \to PP$ modes (97), where P is any pseudoscalar meson, using the $\sqrt{s} = 4170$-MeV sample. The modes (e.g., $K^+\eta$, $K^+\eta'$, π^+K_S, and $K^+\pi^0$) were seen for the first time and were compared with their CF counterparts (e.g., $\pi^+\eta$, $\pi^+\eta'$, and K^+K_S). The ratios observed are reasonably consistent with the value of $r_{CS} \approx 5\%$. The decays $D_s \to \pi^+\pi^0$ have not yet been seen. The dipions would be in an S wave with $I = 2$ and would have to be reached through a $\Delta I = 2$ transition, which is apparently much suppressed.

4.2.2. Doubly Cabibbo-suppressed hadronic decays ($c \to d u \bar{s}$) of D mesons. These decays are expected to be suppressed relative to CF modes by a factor $r_{DCS} = |(V_{cd}V_{us})/(|V_{cs}V_{ud})|^2 \approx 3.1 \times 10^{-3}$. For D^0s, these rates are comparable to the mixing rate so that the two processes interfere; therefore, disentangling the two effects requires some care. We discuss this issue in more detail in Section 5.

With such small branching ratios, one might wonder if DCS transitions could be affected by NP effects. However, because the final state is composed of quarks of different flavors, it is hard to find a well-motivated NP model that can affect DCS transition at an appreciable level (98).

Despite effects expected to arise from final-state interactions and from mixing, the measured D^0 DCS branching fractions compare remarkably well with expectations based on the value of r_{DCS}. Using world averages (34):

$$\Gamma(K^+\pi^-)/\Gamma(K^-\pi^-\pi^+\pi^-) \qquad (1.18 \pm 0.26) \times r_{\text{DCS}}$$
$$\Gamma(K^+\pi^-\pi^0)/\Gamma(K^-\pi^+\pi^0) \qquad (0.71 \pm 0.17) \times r_{\text{DCS}}$$
$$\Gamma(K^-\pi^-\pi^+\pi^-)/\Gamma(K^-\pi^+\pi^+\pi^-) \quad (1.04 \pm 0.25) \times r_{\text{DCS}}.$$

The only decay of D^+ free from mixing effects that has been observed so far is $D^+ \to K^+\pi^0$. This was first measured by BaBar, and its observation has been confirmed by CLEO-c. BaBar (99) obtained $\mathcal{B} = (2.52 \pm 0.47 \pm 0.25 \pm 0.08) \times 10^{-4}$, and CLEO-c (100) obtained $\mathcal{B} = (2.28 \pm 0.36 \pm 0.15 \pm 0.08) \times 10^{-4}$. Both experiments used the $D^+ \to K^-\pi^+\pi^+$ mode as normalization, and the fourth uncertainty in each case is due to this absolute branching fraction.

Combining these measurements with the known lifetimes for D^0 and D^+ and the $D^0 \to K^-\pi^+$ branching fractions from Reference 34, a ratio can be formed:

$$\frac{\Gamma\left(D^+ \to K^+\pi^0\right)}{\Gamma\left(D^0 \to K^-\pi^+\right)} = (2.44 \pm 0.33) \times 10^{-3} = (0.79 \pm 0.20) \times r_{\text{DCS}}.$$

This ratio is clearly compatible with the expected DCS rate. Similarly, the ratio of the two DCS rates is

$$\frac{\Gamma\left(D^+ \to K^+\pi^0\right)}{\Gamma\left(D^0 \to K^+\pi^-\right)} = 0.66 \pm 0.09.$$

A naïve spectator diagram analysis would predict a ratio of 0.5. The difference is probably due to final-state interaction effects, although annihilation or exchange diagrams could also contribute.

4.3. Three-Body Decays

Multibody D meson decays in general can be a rich source of information on long-range strong-interaction effects because of the complex interference patterns between intermediate resonances formed between hadrons in the final state. In addition, some of these decays can be used for measurements of CPV in B decays (75) or $D^0 - \bar{D}^0$ mixing parameters (74). Data from fixed-target experiments, CLEO, BaBar, and Belle [from data sets both near the $\Upsilon(4S)$ and at 3770-MeV center-of-mass energies] have been studied. Proper analysis of these modes can also be used to obtain information on branching ratios for quasi-two-body resonant decay modes of the parent charm meson. The huge sizes of the data samples—of order 10^6 events in many channels—now available from the B factories require a detailed review of the models used to describe the Dalitz plot distributions. Undoubtedly, many results await such review and have yet to be published. Of particular concern is the extent to which phase information, which is essential to the determination of the parameters above, depends on the models assumed for these descriptions. Efforts are under way to attempt less model-dependent approaches (101, 102).

4.3.1. Formalism for three-body D and D_s decays. Decays of D or D_s to three hadrons ABC often proceed through quasi-two-body modes $D \to A + f$ followed by $f \to B + C$, where f is an intermediate isobar state as outlined in Reference 78. When A, B, and C are pseudoscalar hadrons, the Dalitz plot—in which the squared invariant mass of one hadron pair is plotted against the squared invariant mass of one of the other pairs—contains all the dynamical information. These Dalitz plots often show intricate interference patterns between multiple resonances that may be produced in an intermediate state.

The decay amplitude could be constructed from a partial wave expansion in any one of the three possible channels f defined by the particle pair. Here we choose $f = BC$. Each wave would then be characterized by the spin ($J = L$ for pseudoscalar hadrons) and isospin I of f:

$$A(s, s') = \sum_I \sum_{L=0}^{\infty} M_L(p, q) F_{L, I}(s), \qquad 18.$$

where s and s' are squared invariant masses for the BC channel (i.e., f) and for the AC channel, respectively. $F_{L, I}$ is the partial wave decay amplitude for the system f. M is a tensor function appropriate for the conservation of total spin in the decay; it depends on L and the momenta p and q of B and A, respectively, which are defined in the f rest frame. The density of the points on the Dalitz plot is then proportional to $|A|^2$.

The complex function $F_{L, I}(s)$ describes the production and final-state scattering resulting in the observed system f. Two distance scales may be distinguished. In the first, the parent D decays weakly and hadronization occurs, resulting in an intermediate hadron state k that may differ from f. At longer range, rescattering (e.g., $KK \to \pi\pi$) occurs to make the observed system f. Thus, dropping the labels L and I, $F_{L,I}(s)$ can be written as

$$F_f(s) = T_{fk}(s) Q_k(s), \qquad 19.$$

in which $T_{fk}(s)$ is the matrix that describes hadron–hadron scattering. When s is small, T can only include elastic scattering. In this regime, therefore, in the absence of scattering between k and the recoil hadron A, the Watson theorem (103) [which requires that the phase of $F_f(s)$ should have the same s dependence as elastic scattering] should hold. However, $Q_k(s)$ is an unknown function describing the short-range effects and could well have an s-dependent phase when strong $k - f$ scattering takes place. In this case, phases consistent with naïve expectations from the Watson theorem should not be observed. A recent K matrix fit to the $I = 1/2$ $K^- \pi^+$ S wave amplitude from $D^+ \to K^- \pi^+ \pi^+$ data by the FOCUS collaboration (101, 104) indicates that this may be so.

4.3.2. Analysis methods of three-body D and D_s decays. In fitting Dalitz plots, analysts have used several assumptions for the form of $F_f(s)$. The most frequently used assumption is the Breit–Wigner (BW) isobar model, in which $F(s)$ is approximated as a linear combination of resonant terms for each wave. Equation 18 is approximated by a finite sum that includes only terms for the resonant states r observed in the data, no matter in which channel they occur. The amplitude (18) is then a sum of Breit–Wigner propagators,

$$A(s, s') = NR + \sum_r A_r$$

$$A_r = c_r e^{i\delta_r} \frac{M_L(p, q) G_L(q) G_L(p)}{m_r^2 - s + im_r \Gamma(s, L)}, \qquad 20.$$

where $c_r e^{i\delta_r}$ are complex coefficients and NR is a constant term often introduced to describe direct, nonresonant decay to the three hadrons A, B, and C. The parent D and the resonance have form factors G_L that depend on L. Here m_r is the mass and $\Gamma(s, L) = \Gamma_r(m_r/\sqrt{s})(p/p_r)^{2L+1}[G_L(p)/G_L(p_r)]^2$ is the mass-dependent width of the resonance r. The form factors $G_L(q)$ and $G_L(p)$ for the parent and the resonance r, respectively, are usually assumed to take the Blatt–Weisskopf form (105). This model can provide branching fractions for quasi-two-body resonant decays relative to the three-body decays, which are defined for each resonance r as

$$f_r = \frac{\iint |A_r|^2 ds ds'}{\iint |NR + \sum_r A_r|^2 ds ds'}. \qquad 21.$$

The sum of the fractions so defined is not guaranteed to be unity, as the interference terms included in the denominator are missing from the numerator. Although Equation 21 is in standard use, and although it provides a branching fraction that may be an improvement upon the "cut and count" method that preceded it, a better definition would be desirable. In particular, this equation only works to define resonant fractions from the isobar model.

Other models attempt to address the problems associated with the description of the S waves, where the identity of resonances is less well understood and where overlapping, broad BW resonances violate unitarity. Understandably, these methods do not have a convenient definition for quasi-two-body fractions. One model introduces hadron scattering through a K matrix (106, 107) related to the K and T matrices and to the Q and F vectors (discussed above) by

$$
\begin{aligned}
T_{kf}(s) &= (I - i\rho K(s))_{ki}^{-1} K_{if}(s) \\
Q_f(s) &= K_{fk}^{-1}(s) P_k(s) \\
F_f(s) &= (I - i\rho K(s))_{fk}^{-1} P_k(s),
\end{aligned}
\qquad 22.
$$

where ρ is a matrix of phase-space factors, purely imaginary below threshold, for any of the channels included, and $P_k(s)$ is a vector which describes the s dependence of the production of f in the decays. The K matrix is real, guaranteeing the unitarity of T, and it contains poles and nonresonant terms obtained from global fits to available scattering data. One model that is appropriate for the S wave $\pi\pi$ system comes from Anisovich & Sarantsev (108), who found values for K matrix elements through a global fit to all the available $\pi\pi$ scattering data from threshold to 1900 MeV. This model has both pros and cons. It does preserve the unitarity of the T matrix; however, it does not do the same for F, as the P vector is arbitrary and is determined by fitting the data. The form for ρ below threshold is also not suitable for the description of poles for broad resonances, particularly if close to threshold.

Less model-dependent methods have also been used. In restricted regions of the Dalitz plot, the angular moments of f can be used to measure the S, P, etc., amplitudes. A method that works over the whole Dalitz plot was devised by the E791 collaboration (109) in its analysis of $D^+ \to K^-\pi^+\pi^+$ decays. $F(s)$ for the $K^-\pi^+$ S wave was parameterized by a set of complex quantities at discrete s values. These quantities were treated as free parameters in their fit. The method requires a reference phase that, in the E791 fit, was defined by the isobar-model description of the other waves.

Assumptions about the models used to describe Dalitz plots affects results for CKM phases and $D^0 - \bar{D}^0$ mixing parameters. Extending such model independence into fits becomes more important, therefore, as the statistical precision of such measurements improves.

4.3.3. Summary of charm Dalitz plot analyses.

Several experiments have analyzed $D^0 \to K_S\pi^+\pi^-$ decays (34). CLEO (110), the first experiment to do so, used a BW isobar model with 11 resonances: $K_S\rho^0$, $K_S\omega$, $K_S f_0$ (980), $K_S f_2$ (1270), $K_S f_2$ (1270), $K_S b_0$ (1370), $K^\star(892)\pi^+$, $K_0^\star(1430)^-\pi^+$, $K_2^\star(1430)^-\pi^+$, $K^\star(1680)\pi^+$, and the DCS mode $K^\star(892)^+\pi^-$. More recently, to extract information on the CKM angle $\gamma(\phi_3)$, analyses were made by both Belle (111, 112) and BaBar (113) using samples that were two orders of magnitude larger than CLEO's. At this level of statistical precision, the inadequacy of the CLEO model to describe the data is apparent. Amplitudes for the now clearly evident $\rho - \omega$ mixing signals, for two σ isobars at 400 and 1000 MeV/c^2, and for radial excitations for the ρ improved the fit, yet the quality was barely acceptable. BaBar recently added the K matrix description of the S wave $\pi\pi$ system (108) and a model for the S wave $K\pi$ system derived from elastic scattering data from the LASS (Large Aperture Superconducting Solenoid spectrometer) experiment (122). Alternate isobar models lead to uncertainties of about

$10°$ in $\gamma(\phi_3)$, but these are still smaller than the currently obtainable statistical and other systematic uncertainties in this parameter.

Decays to $D^0 \to \pi^+\pi^-\pi^0$ have also been used by BaBar (114) to measure the CKM unitarity angle γ. An earlier K matrix analysis by CLEO (115) was found to have a negligibly small NR component and to be dominated by $\rho\pi$ in all three charge modes. The structure of the plot showed strong, destructive interference between these modes in a sixfold symmetry suggestive of a dominant $I = 0$ (93). This is consistent with the observation, noted in Section 4.2.1, that $D^0 \to 3\pi^0$ decays are strongly suppressed.

The decay $D^+ \to \pi^+\pi^+\pi^-$ was studied by E687, E791, FOCUS, and more recently, CLEO (117). The CLEO analysis used the largest sample ($\sim$4000 events) to date. The BW isobar-model analysis by E791 had reported the need to add a $\sigma(500)$ to the $\pi^+\pi^-$ S wave in order to get an acceptable fit. FOCUS reexamined this decay using a K matrix model for the $\pi^+\pi^-$ S wave. The fit was acceptable, but the question of whether or not there was a $\sigma(500)$ was not clear. CLEO tried various other parameterizations for $\sigma(500)$. Following a suggestion by Oller (118), CLEO used a simple pole of the form $1/(m_0^2 - s)$, where $m_0^2 = (0.47 - 0.22i)$, rather than the BW used by E791. A scalar term based on the linear sigma model (119) was also used. Both of these approaches produced a slightly improved fit. This suggests that a low-mass σ resonance is likely to play a role in this mode, but because it is broad and close to threshold, even larger data samples will be needed to find its pole parameters.

In $D^+ \to K^+\pi^+\pi^+$ decays, E791 found evidence for a broad $K\pi$ scalar resonance (120) labeled as $\kappa(800)$. Without this, the BW isobar-model fit required an NR component with a fraction in excess of 90%. The $\kappa(800)$, with mass $797 \pm 19 \pm 43$ MeV and width $410 \pm 19 \pm 43$ MeV, improved the fit considerably and reduced the nonresonant fit fraction to $13 \pm 5.8 \pm 4.4$%. FOCUS, using three times the sample size and a K matrix obtained from $K\pi$ scattering data, found that an $I = 3/2$ $K\pi$ component is probably also present. Their formulation of the scattering, however, is unable to address the existence of a κ pole.

Charged S wave $K^\pm\pi^0$ systems could provide new information on the $\kappa(800)$ so far seen only in the neutral $K^-\pi^+$ system. If it is a true $I = 1/2$ scalar resonance, the κ should also appear, with similar mass and width, in charged $K\pi$ systems such as this one. This was one motivation for BaBar to study a large (11,000-event) sample with 98% purity of the decays $D^0 \to K^+K^-\pi^0$ (121). An isobar-model fit provided a satisfactory (although ambiguous) description of the BaBar data. In each model applied, the $K^{*+}(890)$ resonance was included among the components and was used as the reference for other phases. An S wave K^+K^- resonance was always required to obtain a satisfactory fit, but there was no distinction between $a_0(980)$ and $f_0(980)$ at low masses. The higher-mass K^+K^- system, either an $f_2'(1525)$ or an f_0 with a similar mass, was also required, again with little distinction.

Three models for the $K\pi$ S waves were compared. The first was a linear combination of BW terms for $\kappa(800)$, $K^*(1430)$, and an NR term. The $\kappa^\pm$ mass and width were allowed to vary. The second used the $K\pi$ scattering amplitude from Reference 122. The third used the results for the S wave amplitude measured in the E791 model-independent $D^+ \to K^-\pi^+\pi^+$ analysis (109). The second model gave the best fit, with the LASS phases shifted by approximately $-90°$. The fit with $\kappa^\pm$ was poor and required a mass (870 ± 30) MeV/c^2 and width (150 ± 20) MeV/c^2, the latter differing significantly from the width of $\sim$400 MeV/c^2 reported for the neutral state. Establishing the existence of a κ state with such a width requires a more sophisticated analysis to find its pole parameters in the T matrix; therefore, although poor, this result does not rule out the possibility of the κ as a genuine resonance.

In this Dalitz plot, the ϕ is relatively far from other interfering resonances. BaBar made a model-independent study of the angular moments in this region to learn more about the underlying

S wave. Events were evaluated in slices of K^+K^- invariant mass that were selected for the acceptance-corrected mean values, X_ℓ, of the quantity $\sqrt{2\ell + \pi/4}P_\ell(\theta)$ (for $\ell = 0$, 1, and 2), where θ is the angle between the K^- and the π^0 in the K^+K^- rest frame and where P_ℓ is the Legendre polynomial function of order ℓ. Assuming that only S and P amplitudes ($L = 0$ and 1) contribute to the K^+K^- system, these moments provided values for these two amplitudes:

$$X_0 = \frac{|S|^2 + |P|^2}{\sqrt{2}}; \quad X_1 = \sqrt{2}|S||P|\cos\theta_{SP}; \quad X_2 = \sqrt{\frac{2}{5}}|P|^2. \qquad 23.$$

In **Figure 5** the resulting magnitudes $|S|$ and $|P|$, corrected for the phase space in the Dalitz plot (i.e., the length of the K^+K^- mass strips) are plotted. $|P|$ (**Figure 5b**) follows the ϕ line shape well, with no asymmetry and little background, up to about 1040 MeV/c^2.

In **Figure 5a**, $|S|$ values determined from this channel are compared with similar measurements of $|S|$ from an earlier analysis (116) of $D^0 \to K^+K^-K_S$ decays. In that analysis, $a_0^+(980)$ in the

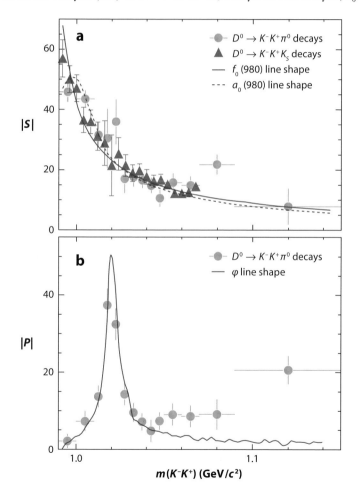

Figure 5

(*a*) The phase-space-corrected S wave amplitude $|S|$ in the K^+K^- system (*yellow points*) from $D^0 \to K^+K^-\pi^0$ decays. Red points are from an earlier analysis of $D^0 \to K^-K^+K_S$ decays. The solid blue curve is the line shape for $f_0(980)$ and the dotted blue curve is for $a_0(980)$. (*b*) Data for $|P|$ (*yellow points*) from $D^0 \to K^+K^-\pi^0$ decays. The solid blue curve is the ϕ line shape. The figure is taken from Reference 121.

$K^+ K_S$ system was compared with the S wave in the $K^+ K^-$ system and was found to agree well, suggesting that $a_0(980)$, as opposed to $f_0(980)$, was present in both charge states. It is possible that the excellent agreement observed here is also evidence that $a_0(980)$ is the main contributor to the $K^- K^+$ S wave in this decay as well. A more convincing test, however, would be to analyze the $D^0 \to K^- \pi^+ \eta$ and $D^0 \to \eta \pi^0 K_S$ systems because the a_0 would then be more obvious in its $\eta \pi^+$ decay modes.

Finally, we discuss the Dalitz plot analysis of the decay $D_s \to K^+ K^- \pi^+$. E687 (123) reported the first Dalitz plot analysis of this channel with a sample of $\sim$300 events. This analysis found significant scalar contributions from $f_0(980)$ [or $a_0(980)$]. CLEO studied the $K^+ K^-$ invariant mass spectrum in this decay (84) and found a clear peak at the ϕ mass but also a broad component with kinematic properties indicative of a scalar. This component is important because the mode $D_s \to \phi \pi$ is commonly used for D_s decay normalization and because the presence of this scalar component introduces an additional uncertainty in this branching fraction, as the scalar channel that is absorbed in the $\phi \pi$ signal depends upon the experimental cuts used. For example, CLEO found that an uncertainty of the order of 5% was introduced depending upon the cut choices. The BaBar group (124) recently reported a preliminary fit of the Dalitz plot structure of this decay with over 100,000 events. It studied moments in the low-mass $K^+ K^-$ and $K^- \pi^+$ systems, which showed clear evidence for an S wave contribution in the former, but not in the latter. An isobar-model fit indeed shows a strong $f_0(980)$ component, thus confirming that using quasi-two-body decay modes such as the $Ds \to \phi \pi$ branching fraction as a normalization channel requires care.

There is still a great deal of experimental work in progress, including further exploration of modes relevant to CPV studies in both D and B decays. Ongoing theoretical work aims to identify tools that reduce the model dependence in the Dalitz plot analyses, in particular when broad scalar resonances are involved. The rich structure of the Dalitz plots is not only a unique and powerful asset in understanding heavy flavor decay dynamics, but it is also a tool for disentangling the intricacies of nonperturbative strong-interaction effects.

5. CHARM MIXING AND CP VIOLATION

The phenomena of mixing and CPV in the charm sector were first considered three decades ago (125), but the effects are so small that experimental evidence is scarce. With upper limits currently at about the 1% level, CPV has not yet been observed. After years of experimental investigation (34), however, evidence for mixing has finally been seen in two kinds of time-dependent measurements. The BaBar collaboration (126) has reported a 3.9–standard deviation effect in WS decays of $D^0 \to K^+ \pi^-$.[1] The CDF collaboration has reported a 3.8–standard deviation effect (149). Also, the Belle collaboration (147) has reported a 3.2–standard deviation effect arising from the observed difference in lifetimes for decays to CP-even final states $D^0 \to K^+ K^-$ and $\pi^+ \pi^-$, compared to the mixed CP state $K^- \pi^+$. This was confirmed by the BaBar experiment (150). In addition, there is useful information on the strong-phase $\delta_{K\pi}$ affecting $D^0 \to K^+ \pi^-$ mixing results coming from CLEO-c studies that exploit the quantum coherence of the $D^0 \bar{D}^0$ pair produced near threshold (34).

5.1. Charm Mixing Predictions in the Standard Model

Charm mixing arises from $|\Delta C| = 2$ interactions that generate off-diagonal terms in the mass matrix for D^0 and $\bar{D}^0$ mesons. The expansion of the off-diagonal terms in the neutral D mass

---

[1] Unless otherwise noted, charge conjugate states are assumed throughout this paper.

matrix to second order in the weak interaction is

$$\left(M - \frac{i}{2}\Gamma\right)_{21} = \frac{1}{2M_D}\langle\bar{D}^0|H_w^{|\Delta C|=2}|D^0\rangle + \frac{1}{2M_D}\sum_n \frac{\langle\bar{D}^0|H_w^{|\Delta C|=1}|n\rangle\langle n|H_w^{|\Delta C|=1}|D^0\rangle}{M_D - E_n + i\varepsilon}, \qquad 24.$$

where $H_w^{|\Delta C|=2}$ and $H_w^{|\Delta C|=1}$ are the effective $|\Delta C| = 2$ and $|\Delta C| = 1$ Hamiltonians. The off-diagonal mass-matrix terms induce mass eigenstates D_1 and D_2, which are superpositions of the flavor eigenstates D^0 and $\bar{D}^0$,

$$D_{\frac{1}{2}} = p\, D^0 \pm q\, \bar{D}^0, \qquad 25.$$

where $|p|^2 + |q|^2 = 1$. The key quantities in D^0 mixing are the mass and width differences,

$$\Delta M_D \equiv M_1 - M_2 \quad \text{and} \quad \Delta\Gamma_D \equiv \Gamma_1 - \Gamma_2, \qquad 26.$$

or equivalently their dimensionless equivalents,

$$x_D \equiv \frac{\Delta M_D}{\Gamma_D} \quad \text{and} \quad y_D \equiv \frac{\Delta\Gamma_D}{2\Gamma_D}, \qquad 27.$$

where Γ_D is the average width of the two neutral D meson mass eigenstates. Two quantities, y_D^{CP} and y'_D, which are measured in most experimental determinations of $\Delta\Gamma_D$, are defined as

$$y_D^{CP} \equiv (\Gamma_+ - \Gamma_-)/(\Gamma_+ + \Gamma_-) = y_D\cos\phi - x_D\sin\phi\left(\frac{A_m}{2} - A_{prod}\right),$$
$$x' = x_D\cos\delta_{K\pi} + y_D\sin\delta_{K\pi},$$
$$y' = y_D\cos\delta_{K\pi} - x_D\sin\delta_{K\pi}, \qquad 28.$$

where the transition rates $\Gamma_\pm$ pertain to decay into final states of definite CP, $A_{prod} = (N_{D^0} - N_{\bar{D}^0})/(N_{D^0} + N_{\bar{D}^0})$ is the so-called production asymmetry of D^0 and $\bar{D}^0$ (giving the relative weight of D^0 and $\bar{D}^0$ in the sample), and $\delta_{K\pi}$ is the strong-phase difference between the CF and DCS amplitudes (81). The quantities A_m and ϕ account for the presence of CPV in D^0–$\bar{D}^0$ mixing, where A_m is related to the q, p parameters of Equation 25 as $A_m \equiv |q/p|^2 - 1$ and where ϕ is a CP-violating phase of M_{21} (if one neglects direct CPV) (127).

The charm quark system is rather unique from the theoretical point of view, as its mass places it somewhere on the border between heavy and light quark systems. This makes prediction of $D^0 - \bar{D}^0$-mixing parameters a challenging task. As has been shown (128), in the SM x_D and y_D are generated only at second order in $SU(3)_F$ breaking:

$$x_D, y_D \sim \sin^2\theta_C \times [SU(3)\text{ breaking}]^2, \qquad 29.$$

where θ_C is the Cabibbo angle. Therefore, predicting the SM values of x_D and y_D depends crucially on estimating the size of $SU(3)_F$ breaking.

Theoretical predictions of x_D and y_D within the SM span several orders of magnitude. Roughly, there are two approaches, neither of which gives very reliable results because m_c is in some sense intermediate between heavy and light. The inclusive approach is based on the operator product expansion (OPE). In the $m_c \gg \Lambda$ limit, where Λ is a scale characteristic of the strong interactions, ΔM and $\Delta\Gamma$ can be expanded in terms of matrix elements of local operators (129–133). Such calculations typically yield $x_D, y_D < 10^{-3}$. The use of the OPE relies on local quark–hadron duality and on Λ/m_c being small enough to allow a truncation of the series after the first few terms. The charm mass may not be large enough for these to be good approximations, especially for nonleptonic D decays. An observation of y_D of order 10^{-2} could be ascribed to a breakdown of the OPE or of duality, but such a large value of y_D is certainly not a generic prediction of OPE analyses.

The exclusive approach sums over intermediate hadronic states, which may be modeled or fitted to experimental data (134–136). Because there are cancellations between states within a given $SU(3)$ multiplet, one needs to know the contribution of each state with high precision. However, the D meson is not light enough that its decays are dominated by a few final states. In the absence of sufficiently precise data on many decay rates and on strong phases, one is forced to use certain assumptions. It was shown that phase-space effects alone provide enough $SU(3)_F$ violation to induce $x_D, y_D \sim 10^{-2}$ (128, 137). Large effects in y_D appear for decays close to D threshold, where an analytic expansion in $SU(3)_F$ violation is no longer possible; in addition, a dispersion relation can be used to show that in this case x_D would receive contributions of similar order of magnitude.

5.2. New Physics Contribution to $D^0 - \bar{D}^0$ Mixing

In order to learn how NP might affect the mixing amplitude, it is instructive to consider off-diagonal terms in the neutral D mass matrix of Equation 24.

5.2.1. New physics in $|\Delta C| = 2$ interactions.
Because all NP particles are much heavier than the SM ones, the most natural place for NP to affect mixing amplitudes is in the $|\Delta C| = 2$ piece, which corresponds to a local interaction at the charm quark mass scale. Integrating out NP degrees of freedom at some scale Λ, we are left with an effective Hamiltonian written in the form of a series of operators of increasing dimension (138). The complete basis of those effective operators, which can most conveniently be written in terms of left- and right-handed quark fields, is composed of eight operators,

$$\mathcal{H}_{NP}^{\Delta C=2} = \sum_{i=1} C_i(\mu)\, \mathcal{Q}_i(\mu),$$

30.

where C_i are the Wilson coefficients and $\mathcal{Q}_i$ are the effective operators

$$
\begin{aligned}
\mathcal{Q}_1 &= \bar{u}_L \gamma_\mu c_L \bar{u}_L \gamma^\mu c_L, & \mathcal{Q}_5 &= \bar{u}_R \sigma_{\mu\nu} c_L \bar{u}_R \sigma^{\mu\nu} c_L \\
\mathcal{Q}_2 &= \bar{u}_R \gamma_\mu c_R \bar{u}_L \gamma^\mu c_L, & \mathcal{Q}_6 &= \bar{u}_R \gamma_\mu c_R \bar{u}_R \gamma^\mu c_R, \\
\mathcal{Q}_3 &= \bar{u}_L c_R \bar{u}_R c_L, & \mathcal{Q}_7 &= \bar{u}_L c_R \bar{u}_L c_R, \\
\mathcal{Q}_4 &= \bar{u}_R c_L \bar{u}_R c_L, & \mathcal{Q}_8 &= \bar{u}_L \sigma_{\mu\nu} c_R \bar{u}_L \sigma^{\mu\nu} c_R.
\end{aligned}
$$

31.

Because these operators are generated at the scale $\mu = \Lambda$ (at which NP is integrated out), a nontrivial operator mixing can occur if we take into account RG running of these operators between the $\mu = \Lambda$ and $\mu \simeq m_c$ scales. This running can be accounted for by solving RG equations obeyed by the Wilson coefficient functions,

$$\frac{d}{d\log\mu}\vec{C}(\mu) = \hat{\gamma}^T(\mu)\vec{C}(\mu),$$

32.

where $\hat{\gamma}^T(\mu)$ represents the matrix of anomalous dimensions of operators of Equation 31 (138). A prediction for a mixing parameter x in a particular model of NP is then obtained by computing $C_i(\Lambda)$ for a set of $\mathcal{Q}_i(\Lambda)$ generated by a given model, running the RG equations of Equation 32, and computing matrix elements $\langle \bar{D}^0 | \mathcal{Q}_i(m_c) | D^0 \rangle$.

Depending on the NP model, predictions for x_D vary by orders of magnitude. It is interesting to note that some models require large signals in the charm system if mixing and FCNCs in the strange and beauty systems are to be small (as in, for example, the SUSY alignment model). A list

Table 8 Constraints on new physics (NP) models from D^0 mixing

Model	Approximate constraint
Fourth-generation	$|V_{ub'}V_{cb'}| \cdot m_{b'} < 0.5$ (GeV)
$Q = -1/3$ singlet quark	$s_2 \cdot m_S < 0.27$ (GeV)
$Q = +2/3$ singlet quark	$|\lambda_{uc}| < 2.4 \cdot 10^{-4}$
Little Higgs	Tree: See entry for $Q = -1/3$ singlet quark
	Box: Region of parameter space can reach observed x_D
Generic Z'	$M_{Z'}/C > 2.2 \cdot 10^3$ TeV
Family symmetries	$m_1/f > 1.2 \cdot 10^3$ TeV (with $m_1/m_2 = 0.5$)
Left-right symmetric	No constraint
Alternate left-right symmetric	$M_R > 1.2$ TeV ($m_{D_1} = 0.5$ TeV)
	$(\Delta m/m_{D_1})/M_R > 0.4$ TeV^{-1}
Vector leptoquark bosons	$M_{VLQ} > 55(\lambda_{PP}/0.1)$ TeV
Flavor conserving two-Higgs doublet	No constraint
Flavor changing neutral Higgs	$m_H/C > 2.4 \cdot 10^3$ TeV
Flavor changing neutral Higgs (Cheng–Sher ansatz)	$m_H/|\Delta_{uc}| > 600$ GeV
Scalar leptoquark bosons	See entry for RPV supersymmetry
Higgsless	$M > 100$ TeV
Universal extra dimensions	No constraint
Split fermion	$M/|\Delta y| > (6 \cdot 10^2$ GeV)
Warped geometries	$M_1 > 3.5$ TeV
Minimal supersymmetric standard model	$|(\delta_{12}^u)_{LR, RL}| < 3.5 \cdot 10^{-2}$ for $\tilde{m} \sim 1$ TeV
	$|(\delta_{12}^u)_{LL, RR}| < .25$ for $\tilde{m} \sim 1$ TeV
Supersymmetric alignment	$\tilde{m} > 2$ TeV
Supersymmetry with RPV	$\lambda'_{12k}\lambda'_{11k}/m_{\tilde{d}_{R,k}} < 1.8 \cdot 10^{-3}/100$ GeV
Split supersymmetry	No constraint

Abbreviation: RPV, R-parity violation.

of constraints on NP models is given in **Table 8**; for more informative figures and methodology see Reference 138.

5.2.2. New physics in $|\Delta C| = 1$ interactions. The local $|\Delta C| = 2$ interaction cannot, however, affect $\Delta\Gamma_D$ because it does not have an absorptive part. Thus, naïvely, NP cannot affect lifetime difference y. However, this is not quite correct. Consider a D^0 decay amplitude that includes a small NP contribution, $A[D^0 \to n] = A_n^{(SM)} + A_n^{(NP)}$. Here $A_n^{(NP)}$ is assumed to be smaller than the current experimental uncertainties on those decay rates. It is a good approximation to write y as

$$y_D \simeq \sum_n \frac{\rho_n}{\Gamma_D} A_n^{(SM)} \bar{A}_n^{(SM)} + 2 \sum_n \frac{\rho_n}{\Gamma_D} A_n^{(NP)} \bar{A}_n^{(SM)}. \qquad 33.$$

The SM contribution to y is known to vanish in the limit of exact flavor $SU(3)$. Moreover, the first-order correction is also absent, so the SM contribution arises only as a second-order effect. Thus, those NP contributions that do not vanish in the flavor $SU(3)$ limit must determine the lifetime difference there, even if their contributions are tiny in the individual decay amplitudes (139). A simple calculation reveals that NP contribution to y can be as large as several percent in

R-parity-violating SUSY models or as small as 10^{-10} in the models with interactions mediated by charged Higgs particles (139, 140).

5.3. CP Violation

An observation of CPV in the current round of charm experiments is arguably one of the cleanest signals of physics beyond the SM. It is easy to understand how the manifestation of NP interactions in the charm system is associated with the observation of (large) CPV. This is due to the fact that all quarks that build up the hadronic states in weak decays of charm mesons belong to the first two generations. Because the 2×2 Cabibbo quark-mixing matrix is real, no CPV is possible in the dominant tree-level diagrams that describe the decay amplitudes. CP-violating amplitudes can be introduced in the SM by including penguin or box operators induced by virtual b quarks. However, their contributions are strongly suppressed by the small combination of CKM matrix elements $V_{cb}V_{ub}^*$. It is thus widely believed that the observation of (large) CPV in charm decays or in mixing would be an unambiguous sign of NP. This fact makes charm decays a valuable tool in searching for NP, as the statistics available in charm physics experiments is usually quite large.

As with other flavor physics, CP-violating contributions in charm can be classified into three general categories:

1. CPV in the $\Delta C = 1$ decay amplitudes. This type of CPV occurs when the absolute value of the decay amplitude for D to decay to a final state $f(A_f)$ is different from that of the corresponding CP-conjugated amplitude (termed direct CPV). This can happen if the decay amplitude can be broken into at least two parts associated with different weak and strong phases,

$$A_f = |A_1|e^{i\delta_1}e^{i\phi_1} + |A_2|e^{i\delta_2}e^{i\phi_2},$$ 34.

   where ϕ_i represent weak phases ($\phi_i \to -\phi_i$ under CP transformation) and δ_i represents strong phases ($\delta_i \to \delta_i$ under CP transformation). This ensures that the CP-conjugated amplitude $\bar{A}_{\bar{f}}$ differs from A_f.

2. CPV in $D^0 - \bar{D}^0$ mixing matrix. Introduction of $\Delta C = 2$ transitions, via either SM or NP one-loop or tree-level NP amplitudes, leads to nondiagonal entries in the $D^0 - \bar{D}^0$ mass matrix,

$$\left[M - i\frac{\Gamma}{2}\right]_{ij} = \begin{pmatrix} A & p^2 \\ q^2 & A \end{pmatrix}.$$ 35.

   This type of CPV is manifest when $R_m^2 = |p/q|^2 = (2M_{12} - i\Gamma_{12})/(2M_{12}^* - i\Gamma_{12}^*) \neq 1$.

3. CPV in the interference of decays with and without mixing. This type of CPV is possible for a subset of final states to which both D^0 and $\bar{D}^0$ can decay.

For a given final state f, CP-violating contributions can be summarized in the parameter

$$\lambda_f = \frac{q}{p}\frac{\bar{A}_f}{A_f} = R_m e^{i(\phi_f + \delta)}\left|\frac{\bar{A}_f}{A_f}\right|,$$ 36.

where A_f and $\bar{A}_f$ are the amplitudes for $D^0 \to f$ and $\bar{D}^0 \to f$ transitions, respectively, and where δ is the strong-phase difference between A_f and $\bar{A}_f$. Here ϕ represents the convention-independent weak-phase difference between the ratio of decay amplitudes and the mixing matrix.

Most of the experimental techniques that are sensitive to CPV make use of decay asymmetries that are similar to those employed in B physics (141–143),

$$a_f = \frac{\Gamma(D \to f) - \Gamma(\bar{D} \to \bar{f})}{\Gamma(D \to f) + \Gamma(\bar{D} \to \bar{f})}. \qquad 37.$$

One can also introduce a related asymmetry,

$$a_{\bar{f}} = \frac{\Gamma(D \to \bar{f}) - \Gamma(\bar{D} \to f)}{\Gamma(D \to \bar{f}) + \Gamma(\bar{D} \to f)}. \qquad 38.$$

For charged D decays the only contribution to the asymmetry of Equation 37 comes from the multicomponent structure of the $\Delta C = 1$ decay amplitude of Equation 34. In this case,

$$
\begin{aligned}
a_f &= \frac{2 \, \mathrm{Im}\left(A_1 A_2^*\right) \sin \delta}{|A_1|^2 + |A_2|^2 + 2 \, \mathrm{Re} \, A_1 A_2^* \cos \delta} \\
&= 2 r_f \sin \phi_f \sin \delta,
\end{aligned}
\qquad 39.
$$

where $\delta = \delta_1 - \delta_2$ is the CP-conserving phase difference, ϕ is the CP-violating phase difference, and $r_f = |A_2/A_1|$ is the ratio of amplitudes. Both r_f and δ are extremely difficult to compute reliably in D decays. However, the task can be significantly simplified if one concentrates only on the detection of NP in CP-violating asymmetries in the current round of experiments (144), i.e., at the $\mathcal{O}(1\%)$ level. This is the level at which a_f is currently probed experimentally. In this case one should expect $r_f \sim 0.01$, which follows from Equation 39.

Clearly the SM asymmetries are safely below this estimate. On the one hand, CF ($A_f \sim \lambda^0$) and DCS ($A_f \sim \lambda^2$) decay modes proceed via amplitudes that share the same weak phase, so no CP asymmetry is generated.[2] Moreover, the presence of NP amplitudes does not significantly change this conclusion (98). On the other hand, CS decays ($A_f \sim \lambda^1$) readily have a two-component structure, as they receive contributions from both tree and penguin amplitudes. In this case the same conclusion follows from the consideration of the charm CKM unitarity,

$$V_{ud} V_{cd}^* + V_{us} V_{cs}^* + V_{ub} V_{cb}^* = 0. \qquad 40.$$

In the Wolfenstein parameterization of CKM, the first two terms in this equation are of the order $\mathcal{O}(\lambda)$ (where $\lambda \simeq 0.22$), whereas the last term is $\mathcal{O}(\lambda^5)$. Thus, CP-violating asymmetry is expected to be at most $a_f \sim 10^{-3}$ in the SM. Model-dependent estimates of this asymmetry exist and are consistent with this estimate (145). Other observables are also possible, such as untagged CP asymmetry (146), which for some final states can be written in terms of experimentally measured quantities only and which suffers no theoretical uncertainties.

5.4. Experimental Studies of $D^0 - \bar{D}^0$ Mixing

Studies of $D^0 - \bar{D}^0$ mixing predominantly use samples of D^0 mesons, whose flavor is identified by the sign of the "slow" pion π_s in the decay of a $D^{*+} \to D^0 \pi_s^+$. Effects of mixing in the subsequent decays are then examined in one of two alternative ways. Studies of time-dependent decay rates look either for structure in the WS hadronic final states or for differences between the lifetimes of decays to CP eigenstates and to states of mixed CP. Alternatively, one can study time-integrated rates to look for decays either to semileptonic final states with the WS lepton[3] or for the effects

---

[2] Technically, there is a small $\mathcal{O}(\lambda^4)$ phase difference between the dominant tree T amplitude and the exchange E amplitudes.

[3] The signal for WS decays also uses information from the time dependence from mixed decays to distinguish them from the backgrounds.

upon rates resulting from quantum correlations between the $D^0 - \bar{D}^0$ systems produced in the $\psi(2S)$ decays at CLEO-c.

5.5. Time-Dependent Studies

Mesons produced at time $t = 0$ as $D^0(\bar{D}^0)$ have amplitudes for decay to final-state $f(\bar{f})$ at time t given by

$$\langle f|H|D^0(t)\rangle = e^{-(\Gamma_D + iM_D)t} A_f \left[\cosh \left((y_D + ix_D)\frac{\Gamma_D t}{2} \right) + \lambda_f \sinh \left((y_D + ix_D)\frac{\Gamma_D t}{2} \right) \right]$$

$$\langle \bar{f}|H|\bar{D}^0(t)\rangle = e^{-(\Gamma_D + iM_D)t} \bar{A}_{\bar{f}} \left[\lambda_{\bar{f}}^{-1} \sinh \left((y_D + ix_D)\frac{\Gamma_D t}{2} \right) + \cosh \left((y_D + ix_D)\frac{\Gamma_D t}{2} \right) \right], \quad 41.$$

where $\lambda_f = \frac{q \bar{A}_f}{p A_f}$ is defined in Equation 36, M_D and Γ_D are the mean mass and width of the D_1 and D_2, respectively, and A_f and $\bar{A}_f$ are the amplitudes describing the direct decays of D^0 and $\bar{D}^0$, respectively, to the same final state f.

In the absence of CPV in either mixing or direct decay to f, λ_f is proportional to $e^{i\delta}$, where δ is the strong-phase difference between $D^0 \to f$ and $\bar{D}^0 \to f$ amplitudes. With CPV in mixing ($p \neq q$) or in direct decay, λ_f is complex with weak-phase ϕ_f and strong-phase δ.

Decay rates proportional to the square modulus of these amplitudes provide information on x_D and y_D, but only if the strong-phase δ is known. However, in the important special case where f is a CP eigenstate (with CP $= \eta$), the direct decay amplitudes are related by $A_\eta = \eta \bar{A}_\eta$, so that $\delta = 0$.

5.5.1. Results from $D^0 \to K^+\pi^-$ decays.
These WS decays can take place in two ways: either directly, by a DCS mechanism, or by mixing ($D^0 \to \bar{D}^0$) followed by a right-sign (RS) CF decay $\bar{D}^0 \to K^+\pi^-$. These two processes interfere with one another, giving the time-dependent decay amplitudes given in Equations 41. Neglecting CPV and assuming that $|x_D|$ and $|y_D| \ll 1$, this leads to the decay rate R_{WS} for these decays:

$$\frac{R_{WS}(t)}{e^{-\Gamma_D t}} \propto R_D + \sqrt{R_D} y' t + R_M (\Gamma_D t)^2 / 2. \quad 42.$$

Here R_D is the DCS decay rate alone in the absence of mixing, R_M is the mixing rate, and the middle term (linear in y') results from interference between mixing and DCS amplitudes. Deviation from a purely exponential decay, expressed on the right side of Equation 42, can provide information on x'^2 and y' but not on the values of x_D and y_D or their relative signs.

This method has been used by E691, E791, BaBar, and CLEO (148), resulting in upper limits for mixing. The most stringent limit on $D^0 - \bar{D}^0$ mixing using this method was reported by Belle (151). However, using a 384-fb^{-1} data sample, the BaBar collaboration recently reported evidence for mixing from their sample of $4,030 \pm 90$ decays of D^0 mesons to the WS final state.

The distribution in decay times t (uncertainty δt) for these D^0 and $\bar{D}^0$ events is shown in **Figure 6a**. Precise knowledge of parameters describing the distribution of δt, clearly an important component in these fits, is obtained from a sample of $\sim 1.3 \times 10^6$ RS candidates for the CF decays $D^0 \to K^-\pi^+$. The difference between the fit with mixing and that without is significant, as seen in the residuals in **Figure 6b** and in the ratio of WS to RS decays in **Figure 6c**. The central values from the mixing fit occur at a negative (unphysical) value for x'^2. The likelihood obtained in the fit at the point ($x'^2 = 0$, $y' = 6.4 \times 10^{-3}$) just inside the physical region differs from that at the central point by only 0.7 units, whereas the likelihood at the no-mixing point ($x'^2 = y' = 0$) differs

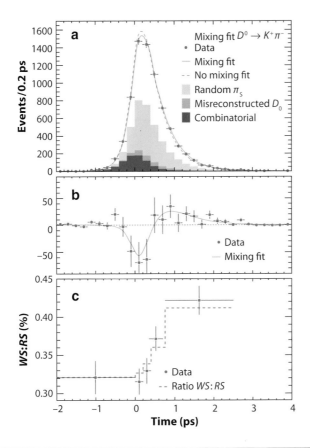

Figure 6

(*a*) Decay times for $D^0 \to K^+\pi^-$ decays. Also shown are the projections onto the time axis of fits made in the (M, ΔM, t, δt) distribution for events near the D^0 signal region. The dashed blue curve represents a fit made on the assumption that $x'^2 = y' = 0$, and the solid orange curve represents a fit where these parameters are allowed to float. (*b*) Residuals of data bins from the fit with no mixing. The solid orange curve represents the fit with mixing. (*c*) Ratio of wrong-sign (WS) to right-sign (RS) decays in time slices. The approximately linear form expected from Equation 42 is evident in the data. Figures are from Reference 126.

by almost 24 units. This difference is taken to indicate evidence for mixing at 3.9-σ significance. The CDF experiment, using data from a 1.5-fb^{-1} $\bar{p}p$ exposure at $\sqrt{s} = 1.96$ TeV, has recently confirmed the BaBar result at a significance of 3.8 standard deviations (149). The results from CDF are also summarized in **Table 9**, which shows that their agreement with BaBar's result is excellent. In the CDF experiment, it was not possible to remove background from D mesons from B decays simply with a momentum cut, as in the BaBar and Belle experiments. However, the background was identified from its vertex distribution and was properly taken into account. In an earlier analysis, the Belle collaboration (151) also performed this analysis; however, their central values for x'^2 and y' were closer to zero and so did not provide evidence for mixing, leading to 95%-CL limits on the mixing parameters.

   Table 9 summarizes the data on mixing derived from this hadronic channel. Generally, the highest sensitivity is achieved with fits assuming CPV. Note that the parameters x' and y' include a strong-phase $\delta_{K\pi}$, the phase of the amplitude ratio $\langle K^+\pi^-|D^0\rangle/\langle K^+\pi^-|\bar{D}^0\rangle$.

Table 9 Mixing and CP violation (CPV) parameters from $D^0 \to K^+\pi^-$ decays

Fit type	Parameter	Fit results/10^{-3}		
		BaBar[a]	CDF[b]	Belle[c]
No CPV or mixing	R_D	3.53 ± 0.09	–	3.77 ± 0.01
No CPV	R_D	3.03 ± 0.19	3.04 ± 0.55	3.64 ± 0.17
	x'^2	-0.22 ± 0.37	-0.12 ± 0.35	$0.18^{+0.21}_{-0.23}$
	y'	9.7 ± 5.4	8.5 ± 7.6	$0.6^{+4.0}_{-3.9}$
CPV allowed	R_D	3.03 ± 0.19	–	–
	a_D	-21 ± 54	–	23 ± 47
	a_M	–	–	670 ± 1200
	x'^{2+}	-0.24 ± 0.52	–	<0.72
	x'^{2-}	-0.20 ± 0.50	–	–
	y'^+	9.8 ± 7.8	–	$-28 < y' < 21$
	y'^-	9.6 ± 7.5	–	–

[a]Data from Reference 126.
[b]Data from Reference 149.
[c]Data from Reference 151.

5.5.2. Lifetime difference measurements. The Belle collaboration has also presented evidence for mixing using a 540-fb^{-1} e^+e^- data at the $\Upsilon(4S)$. They measured lifetimes for CS decays to the $CP = +1$ final states K^+K^- and $\pi^+\pi^-$ and for CF decays to the final state $K^-\pi^+$ with mixed CP (147).

This method was used in several earlier studies (152). The first results were from the E791 collaboration, which was unable to detect mixing due to limited statistical precision. Upper limits were also reported by FOCUS and CLEO. In the approximation that x_D and y_D are small, decays to $CP = +1$ eigenstates follow approximately exponential forms (127) with lifetimes, respectively, for decays of D^0 and $\bar{D}^0$ of

$$\tau^+ = \tau^0 \left[1 + |q/p|(y\cos\phi_f - x\sin\phi_f)\right]^{-1}$$
$$\tau^- = \tau^0 \left[1 + |p/q|(y\cos\phi_f + x\sin\phi_f)\right]^{-1}, \qquad 43.$$

where τ^0 is the lifetime for decays to non-CP eigenstates such as $K^-\pi^+$. For such measurements, we define

$$\Delta Y = -(\tau^0/\langle\tau\rangle)a_\tau, \qquad 44.$$

where $\langle\tau\rangle$ is the average of τ^+ and τ^- and $a_\tau = (\tau^- - \tau^+)/(\tau^- + \tau^+)$ is their asymmetry. In the absence of mixing ($x = y = 0$), both are zero. In the absence of CPV in mixing or in decay (i.e., $\phi_f = 0$), then $\Delta Y = 0$ and $y_D^{CP} = y$.

These measurements require backgrounds to be small and to have a well-understood time dependence. The Belle samples consisted of $1.11 \times 10^5 \, K^+K^-$, $1.22 \times 10^6 \, K^-\pi^+$, and $49 \times 10^3 \, \pi^+\pi^- \, D^0$ decays with purities of 98%, 99%, and 92%, respectively. The decay times for these samples were simultaneously fit to distributions with an exponential for each signal convolved with the time-resolution function over the expected background distributions.

Measurements were obtained for y_D^{CP} using both D^0 and $\bar{D}^0$ samples together and for τ^+ and τ^- from separate fits to each sample. The major systematic uncertainties were from an understanding of time offsets and from possible time dependence of the efficiency for reconstructing events. They measured

$$y_D^{CP} = (1.31 \pm 0.32 \pm 0.25)\%$$
$$a_\tau = (0.01 \pm 0.30 \pm 0.15)\%.$$

Clearly, y_D^{CP} is not consistent with zero, representing evidence for mixing at the 3.2-σ level. However, a_τ is consistent with zero, so there is no evidence for CPV.

A similar analysis by BaBar (147), which used a 384-fb^{-1} data set, confirmed these results. Although the BaBar sample was smaller, it was of higher purity resulting in the values

$$y_D^{CP} = (1.24 \pm 0.39 \pm 0.13)\%$$
$$\Delta Y = (-0.26 \pm 0.36 \pm 0.08)\%,$$

agreeing well with the Belle results. They show evidence for mixing at the 3.0-σ level, but also provide no evidence for CPV.

5.5.3. Mixing in the decays $D^0 \to K_S \pi^+ \pi^-$. For $D^0 \to K_S \pi^+ \pi^-$, the time dependence of the Dalitz plot distribution allows one to measure x_D and y_D directly. This technique was first developed by the CLEO collaboration (153), which used a 9-fb^{-1} data sample. Assuming no CPV, CLEO obtained the limits $(-4.7 < x < 8.6)\%$ and $(-6.1 < y < 3.5)\%$ at 95% CL.

An important feature of this decay mode is that, if K_S is treated as a CP = +1 eigenstate, final states f reached via the $\pi\pi$ channel are also CP eigenstates for which the strong-phase difference between D^0 and $\bar{D}^0$ is $\delta = 0$. This provides a reference phase for a time-dependent Dalitz plot analysis that determines the A_f, $\bar{A}_f$ for all channels everywhere in the plot. Thus, these decays allow measurement of x_D, y_D, and their relative sign, free from any unknown strong phase. This fit can also provide magnitude and phase of λ_fs, providing a test for CPV.

Belle (76) applied this technique to a data sample 60 times larger than CLEO's. The $K_S \pi^+ \pi^-$ Dalitz plot is shown in **Figure 7**. It is expected that RS and WS K^* amplitudes would have opposite

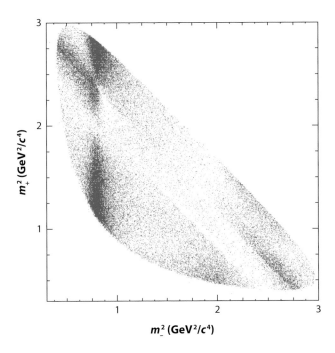

Figure 7

Dalitz plot of the decay $D \to K_S \pi^+ \pi^-$ showing squared invariant mass of $K_S \pi^+$ versus that of $K_S \pi^-$ for data from Reference 76. The RS K^{*-} is the vertical band and ρ^0 is the diagonal band. The wrong-sign (WS) K^{*+} appears as a weak, horizontal band destructively interfering with other structures in the plot.

Table 10 Mixing and CP violation (CPV) parameters from $D^0 \to K_S \pi^+ \pi^-$ decays from the Belle collaboration analysis (76)

Fit type	Parameter	Fit result	95%-CL interval
No CP violation	x (%)	$0.80 \pm 0.29^{+.09+.10}_{-.07-.14}$	(0.0,1.6)
	y (%)	$0.33 \pm 0.24^{+.08+.06}_{-.12-.08}$	(−0.34,0.96)
CP violation allowed	x (%)	$0.81 \pm 0.30^{+.10+.09}_{-.07-.16}$	$|x| < 1.6$
	y (%)	$0.37 \pm 0.25^{+.07+.07}_{-.13-.08}$	$|y| < 1.04$
	$|q/p|$	$0.86^{+.30+.06}_{-.29-.03} \pm 0.08$	
	$\arg q/p$	$\left(-14^{+16+5+2}_{-18-3-4}\right)$	
No direct CP violation	$|q/p|$	$0.95^{+.22}_{-.20}$	
	$\arg q/p$	$\left(-2^{+10}_{-11}\right)$	

The first uncertainty is statistical and the second systematic. The third is due to uncertainties in the isobar structure assumed in the model for the Dalitz plot distribution.

signs because their weak CF or DCS phases differ in sign. A BW isobar-model description of the amplitudes A_f was used, with complex coefficients, as in Equation 20. There were 18 isobars, including $\rho - \omega$ mixing, two $\pi^+\pi^-$ S wave states, and a nonresonant term NR, required to provide a reasonable match to all the features seen. The appropriate time dependencies were included as in Equation 41.

Three fits were made. In the first, no CPV was included (all D^0 and $\bar{D}^0$ events were combined and isobar coefficients for D^0 were constrained to equal those for $\bar{D}^0$). The condition $p = q$ was also imposed. In the second fit these conditions were relaxed, introducing a set of complex isobar coefficients for $\bar{D}^0$ that differed from those for D^0. The modulus and phase of the ratio p/q were also allowed to float. In the third fit, CPV in mixing ($p \neq q$) was allowed, but direct CPV was not (isobar coefficients constrained to be the same for D^0 as for $\bar{D}^0$). The results of these three fits are summarized in **Table 10**.

The Belle collaboration estimates that the best solution differs from the mixing point ($x_D = y_D = 0$) by 2.2 standard deviations. Allowing for CPV, they obtain the CPV parameters $|q/p| = 0.86^{+0.30+0.06}_{-0.29-0.03} \pm 0.08$ and arg $(q/p = (-14^{+16+5+2}_{-18-3-4})°$. This result does not quite establish evidence for mixing nor for CPV. It does, however, illustrate a powerful way to study mixing that can determine x_D, y_D, and their relative signs, as well as the CPV parameters ϕ and $|p/q|$.

5.6. Time-Independent Studies

Rates for WS leptons in semileptonic decays, a clear signal for mixing, could directly determine the mixing rate R_M. So far, with samples available, these have only been able to produce upper limits on this quantity. The most precise limits are from Belle (154), which used a 253-fb^{-1} sample, and from BaBar (155), which used a 344-fb^{-1} sample. The BaBar analysis differed considerably from Belle's in that it adopted a double-tagging approach, which required a fully reconstructed D on the side opposite the semileptonic decay, resulting in much reduced WS backgrounds. Event yields differed by orders of magnitude between the two experiments, yet the limits obtained were very similar:

$$\text{Belle} \quad R_M < 1 \times 10^{-3}$$
$$\text{BaBar} \quad (-1.3 < R_M < +1.2) \times 10^{-3}.$$

CLEO-c exploited the quantum coherence of the $D^0 - \bar{D}^0$ pairs produced via decay of the $\psi(3770)$ resonance to extract several important variables affecting $D^0 - \bar{D}^0$ mixing. Such pairs were produced in a coherent P wave state with $C = -1$, and—assuming no CPV—by reconstructing one neutral D meson decaying into a CP eigenstate, the CP eigenvalue for the other D was therefore constrained to have the opposite CP (156, 157). In principle, mixing observables could then be measured. Decays to $K^-\pi^+$ have rates that depend upon R_M, R_D, y', and δ. A sophisticated fitting technique was developed (158–160) to reach maximum sensitivity. Using a 281-pb^{-1} data sample collected at the $\psi(3770)$, CLEO determined $\cos\delta = 1.03^{+0.31}_{-0.17} \pm 0.06$ (161).

5.6.1. Averaging the results. The decays discussed above provided information in different forms, depending upon the final state. Semileptonic modes determined R_M, and WS hadronic systems measured x'^2 and y' separately for D^0 and $\bar{D}^0$. Decays to CP eigenstates measured y_D^{CP} and ΔY, and quantum correlated states from $\psi(3770) \to D^0$ decays could measure R_M, R_D, y_D, and $\cos\delta$ for various hadron systems. Parameters x_D, y_D, $|p/q|$, and $\arg p/q$ were obtained from time-dependent amplitude analyses of decays of D^0 to final states with more than two hadrons, as long as those amplitudes included at least one CP eigenstate.

The parameters of interest for physics that define values for all these quantities include x_D, y_D, $|p/q|$, $\arg p/q$, $\phi_{K\pi}^{WS}$, $\delta_{K\pi}^{WS}$, and R_D (total WS decay rate) and its asymmetry $a_D = (R_D - \bar{R}_D)/(R_D + \bar{R}_D)$. The Heavy Flavor Averaging Group (162) made a χ^2 fit to obtain values for the parameters that best describe all 26 available observations. Results projected onto the (x_D, y_D) and $(|p/q|, \arg p/q)$ planes are shown in **Figure 8**.

The point at which there is no mixing on the (x_D, y_D) plane lies at the origin, outside the 5-σ contour. This indicates very strong evidence for $D^0 - \bar{D}^0$ mixing. There is no evidence, however, for CPV in the mixing. The point where $p = q$ in the $(|p/q|, \arg p/q)$ plane lies at (1, 0)—right on the 1-σ contour.

Evidence for mixing is convincing, and different experiments and methods agree well. Because $y_D^{CP} > 0$, the CP $= -1$ state has a longer lifetime, as with the other neutral mesons that mix. If the sign of x_D/y_D remains positive as more measurements are made, then the CP $= -1$ state is the lighter state, unlike the K^0 system. Finally, there is no evidence for CPV so far (see following section).

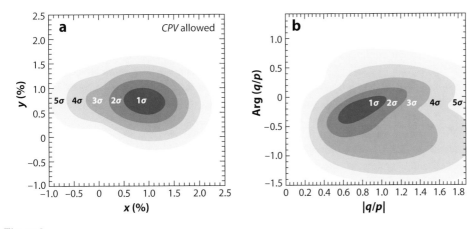

Figure 8

(*a*) Likelihood contours projected onto the (x_D, y_D) plane from an eight-parameter fit to the 26 mixing observables for which data exists. (*b*) Projection onto the $(|p/q|, \arg p/q)$ plane for this fit. Abbreviation: HFAG, Heavy Flavor Averaging Group.

Table 11   Asymmetries in decays of D mesons to various final states f

f	A_{CP} (%)	f	A_{CP} (%)
D^0 decays		**D^+ decays**	
Cabibbo-favored			
$K^-\pi^+$	-0.4 ± 1.0	$K_S\pi^+$	-0.9 ± 0.9
$K_S\pi^0$	$+0.1 \pm 1.3$	$K_S\pi^+\pi^0$	$+0.3 \pm 0.9$
$K^-\pi^+\pi^0$	$+0.2 \pm 0.9$	$K_S\pi^+\pi^-\pi^+$	$+0.1 \pm 1.3$
$K^-\pi^+\pi^-\pi^+$	$+0.7 \pm 1.0$	$K^-\pi^+\pi^+$	-0.5 ± 1.0
		$K^-\pi^+\pi^+\pi^0$	$+1.0 \pm 1.3$
Cabibbo-suppressed			
K^-K^+	$+0.15 \pm 0.34$	K_SK^+	$+7.1 \pm 6.2$
K_SK_S	-2.3 ± 1.9	$K^+K^-\pi^+$	$+0.6 \pm 0.8$
$\pi^-\pi^+$	$+0.02 \pm 0.51$	$K^+K^-\pi^+$	$+0.6 \pm 0.8$
$\pi^0\pi^0$	$+0.1 \pm 4.8$	$\pi^-\pi^+\pi^+$	-1.7 ± 4.2
$\pi^-\pi^+\pi^0$	$+0.1 \pm 5$	$K_SK^+\pi^-\pi^+$	-4.2 ± 6.8
$K^-K^+\pi^-\pi^+$	-8.2 ± 7.3		
$K_S\pi^+\pi^-$	$-0.9^{+2.6}_{-5.7}$		
Doubly Cabibbo-suppressed		Cabibbo-suppressed D_s	
$K^+\pi^-$	-0.8 ± 3.1	$D_s \to K^+\eta$	-20 ± 18
$K^+\pi^-\pi^0$	-0.1 ± 5.2	$D_s \to K^+\eta'$	-17 ± 37
$K^+\pi^-\pi^+\pi^-$	-1.8 ± 4.4	$D_s \to K_S\pi^+$	27 ± 11
		$D_s \to K^+\pi^0$	2 ± 29

5.6.2. Results of experimental searches for CP violation. At the present time, there is no experimental evidence for CPV in weak decays in the charm sector. Finding it in CF or DCS decay modes would signal possible NP. For decays to multibody systems, the decay asymmetry could appear only in certain subchannels and could result in particle–antiparticle differences in phase-space distribution. Searches may also be made for T violation.

5.6.3. Asymmetries in time-integrated partial widths. Until 2008, measurements of the asymmetries in partial widths for time-integrated D decay rates were known with precisions of a few percent. A recent compilation of average values (163) for D decay asymmetries for a number of modes measured by CDF, FOCUS, E791, CLEO, BaBar, and Belle is summarized in **Table 11**. All values are consistent with zero, with a precision of a few percent in most cases. Included in the most recent results are measurements from CLEO-c (6) of CF modes using its $\psi(3770)$ data. Precisions were excellent, of order 1%.

The most precise measurement came from BaBar (164); it has a precision of 0.34% for the decays $D^0 \to K^+K^-$ and a precision of 0.5% for $D^0 \to \pi^+\pi^-$. This sensitivity required careful consideration of systematic effects, notably charge and tagging asymmetries calibrated using data from the $K^-\pi^+$ CF mode. Effects from forward-backward production asymmetry arising from higher-order QED were also taken into account. Systematic uncertainties were 0.13% for K^+K^- and 0.22% for $\pi^+\pi^-$, so the results were limited by statistics. Nevertheless, finding CPV closer to 0.1% in CS modes and even less in CF or DCS modes (the goals to observe NP) will require even better precision.

CPV effects should influence the Dalitz plot distributions in three-body decays such as $D^0 \to \pi^+\pi^-\pi^0$, as asymmetries should affect different partial waves in each of the three channels to differing degrees. Such effects would also be expected to introduce phase differences between D^0 and $\bar{D}^0$, and these could be observed in analysis of the Dalitz plots. The CLEO collaboration, using a BW isobar-model analysis of the $\pi^-\pi^+\pi^0$ decay, saw no such effects at the few-percent level (115). More recently, this was repeated, and a model-independent approach was developed by BaBar (165) to search for CPV in both $\pi^-\pi^+\pi^0$ and $K^-K^+\pi^0$ final-state Dalitz plots with samples an order of magnitude larger than CLEO's. They found no effect at the 1–2% level.

5.6.4. T-violation studies. It has been pointed out (141) that T violation in charmed meson decays may also be observed in the asymmetry of triple scalar products (T-odd) of the momenta of the particles emerging from four-body decays (141). The only such measurements to date are from the FOCUS collaboration (166), which studied the decays $D^0 \to K^+K^-\pi^+\pi^-$, $D^+ \to K^+K_S\pi^+\pi^-$, and $D_s^+ \to K^+K_S\pi^+\pi^-$ and measured the quantities (defined in terms of momenta $\vec{p}$ with suffices indicating each product from four-body D^0, $\bar{D}^0$, and D_s^+ decays):

$$C_T = \vec{p}_{K^+} \cdot (\vec{p}_{\pi^+} \times \vec{p}_{\pi^-})$$
$$A_T = \frac{\Gamma(C_T > 0) - \Gamma(C_T < 0)}{\Gamma(C_T > 0 + \Gamma(C_T < 0)}.$$

The conjugate quantities $\bar{C}_T$ and $\bar{A}_T$ for $\bar{D}^0$, D^-, and D_s^- decays were also measured. Any asymmetry not consistent with zero would indicate T violation in the absence of strong interactions. These interactions introduced the same asymmetries in particle and antiparticle decay, so the quantity $A_{T\text{-viol}} = (1/2)(A_T - \bar{A}_T)$, which would be zero if T were conserved, was evaluated as

$$
\begin{aligned}
D^0 &\to K^+K^-\pi^+\pi^- &\quad 0.010 \pm 0.057 \pm 0.037 \\
D^+ &\to K^+K_S\pi^+\pi^- &\quad 0.023 \pm 0.062 \pm 0.022 \\
D^0 &\to K^+K^-\pi^+\pi^- &\quad -0.036 \pm 0.067 \pm 0.023,
\end{aligned}
$$

all consistent with zero.

5.6.5. Summary. Clearly, experimental precision is not yet sufficient to challenge the SM with respect to its predictions of CPV in the charm sector. However, the outlook is good, as the precision of asymmetry measurements is not yet limited by systematics. Also, model-independent studies of the multibody channels $\pi^+\pi^-\pi^0$ and $K^+K^-\pi^0$, less prone to systematic uncertainties, show promise as a tool for observing effects of CPV.

Both BaBar and Belle still have large samples of four-body decays in which T violation tests similar to that made by FOCUS can be repeated. Also, more data is yet to come from B factories on the K^-K^+ and $\pi^-\pi^+$ channels, where the precisions are beginning to become interesting. Even larger samples from charm factories, LHCb, or possibly super B factories in Italy or at KEK may provide a definitive answer on NP manifested in these studies.

6. CONCLUSIONS AND OUTLOOK

Charm decays remain a powerful ground for both theoretical and experimental investigations. The charm quark transition amplitudes described in this review represent a crucial tool to understand strong interaction dynamics in the nonperturbative regime. The validation of theoretical tools that tackle nonperturbative processes is critical to precision tests of the Yukawa sector of the SM, in particular to unitarity checks of the CKM matrix.

Finally, charm decays provide a unique window on NP, which affects up-type quark dynamics. If so, charm phenomenology can have an impact on the interpretation of results from the direct searches for new physics to be performed at the LHC. The charm quark is the only up-type quark that can have flavor oscillations; thus, the observation of $D^0 - \bar{D}^0$ mixing is already constraining many scenarios of physics beyond the SM. In addition, a multitude of NP models predict enhancements on CP-violating phases in D decays beyond the 10^{-3} level generally predicted within the SM. A full exploration of CPV in the charm sector—which will hopefully be achieved within the next decade—will be critical for further narrowing the vast parameter space presently characterizing all the NP models.

DISCLOSURE STATEMENT

The authors are not aware of any biases that might be perceived as affecting the objectivity of this review.

ACKNOWLEDGMENTS

The authors would like to thank their colleagues for helpful conversations during the course of writing of this review, especially D. Asner, D. Cinabro, R. Harr, S. Pakvasa, A. Schwartz, and S. Stone for their careful reading of the manuscript and useful comments. The work of M.A. was supported in part by the U.S. National Science Foundation under grant number PHY-0553004. B.M. was supported by the U.S. National Science Foundation under grant number PHY-0457336. A.A.P. was supported in part by the U.S. National Science Foundation CAREER Award number PHY-0547794 and by the U.S. Department of Energy under contract number DE-FG02-96ER41005.

LITERATURE CITED

1. Gaillard MK, Lee BW, Rosner JL. *Rev. Mod. Phys.* 47:277 (1975)
2. Petrov AA. hep-ph/0311371 (2003)
3. Adler J, et al. (Mark III Collab.) *Phys. Rev. Lett.* 60:89 (1988)
4. Briere RA, et al. Preprint CLNS-01-1742 (2001)
5. Li WG, et al. (BES Collab.) *Int. J. Mod. Phys. A* 20:1560 (2005)
6. Dobbs S, et al. *Phys. Rev. D* 76:112001 (2007)
7. Widhalm L, et al. *Phys. Rev. Lett.* 97:061804 (2006)
8. Albini E, et al. *Phys. Lett.* 110B:339 (1982)
9. Artuso M. In *Proc. Int. Workshop Vertex Detectors, 16th, Lake Placid, NY, Sept. 23–27, 2007,* 9 pp. Trieste: Proc. Sci. (2008)
10. Aubin C, et al. *Phys. Rev. Lett.* 95:122002 (2005)
11. Follana E, Davies CTH, Lepage GP, Shigemitsu J. *Phys. Rev. Lett.* 100:062002 (2008)
12. Aubin C, et al. *Phys. Rev. Lett.* 94:011601 (2005)
13. Shifman MA, Vainshtein AI, Zakharov VI. *Nucl. Phys. B* 147:385 (1979)
14. Narison S. hep-ph/0202200 (2002)
15. Rosner JL, Stone S. hep-ex/0802.1043 (2008)
16. Aubert B, et al. *Phys. Rev. D* 74:031103 (2006); Aubert B, et al. *Phys. Rev. D* 71:091104 (2005)
17. Scora D, Isgur N. *Phys. Rev. D* 52:2783 (1995)
18. Isgur N, Wise MB. *Phys. Lett. B* 232:113 (1989)
19. Isgur N, Wise MB. *Phys. Rev. D* 42:2388 (1990)
20. Grinstein B, Pirjol D. *Phys. Rev. D* 70:114005 (2004)
21. Chiu WT, et al. *Phys. Lett. B* 624:31 (2005)
22. Lellouch L, Lin CJ. *Phys. Rev. D* 64:094501 (2005)
23. Becirevic D. *Phys. Rev. D* 60:074501 (1999)

24. Bordes J, Penarrocha J, Schilcher K. *JHEP* 0522:014 (2005)
25. Narison S. hep-ph/0202200 (2002)
26. Badalian AM, et al. *Phys. Rev. D* 75:116001 (2007); Badalian AM, Bakker BLG. hep-ph/0702229 (2007)
27. Amundson J. *Phys. Rev. D* 47:3059 (1993)
28. Artuso M, et al. *Phys. Rev. Lett.* 95:251801 (2005); Eisenstein BI, hep-ex/0806.211v2 (2008)
29. Aubert B, et al. *Phys. Rev. Lett.* 98:141801 (2007)
30. Hewett JL. hep-ph/9505246 (1995); Akeroyd AG, Chen CH. *Phys. Rev. D* 75:075004 (2007); Akeroyd AG. *Prog. Theor. Phys.* 111:295 (2004)
31. Ikado K, et al. *Phys. Rev. Lett.* 97:251802 (2006)
32. Coan TE, et al. *Phys. Rev. Lett.* 95:191802 (2005); Huang GS, et al. *Phys. Rev. Lett.* 95:101801 (2005)
33. Ablikim M, et al. *Phys. Lett. B* 608:24 (2005); Ablikim M, et al. *Phys. Lett. B* 597:39 (2004)
34. Yao WM, et al. *J. Phys. G* 33:1 (2006); Part. Data Group, **http://pdg.lbl.gov** (2008)
35. Artuso M, et al. *Phys. Rev. Lett.* 99:071802 (2007)
36. Ecklund KM. *Phys. Rev. Lett.* 100:161801 (2008)
37. Abe K, et al. hep-ex/0709.1340 (2007)
38. Chadha M, et al. *Phys. Rev. D* 58:032002 (1998)
39. Alexandrov Y, et al. *Phys. Lett. B* 478:31 (2000)
40. Heister A, et al. *Phys. Lett. B* 528:1 (2002)
41. Acciarri M, et al. *Phys. Lett. B* 396:327 (1997)
42. Abbiendi G, et al. *Phys. Lett. B* 516:236 (2001)
43. Adam N, et al. *Phys. Rev. Lett.* 97:251801 (2006)
44. Stone S. *AIP Conf. Proc.* 842:253 (2006)
45. Boyd CG, Grinstein B, Lebed RF. *Phys. Rev. D* 56:6895 (1997)
46. Becirevic D, Kaidalov AB. *Phys. Lett. B* 478:417 (2000)
47. Link JM, et al. *Phys. Lett. B* 607:233 (2005)
48. Nierste U. *Int. J. Mod. Phys. A* 21:1724 (2005)
49. Eur. Org. Nucl. Res. Large Electron-Positron Collid. **http://lepewwg.web.cern.ch/LEPEWWG/lepww/4f/Winter05/** (2005)
50. Cronin-Hennessy D, et al. hep-ex/0712.0998 (2007)
51. Becher T, Hill RJ. *Phys. Lett. B* 633:61 (2006)
52. Link JM, et al. *Phys. Lett. B* 607:233 (2005)
53. Pavlunin V. *PoS HEP* 2005:206 (2006)
54. Aubert B, et al. hep-ex/0704.0020 (2007)
55. Huang GS, et al. *Phys. Rev. Lett.* 94:011802 (2005)
56. Link JM, et al. *Phys. Lett. B* 633:183 (2006)
57. Shepherd MR, et al. *Phys. Rev. D* 74:052001 (2006)
58. Fajfer S, Kamenik JF. *Phys. Rev. D* 73:057503 (2006)
59. Link JM, et al. *Phys. Lett. B* 535:43 (2002)
60. Bianco S, Fabbri FL, Benson D, Bigi I. *Riv. Nuovo Cim.* 26N7:1 (2003)
61. Burdman G, Shipsey I. *Annu. Rev. Nucl. Part. Sci.* 53:431 (2003)
62. Burdman G, Golowich E, Hewett JL, Pakvasa S. *Phys. Rev. D* 52:6383 (1995)
63. Burdman G, Golowich E, Hewett JL, Pakvasa S. *Phys. Rev. D* 66:014009 (2002)
64. Fajfer S, Kosnik N, Prelovsek S. *Phys. Rev. D* 76:074010 (2007)
65. He Q, et al. *Phys. Rev. Lett.* 95:221802 (2005)
66. Abe K, et al. *Phys. Rev. Lett.* 92:101803 (2004)
67. Acosta D, et al. *Phys. Rev. D* 68:091101 (2007)
68. Aubert B, et al. hep-ex/0607051 (2006)
69. Abazov VM, et al. *Phys. Rev. Lett.* 100:101801 (2008)
70. Aubert B, et al. *Phys. Rev. Lett.* 93:191801 (2004)
71. Acosta DE, et al. *Phys. Rev. D* 68:091101 (2003)
72. Freyberger A, et al. *Phys. Rev. Lett.* 76:3065 (1996)
73. Cavoto G, et al. hep-ph/0603019 (2006)
74. Aubert B, et al. *Phys. Rev. D* 71:032005 (2005)

75. Giri A, Grossman Y, Soffer A, Zupan J. *Phys. Rev. D* 68:054018 (2003)
76. Abe K, et al. *Phys. Rev. Lett.* 99:131803 (2007)
77. Buccella F, et al. *Phys. Rev. D* 51:3478 (1995)
78. Bauer M, Stech B, Wirbel M. *Z. Phys. C* 34:103 (1987)
79. Buras AJ, Gerard JM, Ruckl R. *Nucl. Phys. B* 268:16 (1986)
80. Blok B, Shifman MA. *Nucl. Phys. B* 399:441 (1993)
81. Falk AF, Nir Y, Petrov AA. *JHEP* 12:019 (1999)
82. Savage MJ. *Phys. Lett. B* 257:414 (1991)
83. Dobbs S, et al. *Phys. Rev. D* 76:112001 (2007)
84. Alexander J, et al. *Phys. Rev. Lett.* 100:161804 (2008)
85. Baltrusaitis RM, et al. *Phys. Rev. Lett.* 56:2140 (1986)
86. Sun WM. *Nucl. Instrum. Methods A* 556:325 (2006)
87. Aubert B, et al. *Phys. Rev. Lett.* 100:051802 (2008)
88. Abe K, et al. hep-ex/0701053 (2007)
89. White E, He Q. hep-ex/0711.2285 (2007)
90. Bigi IIY, Yamamoto H. *Phys. Lett. B* 349:363 (1995)
91. Rosner JL. *Phys. Rev. D* 74:057502 (2006)
92. Rubin P, et al. *Phys. Rev. Lett.* 96:081802 (2006)
93. Gaspero F, Meadows B, Mishra K, Soffer A. hep-ph/0805.4050 (2008)
94. Selen M, et al. *Phys. Rev. Lett.* 71:1973 (1993)
95. Aubert B, et al. *Phys. Rev. D* 74:091102 (2006)
96. Abe K, et al. *Phys. Lett. B* 662:102 (2008)
97. Adams GS, et al. *Phys. Rev. Lett.* 99:191805 (2007)
98. Bergmann S, Nir Y. *JHEP* 09:031 (1999)
99. Aubert B, et al. *Phys. Rev. D* 74:011107 (2006)
100. Dytman SA, et al. *Phys. Rev. D* 74:071102 (2006)
101. Meadows B. hep-ex/0712.1605 (2007)
102. Bondar A, Poluektov A. hep-ex/0801.0840 (2008)
103. Watson KM. *Phys. Rev.* 88:1163 (1952); Gillespie J. *Final State Interactions.* San Francisco: Holden-Day (1964)
104. Link JM, et al. *Phys. Lett. B* 653:1 (2007)
105. Blatt JM, Weisskopf VF. *Theoretical Nuclear Physics.* New York: Wiley (1952)
106. Wigner EP. *Phys. Rev.* 70:15 (1946)
107. Chung SU, et al. *Ann. Phys.* 4:404 (1995)
108. Anisovich VV, Sarantsev AV. *Eur. Phys. J. A* 16:229 (2003)
109. Aitala EM, et al. *Phys. Rev. D* 73:032004 (2006)
110. Muramatsu H, et al. *Phys. Rev. Lett.* 89:251802 (2002)
111. Poluektov A, et al. *Phys. Rev. D* 73:112009 (2006)
112. Poluektov A, et al. *Phys. Rev. D* 70:072003 (2004)
113. Aubert B, et al. *Phys. Rev. Lett.* 95:121802 (2005); Aubert B, et al., hep-ex/0805.2001 (2008)
114. Aubert B, et al. *Phys. Rev. Lett.* 99:251801 (2007)
115. Cronin-Hennessy D, et al. *Phys. Rev. D* 72:031102 (2005)
116. Aubert B, et al. *Phys. Rev. D* 72:052008 (2005)
117. Bonvicini G, et al. *Phys. Rev. D* 76:012001 (2007)
118. Oller JA. *Phys. Rev. D* 71:054030 (2005)
119. Schechter J. *Int. J. Mod. Phys. A* 20:6149 (2005)
120. Aitala EM, et al. *Phys. Lett. B* 404:187 (1997)
121. Aubert B, et al. *Phys. Rev. D* 76:011102 (2007)
122. Aston D, et al. *Nucl. Phys. B* 296:493 (1988)
123. Frabetti PL, et al. *Phys. Lett. B* 351:591 (1995)
124. Pappagallo M. hep-ex/0711.4769 (2007)
125. Pais A, Treiman SB. *Phys. Rev. D* 12:2744 (1975)
126. Aubert B, et al. *Phys. Rev. Lett.* 98:211802 (2007)

127. Bergmann S, et al. *Phys. Lett. B* 486:418 (2000)

128. Falk AF, Grossman Y, Ligeti Z, Petrov AA. *Phys. Rev. D* 65:054034 (2002)

129. Georgi H. *Phys. Lett. B* 297:353 (1992)

130. Ohl T, Ricciardi G, Simmons EH. *Nucl. Phys. B* 403:605 (1993)

131. Petrov AA. *Phys. Rev. D* 56:1685 (1997)

132. Bigi IIY, Uraltsev NG. *Nucl. Phys. B* 592:92 (2001)

133. Golowich E, Petrov AA. *Phys. Lett. B* 625:53 (2005)

134. Donoghue JF, Golowich E, Holstein BR, Trampetic J. *Phys. Rev. D* 33:179 (1986)

135. Colangelo P, Nardulli G, Paver N. *Phys. Lett. B* 242:71 (1990)

136. Golowich E, Petrov AA. *Phys. Lett. B* 427:172 (1998)

137. Falk AF, et al. *Phys. Rev. D* 69:114021 (2004)

138. Golowich E, Hewett J, Pakvasa S, Petrov AA. *Phys. Rev. D* 76:095009 (2007)

139. Golowich E, Pakvasa S, Petrov AA. *Phys. Rev. Lett.* 98:181801 (2007)

140. Petrov AA, Yeghiyan GK. *Phys. Rev. D* 77:034018 (2008)

141. Bigi IIY, Sanda AI. *Camb. Monogr. Part. Phys. Nucl. Phys. Cosmol.* 9:1 (2000)

142. Petrov AA. hep-ph/0711.1564 (2007)

143. Brown T, Tuan SF, Pakvasa S. *Phys. Rev. Lett.* 51:1823 (1983); Bigi IIY, Sanda AI. *Phys. Rev. D* 29:1393 (1984)

144. Grossman Y, Kagan AL, Nir Y. *Phys. Rev. D* 75:036008 (2007)

145. Buccella F, et al. *Phys. Lett. B* 302:319 (1993)

146. Petrov AA. *Phys. Rev. D* 69:111901 (2004)

147. Staric M, et al. *Phys. Rev. Lett.* 98:211803 (2007)

148. Anjos J, et al. *Phys. Rev. Lett.* 60:1239 (1988); Aitala E, et al. *Phys. Rev. D* 57:13 (1998); Link J, et al. *Phys. Lett. B* 618:23 (2005); Aubert B, et al. *Phys. Rev. Lett.* 91:171801 (2003); Godang R, et al. *Phys. Rev. Lett.* 84:5038 (2000)

149. Aaltonen T. *Phys. Rev. Lett.* 100:121802 (2008)

150. Aubert B, et al. (BaBar Collab.) hep-ex/0712.2249 (2007)

151. Zhang LM, et al. *Phys. Rev. Lett.* 96:151801 (2006)

152. Aitala EM, et al. *Phys. Rev. Lett.* 83:32 (1999); Link J, et al. *Phys. Lett. B* 485:62 (2000); Csorna S, et al. *Phys. Rev. D* 65:092001 (2002)

153. Asner DM, et al. *Phys. Rev. D* 72:012001 (2005)

154. Bitenc U, et al. *Phys. Rev. D* 72:071101 (2005)

155. Aubert B, et al. *Phys. Rev. D* 76:014018 (2007)

156. Gronau M, Grossman Y, Rosner JL. *Phys. Lett. B* 508:37 (2001)

157. Atwood D, Petrov AA. *Phys. Rev. D* 71:054032 (2005)

158. Asner DM, Sun WM. *Phys. Rev. D* 73:034024 (2006)

159. Asner DM, et al. *Int. J. Mod. Phys. A* 21:5456 (2006)

160. Sun WM. hep-ex/0712.0498 (2007)

161. Rosner J, et al. *Phys. Rev. Lett.* 100:221801 (2008); Asner D, et al. hep-ex/0802.2268v1 (2008)

162. Schwartz A, et al. hep-ex/0803.0082 (2008)

163. Schwartz A, et al. (Heavy Flavor Averaging Group) **http://www.slac.stanford.edu/xorg/hfag/charm/charm_asymcp.html** (2007)

164. Aubert B, et al. *Phys. Rev. Lett.* 100:061803 (2008)

165. Aubert B, et al. hep-ex/0802.4035 (2008)

166. Link JM, et al. *Phys. Lett. B* 622:239 (2005)

Strategies for Determining the Nature of Dark Matter

Dan Hooper[1] and Edward A. Baltz[2]

[1] Theoretical Astrophysics, Fermi National Accelerator Laboratory, Batavia, Illinois 60510;
email: dhooper@fnal.gov

[2] Kavli Institute for Particle Astrophysics and Cosmology, Stanford Linear Accelerator Center,
Menlo Park, California 94025; email: eabaltz@slac.stanford.edu

Annu. Rev. Nucl. Part. Sci. 2008. 58:293–314

First published online as a Review in Advance on
July 28, 2008

The *Annual Review of Nuclear and Particle Science*
is online at nucl.annualreviews.org

This article's doi:
10.1146/annurev.nucl.58.110707.171217

0163-8998/08/1123-0293$20.00

Key Words

dark matter, supersymmetry, weakly interacting massive particles, gamma
rays, neutrinos, cosmic rays

Abstract

In this review, we discuss the role of the various experimental programs
taking part in the effort to identify the particle nature of dark matter. In
particular, we focus on electroweak-scale dark matter particles and discuss a
wide range of search strategies that are being developed and utilized to detect
them. These efforts include direct detection experiments, which attempt to
observe the elastic scattering of dark matter particles with nuclei; indirect
detection experiments, which search for photons, antimatter, and neutrinos produced as a result of dark matter annihilations; and collider searches
for new teraelectronvolt-scale physics. Each of these techniques could potentially provide a unique and complementary set of information related to
the mass, interactions, and distribution of dark matter. Ideally, these many
different tools will be used together to conclusively identify the particle or
particles that constitute the dark matter of the universe.

Contents

1. INTRODUCTION

There exists a wide array of evidence in support of the conclusion that most of the matter in our universe is nonluminous. The evidence includes observations of the rotational speeds of galaxies (1), the orbital velocities of galaxies within clusters (2), gravitational lensing (3), the cosmic microwave background (4), the light element abundances (5), and large scale structure (6). Despite these many observational indications, it is clear that the majority of the dark matter does not consist of baryonic material or any other known form of matter (7). At present, we remain ignorant of the particle identity of this substance.

In this review, we summarize some of the most promising strategies and techniques being pursued to elucidate the nature of dark matter. These efforts include direct detection experiments designed to observe the elastic scattering of dark matter particles with nuclei; indirect detection experiments that aim to detect the annihilation products of dark matter, such as gamma rays, neutrinos, positrons, antiprotons, antideuterons, synchrotron radiation, and X-rays; and collider searches for dark matter and associated particles. The material presented here is not intended to be an exhaustive summary of the field of dark matter physics. Such reviews can be found elsewhere (7). In this article, we limit our discussion to the case of candidate dark matter particles with electroweak-scale masses and couplings. Furthermore, for the sake of conciseness, we do not discuss every experimental approach being pursued, but rather focus on several of the most promising direct, indirect, and collider efforts as well as on the interplay and complementarity among these various programs.

We emphasize that the detection of dark matter particles in any one of the experimental channels discussed here will not be sufficient to conclusively identify the nature of dark matter. The direct or indirect detection of the dark matter particles making up our galaxy's halo is highly unlikely to provide enough information to reveal the underlying physics (supersymmetry, etc.) behind these particles. In contrast, collider experiments may identify a long-lived, weakly interacting particle, but they will not be able to test its cosmological stability or abundance. Only by combining the information provided by many different experimental approaches are we likely to solve the mystery of dark matter's particle nature. Although the detection of dark matter in any one search channel would constitute a discovery of the utmost importance, it would almost certainly leave many important questions unanswered.

2. THE WIMP HYPOTHESIS

In this review, we limit our discussion to dark matter candidates that are heavy, electrically neutral, and weakly interacting. Such particles, collectively known as weakly interacting massive particles (WIMPs), are particularly well motivated, especially when their mass and couplings are tied to the physics of the electroweak scale. Before we discuss the experimental techniques for detecting dark matter particles, we briefly describe some of the most compelling motivations for electroweak-scale dark matter.

The challenge of stabilizing the mass of the Higgs boson (i.e., the hierarchy problem) leads us to expect new forms of matter to appear at or near the electroweak scale. The nature of any physics beyond the Standard Model that might appear at the teraelectronvolt scale, however, is tightly constrained by the precision electroweak measurements made at the Large Electron-Positron Collider (LEP). In particular, new discrete symmetries are required of most phenomenologically viable models of teraelectronvolt-scale physics (8). Such symmetries naturally lead to a stable particle or particles, which may potentially constitute the dark matter of our universe.

Numerous proposed extensions of the Standard Model introduce new particle content at or near the electroweak scale and include a discrete symmetry of the form required to stabilize a potential dark matter candidate. The most well-studied example is the lightest neutralino in supersymmetric models. Other examples include Kaluza–Klein hypercharge gauge bosons in models with universal extra dimensions (9) and the lightest T-parity-odd particle in little Higgs theories (8, 10). These candidates have similar masses and couplings and thus have undergone similar thermal histories in the early universe. At high temperatures WIMPs are abundant, being freely created and annihilated in pairs. As the universe expands and the temperature drops below the WIMPs' production threshold, however, the number density of these particles is rapidly suppressed. Ultimately, the WIMPs will "freeze out" and remain as a thermal relic of the universe's hot youth. The resulting density of WIMPs is given by

$$\Omega_\chi h^2 = \frac{s_0}{\rho_c/h^2} \left(\frac{45}{\pi g_*}\right)^{1/2} \frac{x_f}{m_{Pl}} \frac{1}{\langle \sigma v \rangle}, \qquad 1.$$

where s_0 is the current entropy density of the universe, ρ_c is the critical density, h is the (scaled) Hubble constant, g_* is the effective number of relativistic degrees of freedom at the time that the dark matter particle goes out of thermal equilibrium, m_{Pl} is the Planck mass, $x_f = m/T_f \approx 25$ is the inverse freeze-out temperature in units of the WIMP mass, and $\langle \sigma v \rangle$ is the thermal average of the dark matter pair-annihilation cross section multiplied by the relative velocity.

In order for this process to yield a thermal abundance of dark matter within the range measured by WMAP ($0.095 < \Omega h^2 < 0.129$) (4), the thermally averaged annihilation cross section is required to be $\langle \sigma v \rangle \approx 3 \times 10^{-26}$ cm^3 s^{-1} [or, alternatively, $\langle \sigma v \rangle \approx 0.9$ picobarns (pb)]. Remarkably, this measurement is quite similar to the value obtained for a generic electroweak-mass particle annihilating through the exchange of the electroweak gauge or Higgs bosons. In particular, $\langle \sigma v \rangle = \pi \alpha^2/8m^2$ leads us to a WIMP mass on the order of $m \sim 100$ GeV.

We conclude that if a stable, weakly interacting, electroweak-scale particle exists, then it is likely to be present in the universe today with an abundance similar to the measured dark matter density. With this in mind, we focus our dark matter search strategy on this particularly well-motivated scenario wherein the dark matter particle has electroweak interactions and a mass near the electroweak scale.

3. DIRECT DETECTION

Experiments such as XENON (11), CDMS (Cryogenic Dark Matter Search) (12, 13), ZEPLIN (Zoned Proportional Scintillation in Liquid Noble Gases) (14), EDELWEISS (Expérience pour Détecter les WIMPs en Site Souterrain) (15), CRESST (Center for Research and Exploration in Space Science and Technology) (16), WARP (WIMP Argon Programme) (17), COUPP (Chicagoland Observatory for Underground Particle Physics), and DAMA (Dark Matter) (18) are designed to detect dark matter particles through their elastic scattering with nuclei. This class of techniques is collectively known as direct detection, in contrast to indirect detection efforts, which attempt to observe the annihilation products of dark matter particles.

The role played by direct detection is important for a number of reasons. First, although collider experiments may be capable of detecting dark matter particles, they will not be able to distinguish a cosmologically stable WIMP from a long-lived but unstable particle. Generally speaking, colliders cannot record the cosmological abundance of an observed WIMP. Second, although the mass of the dark matter particle could potentially be measured in Large Hadron Collider (LHC) experiments, its couplings are much more difficult to access in this way. Direct detection experiments, in contrast, provide a valuable probe of the dark matter's couplings to the Standard Model. Third, the uncertainties involved in direct detection are likely to be significantly smaller than in most indirect detection channels. Whereas indirect detection rates rely critically on the distribution of dark matter, especially in high-density regions, and on other astrophysical properties such as the galactic magnetic and radiation fields, direct detection experiments rely only on the local dark matter density and velocity distribution.

The density of dark matter in the local neighborhood is inferred by fitting observations to models of the galactic halo. These observations include the rotational speed of stars at the solar circle and other locations, the total projected mass density (estimated by considering the motion of stars perpendicular to the galactic disk), peak-to-trough variations in the rotation curve (i.e., the flatness constraint), and microlensing. Taken together, these constraints can be used to estimate the local halo density to lie between 4×10^{-25} g cm^3 and 13×10^{-25} g cm^{-3} (0.22–0.73 GeV cm^{-3}) (19). Limits on the density of MACHO (massive astrophysical compact halo objects) imply that at least 80% of this is cold dark matter. The velocity of the WIMPs is expected be close to the galactic rotation velocity, 230 ± 20 km s^{-1} (20).

These observations, however, only constrain the dark matter density as averaged over scales larger than about one kiloparsec. In contrast, the solar system moves a distance of $\sim 10^{-3}$ parsecs relative to the dark matter halo each year. If dark matter is distributed in an inhomogeneous way over milliparsec scales (i.e., as a collection of dense clumps and voids), then the density along the path of the Earth, as seen by direct detection experiments, could be much larger or smaller than is inferred by the rotational dynamics of our galaxy.

Throughout most of our galaxy's halo, however, inhomogeneities in the small-scale dark matter distribution are not anticipated to be large. The vast majority of the dark matter in the inner regions of our galaxy has been in place for $\sim 10^{10}$ years, ample time for the destruction of clumps through tidal interactions. Using high-resolution simulations, Helmi et al. found that the dark matter in the solar neighborhood is likely to consist of a superposition of hundreds of thousands of dark matter streams, collectively representing a very smooth and homogeneous distribution (21). However, if we happen to find that our Solar System resides in an overdense clump or stream of dark matter, high direct detection rates could lead us to mistakenly infer an artificially large WIMP-nucleon elastic scattering cross section.

The nuclear physics involved in WIMP-nuclei elastic scattering also introduces uncertainties that may ultimately limit the accuracy to which the dark matter's couplings to the Standard Model can be measured. In many models, including many supersymmetric models, the WIMP-nucleon scattering cross section is dominated by the t channel exchange of a Higgs boson. The coupling of the Higgs boson to the proton receives its dominant contributions from two sources: the coupling of the Higgs to gluons through a heavy quark loop and the direct coupling of the Higgs to strange quarks (22). Therefore this coupling depends on the parameter

$$f_{Ts} = \frac{\langle p | m_s \bar{s} s | p \rangle}{\langle p | H_{QCD} | p \rangle}, \qquad 2.$$

that is, the fraction of the mass of the proton that arises from the mass of the nonvalence strange quarks in the proton wave function. Researchers have known for some time that there is significant uncertainty in this quantity (23), and several recent papers have pointed out the uncertainty this introduces to calculations of the WIMP-nucleon elastic scattering cross section (24, 25). In particular, in the case of WIMPs that couple dominantly to the strange content of the nucleon, this can lead to an uncertainty in the direct detection cross section of a factor of four or even larger (24). It is possible that in the future this uncertainty could be reduced through the use of lattice gauge theory (26, 27).

The processes of WIMP-nuclei elastic scattering can be naturally divided into spin-dependent and spin-independent contributions. The spin-independent (or coherent scattering) term is enhanced in WIMP-nucleus cross sections by factors of A^2; thus it is advantageous to use targets consisting of heavy nuclei. This enhancement is due to the fact that the WIMP wavelength is of order the size of the nucleus; therefore the scattering amplitudes on individual nucleons add coherently. The spin-dependent contribution, in contrast, couples to the spin of the target nuclei and scales with $J(J + 1)$. Naïvely, this could be considered a coherent subtraction of amplitudes of opposite signs of pairs of nucleons. As the current spin-dependent scattering constraints are not strong enough to test many dark matter models, we primarily focus upon the process of spin-independent scattering.

The spin-independent WIMP-nucleus elastic scattering cross section is given by

$$\sigma \approx \frac{4 m_X^2 m_T^2}{\pi (m_X + m_T)^2} [Z f_p + (A - Z) f_n]^2, \qquad 3.$$

where m_T is the mass of the target nucleus, m_X is the WIMP's mass, and Z and A are the atomic number and atomic mass of the nucleus. f_p and f_n are the WIMP's couplings to protons and neutrons, given by

$$f_{p,n} = \sum_{q=u,d,s} f_{T_q}^{(p,n)} a_q \frac{m_{p,n}}{m_q} + \frac{2}{27} f_{TG}^{(p,n)} \sum_{q=c,b,t} a_q \frac{m_{p,n}}{m_q}, \qquad 4.$$

where a_q are the WIMP-quark couplings and $f_{T_q}^{(p,n)}$ denote the quark content of the nucleon.

The first term in Equation 4 corresponds to interactions with the quarks in the target nuclei. In the case of neutralino dark matter, spin-independent elastic scattering can occur through either t channel CP-even Higgs exchange, or s channel squark exchange:

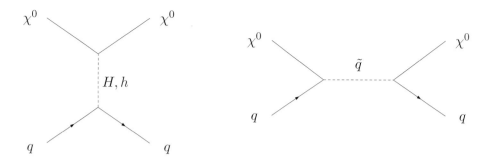

The second term corresponds to interactions with the gluons in the target through a loop diagram (a quark/squark loop in the case of supersymmetry). $f_{TG}^{(p)}$ is given by $1 - f_{T_u}^{(p)} - f_{T_d}^{(p)} - f_{T_s}^{(p)} \approx 0.84$, and analogously, $f_{TG}^{(n)} \approx 0.83$.

The WIMP cross section depends on both its mass and its couplings to quarks, a_q. In the case of neutralino dark matter, the value of this coupling depends on many features of the supersymmetric spectrum. The contribution resulting from Higgs exchange depends on the neutralino composition as well as the Higgs masses and couplings. In the case of heavy squarks, small wino component, and little mixing between the CP-even Higgs bosons ($\cos\alpha \approx 1$), neutralino-nuclei elastic scattering is dominated by H exchange with strange and bottom quarks, leading to a neutralino-nucleon cross section approximately given by

$$\sigma_{\chi N} \sim \frac{g_1^2 g_2^2 f_{\tilde{B}} f_{\tilde{H}} m_N^4}{4\pi m_W^2 \cos^2\beta m_H^4} \left(f_{T_s} + \frac{2}{27} f_{TG} \right)^2 , \quad (m_{\tilde{q}} \text{ large, } \cos\alpha \approx 1), \qquad 5.$$

where $f_{\tilde{B}}$ and $f_{\tilde{H}}$ denote the bino and higgsino fractions of the lightest neutralino and $\tan\beta$ is the ratio of the vevs of the two Higgs doublets in the minimal supersymmetric Standard Model (MSSM). Note that the coupling involves the product of $f_{\tilde{B}}$ and $f_{\tilde{H}}$. Purely gaugino or purely higgsino neutralinos have a suppressed cross section with nuclei. The fundamental reason for this is that the relevant vertex is gaugino-higgsino-Higgs.

If the heavier of the two CP-even Higgs bosons is very heavy and/or $\tan\beta$ is small, scattering with up-type quarks through light Higgs exchange can dominate:

$$\sigma_{\chi N} \sim \frac{g_1^2 g_2^2 f_{\tilde{B}} f_{\tilde{H}} m_N^4}{4\pi m_W^2 m_h^4} \left(f_{T_u} + \frac{4}{27} f_{TG} \right)^2 , \quad (m_{\tilde{q}}, \ m_H \text{ large, } \cos\alpha \approx 1). \qquad 6.$$

If $\tan\beta$ and m_H are large and the squarks are somewhat light, elastic scattering can instead be dominated by squark exchange:

$$\sigma_{\chi N} \sim \frac{g_1^2 g_2^2 f_{\tilde{B}} f_{\tilde{H}} m_N^4}{4\pi m_W^2 \cos^2\beta \, m_{\tilde{q}}^4} \left(f_{T_s} + \frac{2}{27} f_{TG} \right)^2 , \quad (\tilde{q} \text{ dominated, } \tan\beta \gg 1). \qquad 7.$$

From these expressions (28), it is clear that the direct detection of dark matter alone will not be capable of revealing much about supersymmetry or the other underlying physics. There are many different sets of supersymmetric parameters that can lead to a given value of the WIMP-nucleon cross section. Only by combining this information with collider and/or indirect detection data can one hope to infer the nature of the dark matter particle.

Currently, the strongest limits on the spin-independent WIMP-nucleon cross section come from the XENON (11) and CDMS (12) experiments, which have obtained an upper bound on the cross section of a ∼100-GeV WIMP at the ∼10^{-7}-pb level. These constraints, along with those of other experiments, are shown in **Figure 1**.

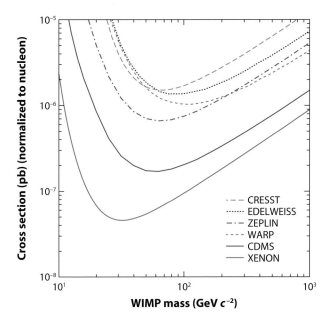

Figure 1

The current limits on the spin-independent weakly interacting massive particle (WIMP)-nuclei (normalized per nucleon) elastic scattering cross section as a function of the WIMP mass. *From bottom to top*: constraints from the XENON (11), CDMS (Cryogenic Dark Matter Search) (12), WARP (WIMP Argon Programme) (17), ZEPLIN (Zoned Proportional Scintillation in Liquid Noble Gases) (14), EDELWEISS (Expérience pour Détecter les WIMPs en Site Souterrain) (15), and CRESST (Center for Research and Exploration in Space Science and Technology) (16) experiments. The plot was generated using the tool found at **http://dmtools.berkeley.edu/limitplots/**.

Currently investigators are making a great deal of progress in the experimental field of direct detection. In February 2008, the CDMS collaboration released a new limit that is more stringent than those of any other experiment. Also, the XENON collaboration is preparing for a run with a larger detector, with results expected within a year or so of this writing. Beyond the next year or two, it is difficult to foresee which experiment(s) will be leading this search. It is still not clear whether detectors using liquid noble elements or those using cryogenic technologies will advance more rapidly. For the time being, there are clear advantages to proceeding with multiple technologies.

Despite our inability to predict how this field will develop, it is reasonable to expect that by 2010 direct detection experiments will reach sensitivities of $\sim 10^{-9}$-pb level of sensitivity. Generally speaking, such cross sections are sufficient to test many (if not most) supersymmetric models as well as many WIMP candidates in other particle physics frameworks. Given the rate at which direct dark matter experiments are developing, it is important to recognize that such experiments are likely to see their first evidence for WIMPs within the same time frame in which the LHC is expected to reveal the presence of the associated physics. Therefore it will be essential to compare the mass of the WIMP observed in each experimental program.

Direct detection experiments can determine the mass of the WIMP by measuring the distribution of the recoil energy, E_R (29). The energy varies with the mass of the WIMP with a resonance where the WIMP mass equals the target mass. Generally, one expects

$$\langle E_R \rangle \approx \frac{2v^2 m_T}{(1 + m_T/m_\chi)^2},$$

8.

where m_T is the target mass and v is the WIMP velocity, with corrections depending on the precise target material and the properties of the detector (30). Assuming the standard velocity distribution in smooth halo models, with approximately 10% uncertainty, an experiment with a xenon or germanium target that detects 100 signal events for a WIMP of mass $m_X = 100$ GeV can expect to measure the mass of this particle at the 20% level, thus potentially confirming the cosmological stability (and abundance) of a WIMP detected at the LHC.

If the WIMP mass inferred in a direct detection experiment were inconsistent with that measured at the LHC, it could imply that different particle species are being observed, or it could be the result of a nonstandard dark matter velocity distribution. In the future, directional dark matter detectors may help to prevent such confusion.

4. INDIRECT DETECTION

In parallel to direct detection experiments, a wide range of indirect detection programs have been developed to search for the annihilation products of dark matter particles. In particular, searches are underway to detect (*a*) neutrinos from dark matter annihilations in the core of the Sun, (*b*) antimatter particles from dark matter annihilations in the galactic halo, and (*c*) photons from dark matter annihilations in the halo of the Milky Way, galactic substructure, and the dark matter distribution integrated over cosmological volumes. In this section, we briefly describe the role of these experimental programs in the overall strategy to reveal the identity of dark matter.

4.1. Gamma Rays

Searches for prompt photons generated in dark matter annihilations have a key advantage over other indirect detection channels in that photons travel essentially unimpeded from their production site. In particular, gamma rays are not deflected by magnetic fields, and thus can potentially provide valuable directional information. For example, point sources of dark matter annihilation radiation might appear from high-density regions such as the Galactic Center or dwarf spheroidal galaxies. Furthermore, over galactic distance scales gamma rays are not attenuated; thus they retain their spectral information. In other words, the spectrum observed at Earth is the same spectrum that was generated in the dark matter annihilations.

The spectrum of photons produced in dark matter annihilations depends on the details of the WIMP being considered. Supersymmetric neutralinos, for example, typically annihilate to final states consisting of heavy fermions and gauge or Higgs bosons (22). Generally speaking, each of these annihilation modes typically results in a very similar spectrum of gamma rays. The gamma ray spectrum from a WIMP that annihilates to light leptons can be quite different, however. This difference can be particularly important in the case of Kaluza–Klein dark matter in models with one universal extra dimension, for example, in which dark matter particles annihilate significantly to e^+e^- and $\mu^+\mu^-$ (9).

The Galactic Center has long been considered one of the most promising regions of the sky in which to search for gamma rays from dark matter annihilations (31). However, the prospects for such a search depend on a number of factors, including the nature of the WIMP, the distribution of dark matter in the region around the Galactic Center, and our understanding of the astrophysical backgrounds. The gamma ray spectrum produced through dark matter annihilations is given by

$$\Phi_\gamma(E_\gamma, \psi) = \frac{1}{2} \langle \sigma v \rangle \frac{d N_\gamma}{d E_\gamma} \frac{1}{4\pi m_X^2} \int_{\text{los}} \rho^2(r) dl(\psi) d\psi.$$ 9.

Here, $\langle\sigma v\rangle$ is the thermally averaged WIMP annihilation cross section, m_X is the mass of the WIMP, ψ is the angle observed relative to the direction of the Galactic Center, $\rho(r)$ is the dark matter density as a function of distance to the Galactic Center, and the integral is performed over the line of sight. dN_γ/dE_γ is the gamma ray spectrum generated per WIMP annihilation. Averaging over a solid angle centered around a direction, ψ, we arrive at

$$\Phi_\gamma(E_\gamma) \approx 2.8 \times 10^{-12} \text{ cm}^{-2}\text{ s}^{-1} \frac{dN_\gamma}{dE_\gamma} \left(\frac{\langle\sigma v\rangle}{3 \times 10^{-26} \text{ cm}^3/\text{s}} \right) \left(\frac{1 \text{ TeV}}{m_X} \right)^2 \bar{\mathcal{J}}(\Delta\Omega, \psi)\Delta\Omega, \qquad 10.$$

where $\Delta\Omega$ is the solid angle observed. The quantity $\bar{\mathcal{J}}(\Delta\Omega, \psi)$ depends only on the dark matter distribution and is the average over the solid angle of the quantity

$$\mathcal{J}(\psi) = \frac{1}{8.5 \text{ kpc}} \left(\frac{1}{0.3 \text{ GeV/cm}^3} \right)^2 \int_{\text{los}} \rho^2(r(l, \psi))dl. \qquad 11.$$

$\mathcal{J}(\psi)$ is normalized such that a completely flat halo profile, with a density equal to the value at the solar circle and integrated along the line of sight to the Galactic Center, would yield a value of one. In dark matter distributions favored by N-body simulations, however, this value can be much larger. The Navarro–Frenk–White profile (32), a commonly used benchmark halo model, leads to values of $\bar{\mathcal{J}}(\Delta\Omega = 10^{-5} \text{ sr}, \psi = 0) \sim 10^5$. The effects of adiabatic contraction due to the cooling of baryons are expected to further increase this quantity (33).

The recent discovery of a bright, very high energy gamma ray source in the Galactic Center region by the telescopes HESS (High-Energy Stereoscopic System) (34), MAGIC (Major Atmospheric Gamma-ray Imaging Cherenkov) (35), VERITAS (Very Energetic Radiation Imaging Telescope Array System) (36), and CANGAROO-II [Collaboration of Australia and Nippon (Japan) for a Gamma Ray Observatory in the Outback II] (37) has complicated efforts to identify gamma rays from dark matter annihilations. This source appears to be coincident with the dynamical center of the Milky Way (Sgr A*) and has no detectable angular extension (less than 1.2 arcmin). Its spectrum is well described by a power law, $dN_\gamma/dE_\gamma \propto E_\gamma^{-\alpha}$, where $\alpha = 2.25 \pm 0.04(\text{stat}) \pm 0.10(\text{syst})$ over the range of 160 GeV to 20 TeV. Although investigators initially speculated that this source could be the product of annihilations of very heavy ($\gtrsim$10 TeV) dark matter particles (38), the spectral shape appears inconsistent with a dark matter interpretation. The source of these gamma rays is more likely an astrophysical accelerator associated with our galaxy's central supermassive black hole (39). Although this gamma ray source represents a formidable background for GLAST (Gamma-Ray Large Area Space Telescope) and other experiments searching for dark matter annihilation radiation (40), it may be possible to reduce the impact of this and other backgrounds by studying the angular distribution of gamma rays from this region of the sky (41).

The prospects for identifying dark matter annihilation radiation from the Galactic Center depend critically on the unknown dark matter density within the inner parsecs of the Milky Way and on the properties of the astrophysical backgrounds present. If these characteristics are favorable, then the Galactic Center is very likely to be the most promising region of the sky to study. If not, other regions with high dark matter densities may be more advantageous.

Dwarf spheroidal galaxies within and near the Milky Way provide an opportunity to search for dark matter annihilation radiation with considerably less contamination from astrophysical backgrounds. The flux of gamma rays from dark matter annihilations in such objects, however, is also expected to be lower than from a cusp in the center of the Milky Way (42–44). As a result, planned experiments are likely to observe dark matter annihilation radiation from dwarf galaxies only in the most favorable range of particle physics models.

The integrated gamma ray signal from dark matter annihilations throughout the cosmological distribution of dark matter may also provide an opportunity to identify the products of dark matter annihilations. The ability of future gamma ray telescopes to identify a dark matter component of the diffuse flux depends strongly on the fraction of the extragalactic gamma ray background observed by the EGRET (Energetic Gamma Ray Experiment Telescope), which will be resolved as individual sources such as blazars. If a large fraction of this background is resolved, the remaining extragalactic signal could potentially contain identifiable signatures of dark matter annihilations (45).

The telescopes potentially capable of detecting gamma rays from dark matter annihilations in the near future include the satellite-based experiment GLAST (46) and a number of ground-based Atmospheric Cherenkov Telescopes such as HESS, MAGIC, and VERITAS. The roles played by these two classes of experiments in the search for dark matter are quite different. GLAST will continuously observe a large fraction of the sky, but with an effective area far smaller than that of ground-based telescopes. Ground-based telescopes, in contrast, study the emission from a small angular field, but with far greater exposure. Furthermore, whereas ground-based telescopes can only study gamma rays with energy greater than $\sim$100 GeV, GLAST will be able to directly study gamma rays with energies ranging from 100 MeV to 300 GeV.

As a result of the different energy ranges accessible by these experiments, searches for dark matter particles lighter than a few hundred GeV are most promising with GLAST, whereas ground-based telescopes are better suited for heavier WIMPs. The large field of view of GLAST also makes it well suited for measurements of the diffuse gamma ray background. GLAST is also expected to detect a number of unidentified sources, some of which could potentially be signals of dark matter substructures. Follow-up observations with ground-based gamma ray telescopes would be very useful for clarifying the nature of such sources.

4.2. Antimatter

WIMP annihilations in the galactic halo generate charged antimatter particles: positrons, antiprotons, and antideuterons. Unlike gamma rays, which travel along straight lines, charged particles move under the influence of the Galactic Magnetic Field, diffusing and losing energy; this results in a diffuse spectrum at Earth. By studying the cosmic antimatter spectra, satellite-based experiments such as PAMELA (Payload for Antimatter Matter Exploration and Light-Nuclei Astrophysics) (47) and AMS-02 (Alpha Magnetic Spectrometer) (48) may be able to identify signatures of dark matter. PAMELA began its three-year satellite mission in June 2006. AMS-02 is planned for later deployment aboard the International Space Station.

Compared to antiprotons and antideuterons, cosmic positrons are more attractive probes of dark matter for several reasons. Positrons lose the majority of their energy over typical length scales of up to a few kiloparsecs (49). The cosmic positron spectrum, therefore, samples only the local dark matter distribution and is thus subject to considerably less uncertainty than the other antimatter species. Additionally, data from the HEAT (High-Energy Antimatter Telescope) (50) and AMS-01 experiments (51) contain features that could plausibly be the consequence of dark matter annihilations in the local halo.

The spectral shape of the cosmic positron spectrum generated in dark matter annihilation depends on the leading annihilation modes of the WIMP in the low velocity limit. Bino-like neutralinos, for example, typically annihilate to heavy fermion pairs: $b\bar{b}$ with a small $\tau^+\tau^-$ admixture, along with a fraction to $t\bar{t}$ if $m_\chi \gtrsim m_t$. Wino- or higgsino-like neutralinos annihilate most efficiently to combinations of Higgs and gauge bosons. In other particle dark matter candidates, such as Kaluza–Klein dark matter in models with universal extra dimensions, annihilation to light charged leptons can lead to a much harder positron spectrum than is expected from neutralinos (52).

Once positrons are injected into the local halo through dark matter annihilations, they propagate under the influence of galactic magnetic fields, gradually losing energy through synchrotron emission and inverse Compton scattering with radiation fields such as starlight and the cosmic microwave background. The spectrum observed at Earth is found by solving the diffusion-loss equation (53)

$$\frac{\partial}{\partial t}\frac{dn_{e^+}}{dE_{e^+}} = \vec{\nabla} \cdot \left[K(E_{e^+}, \vec{x})\vec{\nabla}\frac{dn_{e^+}}{dE_{e^+}} \right] + \frac{\partial}{\partial E_{e^+}}\left[b(E_{e^+}, \vec{x})\frac{dn_{e^+}}{dE_{e^+}} \right] + Q(E_{e^+}, \vec{x}), \qquad 12.$$

where dn_{e^+}/dE_{e^+} is the number density of positrons per unit energy, $K(E_{e^+}, \vec{x})$ is the diffusion constant, $b(E_{e^+}, \vec{x})$ is the rate of energy loss, and $Q(E_{e^+}, \vec{x})$ is the source term that contains all of the information about the dark matter annihilation modes, cross section, and distribution. To solve the diffusion-loss equation, a set of boundary conditions must be adopted. In this application, the boundary condition is described as the distance from the galactic plane at which the positrons can freely escape, L. These diffusion parameters can be constrained by studying the spectra of various species of cosmic ray nuclei, most importantly the boron-to-carbon ratio (54).

In **Figure 2**, the ratio of positrons to positrons plus electrons in the cosmic ray spectrum is shown as a function of energy and includes a possible contribution from dark matter annihilations. Also shown in **Figure 2** are the measurements from the HEAT experiment (50), which might contain an excess of positrons relative to electrons in comparison to standard astrophysical expectations at energies above ~7 GeV. Although positrons from dark matter annihilations are

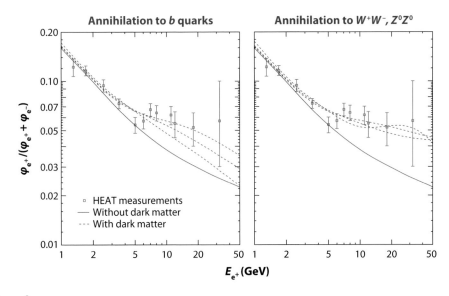

Figure 2

The positron fraction including the contribution from dark matter annihilations compared to the measurements of the HEAT (High-Energy Antimatter Telescope) experiment (50). Results are shown for weakly interacting massive particle (WIMP) masses of 100, 300, and 600 GeV. In panel a (b), the WIMP is assumed to annihilate to $b\bar{b}$ (a mixture of ZZ and W^+W^-). If an annihilation cross section of $\sigma v \approx 3 \times 10^{-26}$ cm^3 s^{-1} and a local density of 0.3 GeV cm^{-3} are assumed, the annihilation rate must be boosted by a factor of approximately 50 or more to normalize to the HEAT data. The solid line denotes the prediction from the galactic cosmic ray model in Reference 56.

indeed able to generate this possible excess, this requires a somewhat larger annihilation rate than is typically expected. In particular, if a smooth dark matter halo and an annihilation cross section of $\sigma v \approx 3 \times 10^{-26}$ cm^3 s^{-1} (as required to thermally produce the observed dark matter abundance via S wave processes) are assumed, the annihilation rate will be a factor of 50 or more too low to generate the spectrum measured by HEAT. Fluctuations in the local dark matter density, however, could lead to enhancements in the local annihilation rate, known as the boost factor. It is typically expected that this quantity could be as large as five to ten. Although boost factors of 50 or more are not impossible, such large values would be somewhat surprising.

If the positron flux observed by HEAT is in fact the result of annihilating dark matter, then the corresponding spectrum will be precisely measured by PAMELA (47) and AMS-02 (48). If not, then the detection of positrons from dark matter annihilations will be more difficult, but perhaps still possible (55).

Unlike gamma ray measurements of the Galactic Center or dwarf galaxies, observations of the cosmic positron spectrum (as well as the antiproton and antideuteron spectra) could potentially provide a measurement of the dark matter annihilation rate over large volumes of space. Such a measurement, therefore, could be used to determine the product of the WIMP's annihilation cross section and its density squared, averaged over the sampled volume (a region of roughly a few cubic kiloparsecs, which corresponds to the distance a typical positron travels from its point of origin before losing the majority of its energy). As a result of this limited range, only the dark matter distribution in the local halo is relevant to the observed cosmic positron flux. Assuming there are no very large and unknown clumps of dark matter in the surrounding kiloparsecs (which, although not impossible, is very unlikely; see Reference 57), a measurement of the cosmic positron spectrum could be used to infer the dark matter particle's annihilation cross section (in the low velocity limit) with a comparatively modest degree of uncertainty coming from the unknown distribution of dark matter.

4.3. Neutrino Telescopes

Although dark matter annihilations in the galactic halo produce too few neutrinos to be detected (58), annihilations that occur in the center of the Sun could potentially generate an observable flux of high-energy neutrinos (59). Dark matter particles scatter elastically with and become captured in the Sun at a rate given by (60)

$$C^{\odot} \approx 3.35 \times 10^{19} \text{ s}^{-1} \left(\frac{\sigma_{H,SD} + \sigma_{H,SI} + 0.07 \, \sigma_{He,SI}}{10^{-7} \text{ pb}} \right) \left(\frac{100 \, \text{GeV}}{m_X} \right)^2, \qquad 13.$$

where m_X is the dark matter particle's mass and $\sigma_{H,SD}$, $\sigma_{H,SI}$, and $\sigma_{He,SI}$ are the spin-dependent and spin-independent elastic scattering cross sections of the WIMP with hydrogen and helium nuclei, respectively. The factor of 0.07 reflects the solar abundance of helium relative to hydrogen as well as dynamical factors and form factor suppression.

Notice that the capture rate is suppressed by two factors of the WIMP mass. One of these factors is simply the result of the depleted number density of WIMPs in the local halo ($n \propto 1/m$), whereas the second factor is the result of kinematic suppression for the capture of a WIMP much heavier than the target nuclei, in this case hydrogen or helium. If the WIMP's mass were comparable to the masses of hydrogen or helium nuclei, these expressions would no longer be valid. For WIMPs heavy enough to generate neutrinos detectable in the high-energy neutrino telescopes, Equation 13 should apply.

If the capture rate and annihilation cross sections are sufficiently large, equilibrium will be reached between these processes. For a number of WIMPs in the Sun, N, the rate of change of this quantity is given by

$$\dot{N} = C^{\odot} - A^{\odot} N^2, \tag{14.}$$

where $C^{\odot}$ is the capture rate and $A^{\odot}$ is the annihilation cross section multiplied by the relative WIMP velocity per volume. $A^{\odot}$ can be approximated by

$$A^{\odot} \approx \frac{\langle \sigma v \rangle}{V_{\text{eff}}}, \tag{15.}$$

where V_{eff} is the effective volume of the core of the Sun determined approximately by matching the core temperature with the gravitational potential energy of a single WIMP at the core radius. The authors of References 61 and 62 calculated this to be

$$V_{\text{eff}} \approx 5.7 \times 10^{27} \text{ cm}^3 \left(\frac{100 \text{ GeV}}{m_X} \right)^{3/2}. \tag{16.}$$

The present WIMP annihilation rate in the Sun is given by

$$\Gamma = \frac{1}{2} A^{\odot} N^2 = \frac{1}{2} C^{\odot} \tanh^2 \left(\sqrt{C^{\odot} A^{\odot}} t_{\odot} \right), \tag{17.}$$

where $t_{\odot} \approx 4.5$ billion years is the age of the solar system. The annihilation rate is maximized when it reaches equilibrium with the capture rate; this occurs when

$$\sqrt{C^{\odot} A^{\odot}} t_{\odot} \gg 1. \tag{18.}$$

If this condition is met, the final annihilation rate (and corresponding neutrino flux and event rate) has no further dependence on the dark matter particle's annihilation cross section.

WIMPs can generate neutrinos through a wide range of annihilation channels. Annihilations to heavy quarks, tau leptons, gauge bosons, and Higgs bosons can all generate neutrinos in the subsequent decay. In some models, WIMPs can also annihilate directly to neutrino pairs. Once produced, neutrinos can travel to Earth where they can be detected. The muon–neutrino spectrum at Earth from WIMP annihilations in the Sun is given by

$$\frac{dN_{\nu_\mu}}{dE_{\nu_\mu}} = \frac{C_{\odot} F_{\text{Eq}}}{4 \pi D_{\text{ES}}^2} \left(\frac{dN_\nu}{dE_\nu} \right)^{\text{Inj}}, \tag{19.}$$

where $C_{\odot}$ is the WIMP capture rate in the Sun, F_{Eq} is the nonequilibrium suppression factor (≈ 1 for capture-annihilation equilibrium), D_{ES} is the distance from Earth to Sun, and $(\frac{dN_\nu}{dE_\nu})^{\text{Inj}}$ is the neutrino spectrum from the Sun per WIMP annihilating. Due to $\nu_\mu - \nu_\tau$ vacuum oscillations, the muon neutrino flux from WIMP annihilations in the Sun observed at Earth is the average of the ν_μ and ν_τ components.

Muon neutrinos produce muons in charged current interactions with ice or water nuclei inside or near the detector volume of a high-energy neutrino telescope. The rate of neutrino-induced muons observed in a high-energy neutrino telescope is estimated by

$$N_{\text{events}} \simeq \iint \frac{dN_{\nu_\mu}}{dE_{\nu_\mu}} \frac{d\sigma_\nu}{dy} (E_{\nu_\mu}, y) R_\mu ((1-y)E_\nu) A_{\text{eff}} \, dE_{\nu_\mu} \, dy, \tag{20.}$$

where $\sigma_\nu(E_{\nu_\mu})$ is the neutrino-nucleon charged current interaction cross section; $(1 - y)$ is the fraction of neutrino energy that goes into the muon; A_{eff} is the effective area of the detector; and $R_\mu((1-y)E_\nu)$ is the distance a muon of energy, $(1-y)E_\nu$, travels before falling below the muon energy threshold of the experiment (ranging from ~ 1 to 100 GeV), also known as the muon range.

The spectrum and flux of neutrinos generated in WIMP annihilations depend on the annihilation modes that dominate, and thus are model dependent. For most annihilation modes, however,

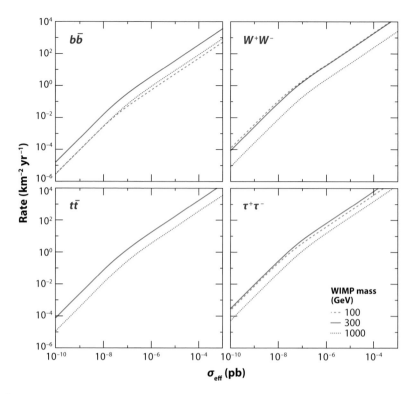

Figure 3

The event rate in a kilometer-scale neutrino telescope such as IceCube as a function of the weakly interacting massive particle's (WIMP's) effective elastic scattering cross section in the Sun for a variety of annihilation modes. The effective elastic scattering cross section is defined as $\sigma_{eff} = \sigma_{H,SD} + \sigma_{H,SI} + 0.07\sigma_{He,SI}$, following Equation 13. The dashed, solid, and dotted lines correspond to WIMPs of mass 100, 300, and 1000 GeV, respectively.

the variation from model to model is not dramatic. In **Figure 3**, the event rate in a kilometer-scale neutrino telescope (with a 50-GeV muon energy threshold) is shown as a function of the WIMP's effective elastic scattering cross section for a variety of annihilation modes (63). The effective elastic scattering cross section is defined as $\sigma_{eff} = \sigma_{H,SD} + \sigma_{H,SI} + 0.07\sigma_{He,SI}$, following Equation 13. These rates are indicative of those expected for experiments such as IceCube at the South Pole (64), or a future kilometer-scale neutrino telescope in the Mediterranean Sea (65). To detect neutrinos from WIMP annihilations in the Sun over the background of atmospheric neutrinos, a rate within the range of 10–100 km^{-2} year^{-1} events is required.

Currently the Super-Kamiokande (Super-K) experiment has placed the strongest bounds on high-energy neutrinos from the direction of the Sun (66). In this application, Super-K has two primary advantages over other neutrino detectors. First, it has analyzed data over a longer period than most of its competitors—a total of nearly 1700 live days. Second, Super-K was designed to be sensitive to low-energy ($\sim$GeV) neutrinos, which gives it an advantage in searching for lighter WIMPs. Super-K's upper limit on neutrino-induced muons above 1 GeV from WIMP annihilations in the Sun is approximately 1000 to 2000 km^{-2} year^{-1} for WIMPs heavier than 100 GeV and approximately 2000 to 5000 km^{-2} year^{-1} for WIMPs in the 20–100 GeV range. The precise value of these limits depends on the WIMP annihilation mode considered.

The AMANDA-II (Antarctic Muon and Neutrino Detector Array) (67), Baksan (68), and MACRO (Monopole, Astrophysics, and Cosmic Ray Observatory) (69) experiments have all placed limits on the flux of neutrino-induced muons from the Sun that are only slightly weaker than those of Super-K. The limit placed by the AMANDA experiment resulted from only 144 live days of data. Having operated the detector for seven years, AMANDA is expected to produce significantly improved bounds in the future.

In addition to these experiments, two next-generation neutrino telescopes, IceCube and ANTARES (Astronomy with a Neutrino Telescope and Abyss Environmental Research Project), are currently under construction at the South Pole and in the Mediterranean Sea, respectively. IceCube, with a full cubic kilometer of instrumented volume, will be considerably more sensitive to WIMP annihilations in the Sun than other planned or existing experiments (64). ANTARES, which will have less than one-tenth of the effective area of IceCube, will have the advantage of a lower energy threshold and thus may be more sensitive to low-mass WIMPs (70). Beyond ANTARES, there are also plans to build a kilometer-scale detector in the Mediterranean Sea (65).

From **Figure 3**, we see that a WIMP-proton elastic scattering cross section on the order of 10^{-6} pb or greater is needed if kilometer-scale neutrino telescopes are to detect a signal from dark matter annihilations. Elastic scattering cross sections of this size are constrained by the absence of a positive signal in direct detection experiments, however. Currently, the strongest constraints on the WIMP-nucleon spin-independent elastic scattering cross section have been made by the XENON (11) and CDMS experiments (12), both of which place limits below 10^{-6} pb. Therefore, if current or planned neutrino telescopes are to detect neutrinos from dark matter annihilations in the Sun, they must scatter elastically with nuclei in the Sun via spin-dependent interactions, which are far less strongly constrained by direct detection experiments. The strongest bounds on the WIMP-proton spin-dependent cross section have been made by the NAIAD (NaI Advanced Detector) experiment (71). This result limits the spin-dependent cross section with protons to be less than approximately 0.3 pb for a WIMP in the mass range of 50 to 100 GeV and less than 0.8 pb $(m_X/500 \text{ GeV})$ for a heavier WIMP. The PICASSO (Projet d'Identification de Candidats Supersymétriques Sombres) (72) and CDMS (13) experiments have placed limits on the spin-dependent WIMP-proton cross section approximately one order of magnitude weaker than the NAIAD result. A WIMP with a largely spin-dependent scattering cross section with protons may thus be capable of generating large event rates in high-energy neutrino telescopes. For example, given a 300-GeV WIMP with an elastic scattering cross section near the experimental limit, **Figure 3** suggests that rates as high as $\sim 10^6$ year^{-1} could be generated if purely spin-dependent scattering contributes to the capture rate of WIMPs in the Sun.

The relative size of the spin-independent and spin-dependent elastic scattering cross sections depends on the nature of the WIMP in question. For a neutralino, these cross sections depend on its composition and on the mass spectrum of the exchanged Higgs bosons and squarks. Spin-dependent axial-vector scattering of neutralinos with quarks within a nucleon is made possible through the t channel exchange of a Z, or the s channel exchange of a squark. Spin-independent scattering occurs (*a*) at the tree level through s channel squark exchange and t channel Higgs exchange and (*b*) at the one-loop level through diagrams involving a loop of quarks and/or squarks.

For higgsino-like or mixed higgsino-bino neutralinos, the spin-dependent cross section can be somewhat larger than the spin-independent cross section, which is potentially well suited for the prospects for indirect detection. In particular, spin-dependent cross sections as large as $\sim 10^{-3}$ pb are possible even in models with very small spin-independent scattering rates. Such neutralinos would remain easily undetected in all planned direct detection experiments, while still generating on the order of ~ 1000 events per year at IceCube.

4.4. Synchrotron Emission

As described in Section 4.2, electrons and positrons produced in dark matter annihilations travel under the influence of the Galactic Magnetic Field, losing energy through Compton scattering off of starlight, cosmic microwave background photons, and far infrared emission from dust, and through synchrotron emission from interactions with the Galactic Magnetic Field. The relative importance of these processes depends on the energy densities of radiation and magnetic fields.

The processes of synchrotron emission and inverse Compton scattering both lead to potentially observable byproducts (73). For dark matter particles with electroweak-scale masses, the resulting synchrotron photons typically fall within the microwave frequency band, and thus are well suited for study with cosmic microwave background experiments (74). The inverse Compton scattering of highly relativistic electrons and positrons with starlight photons, on the other hand, can generate photons with megaelectronvolt to gigaelectronvolt energies.

5. THE ROLE OF COLLIDERS

Among other new states, particles with TeV-scale masses and quantum chromodynamics color are generic features of models of electroweak symmetry breaking. These particles appear as counterparts to the quarks to provide new physics associated with the generation of the large top quark mass. In many scenarios, including supersymmetry, electroweak symmetry breaking arises as a result of radiative corrections due to these particles, enhanced by the large coupling of the Higgs boson to the top quark.

Any particle with these properties will be pair-produced at the LHC with a cross section of tens of picobarns (75). That particle (or particles) will then subsequently decay to particles including quarks or gluon jets and the lightest particle in the new sector (i.e., the dark matter candidate), which will proceed to exit the detector unseen. For any such model the LHC experiments are, therefore, expected to observe large numbers of events with many hadronic jets and an imbalance of measured momentum. These "missing energy" events are signatures of a wide range of models that contain an electroweak-scale candidate for dark matter.

If TeV-scale supersymmetry exists in nature, it will very likely be within the discovery reach of the LHC. The rate of missing energy events depends strongly on the mass of the colored particles that are produced and depends only weakly on other properties of the model. In **Figure 4**, the estimates of the ATLAS (A Toroidal LHC Apparatus) collaboration are shown for the discovery of missing energy events (76). If squarks or gluinos have masses below 1 TeV, the missing energy events can be discovered with an integrated luminosity of 100 pb^{-1}, about 1% of the LHC first-year design luminosity. Thus, we will know very early in the LHC program whether a WIMP candidate is being produced.

In studying the decays of squarks and/or gluinos, it will also be possible to discover other superpartners at the LHC. For example, in many models, decays of the variety $\tilde{q} \rightarrow \chi_2^0 q \rightarrow \tilde{l}^\pm l^\mp q \rightarrow \chi_1^0 l^+ l^- q$ provide a clean signal of supersymmetry in the form of $l^+ l^- + \text{jets} + \text{missing } E_\mathrm{T}$. By studying the kinematics of these decays, the quantities $m_{\tilde{q}}$, $m_{\chi_2^0}$, $m_{\tilde{l}}$, and $m_{\chi_1^0}$ could each be potentially reconstructed (77–79). More generally speaking, the LHC—in most models—is likely to measure the mass of the lightest neutralino to approximately 10% accuracy, and it may also be able to determine the masses of one or more of the other neutralinos and any light sleptons (80). Charginos are more difficult to study at the LHC.

The heavy, neutral Higgs bosons of the MSSM (A, H) can also be potentially produced and studied at the LHC. In particular, in models with large tan β heavy Higgs bosons have enhanced couplings to down-type fermions, thereby leading to potentially observable ditau final states. If

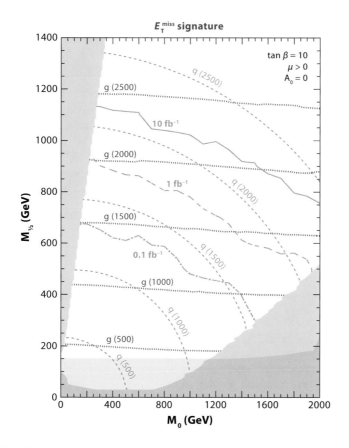

E_T^{miss} **signature**

$\tan\beta = 10$
$\mu > 0$
$A_0 = 0$

Figure 4

The discovery reach for supersymmetry via the missing energy plus jets signature by the ATLAS (A Toroidal LHC Apparatus) experiment at the Large Hadron Collider (LHC). The three sets of contours correspond to levels of integrated luminosity at the LHC (in fb^{-1}), contours of constant squark mass, and contours of constant gluino mass. Reproduced with permission from Reference 76.

enough of these events are observed, the masses of the heavy Higgs bosons could be potentially reconstructed and $\tan\beta$ measured (81, 82).

Prospects for the discovery of supersymmetry at the Tevatron, although not nearly as strong as at the LHC, are also exciting. The most likely discovery channel at the Tevatron is probably through clean trilepton plus missing energy events originating from the production of a chargino and a heavy neutralino, followed by a decay of the form $\chi^\pm \chi_2^0 \to \tilde{\nu} l^\pm \tilde{l}^- \to \nu \chi_1^0 l^\pm l^+ l^- \chi_1^0$ (83). Only models with rather light gauginos (neutralinos and charginos) and sleptons can be discovered in this way, however. For some of the recent results from supersymmetry searches at the Tevatron, see Reference 84.

Measurements of particle masses and other properties at the LHC can provide an essential cross check for direct and indirect detection channels. In particular, neither direct nor indirect detection experiments can provide information capable of identifying the overall cosmological abundance of a WIMP; instead, we infer only combinations of density and interaction cross section, leaving open the possibility that an observation may be generated by a subdominant component of the cosmological dark matter with a somewhat larger elastic scattering or annihilation cross section. Collider measurements can help to clarify this situation.

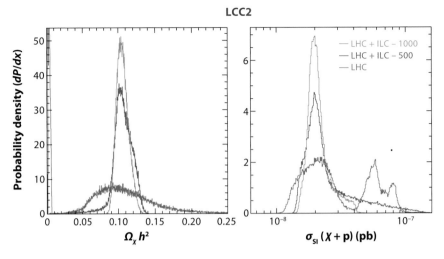

Figure 5

The neutralino relic abundance (*left*) and elastic scattering cross section (*right*) that might be extracted from future Large Hadron Collider (LHC) and a future International Linear Collider (ILC) experiments. The results shown are for a specific benchmark supersymmetry model (LCC2). See Reference 85 for more details.

In **Figure 5**, we show the thermal neutrino relic abundance that might be deduced from future LHC measurements of sparticle masses and other properties. The results shown are for a specific benchmark supersymmetric model (see Reference 85), but are not atypical. In this case, the LHC can infer $\Omega_\chi h^2$ to lie roughly within 0.05–0.2 (assuming properties such as R-parity conservation). Such an observation, along with a detection in either a direct or an indirect channel, would provide a strong confirmation that the observed neutralino does in fact constitute the bulk of the cosmological dark matter.

The right frame of **Figure 5**, for the same supersymmetric model, illustrates possible future LHC constraints on the neutralino-nucleon elastic scattering cross section. This information would be very useful in combination with a direct detection signal. In particular, it would enable the uncertainties in the local dark matter density to be reduced with confidence.

Also shown **Figure 5** are the results that could be obtained from a future 500-GeV or 1-TeV (center-of-mass) e^+e^- linear collider, such as the International Linear Collider (ILC) (86). Such an experiment would have considerable advantages over hadron colliders such as the Tevatron or the LHC. Although hadron colliders can reach very high center-of-mass energies, and thus can play an essential role as discovery machines, lepton colliders are best suited for lower energy precision measurements. In particular, at an electron-positron collider, the process $e^+e^- \rightarrow X\bar{X}$ can provide an exquisite diagnostic of the quantum numbers of the massive particle X. As long as only the diagrams with annihilation through γ and Z are relevant, the angular distribution and threshold shape of the reaction are characteristic for each spin, and the normalization of the cross section directly determines the $SU(2) \times U(1)$ quantum numbers. These tests can be applied to any particles with electric or weak charge whose pair-production thresholds lie in the range of the collider. Such a measurement could be used to pin down the spin and quantum numbers of a given particle and could bring us a long way toward qualitatively identifying the underlying model.

We cannot emphasize enough the importance of the complementary roles played by the LHC and ILC programs. Whereas the LHC can more easily reach high energies and offers very large cross sections for specific states of a model of new physics, the ILC will likely reach fewer states in the new particle spectrum but will provide extremely incisive measurements of the properties of the particles that are available to it. Furthermore, the particles within the ILC reach are typically the ones on which the dark matter density depends most strongly. Although both the LHC and ILC can make precision measurements, the measurements at the ILC will typically have a more direct interpretation in terms of particle masses and couplings.

6. SUMMARY

In this review, we have attempted to summarize the diverse and complementary roles played by the various direct, indirect, and collider searches for particle dark matter. As of 2008, dark matter's nongravitational interactions have not yet been clearly or conclusively detected. There is reason to be optimistic, however, that such a detection will be made within the next few years, moving the field beyond the discovery phase and into the measurement phase of the quest to reveal dark matter's nature and particle identity. As next-generation direct detection experiments such as Super-CDMS, XENON-plus, LUX, and others come online, they will begin to constrain most TeV-scale models containing a viable WIMP candidate. Indirect detection experiments, including GLAST, VERITAS, HESS, MAGIC, PAMELA, AMS-02, IceCube, and others, are also rapidly advancing and may see the first signals of dark matter annihilations. When the LHC begins operations later this year, it will open a new window into high-energy phenomena. If dark matter is indeed associated with physics of the electroweak scale, it is very likely to be within the reach of LHC experiments.

Each of the various experimental programs we describe in this review is potentially capable of bringing unique measurements to the table. Although any one of these programs may be the first to discover particle dark matter, no single experiment or observation will answer all of our questions concerning this substance. Only by combining several of these detection methods will it be possible to conclusively identify the dark matter of our universe.

DISCLOSURE STATEMENT

The authors are not aware of any biases that might be perceived as affecting the objectivity of this review.

ACKNOWLEDGMENTS

D.H. is supported by the United States Department of Energy and grant number NAG5-10842 from the National Aeronautics and Space Administration. Fermilab is operated by the Fermi Research Alliance, LLC under contract number DE-AC02-07CH11359 with the United States Department of Energy.

LITERATURE CITED

1. Borriello A, Salucci P. *MNRAS* 323:285 (2001)
2. Zwicky F. *Helv. Phys. Acta* 6:110 (1933)
3. Tyson JA, Kochanski GP, Dell'Antonio IP. *Astrophys. J.* 498:L107 (1998); Dahle H. astro-ph/0701598 (2007); Clowe D, et al. astro-ph/0608407 (2006)
4. Spergel DN, et al. (WMAP Collab.) *Astrophys. J. Suppl.* 170:377 (2007)
5. Olive KA, Steigman G, Walker TP. *Phys. Rep.* 333:389 (2000)
6. Tegmark M, et al. (SDSS Collab.) *Astrophys. J.* 606:702 (2004)
7. Bertone G, Hooper D, Silk J. *Phys. Rep.* 405:279 (2005)

8. Cheng HC, Low I. *JHEP* 0309:051 (2003); Wudka J. hep-ph/0307339 (2003)
9. Servant G, Tait TMP. *Nucl. Phys. B* 650:391 (2003); Cheng HC, Feng JL, Matchev KT. *Phys. Rev. Lett.* 89:211301 (2002); Hooper D, Profumo S. *Phys. Rep.* 453:29 (2007)
10. Cheng HC, Low I. *JHEP* 0408:061 (2004)
11. Angle J, et al. (XENON Collab.) astro-ph/07060039 (2007)
12. Akerib DS, et al. (CDMS Collab.) astro-ph/0509259 (2005)
13. Akerib DS, et al. (CDMS Collab.) astro-ph/0509269 (2005)
14. Alner GJ, et al. *Astropart. Phys.* 28:287 (2007); Alner GJ, et al. (UK Dark Matter Collab.) *Astropart. Phys.* 23:444 (2005)
15. Sanglard V, et al. (EDELWEISS Collab.) *Phys. Rev. D* 71:122002 (2005)
16. Angloher G, et al. *Astropart. Phys.* 23:325 (2005)
17. Benetti P, et al. astro-ph/0701286 (2007); Brunetti R, et al. *New Astron. Rev.* 49:265 (2005)
18. Bolte WJ, et al. *J. Phys. Conf. Ser.* 39:126 (2006)
19. Gates EI, Gyuk G, Turner MS. *Phys. Rev. D* 53:4138 (1996); Gates E, Gyuk G, Turner MS. astro-ph/9704253 (1997)
20. Drukier AK, Freese K, Spergel DN. *Phys. Rev. D* 33:3495 (1986)
21. Helmi A, White SDM, Springel V. *Phys. Rev. D* 66:063502 (2002)
22. Jungman G, Kamionkowski M, Griest K. *Phys. Rep.* 267:195 (1996)
23. Nelson AE, Kaplan DB. *Phys. Lett. B* 192:193 (1987); Kaplan DB, Manohar A. *Nucl. Phys. B* 310:527 (1988)
24. Bottino A, Donato F, Fornengo N, Scopel S. *Astropart. Phys.* 18:205 (2002)
25. Ellis JR, Olive KA, Santoso Y, Spanos VC. *Phys. Rev. D* 71:095007 (2005)
26. Michael C, McNeile C, Hepburn D. (UKQCD Collab.) *Nucl. Phys. Proc. Suppl.* 106:293 (2002)
27. Procura M, Hemmert TR, Weise W. *Phys. Rev. D* 69:034505 (2004)
28. Gelmini GB, Gondolo P, Roulet E. *Nucl. Phys. B* 351:623 (1991); Srednicki M, Watkins R. *Phys. Lett. B* 225:140 (1989); Drees M, Nojiri M. *Phys. Rev. D* 48:3483 (1993); Drees M, Nojiri MM. *Phys. Rev. D* 47:4226 (1993); Ellis JR, Ferstl A, Olive KA. *Phys. Lett. B* 481:304 (2000)
29. Green AM. *JCAP* 0708:022 hep-ph/0703217 (2007)
30. Lewin JD, Smith PF. *Astropart. Phys.* 6:87 (1996)
31. Bergstrom L, Ullio P, Buckley JH. *Astropart. Phys.* 9:137 (1998); Bergstrom L, Edsjo J, Ullio P. *Phys. Rev. Lett.* 87:251301 (2001); Berezinsky V, Bottino A, Mignola G. *Phys. Lett. B* 325:136 (1994); Cesarini A, et al. *Astropart. Phys.* 21:267 (2004); Ullio P, Bergstrom L, Edsjo J, Lacey CG. *Phys. Rev. D* 66:123502 (2002)
32. Navarro JF, Frenk CS, White SDM. *Astrophys. J.* 462:563 (1996); Navarro JF, Frenk CS, White SDM. *Astrophys. J.* 490:493 (1997)
33. Prada F, et al. astro-ph/0401512 (2004); Bertone G, Merritt D. *Mod. Phys. Lett. A* 20:1021 (2005); Bertone G, Merritt D. *Phys. Rev. D* 72:103502 (2005)
34. Aharonian F, et al. (HESS Collab.) astro-ph/0408145 (2004); Ahronian F. Presented at *TeV Part. Astrophys, Workshop, Batavia, IL.* (2005)
35. Albert J, et al. (MAGIC Collab.) *Astrophys. J.* 638:L101 (2006)
36. Kosack K, et al. (VERITAS Collab.) *Astrophys. J.* 608:L97 (2004)
37. Tsuchiya K, et al. (CANGAROO-II Collab.) *Astrophys. J.* 606:L115 (2004)
38. Hooper D, March-Russell J. *Phys. Lett. B* 608:17 (2005); Hooper D, et al. *JCAP* 0409:002 (2004); Profumo S. *Phys. Rev. D* 72:103521 (2005); Bergstrom L, Bringmann T, Eriksson M, Gustafsson M. *Phys. Rev. Lett.* 94:131301 (2005)
39. Aharonian F, Neronov A. *Astrophys. J.* 619:306 (2005); Aharonian F, Neronov A. astro-ph/0503354 (2005); Aharonian F, Neronov A. *AIP Conf. Proc.* 745:409 (2005); Atoyan A, Dermer CD. *Astrophys. J.* 617:L123 (2004)
40. Zaharijas G, Hooper D. *Phys. Rev. D* 73:103501 (2006)
41. Dodelson S, Hooper D, Serpico PD. astro-ph/0711.4621 (2007)
42. Evans NW, Ferrer F, Sarkar S. *Phys. Rev. D* 69:123501 (2004)
43. Bergstrom L, Hooper D. *Phys. Rev. D* 73:063510 (2006)
44. Strigari LE, et al. astro-ph/0709.1510 (2007)

45. Bergstrom L, Edsjo J, Ullio P. *Phys. Rev. Lett.* 87:251301 (2001); Ullio P, Bergstrom L, Edsjo J, Lacey CG. *Phys. Rev. D* 66:123502 (2002); Elsaesser D, Mannheim K. *Astropart. Phys.* 22:65 (2004); Hooper D, Serpico PD. *JCAP* 0706:013 (2007)

46. Gehrels N, Michelson P. *Astropart. Phys.* 11:277 (1999); Peirani S, Mohayaee R, de Freitas Pacheco JA. *Phys. Rev. D* 70:043503 (2004); Cesarini A, et al. *Astropart. Phys.* 21:267 (2004)

47. Morselli A, Picozza P. Presented at *Int. Workshop Identif. Dark Matter, 4th, York, England* (2002)

48. Sapinski M. (AMS Collab.) *Acta Phys. Polon. B* 37:1991 (2006); Goy C. (AMS Collab) *J. Phys. Conf. Ser.* 39:185 (2006)

49. Baltz EA, Edsjo J. *Phys. Rev. D* 59:023511 (1999)

50. Barwick SW, et al. (HEAT Collab.) *Astrophys. J.* 482:L191 (1997); Coutu S, et al. (HEAT-pbar Collab.) Presented at *Int. Cosm. Ray Conf., 27th, Hamburg, Ger.* (2001)

51. Olzem J. (AMS Collab.) Presented at *UCLA Symp. Sources Detect. Dark Matter Dark Energy Universe, 7th, Marina del Ray, CA, Feb. 22–24* (2006)

52. Hooper D, Kribs GD. *Phys. Rev. D* 70:115004 (2004)

53. Webber WR, Lee MA, Gupta M. *Astrophys. J.* 390:96 (1992); Moskalenko IV, Strong AW, Mashnik SG, Ormes JF. *Astrophys. J.* 586:1050 (2003); Moskalenko IV, Strong AW. *Phys. Rev. D* 60:063003 (1999)

54. Maurin D, Donato F, Taillet R, Salati P. *Astrophys. J.* 555:585 (2001); Maurin D, Taillet R, Donato F. *Astron. Astrophys.* 394:1039 (2002)

55. Hooper D, Silk J. *Phys. Rev. D* 71:083503 (2005)

56. Moskalenko IV, Strong AW. *Astrophys. J.* 493:694 (1998)

57. Hooper D, Taylor JE, Silk J. *Phys. Rev. D* 69:103509 (2004)

58. Bertone G, Nezri E, Orloff J, Silk J. *Phys. Rev. D* 70:063503 (2004)

59. Bergstrom L, Edsjo J, Gondolo P. *Phys. Rev. D* 55:1765 (1997); *Phys. Rev. D* 58:103519 (1998); Barger VD, Halzen F, Hooper D, Kao C. *Phys. Rev. D* 65:075022 (2002)

60. Gould A. *Astrophys. J.* 388:338 (1991)

61. Griest K, Seckel D. *Nucl. Phys. B* 283:681 (1987); Erratum. *Nucl. Phys. B* 296:1034 (1988)

62. Gould A. *Astrophys. J.* 321:571 (1987)

63. Halzen F, Hooper D. *Phys. Rev. D* 73:123507 (2006)

64. DeYoung T. (IceCube Collab.) *Int. J. Mod. Phys. A* 20:3160 (2005); Ahrens J, et al. (IceCube Collab.) *Nucl. Phys. Proc. Suppl.* 118:388 (2003)

65. Sapienza P. *Nucl. Phys. Proc. Suppl.* 145:331 (2005)

66. Abazov VM, et al. (DØ Collab.) *Phys. Rev. Lett.* 93:141801 (2004)

67. Ackermann M, et al. (AMANDA Collab.) astro-ph/0508518 (2005)

68. Boliev MM, et al. Presented at *Int. Workshop Asp. Dark Matter Astrophys. Part. Phys., 20th, Heidelberg, Ger.* (1997)

69. Ambrosio M, et al. (MACRO Collab.) *Phys. Rev. D* 60:082002 (1999)

70. Hossl J. (ANTARES Collab.) Presented at *Int. Workshop Identif. Dark Matter, 6th*, Edinburgh, Scotl. (2004); Brunner J. (ANTARES Collab.) *Nucl. Phys. Proc. Suppl.* 145:323 (2005)

71. Alner GJ, et al. (UK Dark Matter Collab.) *Phys. Lett. B* 616:17 (2005)

72. Barnabe-Heider M, et al. (PICASSO Collab.) hep-ex/0502028 (2005)

73. Baltz EA, Wai L. *Phys. Rev. D* 70:023512 (2004); Baltz EA, Wai L. astro-ph/0403528 (2004); Colafrancesco S, Profumo S, Ullio P. *Astron. Astrophys.* 455:21 (2006); Bergstrom L, Fairbairn M, Pieri L. *Phys. Rev. D* 74:123515 (2006)

74. Finkbeiner DP. astro-ph/0409027 (2004); Hooper D, Finkbeiner DP, Dobler G. *Phys. Rev. D* 76:083012 (2007)

75. Dawson S, Eichten E, Quigg C. *Phys. Rev. D* 31:1581 (1985)

76. Tovey DR. *Eur. Phys. J. Direct C* 4:N4 (2002)

77. Bachacou H, Hinchliffe I, Paige FE. *Phys. Rev. D* 62:015009 (2000)

78. Drees M, et al. *Phys. Rev. D* 63:035008 (2001)

79. Lafaye R, Plehn T, Zerwas D. hep-ph/0404282 (2004); Bechtle P, Desch K, Wienemann P. *Comput. Phys. Commun.* 174:47 (2006)

80. Bachacou H, Hinchliffe I, Paige FE. *Phys. Rev. D* 62:015009 (2000); Allanach BC, Lester CG, Parker MA, Webber BR. *JHEP* 0009:004 (2000); Baer H, Chen CH, Paige F, Tata X. *Phys. Rev. D* 52:2746 (1995); Baer H, Chen CH, Paige F, Tata X. *Phys. Rev. D* 53:6241 (1996); Abdullin S, Charles F. *Nucl. Phys. B* 547:60 (1999)

81. Abdullin S, et al. *Eur. Phys. J. C* 39S2:41 (2005); Datta A, Djouadi A, Guchait M, Moortgat F. *Nucl. Phys. B* 681:31 (2004)

82. Kinnunen R, et al. *Eur. Phys. J. C* 40N5:23 (2005)

83. Abel S, et al. (SUGRA Working Group Collab.) hep-ph/0003154 (2000)

84. Bortoletto D. (CDF, DØ Collabs.) *PoS* HEP2005:347 (2006); Canepa A. (CDF Collab.) hep-ex/0603032 (2006); Anastassov A. (CDF, DØ Collabs.) *PoS* HEP2005:326 (2006); Abazov V. (DØ Collab.) hep-ex/0604029 (2006)

85. Baltz EA, Battaglia M, Peskin ME, Wizansky T. *Phys. Rev. D* 74:103521 (2006)

86. Weiglein G, et al. (LHC/LC Study Group) hep-ph/0410364 (2004)

Charged Lepton Flavor Violation Experiments*

William J. Marciano,[1] Toshinori Mori,[2] and J. Michael Roney[3]

[1] Brookhaven National Laboratory, Upton, New York 11973; email: marciano@bnl.gov

[2] International Center for Elementary Particle Physics, The University of Tokyo, Tokyo 113-0033, Japan; email: mori@icepp.s.u-tokyo.ac.jp

[3] Department of Physics and Astronomy, University of Victoria, Victoria, British Columbia V8W 3P6, Canada; email: mroney@uvic.ca

Annu. Rev. Nucl. Part. Sci. 2008. 58:315–41

First published online as a Review in Advance on July 29, 2008

The *Annual Review of Nuclear and Particle Science* is online at nucl.annualreviews.org

This article's doi: 10.1146/annurev.nucl.58.110707.171126

0163-8998/08/1123-0315$20.00

Key Words

electron, muon, tau

Abstract

We provide a review of the status of experimental searches for lepton flavor violation involving electrons, muons, and tau leptons. Future experimental programs are discussed and placed in the context of theories beyond the standard model.

Contents

1. INTRODUCTION

After more than a century of great discoveries, we now have a standard model of elementary particle physics. It describes three generations of fundamental spin $\frac{1}{2}$ fermions (quarks and leptons), each containing particles of electric charges $\frac{2}{3}$, $-\frac{1}{3}$, 0, and –1 (and their antiparticles). Grouped by (ordered) mass eigenstates, they are:

First generation	u,	d,	ν_1,	e
Second generation	c,	s,	ν_2,	μ
Third generation	t,	b,	ν_3,	τ.

Neutrino masses (the newest addition to the standard model paradigm), m_1, m_2, and m_3, are very small [$< \mathcal{O}(1 \text{ eV})$], whereas the top quark is extremely heavy ($\sim$171 GeV). Other quarks and charged leptons have masses in between these extremes, showing no discernible pattern (1). Is the top quark anomalously massive or are the other fermions unusually light? Deciphering the spectrum of fermion masses is an outstanding problem in elementary particle physics.

Interactions among elementary particles are described by $SU(3)_C \times SU(2)_L \times U(1)_Y$ local gauge symmetries whereby strong, weak, and electromagnetic forces are mediated by gluons, $W^\pm$, Z^0, and γ spin 1 bosons. Standard model weak interaction properties and predictions have been successfully tested at approximately the $\pm 0.1\%$ level by probing tree level as well as quantum loop effects. (The standard model's quantum electrodynamics sector, of course, has been much more precisely established.) Only the anticipated spin-0 Higgs scalar particle, a remnant of $SU(2)_L \times U(1)_Y$ electroweak symmetry breaking and mass generation, remains undiscovered with a current experimental lower bound on m_{Higgs} from direct searches of 114.4 GeV (2) and a quantum loop indirect upper bound of 144 GeV (3). Nevertheless, it is anticipated that some new physics beyond standard model expectations, such as supersymmetric particle partners, heavy fermions, additional gauge bosons, strong dynamics, etc., will eventually emerge that will help explain some of the observed subtle features of nature, including the true origin of the broadly disparate masses, parity violation, and three distinct generations.

The primary way to uncover new physics is to explore the high-energy frontier at colliders, where heavy new particles can be directly produced and studied. Less direct means, which are complementary and in some cases capable of exploring much higher mass scales (even >1000 TeV), involve searches for new physics in rare or highly suppressed flavor changing neutral current reactions. Experimental searches for such effects involving charged leptons (e, μ, and τ) are the subject of this review.

1.1. Flavor Changing Neutral Currents

Individual quarks and leptons are assigned a quantum number called flavor. For example, electron, muon, and tau numbers (or flavors) are assigned to the charged leptons. Flavor is conserved at the tree level by all neutral current interactions (mediated by gluons, Z^0, and γ), but is violated in charged current weak interactions mediated by $W^\pm$ bosons. Due to mixing among generations of fermions, charged current loop effects can induce flavor changing weak neutral current interactions at the quantum level. Naïvely, such effects could be of $\mathcal{O}(\alpha/\pi) \simeq \frac{1}{400}$ relative to ordinary weak interactions, but in fact they are often found to be much more strongly suppressed.

In the case of quarks, such loop-induced effects lead to small but observable $s \to d$ transitions. Their observed suppression, e.g., in $K_L^0 \to \mu^+\mu^-$, was extremely important in unveiling the existence of charm via the GIM (Glashow–Iliopolous–Maiani) mechanism (4) and in predicting its properties. Such loops were also instrumental in explaining CP violation as a manifestation of predicted three-generation Cabibbo–Kobayashi–Maskawa (CKM) mixing. More recently, the study of CP violation in $b \to d$ amplitudes confirmed the CKM model (5, 6). Also, the measurement of $b \to s\gamma$ decays and the search for $B_s \to \mu^+\mu^-$ have been at the forefront of (low-energy) supersymmetry (SUSY) constraints.

In the case of charged leptons, searches for flavor changing neutral current effects have, so far, yielded null results. Nevertheless, they have had important historical significance. For example, the nonobservation of $\mu \to e\gamma$ during the early days following the discovery of the muon (7) helped establish the muon as a distinct elementary lepton rather than an excited electron (8). The same is true for the early tau days, when lack of $\tau^\pm \to e^\pm\gamma$ and $\tau^\pm \to \mu^\pm\gamma$ decays helped establish the tau as elementary. Follow-up constraints on $\mathcal{B}(\mu^+ \to e^+\gamma)$ below $\sim 10^{-5}$ were later used to argue for the existence of a second neutrino (the ν_μ) needed to cancel possible large but unobserved loop-induced neutral current effects inferred in a single-neutrino scenario (9). The search and subsequent discovery of the second neutrino (10) using neutrino beams (11, 12) was not only a quantum loop success, but it also led to the establishment of accelerator-based neutrino physics as a viable science. Introduction of the ν_μ to suppress flavor changing neutral current charged lepton interactions was completely analogous to the GIM mechanism introduction of charm to suppress strangeness changing neutral currents (13, 14).

The sensitivity in the search for $\mu^+ \to e^+\gamma$ and other rare lepton flavor violating (LFV) reactions has been increased by many orders of magnitude over the years (shown in **Figure 1**). As the bounds were lowered, speculative theoretical new physics models were ruled out or constrained. Some current experimental bounds on various LFV reactions are given in **Table 1**, where we also list goals of ongoing, proposed, and possible future experiments. Most of the bounds are from unobserved decays such as $\mu^+ \to e^+\gamma$, $\mu^\pm \to e^\pm e^+ e^-$, $\tau^\pm \to \mu^\pm\gamma$, $\tau^\pm \to \mu^\pm\mu^+\mu^-$, etc. However, one very stringent constraint (currently the best bound) comes from the search for coherent $\mu^- \to e^-$ conversions in the field of a nucleus, $\mu^- N \to e^- N$. It potentially occurs in the following sequential manner. Stopped muons are quickly captured by atoms ($\sim 10^{-10}$ s) and

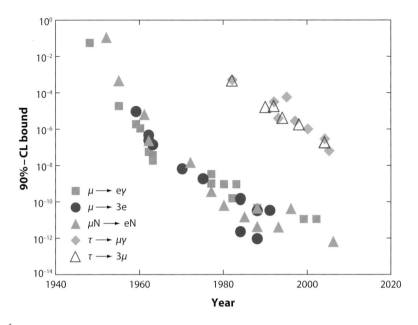

Figure 1

Record of selected lepton flavor violation searches.

cascade down to 1S orbitals. There, they can undergo (*a*) ordinary decay with a rate of $\sim 5 \times 10^5$ s^{-1}, (*b*) weak capture, $\mu^- \mathrm{p} \rightarrow \nu_\mu \mathrm{n}$ (which exceeds the ordinary decay rate for nuclei with Z > 6), or (*c*) coherent flavor changing conversion, $\mu^- N \rightarrow \mathrm{e}^- N$. The last of these reactions has already been significantly constrained using various targets. Indeed, the ratio of conversions to capture,

Table 1   A sample of various charged lepton flavor violating reactions

Reaction	Current bound	Reference	Expected	Possible
$\mathcal{B}(\mu^+ \rightarrow \mathrm{e}^+\gamma)$	$<1.2 \times 10^{-11}$	28	2×10^{-13}	2×10^{-14}
$\mathcal{B}(\mu^\pm \rightarrow \mathrm{e}^\pm\mathrm{e}^+\mathrm{e}^-)$	$<1.0 \times 10^{-12}$	37	–	10^{-14}
$\mathcal{B}(\mu^\pm \rightarrow \mathrm{e}^\pm\gamma\gamma)$	$<7.2 \times 10^{-11}$	92	–	–
$R(\mu^-\mathrm{Au} \rightarrow \mathrm{e}^-\mathrm{Au})$	$<7 \times 10^{-13}$	15	–	–
$R(\mu^-\mathrm{Al} \rightarrow \mathrm{e}^-\mathrm{Al})$	–		10^{-16}	10^{-18}
$\mathcal{B}(\tau^\pm \rightarrow \mu^\pm\gamma)$	$<5.9 \times 10^{-8}$	Table 2		$\mathcal{O}(10^{-9})$
$\mathcal{B}(\tau^\pm \rightarrow \mathrm{e}^\pm\gamma)$	$<8.5 \times 10^{-8}$	Table 2		$\mathcal{O}(10^{-9})$
$\mathcal{B}(\tau^\pm \rightarrow \mu^\pm\mu^+\mu^-)$	$<2.0 \times 10^{-8}$	Table 2		$\mathcal{O}(10^{-10})$
$\mathcal{B}(\tau^\pm \rightarrow \mathrm{e}^\pm\mathrm{e}^+\mathrm{e}^-)$	$<2.6 \times 10^{-8}$	Table 2		$\mathcal{O}(10^{-10})$
$Z^0 \rightarrow \mathrm{e}^\pm\mu^\mp$	$<1.7 \times 10^{-6}$	90		
$Z^0 \rightarrow \mathrm{e}^\pm\tau^\mp$	$<9.8 \times 10^{-6}$	90		
$Z^0 \rightarrow \mu^\pm\tau^\mp$	$<1.2 \times 10^{-5}$	91		
$K_L^0 \rightarrow \mathrm{e}^\pm\mu^\mp$	$<4.7 \times 10^{-12}$	74		10^{-13}
$D^0 \rightarrow \mathrm{e}^\pm\mu^\mp$	$<8.1 \times 10^{-7}$	78		10^{-8}
$B^0 \rightarrow \mathrm{e}^\pm\mu^\mp$	$<9.2 \times 10^{-8}$	79		10^{-9}

Data from current experimental bounds, expected improvements from existing or funded experiments, and possible long-term advances.

$$R(\mu^- N \to e^- N) = \frac{\omega(\mu^- N \to e^- N)}{\omega(\mu^- N \to \nu_\mu N')}, \qquad \text{1.}$$

has reached the $<7 \times 10^{-13}$ bound for gold nuclei (15), and a similar (unpublished) result by the same SINDRUM II collaboration exists for titanium. The simplicity and distinctive signal, a monoenergetic electron of energy

$$E_{\text{mec}} = m_\mu - B_\mu(Z, A) - R(A) \sim 105 \text{ MeV}, \qquad \text{2.}$$

where m_μ is the muon mass, $B_\mu(Z, A)$ is the muonic atom binding energy, and $R(A)$ is the nuclear recoil energy for a nucleus with atomic number Z and mass number A, promise to allow the bound or discovery potential to be pushed much further. Indeed, with only a single final-state particle (as opposed to two in $\mu^+ \to e^+\gamma$), accidentals are not a problem and extremely high rates are possible. Those features allow the unique opportunity of pushing $R(\mu^- N \to e^- N)$ to $10^{-17} \sim 10^{-18}$. This represents an improvement in sensitivity of four to five orders of magnitude over current bounds, which in a mature experimental area is generally unheard of.

1.2. Electromagnetic Transitions

Radiative decays of the generic form $\ell_1 \to \ell_2 + \gamma$ ($\ell_1 = \mu, \tau; \ell_2 = e, \mu$) proceed through electromagnetic gauge–invariant transition amplitudes of the form

$$\mathcal{M} = \frac{e\, G_F m_{\ell_1}}{16\sqrt{2}\pi^2} \varepsilon^\mu q^\nu \overline{\ell_2}(p_2)\sigma_{\mu\nu}\left(D_R \frac{1+\gamma_5}{2} + D_L \frac{1-\gamma_5}{2}\right)\ell_1(p_1), \qquad \text{3.}$$

where $q = p_1 - p_2$ and $\sigma_{\mu\nu} = \frac{i}{2}[\gamma_\mu, \gamma_\nu]$; we have normalized with respect to the Fermi constant, $G_F = 1.16637(1) \times 10^{-5} \text{ GeV}^{-2}$, along with a $\frac{1}{16}\pi^2$ that generally results from a loop integration. D_R and D_L are model-dependent transition dipole moments. For $m_{\ell_2} \ll m_{\ell_1}$, that amplitude leads to the decay rate

$$\Gamma(\ell_1 \to \ell_2\gamma) = \frac{\alpha G_F^2 m_{\ell_1}^5}{2048\pi^4}(|D_R|^2 + |D_L|^2) \qquad \text{4.}$$

and the branching ratio

$$\mathcal{B}(\ell_1 \to \ell_2\gamma) = \frac{3\alpha}{32\pi}(|D_R|^2 + |D_L|^2)\mathcal{B}(\ell_1 \to \ell_2\nu\bar{\nu}), \qquad \text{5.}$$

where $\mathcal{B}(\mu \to e\nu\bar{\nu}) \simeq 1$ and $\mathcal{B}(\tau \to \mu\nu\bar{\nu}) = 0.973\mathcal{B}(\tau \to e\nu\bar{\nu}) \simeq 0.1736$. The amplitude of Equation 3 results from a dimension-five operator that cannot exist at tree level in a renormalizable theory. It can and generally will be induced at loop level due to LFV effects (16, 17).

To obtain a rough estimate regarding the mass scale of new physics probed by searches such as $\mu^+ \to e^+\gamma$, we can reparameterize the amplitude in Equation 3 by $em_\mu/\Lambda^2\varepsilon^\mu q^\nu \bar{e}\sigma_{\mu\nu}\mu$ or $D_R = D_L = 16\sqrt{2}\pi^2/G_F\Lambda^2$, where Λ is the scale of new physics responsible for muon number violation. Comparing this result with the current bound on $\mathcal{B}(\mu^+ \to e^+\gamma)$ in **Table 1** leads to the constraint $\Lambda \geq 340$ TeV. Of course, the bound depends on exactly how we parameterize the new physics. Nevertheless, such a stringent constraint, which will be extended to about $\sim$1000 TeV by an ongoing Paul Scherrer Institut (PSI) effort, nicely illustrates the reach of LFV reactions. For a detailed discussion on how rare muon decays probe new physics, we refer the reader to the thorough 1999 review by Kuno & Okada (18).

The photon amplitude above can also give rise to $\ell_1 \to \ell_2\bar{\ell}_2\ell_2$ via a virtual photon. One finds (for $m_{\ell_2} \ll m_{\ell_1}$) (18)

$$\frac{\mathcal{B}(\ell_1 \to 3\ell_2)}{\mathcal{B}(\ell_1 \to \ell_2\gamma)} \simeq \frac{\alpha}{3\pi}\left[\ln\left(\frac{m_{\ell_1}^2}{m_{\ell_2}^2}\right) - \frac{11}{4}\right], \qquad \text{6.}$$

which gives $\mathcal{B}(\mu \rightarrow 3e)/\mathcal{B}(\mu \rightarrow e\gamma) \simeq 0.006$. Of course, additional amplitudes (not of the chiral changing structure in Equation 3) such as $\mathcal{M} = i\frac{4G_F}{\sqrt{2}} g\bar{e}_L\gamma_\mu\mu_L\bar{e}_L\gamma^\mu e_L$, which gives rise to $\mathcal{B}(\mu \rightarrow 3e) \approx 2g^2$, could substantially increase $\mathcal{B}(\ell_1 \rightarrow 3\ell_2)$ relative to $\mathcal{B}(\ell_1 \rightarrow \ell_2\gamma)$ in some new physics scenarios. Indeed, one can often find $\mathcal{B}(\ell_1 \rightarrow 3\ell_2) > \mathcal{B}(\ell_1 \rightarrow \ell_2\gamma)$, which could be particularly important for $\tau^\pm \rightarrow \mu^\pm\mu^+\mu^-$ decays: Experiments searching for this three-muon mode are expected to have a greater sensitivity than $\tau^\pm \rightarrow \mu^\mp\gamma$ because of its particularly clean experimental signature of three final-state muons.

In the case of coherent muon-electron conversion in the field of a nucleus, attaching the photon from the amplitude in Equation 3 to the nuclear Coulombic field leads to the coherent rate ratio

$$R(\mu^- N \rightarrow e^- N) \simeq \frac{G_F^2 m_\mu^4}{96\pi^3\alpha} \times 3 \times 10^{12} B(A, Z)\mathcal{B}(\mu \rightarrow e\gamma), \qquad 7.$$

where $B(A, Z)$ is a nucleus-dependent factor that includes atomic and nuclear effects. One finds $B = 1.1, 1.8$, and 1.25 for Al, Ti, and Pb, respectively (19, 20). [Pb and Au have similar $B(A, Z)$ factors.]

For the example of $N = \text{Al}$, one finds,

$$\mathcal{B}(\mu \rightarrow e\gamma) \simeq 389 R(\mu^- Al \rightarrow e^- Al). \qquad 8.$$

Indeed, if the amplitude in Equation 3 dominates,

$$\mathcal{B}(\mu \rightarrow e\gamma) : \mathcal{B}(\mu \rightarrow 3e) : R(\mu^- Al \rightarrow e^- Al) :: 389 : 2.3 : 1, \qquad 9.$$

suggesting that μ-e coherent conversion comes in third. Experimentally, however, conversion can be pushed three to four orders of magnitude beyond the other reactions. In addition, for many types of new physics scenarios the amplitude in Equation 3 does not dominate. Instead, relatively large chiral conserving amplitudes of the form $\bar{e}\gamma_\mu\mu\bar{q}\gamma^\mu q$ could enhance $R(\mu^- N \rightarrow e^- N)$ relative to $\mathcal{B}(\mu^+ \rightarrow e^+\gamma)$. In fact, the coherent conversion can easily be $\mathcal{O}(100)$ times larger, as we discuss below.

1.3. Neutrino Masses and Mixing

We now know that lepton flavor is not exactly conserved. Flavor nonconserving mixing among generations has been observed in neutrino oscillations (1). Neutrinos produced by weak interactions (ν_e, ν_μ, and ν_τ) are related to the mass eigenstates (ν_1, ν_2, and ν_3) via

$$\begin{pmatrix} |\nu_e\rangle \\ |\nu_\mu\rangle \\ |\nu_\tau\rangle \end{pmatrix} = U \begin{pmatrix} |\nu_1\rangle \\ |\nu_2\rangle \\ |\nu_3\rangle \end{pmatrix} \qquad 10.$$

$$U = \begin{pmatrix} c_{12}c_{13} & s_{12}c_{13} & s_{13}e^{-i\delta} \\ -s_{12}c_{23} - c_{12}s_{23}s_{13}e^{i\delta} & c_{12}c_{23} - s_{12}s_{23}s_{13}e^{i\delta} & s_{23}c_{13} \\ s_{12}s_{23} - c_{12}c_{23}s_{13}e^{i\delta} & -c_{12}s_{23} - s_{12}c_{23}s_{13}e^{i\delta} & c_{23}c_{13} \end{pmatrix}$$

$$c_{ij} = \cos\theta_{ij}, \quad s_{ij} = \sin\theta_{ij}, \quad i, j = 1, 2, 3.$$

From a combination of solar, reactor, atmospheric, and accelerator neutrino oscillation results (1), we now know that (roughly)

$$\Delta m_{32}^2 = m_3^2 - m_2^2 \simeq \pm 2.5 \times 10^{-3} \text{ eV}^2$$
$$\Delta m_{21}^2 = m_2^2 - m_1^2 \simeq 8 \times 10^{-5} \text{ eV}^2 \qquad \qquad 11.$$

$$\sin^2 2\theta_{23} \simeq 1 \quad \sin^2 2\theta_{12} \simeq 0.80$$
$$\sin^2 2\theta_{13} < 0.15 \quad 0 \le \delta < 360°. \qquad \qquad 12.$$

The mixing is relatively large (although θ_{13} is currently unknown), but the mass differences are extremely small compared to the weak scale ($m_W \simeq 80.4$ GeV), resulting in accidental approximate lepton flavor conservation. Computing the D_R and D_L in Equation 3 due to neutrino loops gives for $\ell_1 = \mu$, $\ell_2 = e$

$$D_L \simeq \frac{1}{2} \sin 2\theta_{13} \sin \theta_{23} e^{-i\delta} \frac{\Delta m_{32}^2}{m_W^2}, \quad D_R = 0$$

or

$$\mathcal{B}(\mu^+ \to e^+ \gamma) \simeq 10^{-54} \left(\frac{\sin^2 2\theta_{13}}{0.15} \right), \qquad \qquad 13.$$

which is nonzero (if $\sin^2 2\theta_{13} \ne 0$), but which is much too small to access experimentally. Therefore, the actual observation of $\mu^+ \to e^+ \gamma$ at $\mathcal{O}(10^{-12} - 10^{-13})$ would clearly indicate a signal for new physics beyond negligible, ordinary neutrino mass effects.

In the case of coherent $\mu^- N \to e^- N$ conversion, the $W^+ W^-$ loop box diagrams dominate and one finds (roughly) from chiral conserving loop amplitudes (16)

$$R(\mu^- \text{Al} \to e^- \text{Al}) \simeq 2 \times 10^{-52} \frac{\sin^2 2\theta_{13}}{0.15}. \qquad \qquad 14.$$

Again, the predicted rate is negligibly small. However, the rate in Equation 14 is about 200 times larger than that in Equation 13 (16, 17) and illustrates the possibility of $R(\mu^- N \to e^- N)$ being larger than $\mathcal{B}(\mu^+ \to e^+ \gamma)$. The neutrino example also illustrates what can happen if heavy neutrinos exist and mix with the light ones. For a fourth generation with neutrinos $\mathcal{N}$ and mixing-induced couplings $U_{e\mathcal{N}}$ and $U_{\mu\mathcal{N}}$ with the electron and muon, respectively, one finds

$$\mathcal{B}(\mu^+ \to e^+ \gamma) \simeq \frac{3\alpha}{32\pi} |U_{e\mathcal{N}}^* U_{\mu\mathcal{N}}|^2 \frac{m_{\mathcal{N}}^4}{m_W^4}. \qquad \qquad 15.$$

For $m_{\mathcal{N}} \simeq m_W$, $|U_{e\mathcal{N}}^* U_{\mu\mathcal{N}}|$ is already constrained to be less than $\sim 2 \times 10^{-4}$. In the case of $R(\mu^- N \to e^- N)$, the $W^+ W^-$ box diagram with a heavy $\mathcal{N}$ dominates, and one finds (roughly) for $m_{\mathcal{N}} \simeq m_W$

$$R(\mu^- \text{Al} \to e^- \text{Al}) \simeq 4\mathcal{B}(\mu^+ \to e^+ \gamma). \qquad \qquad 16.$$

In such an example, coherent μ-e conversion can be a more powerful probe of heavy neutrino mixing than $\mu^+ \to e^+ \gamma$.

1.4. The Muon Anomalous Magnetic Moment and Lepton Flavor Violations

The muon anomalous magnetic moment, $a_\mu \equiv \frac{g_\mu - 2}{2}$, is very similar in structure to Equation 3, except that it is flavor diagonal ($\ell_1 = \ell_2 = \mu$); i.e., it conserves lepton flavor and has no γ_5 term. It is quite sensitive to some types of new physics, such as SUSY, due to its chiral changing Lorentz

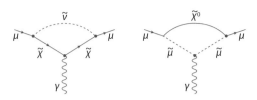

Figure 2

Potential supersymmetric contributions to muon g-2 (21).

structure. If new physics manifests itself in a_μ, it is likely that flavor violation in the new physics sector will also show up in $\mu^+ \to e^+\gamma$ and other LFV reactions (21, 22).

Currently, there is a 3.4-σ discrepancy between experiment and the standard model prediction for a_μ (1):

$$a_\mu^{exp} = 116\ 592\ 080\ (63) \times 10^{-11},$$
$$a_\mu^{SM} = 116\ 591\ 788\ (58) \times 10^{-11},$$
$$\Delta a_\mu = a_\mu^{exp} - a_\mu^{SM} = 292(63)(58) \times 10^{-11}. \qquad 17.$$

The difference, which is sizeable, could indicate an underestimate of standard model hadronic loop effects or a more exciting new physics possibility. In the latter case, the scale of new physics is likely to be in the 100 GeV–2 TeV range, with relatively low–mass scale SUSY being the most natural candidate explanation (see **Figure 2**).

If new physics is responsible for Δa_μ, it should also give rise to off-diagonal LFV electromagnetic transition amplitudes of the type shown in Equation 3, albeit at a reduced level due to the requirement of flavor violation (23, 24). (These amplitudes for SUSY-induced LFV radiative decays are similar to those shown in **Figure 2**, but with different charged leptons in the initial and final states.) Indeed, one expects (roughly)

$$D_R(\text{and/or } D_L) \simeq \frac{16\sqrt{2}\pi^2}{G_F m_\mu^2} \Delta a_\mu \varepsilon_{\ell_1 \ell_2}, \qquad 18.$$

where the $\varepsilon_{\ell_1 \ell_2}$ parameterize the (model-dependent) flavor violating suppression factors. Assuming such a relationship, one expects from Equation 5

$$\mathcal{B}(\ell_1 \to \ell_2 \gamma) \simeq 6.4 \times 10^{14} (\Delta a_\mu)^2 |\varepsilon_{\ell_1 \ell_2}|^2 \mathcal{B}(\ell_1 \to \ell_2 \nu \bar{\nu}). \qquad 19.$$

For the cases of interest (using Δa_μ in Equation 17),

$$\mathcal{B}(\mu^+ \to e^+\gamma) \simeq 6 \times 10^{-3} |\varepsilon_{e\mu}|^2$$
$$\mathcal{B}(\tau^\pm \to \mu^\pm\gamma) \simeq 1 \times 10^{-3} |\varepsilon_{\mu\tau}|^2$$
$$\mathcal{B}(\tau^\pm \to e^\pm\gamma) \simeq 1 \times 10^{-3} |\varepsilon_{e\tau}|^2. \qquad 20.$$

Other LFV rates may be estimated from the relationships described in Section 1.2.

Comparing with the bounds in **Table 1** we see that small $\varepsilon_{\ell_1 \ell_2}$ suppression factors are needed, particularly for $\varepsilon_{e\mu}$, where the current bound on $\mathcal{B}(\mu^+ \to e^+\gamma)$ already requires $\varepsilon_{e\mu} \leq 4.5 \times 10^{-5}$. What makes such a bound particularly interesting is that some models such as SUSY suggest that $\varepsilon_{e\mu}$ should be of order this bound. In fact, $\varepsilon_{e\mu}$ is only small due to a super-GIM mechanism requiring near-mass degeneracies among different generations of superparticles (sparticles).

Indeed, for large mixing this bound translates into a constraint on slepton mass degeneracies within loops

$$\frac{\Delta M^2}{M^2} \simeq \frac{M_1^2 - M_2^2}{M_1^2} < 10^{-4} \qquad 21.$$

or very roughly

$$M_1 - M_2 < 4.5 \times 10^{-5} M_1. \qquad 22.$$

So, for sparticle masses of order several hundred gigaelectronvolts, the degeneracy between generations must be in the tens of megaelectronvolts. Stated differently, if the current $\Delta a_\mu \neq 0$ result is caused by new physics, observation of $\mu^+ \to e^+\gamma$ may be right around the corner.

In the case of tau decays, one might expect a larger breaking of third-generation sparticle degeneracy (relative to the first and second generations). That being the case, and assuming reasonable mixing, rare decays such as $\tau^\pm \to \mu^\pm\gamma$ and $\tau^\pm \to e^\pm\gamma$ may be observable at the 10^{-9} level.

2. RARE MUON DECAYS AND REACTIONS

The best-studied rare muon decays and reactions that involve LFV include $\mu^+ \to e^+\gamma$ and $\mu^+ \to e^+e^-e^+$, as well as muon-to-electron conversion in muonic atoms $\mu^- N \to e^- N$. Because muons are abundantly produced at high-intensity proton accelerators and because their simple final states can be very precisely measured, the current best experimental bounds on LFV were obtained on these processes. Prospects for future experimental developments in these rare muon processes also look very promising. A new experiment searching for $\mu^+ \to e^+\gamma$ decays with two orders of magnitude more sensitivity than the previous search is now starting its physics runs in Switzerland. Proposals to search for $\mu^- N \to e^- N$ with somewhat better sensitivity than the Swiss-based $\mu^+ \to e^+\gamma$ experiment are now being seriously considered in the United States and Japan. Research and development on a muon storage ring to produce a cleaner and higher-rate muon source are also under way, which could further improve $\mu^- N \to e^- N$ sensitivity by another one or two orders of magnitude.

2.1. $\mu^+ \to e^+\gamma$

Experimentally, a $\mu^+ \to e^+\gamma$ event is characterized by a simple two-body final state: The electron and photon are emitted back to back in the rest frame of the decaying muon, with each carrying away an energy equal to half the muon mass (52.8 MeV), neglecting the tiny electron mass. To utilize this simple but powerful kinematic tool, low-energy muons are stopped in a solid (known as a stopping target). However, in order to avoid formation of muonic atoms that would destroy the two-body kinematic signature, only positive muons are used.

Abundant low-energy positive muons, so-called surface muons (25), are produced by bombarding primary protons into a thick production target. The surface muons come from the decays of positive pions that stop near the surface of the production target and have a sharp momentum spectrum of approximately 29 MeV/c, thanks to two-body decays of the stopped pions. Because of their low momentum and narrow momentum spread (typically 8% FWHM), a thin target ($\approx$10 mg cm^{-2}) can be employed. Such a low-mass stopping target is essential for minimizing positron annihilations in the target that generate accidental γ ray backgrounds; it is also needed to achieve a good positron momentum resolution, which is critical for suppression of all backgrounds.

Because the surface muons, which come from a stopped pseudoscalar pion decaying via V-A, are naturally 100% spin polarized, the angular distribution of $\mu^+ \to e^+\gamma$ decays can be measured after discovery of this LFV decay. This distribution may provide important information for helping to pin down the source of the LFV. Researchers have also proposed to reduce backgrounds by limiting the experimental acceptance, as the background positrons and γ rays have angular distributions with respect to the muon spin (26).

The present best upper limit on the branching ratio of $\mathcal{B}(\mu^+ \rightarrow e^+\gamma)$ is 1.2×10^{-11} (90% CL) (shown in **Table 1**), which was established by the MEGA (Muon decays to an Electron and a GAmma ray) experiment at the Los Alamos Meson Physics Facility (LAMPF) (27, 28). The major background in a $\mu^+ \rightarrow e^+\gamma$ search is an accidental coincidence of a positron from the standard Michel decays of muons, $\mu \rightarrow e\nu\bar{\nu}$, and a relatively high energy γ ray from radiative muon decays or annihilation of positrons in material. The physics background from radiative muon decays, $\mu \rightarrow e\nu\bar{\nu}\gamma$ with very low energy neutrinos, on the other hand, is strongly suppressed by reasonably good energy and momentum measurements at a rate more than an order of magnitude smaller than the accidental background.

Because the accidental background increases quadratically with the muon rate, a continuous dc muon beam with the lowest instantaneous rate is better suited for a $\mu^+ \rightarrow e^+\gamma$ search than a pulsed muon beam. In order to achieve a $\mathcal{B}(\mu^+ \rightarrow e^+\gamma)$ sensitivity of 10^{-13} in one year of running ($T \approx 10^7$ s), assuming a detection efficiency of $\varepsilon \approx 10\%$, a dc muon rate of $1/(10^{-13}\varepsilon T) \approx 10^7\,\mathrm{s}^{-1}$ is needed.

Currently there is only one accelerator in the world that is able to provide such a high-rate dc muon beam: the 590-MeV isochronous ring cyclotron at PSI, in Villigen, Switzerland (near Zurich). The cyclotron constantly supplies a 2.0-mA proton beam with 50 MHz rf time structure. Because the 2-μs muon lifetime is much longer than the rf structure, the muon decay rate has no time structure. The cyclotron is currently being upgraded: Its beam current is planned to reach 2.6 mA in one to two years and 3.0 mA some years thereafter. Eventually, the cyclotron will reach an unrivaled beam power exceeding 1.5 MW.

In 1999, a proposal by a group of Japanese physicists to search for $\mu^+ \rightarrow e^+\gamma$ decays was approved by PSI's research committee (29, 30). The experimental collaboration has since evolved to approximately 60 physicists from Japan, Switzerland, Italy, Russia, and the United States and is now known as the MEG (Muon to Electron and Gamma) collaboration. It is currently starting physics runs with a sensitivity of 10^{-13}; with detector upgrades, its sensitivity will eventually reach 10^{-14}. MEG has a clear advantage over the previous MEGA experiment, which used the pulsed LAMPF beam with a macro duty cycle of 7.7% and an instantaneous muon rate of $2.5 \times 10^8\,\mathrm{s}^{-1}$. MEG's dc muon rate is only $3.0 \times 10^7\,\mathrm{s}^{-1}$, resulting in suppression of accidental background by a factor of almost an order of magnitude.

A schematic of the experimental setup of the MEG experiment is shown in **Figure 3**. The main features of the experiment are a novel positron spectrometer with a specially graded magnetic field and an innovative 900-ℓ liquid xenon γ ray detector.

The magnetic field of the positron spectrometer COBRA (Constant Bending Radius) (31) varies from 1.27 T at the center to 0.49 T at both ends. It is designed to quickly sweep away positrons from the drift chamber volume while providing a constant projected bending radius for the trajectory of the 52.8-MeV positrons. This significantly reduces the hit rates in the drift chambers and simplifies the positron tracking.

In the liquid xenon detector (32) (shown in **Figure 4**), the scintillation photons caused by an incident γ ray are viewed from all sides by 846 photomultiplier tubes to make a precise measurement of the conversion point, timing, and energy of the γ ray. To identify and separate pileup γ rays efficiently, fast waveform digitizers are used for all the photomultiplier tube outputs (33). Possible impurities (mostly water) that absorb scintillation light are eliminated by circulating liquid xenon through a purification system (34, 35). Stability monitoring and precise calibration of

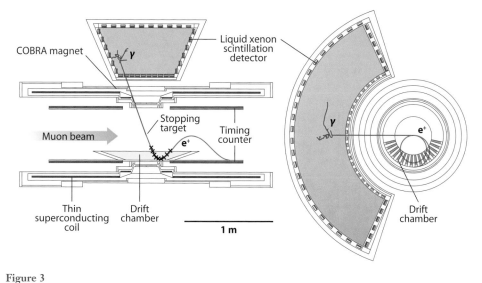

Figure 3

Schematic layout of the Muon to Electron and Gamma (MEG) experiment. Used with permission of the MEG Collaboration.

the liquid xenon detector are key to the success of the experiment. Point-like ^{241}Am α sources deposited on wires (36) and the $^{7}\mathrm{Li}(p, \gamma)^{8}\mathrm{Be}$ reaction provided by a Cockcroft-Walton proton accelerator are used for frequent monitoring and calibration, while 55-MeV γ rays from the pion charge exchange reaction $\pi^{-}\mathrm{p} \rightarrow \pi^{0}\mathrm{n}$ provide the absolute energy calibration.

It is expected that MEG will reach a 90%-CL expected upper limit sensitivity of $1 - 2 \times 10^{-13}$ in two to three years. Possible detector upgrades to maximize the available beam intensity, 1×10^{8} muons s^{-1}, which may further increase with the accelerator upgrade, are being investigated; researchers aim to achieve a 10^{-14} sensitivity.

As no accelerator facility has a higher intensity dc muon beam than PSI, and as there are presently no innovative ideas for experiments to make use of such a high-intensity beam, it seems unlikely that any experiment will exceed 10^{-14} in a $\mu^{+} \rightarrow e^{+}\gamma$ search in the foreseeable future.

Figure 4

Photograph of the inside of the Muon to Electron and Gamma (MEG) liquid xenon photon detector as photomultiplier tubes are assembled. Used with permission of the MEG Collaboration.

2.2. $\mu^{\pm} \to e^{\pm}e^{+}e^{-}$

Just as in $\mu^{+} \to e^{+}\gamma$ experiments, searches for the $\mu^{+} \to e^{+}e^{-}e^{+}$ decay require positive muons to avoid muonic atom formation. With three particles in the final state, these searches also suffer from accidental coincidences: Michel positrons from normal muon decays coincide with $e^{+}e^{-}$ pairs from γ ray conversions or from Bhabha scattering of Michel positrons with atomic electrons. To minimize accidental background, a dc muon beam should be used.

The present upper limit on the branching ratio, 1.0×10^{-12} (37), was obtained by the SINDRUM experiment (38) in 1988. The SINDRUM collaboration used a subsurface dc muon beam of 25 MeV/c with a rate of 6×10^{6} muons s^{-1}. Their spectrometer accepted 24% of $\mu^{+} \to e^{+}e^{-}e^{+}$ assuming a flat transition matrix element, with an 18-MeV/c threshold for transverse momentum.

With the presently available beam intensity of 1×10^{8} muons s^{-1} at PSI, improvement in sensitivity by one to two orders of magnitude ($10^{-13} - 10^{-14}$) might be possible. Because the background increases linearly with the muon rate squared, background reduction must improve by more than two orders of magnitude. The rather modest tracking performance of SINDRUM in momentum resolution (10% FWHM) and vertex constraints seems to leave enough room for improvements. The most significant issue is whether good tracking devices that work at such high rates (10^{8} s^{-1}) can be developed. The COBRA spectrometer of the MEG experiment, which focuses only on the highest end of the Michel spectrum, is certainly not suitable for this purpose.

In order to be highly competitive with $\mu^{+} \to e^{+}\gamma$ and $\mu^{-}N \to e^{-}N$ searches, an experimental sensitivity down to some 10^{-16} is desirable. This would require a dc muon beam of 10^{10} muons s^{-1}, i.e., a new muon facility with an intensity 100 times higher than that of PSI. From an experimental perspective, tracking at such high rates remains a daunting challenge.

2.3. $\mu - e$ Conversion

In muon-to-electron conversion, $\mu^{-}N \to e^{-}N$, a muon converts to an electron by exchanging a virtual photon (or undergoes a nonelectromagnetic interaction) with the capture nucleus. As introduced in Section 1.1 and Equation 2, the experimental signature is simple: a single monochromatic electron with E_{mec} (105.1 MeV for Al target). Because the method requires the formation of muonic atoms with target nuclei, only negative muons can be used. Moreover, the atomic number dependence of the $\mu \to e$ conversion rate can be used to distinguish various theoretical models of LFV after its discovery (20).

As discussed in Section 1.2, for generic chiral-changing dipole photonic vertices that violate lepton flavor, the physics sensitivity of $\mu^{-}N \to e^{-}N$ is two orders of magnitude lower than that of $\mu^{+} \to e^{+}\gamma$: $\frac{1}{389}$ for Al target, $\frac{1}{238}$ for Ti, and $\frac{1}{342}$ for Pb in terms of branching ratios (19, 20). Thus, for LFV electromagnetic transitions a $\mu^{+} \to e^{+}\gamma$ branching ratio of 1×10^{-13} corresponds to approximately 3×10^{-16} for $\mu^{-}N \to e^{-}N$. To achieve this sensitivity, a negative muon beam with an intensity of $10^{10} - 10^{11}$ s^{-1} is necessary.

Obtaining such a high muon rate is a major challenge. Because there is no surface muon beam for negative muons, such a high-intensity beam tends to have a much broader spectrum and is usually contaminated by various other particles, particularly pions.

Major backgrounds in a $\mu^{-}N \to e^{-}N$ search are (*a*) electrons from muon decays in orbit and (*b*) beam-related background. The energy E_{e} of the decay-in-orbit electron has a spectrum falling off rapidly as $(E_{\text{mec}} - E_{e})^{5}$. By improving the electron energy resolution $\sigma_{E_{e}}$, this background decreases as $\sigma_{E_{e}}^{5}$. Because the energy resolution is dominated by energy loss in the stopping target, a thinner target is required. To efficiently stop a broad spectrum of muons, several layers of thin targets are usually used.

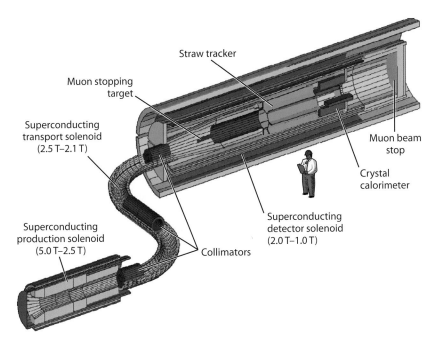

Muon stopping target

Straw tracker

Superconducting transport solenoid (2.5 T–2.1 T)

Muon beam stop

Superconducting production solenoid (5.0 T–2.5 T)

Collimators

Superconducting detector solenoid (2.0 T–1.0 T)

Crystal calorimeter

Figure 5

Layout of the Muon Electron Conversion (MECO) experiment. Used with permission of proponents of MECO.

There are various beam-related backgrounds caused by beam contaminants, specifically pions. The most significant of these is radiative pion capture, wherein pions may be radiatively captured by the target nuclei, emitting γ rays that subsequently convert into electrons.

The SINDRUM II experiment at PSI, which has set the most stringent upper limits of 7×10^{-13} on $\mu^-\text{Au} \rightarrow e^-\text{Au}$ (15), has reduced the pion contamination with an 8-mm-thick CH_2 moderator for a 52-MeV/c beam, where pions have half the range of muons. The main background arises from electrons from radiative pion capture in the degrader or pion decays in flight, which scatter in the target to mimic the signal. They show a time correlation with the cyclotron rf time structure and are thus separated.

The MECO (Muon Electron Conversion) experiment (39) was proposed at Brookhaven National Laboratory to search for $\mu^-\text{Al} \rightarrow e^-\text{Al}$ at a sensitivity below 10^{-16}. Its schematic layout is shown in **Figure 5**. The experimental design of MECO is based on three key concepts:

1. The use of a graded-field solenoid to collect pions, which leads to a 1000-fold increase in muon intensity (to 10^{11} s^{-1}) over the previous experiment. This idea was originally proposed for a Russian experiment at the Moscow Meson Factory (40).
2. A short-pulsed proton beam extracted with a time interval that matches the muon capture lifetime (approximately 0.9 μs for Al target). To avoid beam-related background, data are taken in a delayed time window after the beam pulse, when all the backgrounds have fallen off. No proton should exist during the delayed time window at the level of 10^{-9} (beam extinction).
3. A curved solenoid selects and transports the low-energy negative muons to the stopping targets with a high transmission probability.

To stop a broad spectrum of muons, 17 layers of 0.2-mm-thick Al targets are used. Al is chosen as the target material because its muon capture lifetime (0.9 μs) matches the measurement cycle, whereas heavier elements have much shorter lifetimes.

Unfortunately, MECO was cancelled in 2005 because of budget constraints. However, its importance for physics is still strong. MECO-type experiments are under way both at Fermi National Laboratory (FNAL) and at Japan Proton Accelerator Research Complex (J-PARC). It is expected that minor modifications to the existing accelerators or the accelerators under construction will produce a proton beam with the required structure. The Letter of Intent for the FNAL experiment, Mu2e (41), was submitted in 2007 as was the J-PARC proposal, COMET (42). There is hope that either or both of these experiments may start running soon after the MEG experiment draws to a close.

An ambitious future project is PRISM (Phase-Rotated Intense Slow Muons) (43), designed to produce a high-intensity muon beam with narrow energy spread and low levels of contamination. It is proposed to be built at the J-PARC main proton ring currently under construction at Tokai, Japan. Its schematic layout is shown in **Figure 6**. A fixed-field alternating gradient (FFAG) synchrotron is used to carry out phase rotation, i.e., conversion of an original short-pulse beam with wide momentum spread (±30%) into a long-pulse beam with narrow momentum spread (±3%)

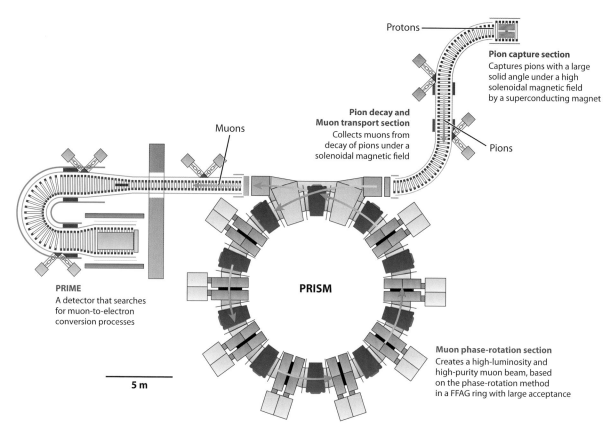

Protons

Pion capture section
Captures pions with a large
solid angle under a high
solenoidal magnetic field
by a superconducting magnet

**Pion decay and
Muon transport section**
Collects muons from
decay of pions under a
solenoidal magnetic field

Muons

Pions

PRISM

PRIME
A detector that searches
for muon-to-electron
conversion processes

Muon phase-rotation section
Creates a high-luminosity and
high-purity muon beam, based
on the phase-rotation method
in a FFAG ring with large acceptance

5 m

Figure 6

A schematic layout of the Phase-Rotated Intense Slow Muons (PRISM) project. Not drawn to scale. Abbreviations: FFAG, fixed-field alternating gradient; PRIME, PRISM Mu E. Used with permission of proponents of PRISM.

by a strong rf field. After five turns in the FFAG ring for the phase rotation, pions in the beam will decay out. Given 10^{14} protons s^{-1} from the J-PARC ring, the PRISM facility should be able to provide 10^{11}–10^{12} muons s^{-1}.

PRIME (PRISM Mu E) (43) is a proposed experiment intended to search for $\mu^- N \rightarrow e^- N$ conversion at the future PRISM facility. Because of a very low duty factor of the PRISM beam, this experiment must handle the extremely high instantaneous rate of 10^{10}–10^{11} muons per beam bunch. In the PRIME experiment, a curved solenoid spectrometer will be used to transport only electrons with desired momenta from the stopping target to the detector. Thanks to the high-quality muon beam at PRISM, which has a high efficiency and a better momentum resolution, we can expect sensitivity of the level of 10^{-18}.

3. LEPTON FLAVOR VIOLATION IN TAU LEPTON DECAYS

It is by incorporating results from many different measurements that we will finally be able to move beyond the standard model. Progress will be made by interpreting within a cohesive theoretical framework the variety of results from, for example, direct searches (and discoveries) of new particles at the energy frontier of the Large Hadron Collider (LHC), neutrino oscillation measurements, and g-2 and electric dipole moment measurements, as well as searches (and discoveries) of LFV in the decays of leptons and mesons. LHC discoveries alone will be insufficient to determine the underlying theoretical structures responsible for new physics. Similarly, a discovery of $\mu^+ \rightarrow e^+ \gamma$ alone will not provide sufficient information to determine the underlying LFV mechanism or even to identify an underlying theory. Nor do we know which LFV decay mode will first be discovered; therefore, it is critical to probe all LFV modes. Consequently, the $\mu^+ \rightarrow e^+ \gamma$ search should be augmented by studies of $\tau^\pm \rightarrow \mu^\pm \gamma$ as well as $\tau^\pm \rightarrow e^\pm \gamma$. For example, even in the presence of the existing and projected $\mu^+ \rightarrow e^+ \gamma$ bounds, $\tau^\pm \rightarrow \mu^\pm \gamma$ decays are predicted to occur at rates that are accessible at current experiments in many models (44). Moreover, the full set of measurements of μ and τ LFV processes are required because, in general, there are strong correlations in many models between the expected rates of the various channels. For instance, in a supersymmetric seesaw model describing potential LFV (45, 46), there is an expectation that the specific relative rates of $\mathcal{B}(\tau^\pm \rightarrow \mu^\pm \gamma)$: $\mathcal{B}(\tau^\pm \rightarrow \mu^\pm \mu^+ \mu^-)$: $\mathcal{B}(\tau^\pm \rightarrow \mu^\pm \eta)$ depend upon the model parameters (45, 46). A detailed analysis of the μ-τ LFV in the unconstrained minimal supersymmetric model (MSSM) framework includes a discussion of various correlations and demonstrates that τ LFV branching fractions can be as high as 10^{-7} (47), even with the strong experimental bounds on muon LFV. Correlations in a constrained MSSM model (48), indicated in **Figure 7**, also illustrate the complementarity of the $\mathcal{B}(\tau^\pm \rightarrow \mu^\pm \gamma)$ and $\mathcal{B}(\mu^+ \rightarrow e^+ \gamma)$ measurements.

3.1. Tau Lepton Data Samples and Search Strategies

Historically, τ lepton samples large enough to be useful for searches for LFV have been pair-produced in $e^+ e^-$ storage ring colliders via the process $e^+ e^- \rightarrow \tau^+ \tau^-$ operating at a center-of-mass energy near the mass of the $\Upsilon(4S)$ meson (10.58 GeV). This is because the $e^+ e^-$ colliders optimized for studying B meson physics and/or CP violation in the B meson system require the highest luminosities possible at the $\Upsilon(4S)$ resonance, which decays almost exclusively to a $B\bar{B}$ pair. These B factories are in fact τ factories as well, as they provide similarly sized $B\bar{B}$ and $\tau^+ \tau^-$ samples.

In recent years the BaBar and Belle experiments have provided new results on LFV in τ decays. Belle, at the Japanese Koo Enerugii Kasokuki Kenkyuu Kikoo (KEKB) $e^+ e^-$ collider, and BaBar, at Stanford Linear Accelerator Center's $e^+ e^-$ Positron Electron Project (PEP-II) B factory, have

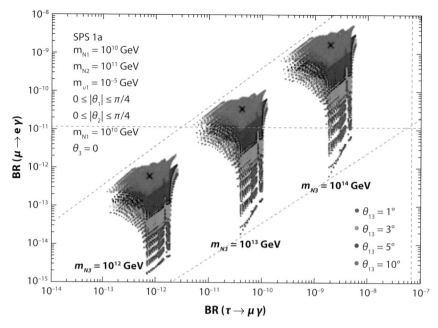

Figure 7

$\mathcal{B}(\mu^+ \rightarrow e^+\gamma)$ versus $\mathcal{B}(\tau^{\pm} \rightarrow \mu^{\pm}\gamma)$ in a constrained minimal supersymmetric model (MSSM) with three right-handed massive neutrinos for three values of the heaviest right-handed neutrino, m_{N_3}, and four values of θ_{13}, for a particular choice of model parameters (48). Used with permission of the authors.

been collecting data at the $\Upsilon(4S)$ since 1999. PEP-II ceased operations in 2008, whereas KEKB's operations will pause for three or four years beginning in 2009 or later in order to implement an upgrade to higher luminosity. The time-dependent B meson CP violation studies require the beams to have different energies in order to introduce a time dilation from the Lorentz boost. This does not affect the measurements involving the τ, but it is an effect that must be taken into account in the analyses. The BaBar (49) and Belle (50) detectors are remarkably similar; the only major difference pertains to the technology used to identify charged particles. Belle uses a threshold Cherenkov detector together with time of flight and tracker dE/dx (see **Figure 8** for a schematic), whereas BaBar mainly relies on a ring-imaging Cherenkov detector augmented by dE/dx in the trackers. With more than 1 ab^{-1} of data currently being collected between the two experiments and the $e^+e^- \rightarrow \tau^+\tau^-$ cross section being 0.919 nb (51), the world sample of τ leptons produced at the e^+e^- colliders now exceeds 10^9, which allows for experimental probing of LFV processes at the $\mathcal{O}(10^{-7})$ to $\mathcal{O}(10^{-8})$ levels.

The general approach of the analyses is to select τ pair events with the appropriate charged-particle topology, removing non-τ events with as minimal an impact as possible on the signal efficiency. This is accomplished by dividing the candidate event into hemispheres in the center of mass, where each hemisphere contains either the τ^+ or the τ^- decay products. Each hemisphere is then considered a possible candidate for the LFV decay under consideration. This can be seen in the BaBar detector's display of a simulated $e^+e^- \rightarrow \tau^+\tau^-$; $\tau^+ \rightarrow e^+\bar{\nu}_\tau\nu_e$; $\tau^- \rightarrow \mu^-\gamma$ event (depicted in **Figure 9**). Unlike standard model τ decays, which have at least one neutrino, the LFV decay products have a combined energy $E_{\ell X}$ equal to the energy of the τ. This energy is approximately equal to the beam energy in the center of mass, $\sqrt{s}/2$, and the decay products' mass ($m_{\ell X}$) is equal to that of the τ. A two-dimensional signal region in the $m_{\ell X}$ versus ΔE plane

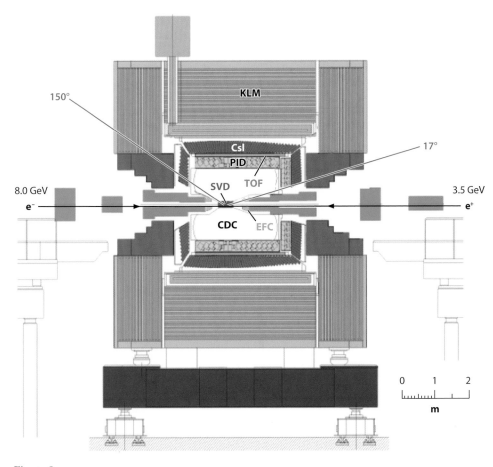

Figure 8

Schematic of the Belle detector. Abbreviations: CDC, central drift chamber; CsI, thallium-doped cesium iodide crystal calorimeter; EFC, extreme forward calorimeter; KLM, K_L^0 detection and muon identification; PID, particle identification system; SVD, silicon vertex detector; TOF, time of flight. Used with permission of the Belle Collaboration.

is therefore used to separate the signal from the standard model τ decay backgrounds, where $\Delta E = E_{\ell X} - \sqrt{s}/2$. **Figure 10** shows the distribution in that plane for simulated $\tau^\pm \to \mu^\pm \gamma$ decays, where the peaking at $\Delta E = 0$ and $m_{\ell X} = m_\tau = 1777$ MeV/c^2 is evident. A signal box in the ΔE-$m_{\ell X}$ encompassing events within approximately two standard deviations of $\Delta E = 0$ and $m_{\ell X} = m_\tau = 1777$ MeV/c^2 is often defined and serves as the most powerful requirement in the searches for LFV in τ decay.

Typically the analyses are optimized using Monte Carlo simulations of the signal and backgrounds to give the best-expected upper limit. The simulation of the signal provides the signal efficiency ε, which typically lies between 2% and 10% depending on the channel under study. The efficiency components of a generic τ LFV decay selection are (roughly) as follows: trigger (90%), acceptance/reconstruction (70%), charged-particle hemisphere topology (1 versus 1 or 1 versus 3: 70%), particle identification (50%), requirements apart from those on ΔE and $m_{\ell X}$ (50%), ΔE versus $m_{\ell X}$ signal box requirements (50%).

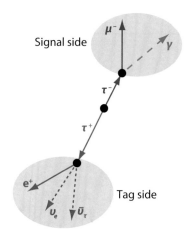

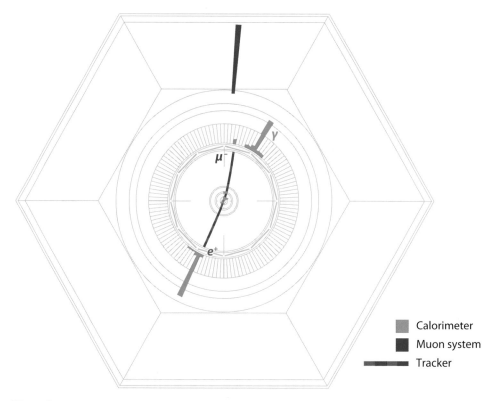

Figure 9

Simulated BaBar event display with a lepton flavor violation $\tau^- \to \mu^- \gamma$ decay opposite a standard model $\tau^+ \to e^+ \bar{\nu}_\tau \nu_e$ decay. Tau leptons decay inside the beam pipe. Used with permission of the Babar Collaboration.

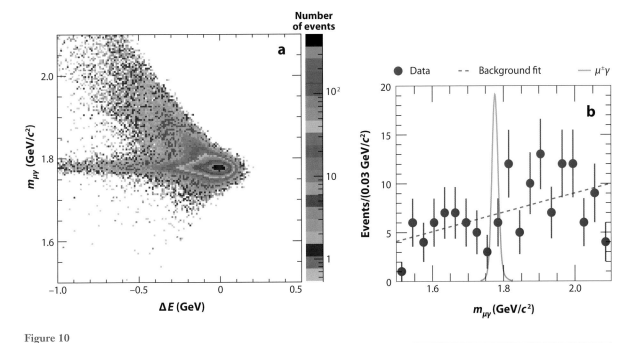

Figure 10

(*a*) The distribution in the $m_{\mu\gamma}$ versus ΔE plane for simulated signal events in the BaBar $\tau^{\pm} \to \mu^{\pm}\gamma$ analysis. (*b*) Distribution of BaBar $m_{\mu\gamma}$ data within a 2σ window in ΔE (52). Used with permission of the BaBar Collaboration.

The expected number of background events (N_{bkd}) is normally estimated using the distribution shapes from the Monte Carlo simulation of backgrounds with the normalization obtained from the data in the regions outside the signal box. These analyses are blind in the sense that the physics analysts have no knowledge of the data in the signal region when the optimization and systematic studies are undertaken. Once these steps are completed, the data in the signal region is unblinded and the analyst learns the number of events observed in the signal region (N_{obs}). The analyst thus either makes a discovery or—as has been the case to date—sets an upper limit on the process.

N_{obs} together with N_{bkd} then gives the number of signal events, N_{sig}: If N_{obs}-N_{bkd} is consistent with zero, an upper limit on N_{sig} (N_{90}^{UL}) is established. Schematically, the 90%-CL branching ratio upper limit is obtained from

$$\mathcal{B}_{90}^{UL} = \frac{N_{90}^{UL}}{2 N_{\tau\tau}\,\varepsilon} = \frac{N_{90}^{UL}}{2\mathcal{L}\sigma_{\tau\tau}\,\varepsilon}, \qquad\qquad 23.$$

where $N_{\tau\tau} = \mathcal{L}\sigma_{\tau\tau}$ is the number of τ pairs produced in e^+e^- collisions obtained from the integrated luminosity $\mathcal{L}$ and from the τ pair production cross section $\sigma_{\tau\tau}$. In practice, if N_{bkd} is more than a few events, then N_{sig} and N_{bkd} are determined from a fit.

3.2. Current Results on Lepton Flavor Violation Decays of the Tau

Experimentally, LFV τ decays can be conveniently classified as $\tau^{\pm} \to \ell^{\pm}\gamma$, $\tau^{\pm} \to \ell_1^{\pm}\ell_2^{+}\ell_3^{-}$, and $\tau^{\pm} \to \ell^{\pm}h^0$, where ℓ is either an electron or a muon and where h^0 represents a hadronic system. In the searches by BaBar and Belle, the h^0 has been categorized in three ways: (*a*) h^0 corresponds to a pseudoscalar meson (e.g., π^0, η, η', K_S^0); (*b*) h^0 corresponds to a neutral vector meson (e.g., ω, $K^*(892)$, ϕ); and (c) h^0 is a pair of oppositely charged mesons, $h^0 = h_1^+ h_2^-$, where $h_{1(2)}^\pm = \pi^\pm$ or $K^\pm$.

The most recent $\tau^\pm \to \mu^\pm \gamma$ and $\tau^\pm \to e^\pm \gamma$ results, as yet unpublished, were reported by Belle (53) using a data sample with an integrated luminosity of 535 fb^{-1} that corresponds to 492×10^6 τ pair events. The main $\tau^\pm \to \mu^\pm \gamma$ backgrounds in these searches arise from $e^+e^- \to \mu^+\mu^-\gamma$ events and $e^+e^- \to \tau^+\tau^-\gamma$ events, where one of the τs decays via $\tau \to \mu\nu\bar{\nu}$. In both cases the photon, from initial-state radiation in the latter case and initial- or final-state radiation in the former, combines with a muon to accidentally fall within the signal box. The $e^+e^- \to \tau^+\tau^-\gamma$; $\tau \to \mu\nu\bar{\nu}$ events can be classified as irreducible because the events are genuine τ pair events and because the μ and the γ are correctly identified and measured. A similarly irreducible background source from $e^+e^- \to \tau^+\tau^-\gamma$; $\tau \to e\nu\bar{\nu}$ exists. Belle set a 90%-CL upper limit on the number of signal events for $\tau \to \mu\gamma (\tau \to e\gamma)$ of 2.0 (3.34) events. These yield upper limits of $\mathcal{B}(\tau \to \mu\gamma) < 4.5 \times 10^{-8}$ and $\mathcal{B}(\tau \to e\gamma) < 1.2 \times 10^{-7}$. In 2005, BaBar published 90%-CL upper limits using a 232-fb^{-1} data sample of 6.8×10^{-8} and 1.1×10^{-7} on $\mathcal{B}(\tau \to \mu\gamma)$ and $\mathcal{B}(\tau \to e\gamma)$, respectively (52, 54).

Both experiments report classical frequentist confidence intervals. These are reported in **Table 2**, along with a combined 90%-CL upper limit calculated using both frequentist and Bayesian analyses that take into account correlations and systematic errors. When results from fits are reported, likelihood functions are combined and the $2 \ln(\Delta\mathcal{L}(\mathcal{B})) = 2.71$ values are used to set the frequentist interval—an approach that reproduces the quoted frequentist intervals of the individual experiments, although both BaBar and Belle use a different approach (55) than that employed here. When event counts in a signal box are reported by both collaborations, the technique of Cousins & Highland (56), following the implementation of Barlow (57), is employed to set a frequentist limit. The Bayesian analysis assumes a prior probability distribution that is uniform in the branching fraction, $\mathcal{B}$, and integrates the combined likelihood function from zero to the value of $\mathcal{B}$ that includes 90% of $\int_0^\infty \mathcal{L}(\mathcal{B})d\mathcal{B}$. Note that when an experiment experiences a downward fluctuation in the background, the reported frequentist interval usually has an upper limit somewhat lower than the Bayesian limit.

Both Belle (58) and BaBar (59) have recently published new results on searches for $\tau \to \ell_1\ell_2\ell_3$, but no evidence for a signal was seen by either experiment. Unlike the $\tau^\pm \to \mu^\pm\gamma$ and $\tau^\pm \to e^\pm\gamma$ searches, there is no irreducible background at the current luminosities. The Belle $\tau \to \ell_1\ell_2\ell_3$ analysis used 492×10^6 τ pairs, whereas BaBar reported on an analysis using 346×10^6

Table 2 Summary of 90%-CL upper limits on $\mathcal{B}(\tau \to \ell\gamma)$ and $\mathcal{B}(\tau \to \ell_1\ell_2\ell_3)$ LFV τ decays[a]

	Belle[b]		BaBar[c]		Combined BF	
Channel	N_{obs} (N_{bkg}) events	BF (10^{-8})	N_{obs} (N_{bkg}) events	BF (10^{-8})	Frequentist (10^{-8})	Bayesian (10^{-8})
$\tau \to \mu\gamma$	10 ($13.9^{+6.0}_{-4.8}$)	4.5	4 (6.2 ± 0.5)	6.8	2.3	5.9
$\tau \to e\gamma$	5 ($5.14^{+3.86}_{-2.81}$)	12	1 (1.9 ± 0.4)	11	7.2	8.5
$\tau \to \mu e^+e^-$	0 (0.04 ± 0.04)	2.7	2 (0.89 ± 0.27)	8.0	3.0	3.0
$\tau \to \mu\mu^+\mu^-$	0 (0.07 ± 0.05)	3.2	0 (0.33 ± 0.19)	5.3	1.7	2.0
$\tau \to e\mu^+\mu^-$	0 (0.05 ± 0.03)	4.1	0 (0.81 ± 0.31)	3.7	1.4	2.2
$\tau \to ee^+e^-$	0 (0.40 ± 0.30)	3.6	1 (1.33 ± 0.25)	4.3	1.8	2.6

[a]Belle results are based on $N_{\tau\tau} = 492 \times 10^6$, whereas BaBar has published on $N_{\tau\tau} = 213 \times 10^6$ for the $\tau \to \ell\gamma$ and $N_{\tau\tau} = 346 \times 10^6$ for the $\tau \to \ell_1\ell_2\ell_3$ results. The combined limits are given in the last two columns. The charge of ℓ_1 is equal to the τ charge. Both frequentist and Bayesian combinations are reported.
[b]Data from References 53 and 58.
[c]Data from References 52, 54, and 59. Abbreviation: BF, branching fraction.

Table 3 Summary of 90%-CL upper limits on $\mathcal{B}(\tau \to \ell h^0)$ in units of (10^{-8})

Channel	$\ell = e\ (10^{-8})$				$\ell = \mu\ (10^{-8})$			
	Belle	BaBar	Combined Frequentist	Bayesian	Belle	BaBar	Combined Frequentist	Bayesian
$\tau \to \ell\pi^0$	8	13	4.2	5.0	12	11	5.5	6.4
$\tau \to \ell\eta$	9.2	16	4.3	6.8	6.5	15	4.9	6.1
$\tau \to \ell\eta'$	16	24	8.9	9.7	13	14	5.2	7.3
$\tau \to \ell K_S^0$	5.6		5.6		4.9		4.9	
$\tau \to \ell\phi$	7.3		7.3		13		13	
$\tau \to \ell\rho^0$	6.3		6.3		6.8		6.8	
$\tau \to \ell\omega$	18	10	8.3	8.5	8.9	11	3.4	5.6
$\tau \to \ell K^{*0}$	7.8		7.8		5.9		5.9	
$\tau \to \ell \bar{K}^{*0}$	7.7		7.7		10		10	

$\ell = \mu$ or e and h^0 is either a pseudoscalar (*upper four rows*) or a vector meson (*lower five rows*) from the Belle (60, 62, 64) and BaBar (61, 63) experiments. Also listed are their frequentist and Bayesian combinations.

τ pairs. Note that, in addition to the reactions listed in **Table 2**, the experiments also report bounds of similar magnitude on $\tau^- \to e^-\mu^+e^-$ and $\tau^- \to \mu^-e^+\mu^-$, which violate lepton flavor twice.

Belle, using 401 fb^{-1} (60), and BaBar, using 339 fb^{-1} (61), have both published bounds on LFV τ decays involving a lepton and a π^0, η, or η' pseudoscalar. Belle has also published results on searches for $\tau \to \ell K_S^0$ (62). Searches for LFV involving the ω vector meson, $\tau \to \ell\omega$, have been reported by both experiments, with BaBar employing a data set of 384 fb^{-1} (63) and Belle, 543 fb^{-1} (64). Using the same data set, Belle has also searched for $\tau \to \ell\phi$, $\tau \to \ell K^{*0}$, and $\tau \to \ell\bar{K}^{*0}$. The 90%-CL bounds on these processes are typically around 10^{-7} and are listed in **Table 3**. BaBar, using 221 fb^{-1}, sets limits on LFV inclusive decays with two charged mesons, $\tau^{\pm} \to \ell^{\pm}h_1^+h_2^-$, where no assumptions are made on the resonance structure of the hadronic final state (65). These bounds range from 1×10^{-7} to 5×10^{-7}, depending on the final state. Belle's equivalent analysis used 158 fb^{-1} and set bounds ranging from 2×10^{-7} to 16×10^{-7} (66).

3.3. Future Prospects

By the end of 2008, Belle and BaBar will have a combined data sample of roughly 1.5 ab^{-1} corresponding to the production of about 2×10^9 τ leptons, and they can be expected to update their analyses using their complete data sets over the following year or two. However, new significantly higher luminosity e$^+$e$^-$ colliders operating on or below the $\Upsilon(4S)$ (67) are on the horizon; these represent exciting new opportunities for the discovery and potential study of LFV decays of the τ. One of these colliders is a proposed upgrade of the KEKB facility, which will operate with substantially higher beam currents and which will see luminosities of 10^{35} cm^{-2} s^{-1} (68). There is also a proposal for a new facility near Frascati, Italy, designed for luminosities of 10^{36} cm^{-2} s^{-1} (44), or 100 times higher the luminosity of present machines. This increase will be achieved not by increasing the current, but by decreasing the interaction spot size. The higher-luminosity "SuperB" flavor factory would go online a couple of years after the proposed KEKB upgrade, and would yield 75 ab^{-1} of data over a five-year period. Such a facility would probe LFV $\tau^{\pm} \to \ell^{\pm}\ell^+\ell^-$ and $\tau^{\pm} \to \ell^{\pm}h^0$ decays, which have no irreducible backgrounds, at the $\mathcal{O}(10^{-10})$ level. However, the initial-state photon accidental backgrounds discussed in Section 3.2 will likely prevent the $\tau^{\pm} \to \ell^{\pm}\gamma$ decays from being probed below the level of a few 10^{-9} for an integrated luminosity of $75 \times ab^{-1}$.

Also, very large numbers of τ leptons will be produced at the LHC (69) via $W \to \tau \bar{\nu}_{\tau}$ (1.7×10^8), $\gamma/Z^0 \to \tau^+\tau^-$ (3.2×10^8), $B \to \tau X$ (7.8×10^{11}), $B_S \to \tau X$ (7.9×10^{10}), and $D_S \to \tau X$ (1.5×10^{12}) decays, where the number of such decays per 10 fb^{-1} are given in parentheses. The LHC will run for a few years at low luminosity (2×10^{33} cm^{-2} s^{-1}), producing integrated luminosities of 10–30 fb^{-1} of data per year. Subsequently, the collider will run at high luminosity (10^{34} cm^{-2} s^{-1}) for a longer period, collecting between 100 fb^{-1} and 300 fb^{-1} of data. Simulation studies with ATLAS (A Toroidal LHC Apparatus) and CMS (Compact Muon Selenoid) focusing on $W^{\pm}$ and Z^0 production (which are less demanding on trigger thresholds) have concluded that, owing to the hostile background, sensitivities to $\tau^{\pm} \to \mu^{\pm}\gamma$ are not competitive with existing limits from the B factories (70), even with statistics from one year of high-luminosity running. The situation for $\tau^{\pm} \to \mu^{\pm}\mu^+\mu^-$, although more promising, is still very challenging. With currently planned trigger configurations and 30 fb^{-1} of data, expected upper limits from $W^{\pm}, Z^0$, and B meson decays are 3.8×10^{-8}, 3.4×10^{-7}, and 2.1×10^{-7}, respectively. To fully exploit the huge τ production rates and to significantly improve these sensitivities would require the development of new trigger configurations and analysis methods providing access to B and D_S production modes under high-luminosity running conditions, which poses a significant challenge to experimenters.

4. SEARCHES FOR CHARGED LEPTON FLAVOR VIOLATION IN MESON DECAYS

In addition to searches for evidence of LFV in the decays of the τ and muon as well as in μ-e conversion, experiments have searched for LFV in the decays of a variety of charged and neutral pseudoscalar and neutral vector mesons (e.g., pions, η, η', kaons, D mesons, B mesons, J/ψ, Υ).

The pseudoscalar meson decays probe $q \to q'\ell_1\ell_2$ transitions and as such are particularly sensitive to lepton-quark models (71). Also, they provide information complementary to the leptonic decay LFV processes, as discussed in Landsberg's recent review (72). The most stringent experimental bounds on mesonic LFV decays are from $K^+ \to \pi^+\mu^+e^-$ and $K_L^0 \to \mu^{\pm}e^{\mp}$, which are bounded at 90% CL to 1.3×10^{-11} (73) and 4.7×10^{-12} (74), respectively. These bounds provide sensitivity to s $\to$ deμ transitions. Other lepton and q and q' combinations in $q \to q'\ell_1\ell_2$ transitions are probed by LFV decays of the π^0, η, η', D^0, D^+, D_s^+, B^0, and B_S^0, along with the $\tau \to \ell h^0$ searches, where h^0 is a light pseudoscalar meson. A sample of the bounds on pseudoscalar meson LFV decays is given in **Table 4**.

Similarly, searches for LFV in $\tau^{\pm} \to \ell^{\pm}h^0$, where h^0 is a neutral vector meson (e.g., ω, ϕ, K^{*0}), are particularly sensitive to sources of LFV arising from the exchange of neutral particles that couple to light neutral vector mesons. The LFV source might involve mass-dependent couplings, so it is worthwhile searching for LFV decays of heavier vector mesons. However, few such searches have been undertaken. The notable exceptions are the BES collaboration's searches for $J/\psi \to \mu^{\pm}e^{\mp}$ ($<1.1 \times 10^{-6}$ at 90% CL), $J/\psi \to \mu^{\pm}\tau^{\mp}$ ($<2.0 \times 10^{-6}$ at 90% CL), and $J/\psi \to e^{\pm}\tau^{\mp}$ ($<8.3 \times 10^{-6}$ at 90% CL) (84, 85). Also, the BaBar collaboration has searched for $e^+e^- \to \mu^{\pm}\tau^{\mp}$ and $e^+e^- \to e^{\pm}\tau^{\mp}$ using 211 fb^{-1} at the $\Upsilon(4S)$ (86). These researchers quote limits on the cross sections of $\sigma_{\mu\tau} < 3.8$ fb^{-1} and $\sigma_{e\tau} < 9.2$ fb^{-1} at 90% CL, which we can interpret as bounds on the $\Upsilon(4S)$ branching fractions of $\mathcal{B}(\Upsilon \to \mu^{\pm}\tau^{\mp}) < 3.5 \times 10^{-6}$ and $\mathcal{B}(\Upsilon \to e^{\pm}\tau^{\mp}) < 8.4 \times 10^{-6}$. Although a complete investigation would in principle require searches for e.g., $\omega \to e^{\pm}\mu^{\mp}$, $\phi \to e^{\pm}\mu^{\mp}$, and $\Upsilon(nS) \to e^{\pm}\mu^{\mp}$, the existing limits on $\mu^{\pm} \to e^{\pm}e^+e^-$ and $\mu^- N \to e^- N$ already greatly constrain such decays.

Table 4 Bounds at 90% CL on selected lepton flavor violating decays of
pseudoscalar mesons

Channel	Upper limit	Experiment	Reference
$\pi^0 \to \mu^\pm e^\mp$	3.59×10^{-10}	KTeV	75
$\eta \to \mu^\pm e^\mp$	6×10^{-6}	Saturne SPES2	76
$K_L^0 \to \pi^0 \mu^\pm e^\mp$	7.56×10^{-11}	KTeV	75
$K_L^0 \to 2\pi^0 \mu^\pm e^\mp$	1.64×10^{-10}	KTeV	75
$K_L^0 \to \mu^+ e^-$	4.7×10^{-12}	BNL E871	74
$K^+ \to \pi^+ \mu^+ e^-$	1.3×10^{-11}	BNL E865, E777	73
$D^+ \to \pi^+ \mu^\pm e^\mp$	3.4×10^{-5}	Fermilab E791	77
$D^+ \to K^+ \mu^\pm e^\mp$	6.8×10^{-5}	Fermilab E791	77
$D^0 \to \mu^\pm e^\mp$	8.1×10^{-7}	BaBar	78
$D_s^+ \to \pi^+ \mu^\pm e^\mp$	6.1×10^{-4}	Fermilab E791	77
$D_s^+ \to K^+ \mu^\pm e^\mp$	6.3×10^{-4}	Fermilab E791	77
$B^0 \to \mu^\pm e^\mp$	9.2×10^{-8}	BaBar (347 fb^{-1})	79
$B^0 \to \tau^\pm e^\mp$	1.1×10^{-4}	CLEO (9.2 fb^{-1})	80
$B^0 \to \tau^\pm \mu^\mp$	3.8×10^{-5}	CLEO (9.2 fb^{-1})	80
$B^+ \to K^+ e^\pm \mu^\mp$	9.1×10^{-8}	BaBar (208 fb^{-1})	81
$B^+ \to K^+ e^\pm \tau^\mp$	7.7×10^{-5}	BaBar (348 fb^{-1})	82
$B_s^0 \to e^\pm \mu^\mp$	6.1×10^{-6}	CDF (102 pb^{-1})	83

Abbreviations: BNL, Brookhaven National Laboratory; CDF, Collider Detector at Fermilab; KTeV,
Kaons at the Tevatron.

5. SEARCHES FOR CHARGED LEPTON FLAVOR VIOLATION IN Z^0 DECAYS

The LFV interactions between charged leptons $\ell_i^\pm$ and $\ell_j^\pm$ involving the Z^0 boson can be expressed in the most general way by (87):

$$
\begin{aligned}
\mathcal{L}_{ij}^{LFV} = &-i g_Z \bar{\ell}_i \gamma^\mu \left[a_L^{ij} \left(\tfrac{1-\gamma_5}{2} \right) + a_R^{ij} \left(\tfrac{1+\gamma_5}{2} \right) \right] Z_\mu \ell_j \\
&+ g_Z \bar{\ell}_i \sigma^{\mu\nu} \tfrac{k_\nu}{M_Z} \left[b_L^{ij} \left(\tfrac{1-\gamma_5}{2} \right) + b_R^{ij} \left(\tfrac{1+\gamma_5}{2} \right) \right] Z_\mu \ell_j + h.c.
\end{aligned}
\qquad 24.
$$

where $g_Z = e/(\sin\theta_W \cos\theta_W)$ is the weak coupling constant, k_ν is the Z^0 boson four momentum, and the couplings a_L^{ij}, a_R^{ij}, b_L^{ij}, and b_R^{ij} are not known a priori. The branching fraction ratio of LFV $Z^0 \to \ell_i^\pm \ell_j^\mp$ decays to standard model $Z^0 \to \mu^+\mu^-$ decays is

$$
\frac{\mathcal{B}(Z^0 \to \ell_i^\pm \ell_j^\mp)}{\mathcal{B}(Z^0 \to \mu^+ \mu^-)} = \frac{2\left(\left(a_L^{ij} \right)^2 + \left(a_R^{ij} \right)^2 \right) + \left(b_L^{ij} \right)^2 + \left(b_R^{ij} \right)^2}{g_{L\ell}^2 + g_{R\ell}^2},
\qquad 25.
$$

where $g_{L\ell}$ and $g_{R\ell}$ are the left- and right-handed standard model couplings of the Z^0 to muons, respectively. At tree level these couplings have the values $g_{L\ell}^{tree} = -\frac{1}{2} + \sin^2\theta_W$ and $g_{R\ell}^{tree} = \sin^2\theta_W$, where $\sin^2\theta_W \approx 0.23$.

The limits on LFV from charged lepton decays can be interpreted as indirect limits on LFV Z^0 decays. However, the k_ν/M_Z factor in Equation 24 completely suppresses the sensitivity of the charged lepton decays to b_L^{ij} and b_R^{ij}, allowing us only to interpret LFV charged lepton decay limits as bounds on $(a_L^{ij})^2$ and $(a_R^{ij})^2$. For example, $\mu^\pm \to e^\pm e^+ e^-$ can be considered to proceed as

$\mu^{\pm} \rightarrow Z^0\, e^{\pm}$, $Z^0 \rightarrow e^+e^-$. In this case (87), we find

$$\frac{\mathcal{B}(\mu^{\pm} \rightarrow e^{\pm}e^+e^-)}{\mathcal{B}(\mu \rightarrow e\nu\bar{\nu})} = 2\left(3\left(\left(a_L^{e\mu}\right)^2 + \left(a_R^{e\mu}\right)^2\right)\left(g_{L\ell}^2 + g_{R\ell}^2\right) + \left(\left(a_L^{e\mu}\right)^2 - \left(a_R^{e\mu}\right)^2\right)\left(g_{L\ell}^2 - g_{R\ell}^2\right)\right), \quad 26.$$

where the highly suppressed b_L^{ij} and b_R^{ij} contributions have been neglected. Using the LEP (Large Electron Positron Collider)– and SLC (Stanford Linear Collider)–measured values for the effective couplings $g_{L\ell} = -0.26939 \pm 0.00022$ and $g_{R\ell} = +0.23186 \pm 0.00023$ (88),

$$\frac{\mathcal{B}(\mu^{\pm} \rightarrow e^{\pm}e^+e^-)}{\mathcal{B}(\mu \rightarrow e\nu\bar{\nu})} = 0.7956[\left(a_L^{e\mu}\right)^2 + 0.9054\left(a_R^{e\mu}\right)^2]. \quad 27.$$

Therefore, the limit of $\mathcal{B}(\mu^{\pm} \rightarrow e^{\pm}e^+e^-) < 1.0 \times 10^{-12}$ at 90% CL (37) can be interpreted as a bound:

$$\left(a_L^{e\mu}\right)^2 + 0.9054\left(a_R^{e\mu}\right)^2 < 1.3 \times 10^{-12}. \quad 28.$$

We note, however, that the b^{ij} in Equation 24 are coefficients of chiral-changing operators and therefore are very likely to be suppressed by the factor m_ℓ/M, where M is a high-mass scale associated with the underlying new physics of LFV. Therefore, assuming that these coefficients are negligible, we find from Equations 25 and 28 that $\mathcal{B}(Z^0 \rightarrow e^{\pm}\mu^{\mp}) < 10^{-12}$. A similar analysis, using constraints from $\mu^-N \rightarrow e^-N$, leads to the even more stringent constraint $\mathcal{B}(Z^0 \rightarrow e^{\pm}\mu^{\mp}) < 10^{-13}$ (89). This bound could be lowered much further as the sensitivity of $\mu^-N \rightarrow e^-N$ in future experiments improves. These indirect bounds suggest that the observation of the mode $Z^0 \rightarrow e^{\pm}\mu^{\mp}$ at future high-energy colliders (even those capable of producing $>10^{10}$ Z^0 bosons) is highly unlikely, even though the signature for $Z^0 \rightarrow e^{\pm}\mu^{\mp}$ would be very clean.

Similarly, the limits from LFV in τ decays can also be used to bound e-τ and μ-τ LFV couplings of the Z^0. An additional feature that the τ decay provides, which is not accessible from muon decays, is individual access to $(a_L^{e\tau})^2$, $(a_R^{e\tau})^2$, $(a_L^{\mu\tau})^2$, and $(a_R^{\mu\tau})^2$. This access occurs because in the $\tau^{\pm} \rightarrow e^{\pm}\mu^+\mu^-$ and $\tau^{\pm} \rightarrow \mu^{\pm}e^+e^-$ decays the $\mu^+\mu^-$ and e^+e^- pairs are produced via a virtual Z^0 leading to the relationships

$$\frac{\mathcal{B}(\tau^{\pm} \rightarrow \ell_1^{\pm}\ell_2^+\ell_2^-)}{\mathcal{B}(\tau \rightarrow e\nu\bar{\nu})} \equiv R_{\ell_1\ell_2\ell_2} = 4\left(\left(a_L^{\ell\tau}\right)^2 + \left(a_R^{\ell\tau}\right)^2\right)\left(g_{L\ell}^2 + g_{R\ell}^2\right), \quad 29.$$

as well as to expressions analogous to Equation 26 for $\tau^{\pm} \rightarrow e^{\pm}e^+e^-$ and $\tau^{\pm} \rightarrow \mu^{\pm}\mu^+\mu^-$ decays. From these relations one can set the following limits at 90% CL using the combined Belle and BaBar branching fractions listed in **Table 2**:

$$\left(a_R^{e\tau}\right)^2 + \left(a_L^{e\tau}\right)^2 < 1.9 \times 10^{-7}; \quad \left(a_R^{e\tau}\right)^2 < 2.0 \times 10^{-6}; \quad \left(a_L^{e\tau}\right)^2 < 1.3 \times 10^{-6} \quad 30.$$

$$\left(a_R^{\mu\tau}\right)^2 + \left(a_L^{\mu\tau}\right)^2 < 3.3 \times 10^{-7}; \quad \left(a_R^{\mu\tau}\right)^2 < 1.3 \times 10^{-6}; \quad \left(a_L^{\mu\tau}\right)^2 < 3.5 \times 10^{-6}. \quad 31.$$

Again, ignoring the chiral-changing b^{ij} terms in Equation 24, we find from these constraints the indirect bounds $\mathcal{B}(Z^0 \rightarrow e^{\pm}\tau^{\mp}) < 10^{-7}$ and $\mathcal{B}(Z^0 \rightarrow \mu^{\pm}\tau^{\mp}) < 2 \times 10^{-7}$.

The most stringent direct limits on $e\mu$ and $e\tau$ decays of the Z^0 from a single experiment were provided by OPAL (Omni Purpose Apparatus for LEP) based on the analysis of a data sample of 5.0×10^6 $e^+e^- \rightarrow Z^0$ events, whereas DELPHI (Detector with Lepton, Photon, and Hadron Identification) provided limits for μ-τ decays using 3.9×10^6 Z^0 events. The OPAL data yielded 95%-CL upper limits of $\mathcal{B}(Z^0 \rightarrow e^{\pm}\mu^{\mp}) < 1.7 \times 10^{-6}$ and $\mathcal{B}(Z^0 \rightarrow e^{\pm}\tau^{\mp}) < 9.8 \times 10^{-6}$ at 95% CL (90). DELPHI set an upper limit of $\mathcal{B}(Z^0 \rightarrow \mu^{\pm}\tau^{\mp}) < 1.2 \times 10^{-5}$ at 95% CL (91). These limits, together with Equation 25 and Equations 28, 30, and 31, enable us to set 95%-CL bounds on the $(b_L^{ij})^2 + (b_R^{ij})^2$ couplings of Equation 25:

$$\left(b_R^{e\mu}\right)^2 + \left(b_L^{e\mu}\right)^2 < 6.3 \times 10^{-6}; \quad \left(b_R^{e\tau}\right)^2 + \left(b_L^{e\tau}\right)^2 < 3.7 \times 10^{-5}; \quad \left(b_R^{\mu\tau}\right)^2 + \left(b_L^{\mu\tau}\right)^2 < 4.5 \times 10^{-5}. \quad 32.$$

Alternatively, one can argue (assuming negligible b^{ij}) that the indirect bounds on $Z^0 \to e^{\pm}\tau^{\mp}$ and $Z^0 \to \mu^{\pm}\tau^{\mp}$ are currently about two orders of magnitude more stringent than the direct Z^0 decay constraints and that those indirect bounds will be further reduced as the sensitivity of rare τ decays improves. Again, it seems that observation of the LFV decays Z^0 into $e\tau$ or $\mu\tau$ is highly unlikely. The above Z^0 decay exercise illustrates a nice complementarity between high-energy collider searches for LFV and lower-energy LFV constraints from muon and τ decay studies. The latter studies are already very stringent and will continue to improve. If an LFV signal is observed at a high-energy collider, any attempt to explain it as underlying new physics must confront the tight constraints arising from rare muon and τ processes.

6. SUMMARY AND OUTLOOK

Historically, searches for charged lepton flavor violation have had an enormous impact on the development of particle physics in spite of the fact that no violation of lepton flavor involving charged leptons has ever been observed. In recent years, the BaBar and Belle experiments have reduced the bounds on third-generation LFV by two orders of magnitude over previous measurements, and plans for SuperB flavor factories on the horizon will see the experiments reach 10^{-9}–10^{-10} levels. Meanwhile, we look forward to seeing what MEG has in store over the next year or two as it reaches the unprecedented sensitivity of 10^{-13} for $\mu^+ \to e^+\gamma$. Later we can expect the sensitivity to reach 10^{-14}. On the μ-e conversion front, we hope to see 10^{-16} and, in the more distant future, 10^{-18}. These high-sensitivity lower-energy particle physics experiments will reach beyond the 1000-TeV energy scales and thereby will provide highly complementary and competitive probes of new physics, which in turn will help us unravel the puzzles that we hope to encounter through direct discoveries at the LHC. Should new physics not reveal itself at the LHC, these experiments will provide some of the best ways to experimentally probe beyond the standard model; as such, they are a critical component of the overall particle physics scientific program. These are exciting times: We are now working in the regime of LFV sensitivity where we can expect to see a positive signal that can only be interpreted in terms of physics beyond the standard model.

DISCLOSURE STATEMENT

The authors are not aware of any biases that might be perceived as affecting the objectivity of this review.

ACKNOWLEDGMENTS

The work of W.J.M. was supported by U.S. Department of Energy grant number DE-AC02-76CH00016. The work of T.M. was supported by a Ministry of Education, Culture, Sports, Science and Technology Grant-in-Aid for Scientific Research on Priority Areas 441. J.M.R. acknowledges support by the Natural Sciences and Engineering Research Council, Canada.

LITERATURE CITED

1. Yao WM, et al. (Particle Data Group Collab.) *J. Phys. G* 33:1 (2006)
2. Barate R, et al. (LEP Higgs Work. Group Collab.) *Phys. Lett. B* 565:61 (2003)
3. Alcaraz J, et al. (ALEPH, DELPHI, L3, OPAL Collab.) hep-ex/0712.0929 (2007)
4. Glashow S, Iliopoulos J, Maiani L. *Phys. Rev. D* 2:1285 (1970)
5. Abe K, et al. (Belle Collab.) *Phys. Rev. D* 66:071102 (2002)

6. Aubert B, et al. (BaBar Collab.) *Phys. Rev. Lett.* 89:201802 (2002)

7. Hinks E, Pontecorvo B. *Phys. Rev.* 73:257 (1948)

8. Lokanathan S, Steinberger J. *Phys. Rev.* 98:240(A) (1955)

9. Feinberg G. *Phys. Rev.* 110:1482 (1958)

10. Danby G, et al. *Phys. Rev. Lett.* 9:36 (1962)

11. Pontecorvo B. *Sov. Phys. JETP* 37:1236 [trans. JETP 37:1751 (1959)] (1960)

12. Schwarz M. *Phys. Rev. Lett* 4:306 (1960)

13. Pontecorvo B. *Sov. Phys. JETP* 7:172 (1958)

14. Maki Z, Nakagawa M, Sakata S. *Prog. Theor. Phys.* 28:870 (1962)

15. Bertl W, et al. (SINDRUM II Collab.) *Eur. Phys. J. C* 47:337 (2006)

16. Marciano WJ, Sanda AI. *Phys. Rev. Lett.* 38:1512 (1977)

17. Marciano WJ, Sanda AI. *Phys. Lett. B* 67:303 (1977)

18. Kuno Y, Okada Y. *Rev. Mod. Phys.* 73:151 (2001)

19. Czarnecki A, Marciano WJ, Melnikov K. *AIP Conf. Proc.* 435:409 (1998)

20. Kitano R, Koike M, Okada Y. *Phys. Rev. D* 66:096002 (2002)

21. Czarnecki A, Marciano WJ. *Phys. Rev. D* 64:013014 (2001)

22. Stockinger D. *J. Phys. G* 34:R45 (2007)

23. Chacko Z, Kribs GD. *Phys. Rev. D* 64:075015 (2001)

24. Graesser M, Thomas SD. *Phys. Rev. D* 65:075012 (2002)

25. Pifer AE, Bowen T, Kendall KR. *Nucl. Instrum. Methods* 135:39 (1976)

26. Kuno Y, Maki A, Okada Y. *Phys. Rev. D* 55:2517 (1997)

27. Brooks ML, et al. (MEGA Collab.) *Phys. Rev. Lett.* 83:1521 (1999)

28. Ahmed M, et al. (MEGA Collab.) *Phys. Rev. D* 65:112002 (2002)

29. Mori T, et al. (MEG Collab.) *UT-ICEPP* 00-02 (1999)

30. Hisamatsu Y. (MEG Collab.) *Eur. Phys. J. C* 52:477 (2007)

31. Ootani W, et al. (MEG Collab.) *IEEE Trans. Appl. Supercond.* 14:568 (2005)

32. Mihara S, et al. (MEG Collab.) *Cryogenics* 44:223 (2004)

33. Ritt S. (MEG Collab.) *Nucl. Instrum. Methods A* 494:520 (2002)

34. Baldini A, et al. (MEG Collab.) *Nucl. Instrum. Methods A* 545:753 (2005)

35. Mihara S, et al. (MEG Collab.) *Cryogenics* 46:688 (2006)

36. Baldini A, et al. (MEG Collab.) *Nucl. Instrum. Methods A* 565:589 (2006)

37. Bellgardt U, et al. (SINDRUM Collab.) *Nucl. Phys. B* 299:1 (1988)

38. Bertl W, et al. (SINDRUM Collab.) *Nucl. Phys. B* 260:1 (1985)

39. Bachman M, et al. (MECO Collab.) *BNL Proposal E 940* (1997)

40. Dzhilkibaev RM, Lobashev VM. (MELC Collab.) *Sov. J. Nucl. Phys.* 49:384 (1989)

41. Carey RM, et al. (Mu2e Collab.) *Fermilab Letter of Intent.* (2007)

42. Bryman D, et al. (COMET Collab.) *J-PARC Proposal P21.* (2007)

43. Kuno Y, et al. (PRISM Collab.) *J-PARC Letter of Intent.* (2006)

44. Bona M, et al. *SuperB: A High-Luminosity Asymmetric e+ e- Super Flavour Factory, Conceptual Design Report.* SLAC-R-709, INFN-AE-07-02, LAL-07-15 (2007)

45. Babu KS, Kolda C. *Phys. Rev. Lett.* 89:241802 (2002)

46. Sher M. *Phys. Rev. D* 66:057301 (2002)

47. Brignole A, Rossi A. *Nucl. Phys. B* 701:3 (2004)

48. Antusch S, Arganda E, Herrero MJ, Teixeira AM. *JHEP* 11:90 (2006)

49. Aubert B, et al. (BaBar Collab.) *Nucl. Instrum. Methods A* 479:1 (2002)

50. Abashian A, et al. (Belle Collab.) *Nucl. Instrum. Methods A* 479:117 (2002)

51. Banerjee S, Pietrzyk B, Roney JM, Was Z. *Phys. Rev. D* 77:054012 (2008)

52. Aubert B, et al. (BaBar Collab.) *Phys. Rev. Lett.* 95:041802 (2005)

53. Hayasaka K, et al. (Belle Collab.) hep-ex/0705.0650 (2007)

54. Aubert B, et al. (BaBar Collab.) *Phys. Rev. Lett.* 96:041801 (2006)

55. Narsky IV. *Nucl. Instrum. Methods A* 450:444 (2000)

56. Cousins RD, Highland VL. *Nucl. Instrum. Methods A* 320:331 (1992)

57. Barlow R. *Comput. Phys. Commun.* 149:97 (2002)

58. Miyazaki Y, et al. (Belle Collab.) hep-ex/0711.2189 (2007)
59. Aubert B, et al. (BaBar Collab.) *Phys. Rev. Lett.* 99:251803 (2007)
60. Miyazaki Y, et al. (Belle Collab.) *Phys. Lett. B* 648:341 (2007)
61. Aubert B, et al. (BaBar Collab.) *Phys. Rev. Lett.* 98:061803 (2007)
62. Miyazaki Y, et al. (Belle Collab.) *Phys. Lett. B* 639:159 (2006)
63. Aubert B, et al. (BaBar Collab.) hep-ex/0711.0980 (2007)
64. Nishio Y, et al. (Belle Collab.) hep-ex/0801.2475 (2007)
65. Aubert B, et al. (BaBar Collab.) *Phys. Rev. Lett.* 95:191801 (2005)
66. Yusa Y, et al. (Belle Collab.) *Phys. Lett. B* 640:138 (2006)
67. Hewett Joanne L, ed. *The Discovery Potential of a Super B Factory. SLAC Workshops.* SLAC-R-709 (2004)
68. Hashimoto ES, et al. *Letter of intent for KEK super B factory,* KEK-REPORT-2004-4 (2004)
69. Raidal M, et al. hep-ph/0801.1826 (2008)
70. Unel NG. hep-ex/0505030 (2005)
71. Pati JC, Salam A. *Phys. Rev. D* 10:275 (1974)
72. Landsberg LG. *Phys. Atom. Nucl.* 68:1190 (2005)
73. Sher A, et al. *Phys. Rev. D* 72:012005 (2005)
74. Ambrose D, et al. (BNL Collab.) *Phys. Rev. Lett.* 81:5734 (1998)
75. Abouzaid E, et al. (KTeV Collab.) hep-ex/0711.3472 (2007)
76. White DB, et al. *Phys. Rev. D* 53:6658 (1996)
77. Aitala EM, et al. (E791 Collab.) *Phys. Lett. B* 462:401 (1999)
78. Aubert B, et al. (BaBar Collab.) *Phys. Rev. Lett.* 93:191801 (2004)
79. Aubert B, et al. (BaBar Collab.) hep-ex/0712.1516 (2007)
80. Bornheim A, et al. (CLEO Collab.) *Phys. Rev. Lett.* 93:241802 (2004)
81. Aubert B, et al. (BaBar Collab.) *Phys. Rev. D* 73:092001 (2006)
82. Aubert B, et al. (BaBar Collab.) *Phys. Rev. Lett.* 99:201801 (2007)
83. Abe F, et al. (CDF Collab.) *Phys. Rev. Lett.* 81:5742 (1998)
84. Bai JZ, et al. (BES Collab.) *Phys. Lett. B* 561:49 (2003)
85. Ablikim M, et al. (BES Collab.) *Phys. Lett. B* 598:172 (2004)
86. Aubert B, et al. (BaBar Collab.) *Phys. Rev. D* 75:031103 (2007)
87. Bernreuther W, et al. In *Proc. Workshop Z Phys. LEP,* ed. G Altarelli, R Kleiss, C Verzegnassi, Vol. 2, p. 34. Zurich: CERN 89-08 (1989)
88. ALEPH, DELPHI, L3, OPAL, SLD Collab.; LEP Electroweak Work. Group; SLD Electroweak Heavy Flavour Group. *Phys. Rep.* 427:257 (2006)
89. Marciano WJ. *Nucl. Phys. Proc. Suppl.* 40:3 (1995)
90. Akers R, et al. (OPAL Collab.) *Z. Phys. C* 67:555 (1995)
91. Abreu P, et al. (DELPHI Collab.) *Z. Phys. C* 73:243 (1997)
92. Bolton RD, et al. *Phys. Rev. Lett.* 53:1415 (1984)

Neutrino Masses and Mixings: Status and Prospects

Leslie Camilleri,[1] Eligio Lisi,[2] and John F. Wilkerson[3]

[1] Department of Physics, Columbia University, New York, New York 10027;
email: camil@nevis.columbia.edu

[2] Istituto Nazionale di Fisica Nucleare, Sezione di Bari, 70126 Bari, Italy;
email: eligio.lisi@ba.infn.it

[3] Center for Experimental Nuclear Physics and Astrophysics, Department of Physics, University of Washington, Seattle, Washington 98195, email: jfw@u.washington.edu

Annu. Rev. Nucl. Part. Sci. 2008. 58:343–69

First published online as a Review in Advance on August 4, 2008

The *Annual Review of Nuclear and Particle Science* is online at nucl.annualreviews.org

This article's doi:
10.1146/annurev.nucl.57.090506.123038

Key Words

neutrino oscillations, neutrino mass spectrum, charge conjugation–parity (CP) violation

Abstract

Neutrino oscillations have been found in experiments observing solar and atmospheric neutrinos. They were confirmed by experiments using neutrinos produced by reactors and accelerators. These observations imply that neutrinos have nonzero masses and that the flavor states are superpositions of mass states through a mixing matrix. Indeed, the observed oscillations have revealed two distinct mass differences and two large mixing angles. In this article we discuss these discoveries, the emerging neutrino standard model, the present knowledge of the neutrino masses and mixing parameters, and the prospects for improving upon this knowledge.

Contents

1. NEUTRINOS: (RE)BUILDING THE STANDARD MODEL

The construction and validation of the standard model of particle physics represent two of the greatest accomplishments in science at the end of the second millennium (1, 2). We are now able to interpret vast amounts of data and processes (with the exception of gravity) in terms of gauge interactions between three families of elementary, spin-$\frac{1}{2}$ particles: the up (u, c, t) and down (d, s, b) quarks, the charged leptons (e, μ, τ), and the neutral leptons, also known as neutrinos (ν_e, ν_μ, ν_τ).

For a long time, the neutrinos were assumed to be massless ($m_\nu = 0$). In recent years, however, this (simplest) possibility has fallen under the growing weight of experimental data. Remarkably, the emerging paradigm does not require new neutrino states or interactions, but is entirely based on the next-to-simplest possibility, namely that neutrinos are massive and mixed—just like quarks, but with much different mass-mixing values. We present a pedagogical overview of the experimental basis for and the theoretical understanding of this new (ν) standard model, and we discuss some of the challenges that it poses for future research.

1.1. Why Are Neutrinos Important to Us?

Several of the physical processes that make life on Earth possible generate neutrinos as byproducts. Below the Earth's surface, the decays of radiogenic elements (e.g., U, Th, and K isotopes) keep our planet heated and produce a flux of $\bar{\nu}_e$, which was recently detected (3). The upper layers of the atmosphere stop a fraction of the cosmic rays, producing charged π and K mesons decaying into ν_μ and μ followed by muons decaying to e, ν_μ, and ν_e (4).

At the astrophysical level, the Sun is a major source of ν_e (6.4×10^{10} cm^{-2} s^{-1} on Earth), produced mainly in the three reactions that form part of the proton-proton chain, as shown in **Figure 1** (5): $p + p \rightarrow d + e^+ + \nu_e$ (pp neutrinos), $e^- + {}^7\text{Be} \rightarrow {}^7\text{Li} + \nu_e$ (beryllium neutrinos) and ${}^8\text{B} \rightarrow {}^8\text{Be}^* + e^+ + \nu_e$ (boron neutrinos). Neutrinos also play an important role in both the stationary and the explosive stellar processes, which produce and disseminate heavy elements in the universe (6); they may also represent an interesting component of high-energy cosmic rays (7).

At the cosmological level, the cosmic microwave background (CMB), with today's observed photon temperature $T_\gamma^0 = 2.725$ K, should be accompanied by a cosmic neutrino background (CνB), with a predicted neutrino temperature $T_\nu^0 = 1.945$ K (9). Direct detection of the CνB seems to be extremely difficult. Such neutrinos left their imprints during primordial nucleosynthesis (when they were relativistic, $T_\nu \gg m_\nu$) (10) and, later on, during the growth of matter fluctuations (until they became nonrelativistic, $T_\nu \ll m_\nu$) (9). Such imprints are consistent, respectively, with three families of neutrinos and with an upper limit on their mass in the subelectronvolt range, in agreement with laboratory data—a triumph of modern precision cosmology (11). Violation of the charge conjugation–parity (CP) symmetry in the neutrino sector might be related to the very existence of a baryon asymmetry in the early Universe and thus to the matter we are made of [baryogenesis through leptogenesis (12)].

Manmade neutrinos, produced in controlled conditions, are also very important. Nuclear reactors produce, via β decays, about 6 $\bar{\nu}_e$ per nuclear fission, corresponding to a very intense isotropic flux of $\bar{\nu}_e$ [$\sim 9.3 \times 10^{20}$ $\bar{\nu}_e$ s^{-1} for a 5-GW (thermal) reactor] (13). Neutrinos can also be produced by accelerators (14): A beam of protons is directed at a carbon or beryllium target, and the positive π and K mesons produced are focused by a system of magnetic horns onto a long decay tunnel in which they decay to produce neutrinos.

Both natural and manmade neutrinos offer a unique tool for our understanding of the Universe from cosmological to subnuclear scales; not surprisingly, they are at center stage in current physics research.

1.2. The Long Path Towards Neutrino Masses and Mixings

The neutrino was "born" in 1930, when Pauli (15) proposed the existence of a new neutral particle with spin $\frac{1}{2}$ in order to save energy and angular momentum conservation in nuclear β decay. He also estimated the new particle to be lighter than 0.01 proton masses (a limit now improved by seven orders of magnitude). This particle, the neutrino, was included by Fermi in a dynamical theory (16), which postulated a pointlike, four-fermion interaction with a relatively weak coupling strength G_F. The Fermi theory has since evolved into the standard model of electroweak interactions, where the pointlike weak force is mediated by a neutral vector boson Z [neutral current (NC)] or a charged boson $W^\pm$ [charged current (CC)], with a strength unified with the electromagnetic one: $G_F \sim O(\alpha/M_{W,Z}^2)$.

These interactions have a chiral nature: Only the left-handed (LH) component of the neutrino field interacts, whereas the right-handed (RH) component is inactive or sterile. (A similar situation holds for antineutrinos, with LH $\leftrightarrow$ RH.) Massless neutrinos provide the simplest framework to

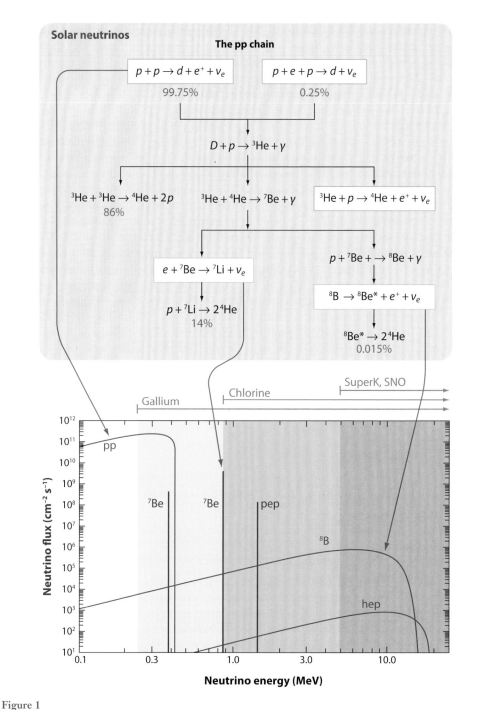

Figure 1

The solar cycle and the resulting solar neutrino energy spectrum. Abbreviations: SNO, Sudbury Neutrino Observatory; SuperK, Super-Kamiokande. Reproduced with permission from Reference 8.

implement such a feature; for $m_v = 0$, chirality would coincide with helicity (i.e., the spin projection on the momentum) and would be strictly conserved: A LH neutrino produced in weak interactions would always remain intrinsically different from its RH antineutrino partner. However, if $m_v \neq 0$, a LH neutrino of energy E can develop the "wrong" RH component at $O(m_v/E)$. An interesting possibility then emerges: The v and $\bar{v}$, endowed with both LH and RH components, instead of being intrinsically different particles (Dirac neutrinos), might be identical—a possibility recognized by Majorana (17) as early as 1937. However, Dirac and Majorana mass effects are indistinguishable in typical experiments (where $m_v/E \ll 10^{-6}$), with one notable exception, which we discuss in Section 4.2: Neutrinoless double-β decay.

Fortunately, neutrino masses can also trigger a different class of effects, namely neutrino flavor changes $v_\alpha \to v_\beta$ (oscillations) on macroscopic length scales, provided that (a) their masses (m_1, m_2, m_3) are not all equal and (b) the states with definite masses (v_1, v_2, v_3) are different from (i.e., mixed with) the states with definite flavor (v_e, v_μ, v_τ), as independently realized by Pontecorvo (18) and Maki, Nakagawa, and Sakata (19).

Neutrino oscillations have been convincingly observed only within the past decade. Section 3 is devoted to the description of the beautiful experiments that have proved the occurrence of $v_e \to v_{\mu,\tau}$ flavor transitions in solar neutrinos and of v_μ disappearance in atmospheric neutrinos, as well as the corresponding oscillation phenomena in reactor and accelerator experiments. The theoretical interpretation has also converged toward a well-defined framework—which we term the v standard model—involving three different v masses m_i in the (sub)electronvolt range and three different mixing angles θ_{ij}.

However, researchers have yet to determine one of the mixing angles, the absolute mass scale and the hierarchical ordering of masses, the Dirac or Majorana nature of the neutrinos, and the possible leptonic CP violation. Each emerging feature of the model will raise new theoretical questions (20). Any answers to these questions in terms of new physics and the existence of new neutrino states or interactions will have far-reaching implications. In the following sections we discuss representative aspects of both established facts and open problems in the v standard model.

2. HOW DO WE KNOW NEUTRINOS HAVE MASS AND MIX? I. THEORY

Neutrino masses can be accessed essentially through (a) kinematical effects on final-state phase space (e.g., in β decay), (b) virtual effects in rare processes (e.g., in neutrinoless double-β decay), (c) gravitational effects on large scales (e.g., on matter density and its distribution in the Universe), and (d) flavor evolution effects during neutrino propagation. The latter has proven to be a very effective probe of nonzero neutrino masses, and is discussed first below. Recent textbooks on these topics include References 21–23.

2.1. Quantum Superposition of Neutrinos and Flavor Change (Oscillations) in Vacuum

Because chirality flips are suppressed at $O(m_v/E)$, we may ignore the spinor properties of neutrinos during their propagation. We can adopt a simple description in terms of wave functions, such as the column vector of states with definite flavor $(v_e, v_\mu, v_\tau)^T$. Then the associated Schrödinger equation is

$$i\frac{d}{dx}\begin{pmatrix} v_e \\ v_\mu \\ v_\tau \end{pmatrix} = \mathbf{H}_{\text{fb}}\begin{pmatrix} v_e \\ v_\mu \\ v_\tau \end{pmatrix}, \qquad \qquad 1.$$

where $t \simeq x$ for ultrarelativistic neutrinos (in natural units), and $\mathbf{H}_{\text{fb}}$ is the 3×3 Hamiltonian matrix in flavor basis (fb). Any observable effect of this equation is invariant under an overall energy shift, $\mathbf{H}_{\text{fb}} \rightarrow \mathbf{H}_{\text{fb}} + \omega \mathbf{1}$ (where $\mathbf{1}$ is the unit matrix), corresponding to an overall phase change of the wave functions by $e^{-i\omega t}$.

If the flavor states $(\nu_e, \nu_\mu, \nu_\tau)$ also have definite masses (m_1, m_2, m_3) and move with momentum $p \gg m_i$, then $E_i = (p^2 + m_i^2)^{1/2} \simeq p + m_i^2/2p$ and

$$\mathbf{H}_{\text{fb}} = \text{diag}(E_1, E_2, E_3) \simeq p\mathbf{1} + \text{diag}\left(m_1^2, m_2^2, m_3^2\right)/2p. \qquad 2.$$

The above matrix is diagonal in flavor basis, and thus flavor-changing processes like $\nu_e \rightarrow \nu_\mu$ are forbidden. This holds, in particular, for the massless neutrino case, $m_i = 0$.

Neutrino masses alone cannot generate off-diagonal elements in $\mathbf{H}_{\text{fb}}$, but neutrino masses combined with mixing can. If the neutrino flavor states ν_α are a quantum superposition of mass states ν_i through a nontrivial unitary matrix U ($U \neq \mathbf{1}$ with $UU^\dagger = 1$),

$$\nu_\alpha = \sum_i U_{\alpha i} \nu_i, \qquad 3.$$

then the matrix $\mathbf{H}_{\text{fb}}$ in Equation 2 transforms as $\mathbf{H}_{\text{fb}} \rightarrow U\,\mathbf{H}_{\text{fb}}\,U^\dagger$, namely

$$\mathbf{H}_{\text{fb}} = \frac{1}{2E} U \begin{pmatrix} -\delta m^2/2 & 0 & 0 \\ 0 & +\delta m^2/2 & 0 \\ 0 & 0 & \pm\Delta m^2 \end{pmatrix} U^\dagger, \qquad 4.$$

where we have set $E \simeq p$, subtracted terms $\propto \mathbf{1}$, and defined two independent squared mass differences,

$$\delta m^2 = m_2^2 - m_1^2 (> 0 \text{ by convention}), \qquad 5.$$

$$\Delta m^2 = |m_3^2 - (m_2^2 + m_1^2)/2|. \qquad 6.$$

The same equations hold for antineutrinos with $U \rightarrow U^*$. The lower- and uppercase deltas refer to the experimental fact that $\delta m^2 \ll \Delta m^2 \simeq |m_3^2 - m_{1,2}^2|$; i.e., the mass spectrum is composed of two close mass states $\nu_{1,2}$ and another state, ν_3, which is more separated in mass. However, it is not yet known whether ν_3 is heavier than $\nu_{1,2}$ (i.e., we have a quarklike or normal mass hierarchy, $+\Delta m^2$) or whether it is lighter than $\nu_{1,2}$ (i.e., we have an inverted mass hierarchy, $-\Delta m^2$).

With the (constant) Hamiltonian in Equation 4, Equation 1 is directly solved by exponentiation, the evolution matrix being (in flavor basis) $\mathbf{S} = \exp(-i\,\mathbf{H}_{\text{fb}}L)$, after a pathlength $L = x$. The square modulus of an off-diagonal matrix element $[\mathbf{S}]_{\beta\alpha}$ ($\beta \neq \alpha$) provides the transition probability $P_{\alpha\beta}$ for the flavor appearance process $\nu_\alpha \rightarrow \nu_\beta$, whereas the square modulus of a diagonal element $[\mathbf{S}]_{\alpha\alpha}$ provides the survival probability $P_{\alpha\alpha}$ for the flavor disappearance process $\nu_\alpha \rightarrow \nu_\alpha$. In a hypothetical two-neutrino (2ν) scenario, and with a 2×2 mixing matrix,

$$U_{2\nu} = \begin{pmatrix} \cos\theta & \sin\theta \\ -\sin\theta & \cos\theta \end{pmatrix}, \qquad 7.$$

one easily obtains the celebrated form of the 2ν transition probability (24),

$$P_{\alpha\beta} = \sin^2 2\theta \, \sin^2 \left(1.27 \frac{(m_i^2 - m_j^2)[\text{eV}^2]L[\text{km}]}{E[\text{GeV}]} \right), \qquad 8.$$

which describes periodic neutrino oscillations. Note that the same parameter $\sin^2 2\theta$ can be obtained either for $\theta < \pi/4$ or for the complementary angle $\pi/2 - \theta > \pi/4$ (the octant ambiguity of vacuum 2ν oscillations).

In the real three-neutrino (3ν) world, the probabilities $P_{\alpha\beta}$ may depend, in general, on both δm^2 and Δm^2, on the mass hierarchy, and on four observable parameters characterizing U (three mixing angles $\theta_{12}, \theta_{13}, \theta_{23}$ and one phase δ), which is usually cast in the factorized form (2)

$$U = \begin{pmatrix} 1 & 0 & 0 \\ 0 & c_{23} & s_{23} \\ 0 & -s_{23} & c_{23} \end{pmatrix} \begin{pmatrix} c_{13} & 0 & s_{13}e^{-i\delta} \\ 0 & 1 & 0 \\ -s_{13}e^{i\delta} & 0 & c_{13} \end{pmatrix} \begin{pmatrix} c_{12} & s_{12} & 0 \\ -s_{12} & c_{12} & 0 \\ 0 & 0 & 1 \end{pmatrix}, \qquad 9.$$

where $c_{ij} = \cos\theta_{ij}$ and $s_{ij} = \sin\theta_{ij}$. Nevertheless, approximate 2ν formulae such as Equation 8 happen to work surprisingly well in a variety of situations (with appropriate replacements for the mass-mixing parameters), essentially because experiments thus far have been sensitive primarily to only one of the two (well-separated) squared mass differences, and also because one of the mixing angles (θ_{13}) is small, if not zero. Sensitivity to all 3ν mass-mixing parameters will be crucial in future oscillation tests of CP symmetry violations $(U \neq U^*)$, which entail differences in the ν and $\bar{\nu}$ oscillation probabilities in vacuum, for example (in natural units):

$$P_{\alpha\beta}(\nu) - P_{\alpha\beta}(\bar{\nu}) = 2\sin 2\theta_{12} \sin 2\theta_{23} \sin 2\theta_{13} \cos\theta_{13} \sin\delta$$

$$\times \sin\left(\frac{\Delta m^2 - \frac{\delta m^2}{2}}{4E}L\right) \sin\left(\frac{\Delta m^2 + \frac{\delta m^2}{2}}{4E}L\right) \sin\left(\frac{\delta m^2}{4E}L\right), \qquad 10.$$

where $\alpha\beta = e\mu, \mu\tau$, or τe. Current experiments are basically insensitive to such (if any) difference.

Finally, Majorana ν mixing involves two extra phases, $U \to U \cdot \text{diag}(1, e^{i\phi_2}, e^{i\phi_3})$ in usual notation. These Majorana phases cancel out in the matrix product of Equation 4 and thus cannot be probed via oscillations.

2.2. Neutrino Flavor Change in Matter

Neutrinos propagating in matter may experience elastic scattering (ES) on background fermions $(\nu_\alpha + f \to \nu_\alpha + f)$ in the forward direction, i.e., with no change in momentum. Forward scattering via NC proceeds with the same amplitude for all neutrino flavors and thus has no observable effects on flavor oscillations. However, forward scattering via CC involves only ν_e, as ordinary matter contains $f = e$ (but not $f = \mu, \tau$). Wolfenstein (25) and Mikheev & Smirnov (26) (MSW) noted that the ν_e acquires an extra CC interaction energy $V_{CC} = \sqrt{2}G_F N_e$ (where N_e is the electron number density), which only affects the ee element of the Hamiltonian matrix shown in Equation 4,

$$\mathbf{H}_{\text{fb}}^{\text{mat}} = \frac{1}{2E}U\begin{pmatrix} -\delta m^2/2 & 0 & 0 \\ 0 & +\delta m^2/2 & 0 \\ 0 & 0 & \pm\Delta m^2 \end{pmatrix}U^\dagger + \begin{pmatrix} \sqrt{2}G_F N_e & 0 & 0 \\ 0 & 0 & 0 \\ 0 & 0 & 0 \end{pmatrix}, \qquad 11.$$

where $V_{CC} \to -V_{CC}$ for antineutrinos.

In the Sun, the Earth's interior, and the cores of supernovae, the density N_e (and thus also the matrix $\mathbf{H}_{\text{fb}}^{\text{mat}}$) may change significantly with x—the solutions to Equation 1 may be profoundly different from Equation 8—and may even lack any periodic behavior, in which case we use the term flavor transition or flavor change, rather than oscillation. Moreover, the flavor-transition amplitude typically becomes octant asymmetric (in contrast to Equation 8), even for constant N_e.

Matter effects are manifest only when the ν_e is significantly involved, and they are best observed when the two matrices in Equation 11 have entries of comparable magnitude, i.e., when either (a) $V_{CC} \sim \delta m^2/2E$ or (b) $V_{CC} \sim \Delta m^2/2E$. Solar $\nu_e \to \nu_{\mu,\tau}$ transitions fulfill the former condition, and indeed they provide evidence for MSW effects (27). Future accelerator $\nu_\mu \to \nu_e$ experiments fulfilling the latter condition in the Earth might probe the mass hierarchy ($\pm\Delta m^2$) via matter effects.

2.3. Other Effects of Masses and Mixings

Neutrinos appear in the final states of many decays in association with charged particles. The larger the neutrino mass, the smaller the maximal energy available to the charged partners. In β decay, the electron spectrum endpoint probes a combination of neutrino squared masses weighted by the ν_e mixings (28),

$$m_\beta = \left[\sum_i |U_{ei}|^2 m_i^2\right]^{\frac{1}{2}} = \left[c_{13}^2 c_{12}^2 m_1^2 + c_{13}^2 s_{12}^2 m_2^2 + s_{13}^2 m_3^2\right]^{\frac{1}{2}}, \qquad 12.$$

which is sometimes termed effective ν_e mass.

Neutrino masses are also a source of gravity, with potentially observable effects on cosmic scales. The current cosmological model predicts a CνB with number density $n_\nu^0 = 112/\text{cm}^3$ (for each $\nu + \bar\nu$ family). The fractional contribution of their rest masses to the energy density of the Universe should then be $\Omega_\nu = n_\nu^0 \Sigma / \rho_{\text{crit}} \simeq \Sigma/(50\,\text{eV})$, where

$$\Sigma = m_1 + m_2 + m_3 \qquad 13.$$

and $\rho_{\text{crit}} \simeq 5.6 \times 10^3\,\text{eVcm}^{-3}$ is the so-called critical density (2, 9). Cosmological data provide tight upper limits on Ω_ν and thus on Σ.

Finally, if massive neutrinos are of Majorana type (i.e., not distinguishable from their antiparticles), they may trigger in some nuclei the rare process of neutrinoless double-β decay ($0\nu2\beta$): $(A, Z) \rightarrow (A, Z + 2) + 2e^-$. This second-order weak process is thought to proceed as follows. (*a*) Within the nucleus, the decay $n \rightarrow p + e^- + \bar\nu_e$ occurs (where the $\bar\nu_e$ is RH); (*b*) the $\bar\nu_e$ develops a LH component at $O(m_\nu/E)$; (*c*) this component—if of Majorana type—is nothing but the LH component of the ν_e and is absorbed by a nearby neutron, $\nu_e + n \rightarrow p + e^-$. The final states contain $2e^-$ and no neutrinos, violating lepton number conservation by two units. Because all three mass states can contribute to $0\nu2\beta$ decay at $O(m_i/E)$, with weights given by U_{ei} (including the unknown Majorana phases $e^{i\phi_i}$) at both the production and absorption points, the process is sensitive to (29)

$$m_{\beta\beta} = \left|\sum_i U_{ei}^2 m_i\right| = \left|c_{13}^2 c_{12}^2 m_1 + c_{13}^2 s_{12}^2 m_2 e^{i2\phi_2} + s_{13}^2 m_3 e^{i2\phi_3}\right|, \qquad 14.$$

which is often termed effective Majorana mass. The observables m_β, Σ, and $m_{\beta\beta}$ are currently the main means of accessing the absolute neutrino mass scale, which is not probed by neutrino oscillation.

The above standard 3ν framework represents a grid for the interpretation of neutrino oscillation and nonoscillation data. It may be supplemented by the study of nonstandard theoretical possibilities, including (*a*) mixing involving "sterile" (i.e., not coupled to the Z boson) neutrino states and (*b*) new neutrino interactions or decays. As yet, there is no convincing evidence for these possibilities.

3. HOW DO WE KNOW NEUTRINOS HAVE MASS AND MIX?
II. EXPERIMENTS

Neutrino oscillation experiments aim to probe either the flavor disappearance ($P_{\alpha\alpha} < 1$) or the flavor appearance ($P_{\alpha\beta} > 0$) of neutrinos with known energy spectra at the source. They also aim to test the profile of the oscillation probability in terms of the neutrino energy E and the pathlength L.

3.1. Muon Flavor Change of Atmospheric Neutrinos

As mentioned in Section 1.1, the interaction of cosmic rays with nuclei in the upper atmosphere creates pions and kaons which, through the $\pi, K \to \mu \to e$ decay chains, yield approximately two $\nu_\mu + \bar{\nu}_\mu$ for every $\nu_e + \bar{\nu}_e$. Despite uncertainties in the absolute fluxes of atmospheric neutrinos, the flavor ratio $R = (\nu_\mu + \bar{\nu}_\mu)/(\nu_e + \bar{\nu}_e) \sim 2$ is a robust prediction, with an estimated theoretical uncertainty of $\sim 5\%$ for $E_\nu \sim 0.1$–10 GeV (30). In addition, owing to the isotropy of cosmic rays and to the spherical symmetry of the atmosphere, one expects atmospheric neutrino fluxes to be up-down symmetric with respect to zenith angle at any detector location.

Atmospheric ν_μ and ν_e are observed underground (to reject cosmic muons), essentially by detecting the final-state leptons (μ and e) produced via CC interactions on nuclei. In a water detector, μ-like and e-like events can be distinguished through the Cherenkov light pattern, where muons, being more massive, scatter less than electrons and hence produce a better-defined ring of light. Events produced by ν_τs cannot be practically identified due to the very short τ lifetime.

Following a number of pioneering, low-statistics experiments (31, 32), in the 1980s several larger nucleon-decay detectors–Kamioka (33), IMB (Irvine–Michigan–Brookhaven) (34), and Soudan (35)—were constructed. These detectors observed an anomalously low flavor ratio R. However, it was not possible to ascribe this low ratio to a deficit of ν_μ or to an excess of ν_e (see below). The directional information was also relatively poor.

In 1998, the Super-Kamiokande collaboration, using a much larger (50-kt) water Cherenkov detector, presented compelling evidence (36) that the anomalous flavor ratio was a neutrino physics effect involving a deficit of ν_μ coming from below (i.e., through the Earth). In addition to its increased statistical sensitivity, this larger detector had an increased percentage of fully contained μ and e events, where the entire energy from the interaction was deposited in the active detector volume. The event analysis reconstructed the most probable ν direction, and hence could determine the pathlength L from the atmosphere to the detector, ranging from a minimum $L \sim 15$ km for downgoing neutrinos to a maximum $L \sim 13,000$ km for upgoing neutrinos. The data showed a clear up-down angular asymmetry of the atmospheric ν_μ flux, with less ν_μ coming from the longest distances L, as was later observed in MACRO (Monopole, Astrophysics and Cosmic Ray Observatory) (37) and Soudan-2 (38). Conversely, no up-down asymmetry has been found for ν_e (39, 40). Atmospheric zenith distribution data can thus be interpreted as arising from dominant $\nu_\mu \to \nu_\tau$ flavor changes, with at most a subdominant contribution from $\nu_\mu \to \nu_e$.

The data from atmospheric ν_μ oscillations are consistent with the final state being ν_τ at 2.4σ CL (41). This result is also consistent with strong limits on ν_e admixture set by short-baseline reactor experiments (see Section 3.5) and with upper limits on a potential sterile neutrino (ν_s) admixture set by Super-Kamiokande atmospheric neutrino data themselves. [A ν_s would reduce both CC and NC interactions but would leave the NC/CC ratio unchanged (42).]

For dominant $\nu_\mu \to \nu_\tau$ oscillations, matter (i.e., MSW) effects related to ν_e play little or no role, and the data essentially probe vacuum ν_μ oscillations between the second and third generations, governed by the $(\Delta m^2, \theta_{23})$ parameters:

$$P_{\mu\mu} \simeq 1 - P_{\mu\tau} \simeq 1 - \sin^2 2\theta_{23} \, \sin^2 \left(1.27 \frac{\Delta m^2 [\mathrm{eV}^2] L[\mathrm{km}]}{E[\mathrm{GeV}]} \right). \qquad 15.$$

Figure 2 (39) shows the muonlike data events divided by the no-oscillation Monte Carlo predictions versus the reconstructed neutrino L/E parameter—i.e., an averaged form of the above $P_{\mu\mu}$. The fact that atmospheric neutrino data can be well described by a formula as simple as Equation 15 over several decades in L/E is impressive.

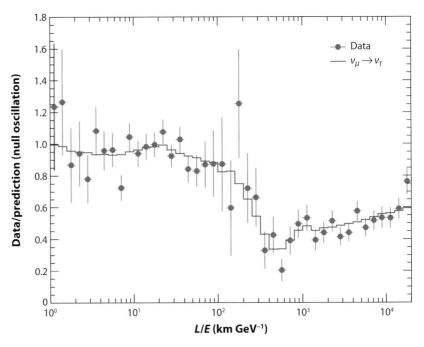

Figure 2

The ratio of the muonlike data events in Super-Kamiokande to no-oscillation Monte Carlo predictions (*red data points*) versus the reconstructed neutrino pathlength-to-energy ratio (*L/E*). The first half-cycle of oscillation is visible as a dip, whereas subsequent oscillations at large *L/E* are completely averaged out ($P_{\mu\mu} \sim 1/2$). The *L/E* position of the dip fixes $\Delta m^2 \sim 2.5 \times 10^{-3}$ eV^2, while its depth fixes $\sin^2 2\theta_{23} \sim 1$ (nearly maximal mixing). The ratio is consistent with $\nu_\mu \to \nu_\tau$ oscillations (*solid blue line*) (39).

3.2. Muon Flavor Change of Accelerator Neutrinos

Given that atmospheric ν_μ disappear, it is important to confirm in a controlled experimental setting both the oscillatory pattern and the $\nu_\mu \to \nu_\tau$ dominance. The High Energy Research Organization, Tsukuba, Japan (KEK) to Kamioka Long-Baseline Neutrino Oscillation Experiment (K2K) (43) and the Main Injector Neutrino Oscillation Search (MINOS) (44) are experiments designed to study ν_μ disappearance in accelerator-produced ν_μ beams. Each includes a near detector designed to study the unoscillated ($\Delta m^2 L_{\text{near}}/E \ll 1$) beam spectrum and composition, thus reducing systematic uncertainties. Their far detector distance L and the average energy $\langle E \rangle$ of the beam are such that $L/\langle E \rangle$ corresponds to the first oscillation maximum of atmospheric neutrinos in **Figure 2**. One should observe in the far detector a distortion of the energy spectrum consistent with Equation 15.

K2K used the 12-GeV KEK proton synchrotron to produce a ν_μ beam with $\langle E_\nu \rangle \sim 1.4$ GeV directed at the Super-Kamiokande detector 250 km away. The neutrino energy could be reconstructed event by event in the quasi-elastic channel. The completed experiment observed a distortion and suppression of the energy spectrum, with an associated allowed region of Δm^2 and $\sin^2 2\theta_{23}$ consistent with the region indicated by the atmospheric neutrino experiments.

MINOS, an ongoing experiment, uses the 120-GeV Fermilab Main Injector to produce a neutrino beam of 4 GeV average energy and a detector positioned in the Soudan mine in Minnesota 735 km away. The 5.4-kt detector consists of iron plates interleaved with planes of scintillator strips. A coil provides a toroidal magnetic field in the iron, allowing the measurement of the momentum

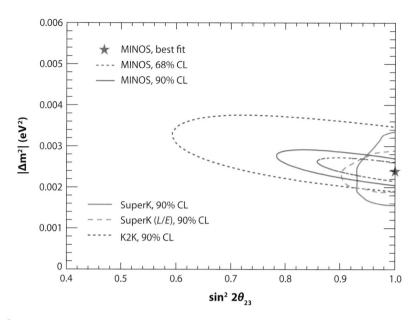

Figure 3

The 90%-CL allowed region on Δm^2 and $\sin^2 2\theta_{23}$ obtained by the High-Energy Research Organization, Tsukuba, Japan (KEK) to Kamioka Long-Baseline Neutrino Oscillation Experiment (K2K) and by the Main Injector Neutrino Oscillation Search (MINOS) compared with the atmospheric neutrino results from Super-Kamiokande (SuperK).

and charge of muons. MINOS also observes distortions of the ν_μ energy spectrum (44), from which the allowed parameter space is extracted.

The allowed regions of Δm^2 and $\sin^2 2\theta_{23}$ of the two experiments are shown in **Figure 3** (44). They are consistent with each other and with the Super-Kamiokande atmospheric neutrino results (40). All these bounds basically constrain the 2ν vacuum-like probability in Equation 15. Removal of the inherent octant ambiguity for θ_{23} (if it is at all possible) will require sensitivity to subleading matter and 3ν effects in future experiments.

Finally, τ flavor appearance will be directly probed in the Oscillation Project with Emulsion-Tracking Apparatus (OPERA) (45), an experiment designed to observe ν_τ downstream from a ν_μ beam (46, 47). This operating experiment is located in the Gran Sasso laboratory in Italy, 732 km away from the source [the Super Proton Synchrotron at the European Organization for Nuclear Research (CERN)]. The average energy of the beam, 20 GeV, was chosen to be well above the 3.5-GeV ν_τ CC production threshold and to be at the maximum of the ν_τ CC production rate, given the oscillation probability and the production cross section. The photographic emulsion technology was chosen because of its micrometer-scale spatial resolution, which allows it to measure accurately the approximately millimeter-long flight path of the τ, followed by a decay kink or a secondary vertex. The 1.8-kt detector is made up of bricks, each of which consists of alternating layers of lead and emulsions. This technique was successfully used to observe the first ν_τ CC interactions in the DONUT (Direct Observation of the Nu Tau) experiment (48). About a dozen ν_τ CC interactions are expected to be observed using various τ-decay modes.

3.3. Electron Flavor Change of Solar Neutrinos

Shortly after Bethe & Critchfield (49) first described the solar fusion chain, Pontecorvo (50) and Alvarez (51) independently suggested that solar ν_e could be detected through the process $\nu_e + {}^{37}\text{Cl} \rightarrow {}^{37}\text{Ar} + e^-$ (for $E_\nu > 0.814$ MeV). Davis (52), motivated by improved standard solar model (SSM) neutrino flux predictions generated by Bahcall (53), built a 615-t tetrachloroethylene detector. The radiochemical technique exposed the detector to solar neutrinos for several months. Thereafter, helium gas was bubbled through the liquid to extract and collect ${}^{37}\text{Ar}$ atoms, which were placed into a ~0.5-cm^3-volume proportional counter to record the ${}^{37}\text{Ar}$ decays. The experiment provided average neutrino rates but no real-time or directional information.

The Davis (54) experiment observed significantly less signal than expected. Explanations for what became known as the solar neutrino problem included problems with the measurement, the underlying SSM assumptions, and unexpected neutrino properties. Of particular concern was the fact that the Davis experiment was only sensitive to the higher-energy beryllium and boron neutrinos, a very small fraction of the total flux, with strongly temperature-dependent rates (5, 55).

In the 1980s, the Kamiokande collaboration detected ${}^{8}\text{B}$ solar neutrinos from $\nu_\alpha + e^- \rightarrow \nu_\alpha + e^-$ scattering. This reaction is dominated by the ν_e cross section, but it also has reduced sensitivity to ν_μ and ν_τ. With directional sensitivity, Kamiokande provided direct proof that it observed neutrinos from the Sun. However, the experiment saw only half the number of neutrinos predicted by the solar model (56). Neither the SSM nor most nonstandard solar models were able to reconcile the different suppressions observed by Kamiokande and Davis. One reason for this is because in the solar fusion chain boron is created via the ${}^{7}\text{Be}$ reaction, and yet Kamiokande—which was sensitive only to boron neutrinos—saw a larger flux than did the Chlorine experiment, which was sensitive to both beryllium and boron neutrinos.

Two Ga radiochemical experiments, SAGE (the Russian-American Gallium Experiment) (57) and GALLEX (the Gallium Experiment) (58), utilized the lower-threshold reaction $\nu_e + {}^{71}\text{Ga} \rightarrow {}^{71}\text{Ge} + e^-$ ($E_\nu > 0.233$ MeV), suggested by Kuzmin (59), to measure the primary low-energy pp solar neutrino flux, which is linked directly to the solar luminosity. Both experiments observed just over half of the total signal predicted by the SSM (dominated by pp neutrinos).

The Davis Cl experiment, Kamiokande, SAGE, and GALLEX, and later the high-statistics Super-Kamiokande electron scattering measurements (60) and the GNO (Gallium Neutrino Observatory) experiment (61), produced results that were incompatible with either standard or nonstandard solar model predictions (62, 63). The results did, however, accord with the hypothesis of neutrino oscillations in the (ν_1, ν_2) sector, which is governed by the mass-mixing parameters (δm^2, θ_{12}). For a long time the hypothesis admitted a multiplicity of possible solutions resulting from either the vacuum or MSW terms in Equation 11 and spanning several orders of magnitude in both mass and mixing parameters. A clear preference for MSW solutions at large mixing angle only emerged with high-statistics Super-Kamiokande data (64).

A direct proof that solar ν_e underwent a flavor change (affected by solar matter) came only recently with the Sudbury Neutrino Observatory (SNO) experiment, a heavy water Cherenkov detector.

The heavy water target provided three different reactions for ${}^{8}\text{B}$ solar neutrinos:

$$\nu_e + d \rightarrow p + p + e^- \quad (d\text{CC}), \qquad\qquad 16.$$

$$\nu_\alpha + d \rightarrow p + n + \nu_\alpha \quad (d\text{NC}), \qquad\qquad 17.$$

$$\nu_\alpha + e^- \rightarrow \nu_\alpha + e^- \quad (\text{ES}). \qquad\qquad 18.$$

The d CC reaction is only sensitive to the ν_e flux ($\Phi_{CC} = \Phi_e$), whereas the d NC reaction is equally sensitive to all three flavors of neutrinos ($\Phi_{NC} = \Phi_e + \Phi_{\mu\tau}$, where $\Phi_{\mu\tau} = \Phi_\mu + \Phi_\tau$). The ES reaction basically probes the combination $\Phi_{ES} \simeq \Phi_e + 0.154\Phi_{\mu\tau}$, where $\sigma_{\mu\tau}/\sigma_e \simeq 0.154$ is the ES cross section ratio. Thus there are three independent observations (the CC, NC, and ES event rates) that overconstrain two fluxes (Φ_e and $\Phi_{\mu\tau}$).

If solar ν_e change flavor, the averaged survival probability at the Earth is given by $\langle P_{ee} \rangle = \Phi_{CC}/\Phi_{NC}$. Moreover, if the SSM is correct, its predicted flux Φ_{SSM} must be equal to the total flux Φ_{NC} measured by SNO, independent of oscillations. The ES rate acts as a further consistency check.

The SNO experiment was performed in several stages. In the first stage, measurements were made with pure D_2O (65). Next, salt (NaCl) was added to enhance the sensitivity to the NC signal through the large neutron capture cross section of ^{35}Cl (66, 67). In the final stage, an array of ^3He proportional counters (68) was inserted into the detector to allow for an independent event-by-event discrimination between the NC events and the CC or ES events. **Figure 4** shows the salt-phase results for the combined flux $\Phi_{\mu\tau}$ versus the flux Φ_e. These results disagree with the null hypothesis of no neutrino flavor change by 7σ, and the NC results are in excellent agreement

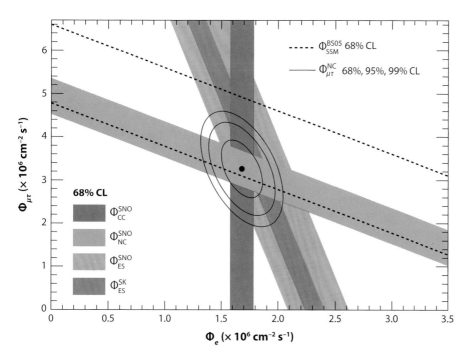

Figure 4

Combined flux of ν_μ and ν_τ versus flux of ν_e (67). The charged currents (CC), neutral currents (NC), and elastic scattering (ES) flux measurements are indicated by the filled bands. The total ^8B solar neutrino flux predicted by the standard solar model (SSM) is shown as dashed black lines, and the flux measured with the NC channel is represented by the solid blue band parallel to the model prediction. The narrow gray band parallel to the Sudbury Neutrino Observatory (SNO) ES result corresponds to the Super-Kamiokande (SK) result (64). The intercepts of these bands with the axes represent the $\pm 1\sigma$ uncertainties. The nonzero value of $\Phi_{\mu\tau}$ provides direct evidence for neutrino flavor transformation. The black point represents Φ_e from the CC flux and $\Phi_{\mu\tau}$ from the NC–CC difference with 68%-, 95%-, and 99%-CL contours included.

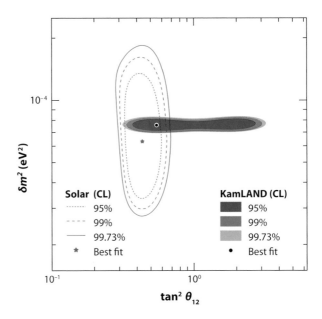

Figure 5

Allowed regions of δm^2 and $\tan^2 \theta_{12}$ for the Kamioka Liquid Scintillator Anti-Neutrino Detector (KamLAND) reactor $\bar{\nu}_e$ disappearance measurement and the global solar ν_e analysis (72).

with the SSM predictions for the flux of ^{8}B neutrinos (69). The CC-to-NC ratio also tells us that $P_{ee} \simeq \frac{1}{3}$ in the SNO energy range.

The latter information, together with the KamLAND (Kamioka Liquid Scintillator Anti-Neutrino Detector) evidence for $\delta m^2 \sim O(10^{-4})$ eV^2 (see Section 3.5), proves the occurrence of solar matter effects (27) and fixes θ_{12}. Indeed, hypothetical vacuumlike oscillations should be completely averaged out ($\delta m^2 L/E \gg 1$ over $L = 1$ a.u.) to yield $\langle P_{ee} \rangle_{\text{vac}} = 1 - 0.5 \sin^2 2\theta_{12} \geq 1/2$, which contrasts with SNO data. Including matter effects, one obtains $\langle P_{ee} \rangle_{\text{mat}} \simeq \sin^2 \theta_{12}$ in the SNO energy range (see Reference 70 and references therein), which is consistent with SNO data for $\sin^2 \theta_{12} \simeq \frac{1}{3}$. Note that at much lower energies (pp neutrinos) the MSW term in Equation 11 vanishes, and the oscillation probability tends toward its vacuumlike expression. A smooth transition between vacuum- and matter-dominated transitions should then be observed at intermediate energies. First results measuring submegaelectronvolt beryllium solar neutrinos reported by Borexino (71), a liquid scintillator–based experiment, are consistent with the expected value for MSW neutrino oscillations.

Figure 5 (72) shows the results of a global χ^2 analysis from all solar neutrino experiments, assuming the SSM and MSW neutrino oscillations for 2ν mixing, which produce a very good fit to all the measurements and constrain the best-fit mass-mixing parameters around $\theta_{12} \sim 34°$ and $\delta m^2 \sim 6.5 \times 10^{-5}$ eV^2 (67). Also shown are the KamLAND constraints, which we discuss in the next section. Note that only the solar neutrino data can solve the octant ambiguity for θ_{12}, thanks to the (octant-asymmetric) matter effects that occur as neutrinos travel through the Sun.

3.4. Electron Flavor Change of Reactor Neutrinos

Neutrinos were first experimentally detected by Reines & Cowan (73, 74), who used $\bar{\nu}_e$ produced at a nuclear reactor. Reactor $\bar{\nu}_e$ are suitable for $\bar{\nu}_e \rightarrow \bar{\nu}_e$ disappearance searches, having typical energies (approximately a few megaelectronvolts) below the μ- and τ-production threshold. These searches require an accurately known reactor thermal power, a good understanding of the initial fuel composition, the relevant fuel-burning process, the fission yields, and the resulting overall $\bar{\nu}_e$ energy spectrum.

Nearly all of the reactor neutrino oscillation experiments performed so far have utilized the $\bar{\nu}_e + p \rightarrow n + e^+$ inverse β-decay reaction to detect the $\bar{\nu}_e$, which has a favorable cross section ($\sim 10^{-43}$ cm^2), and the advantage that it provides a characteristic coincidence detection signature—a positron that annihilates, producing prompt back-to-back 0.511-MeV γs, followed by a delayed neutron capture, providing significant background reduction.

In these reactor experiments, the neutrino baseline was progressively increased from a few meters in early searches to approximately 1 km in the CHOOZ (75) and Palo Verde (76) oscillation searches. None of these measurements observed evidence of $\bar{\nu}_e$ disappearance (13), thus setting severe limits on electron neutrino mixing for $\Delta m^2 > 10^{-3}$ eV^2 (see Section 3.5).

The KamLAND experiment was built to search for neutrino oscillations down to the much-lower δm^2 region of 10^{-5} eV^2. It is therefore capable of checking the predicted MSW large-angle solution of the solar neutrino problem using reactor neutrinos. The 1-kt experiment was ideally situated to see a substantial $\bar{\nu}_e$ flux 4×10^6 cm^{-2} s^{-1} from 16 Japanese reactor power complexes, mostly located between 138 and 214 km from the detector. In 2002, KamLAND reported the first definitive evidence for $\bar{\nu}_e$ disappearance (77); more recently it reported improved precision results yielding $\theta_{12} \simeq 37°$ and $\delta m^2 \simeq 7.6 \times 10^{-5}$ eV^2 (72). Notably, as shown in **Figure 6** the $\bar{\nu}_e$ survival probability versus L_0/E (where $L_0 \simeq 180$ km) displays a clear and statistically significant oscillatory pattern, in excellent agreement with the neutrino oscillation hypothesis in vacuum

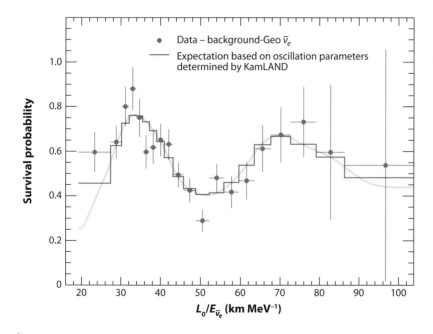

Figure 6

The Kamioka Liquid Scintillator Anti-Neutrino Detector (KamLAND) survival probability ratio for background and geo-neutrino subtracted $\bar{\nu}_e$ versus the reconstructed neutrino pathlength-to-energy ratio (L_0/E), where $L_0 \simeq 180$ km. The clear and statistically significant oscillatory pattern is in excellent agreement with neutrino oscillation predictions (*blue line*) (72).

(matter effects in the Earth's crust are negligible). **Figure 5** demonstrates that the KamLAND best-fit values are in excellent agreement with the global solar neutrino results obtained under the assumption of MSW oscillations. Note the complementarity of the solar neutrino results, which strongly constrain θ_{12} (i.e., the $\nu_{1,2}$ oscillation amplitude), and of the reactor measurements, which tightly constrain δm^2 (i.e., the $\nu_{1,2}$ oscillation frequency).

3.5. No Flavor Change on Short Baselines: Lessons from Reactors and Accelerators

Neutrino oscillations have also been searched for using short-baseline experiments, both at reactors and at accelerators. As described in the previous section, the CHOOZ (78) and Palo Verde (79) reactor experiments looked for the suppression of the flux produced by a nuclear reactor. Their baseline of 1 km, coupled with the few-megaelectronvolt energy of reactor $\bar{\nu}_e$, made them sensitive to the same Δm^2 as atmospheric neutrinos. The ratio of observed to expected rates of events measured by CHOOZ was $1.01 \pm 2.8\%$ (stat) $\pm 2.7\%$ (syst), with the largest systematic uncertainties arising from a knowledge of the $\bar{\nu}_e$ flux and interaction cross sections. These experiments' failure to observe a suppression or distortion of the expected $\bar{\nu}_e$ spectrum led to the conclusion that the $\nu_e \rightarrow \nu_{\mu,\tau}$ transition was not a significant contribution to atmospheric ν_μ disappearance. The experiments set a limit on $\sin^2 \theta_{13}$ of less than a few percent, the precise value depending on the chosen Δm^2 value. Remarkably, all current oscillation searches show a preference for $\sin^2 2\theta_{13} \sim 0$ (although not as strong as in CHOOZ), whenever the simplified 2ν analysis [in either the (Δm^2, θ_{23}) or the (δm^2, θ_{12}) parameters] is promoted to a full 3ν oscillation analysis with $\theta_{13} \geq 0$ (70). This consistency is a nontrivial check of the emerging ν standard model.

Short-baseline accelerator searches have also probed mass-squared differences $\Delta M^2 \sim O(1)$ eV^2, much higher than the atmospheric Δm^2 (hence the uppercase M here) in various channels. The CHORUS (CERN Hybrid Oscillation Research Apparatus) and NOMAD (Neutrino Oscillation Magnetic Detector) experiments (80, 81) found no $\nu_\mu \rightarrow \nu_\tau$ signal at such ΔM^2.

The LSND (Liquid Scintillator Neutrino Detector) (82) used neutrinos produced by the Los Alamos 798-MeV proton beam impinging on a beam stop. Negative pions are mostly absorbed, leaving π^+ to decay ($\pi^+ \rightarrow \mu^+ + \nu_\mu$), followed by muon decays ($\mu^+ \rightarrow e^+ + \nu_e + \bar{\nu}_\mu$), mostly at rest. LSND searched for $\bar{\nu}_\mu \rightarrow \bar{\nu}_e$ oscillations using the same reaction ($\bar{\nu}_e + p \rightarrow n + e^+$) and identification procedure as reactor experiments. An excess of e^+ events was observed, corresponding to an oscillation probability of $P_{\mu e} \simeq 0.26\%$ and $\Delta M^2 \simeq 0.2$–10 eV^2. This high ΔM^2, inconsistent with the solar δm^2 and the atmospheric Δm^2, implied the existence of at least one additional neutrino. Coupled with the LEP (Large Electron-Positron collider) and SLC (Stanford Linear Collider) measurement of the Z^0 width indicating the existence of just three neutrinos (2), this observation further implied that this additional neutrino does not couple to the Z^0 and is therefore sterile. This effect was not confirmed by MiniBooNE (the Mini–Booster Neutrino Experiment) (83), a dedicated experiment looking for ν_e appearance in the Fermilab Booster Neutrino beam consisting mostly of ν_μ. It used a detector consisting of 800 t of mineral oil, in which charged particles emitted both scintillation and Cherenkov light. The observed ν_e energy spectrum was consistent with expectations in the region where an excess would have been expected on the basis of the LSND result. In the following sections, therefore, we ignore the LNSD signal claim.

3.6. The Current Synthesis

The various experiments examined in the above sections probe different parts of the mass-mixing parameter space. Short-baseline reactor neutrinos are dominantly sensitive to (Δm^2, θ_{13}), and their negative oscillation results set the most stringent upper limits to θ_{13}. Atmospheric and long-baseline accelerator neutrinos probe dominantly $(\Delta m^2, \theta_{23})$ and subdominantly θ_{13}. Finally, solar and long-baseline reactor neutrinos probe dominantly $(\delta m^2, \theta_{12})$ and subdominantly θ_{13}. All classes of experiments are consistent with θ_{13} being small. The three-family neutrino mass parameters $(\delta m^2, \Delta m^2)$ and mixing angles $(\theta_{12}, \theta_{23}, \theta_{13})$ are sufficient to describe established neutrino oscillation data. Unfortunately, the smaller the θ_{13}, the lower the sensitivity to the CP-violating phase δ (which enters as the combination $\sin\theta_{13}e^{i\delta}$; see Equation 9) and the smaller the matter effects in atmospheric or long-baseline accelerator neutrinos (to which the vacuum term driven by $\pm\Delta m^2$ would add or subtract in Equation 11, according to the hierarchy). Therefore, the absence of an indication in favor of $\theta_{13} > 0$ implies that the CP phase δ and the mass hierarchy are currently unconstrained.

Various global 3ν analyses of neutrino oscillation data have been performed (see, e.g., References 70 and 84–86). The results of these analyses show a high degree of consistency and stability in the parameter determination. A recent global fit (87) provides the following $\pm2\sigma$ ranges (95% CL) for each parameter:

$$\Delta m^2/\text{eV}^2 = 2.39 \pm^{0.27}_{0.20} \times 10^{-3}, \qquad\qquad 19.$$

$$\delta m^2/\text{eV}^2 = 7.67 \pm^{0.34}_{0.36} \times 10^{-5}, \qquad\qquad 20.$$

$$\sin^2\theta_{12} = 0.312 \pm^{0.040}_{0.034}, \qquad\qquad 21.$$

$$\sin^2\theta_{23} = 0.466 \pm^{0.136}_{0.100}, \qquad\qquad 22.$$

$$\sin^2\theta_{13} < 3.6 \times 10^{-2}. \qquad\qquad 23.$$

4. CONSTRAINTS ON THE ABSOLUTE NEUTRINO MASS SCALE

Oscillation experiments have good sensitivity to mass splittings $m_i^2 - m_j^2$, but they are insensitive to the absolute neutrino masses m_i. Absolute neutrino masses can be probed both directly (via precise observations of decay kinematics in nuclear or particle-decay processes or via time-of-flight measurements in the detection of supernova neutrinos) and indirectly (via virtual effects in neutrinoless double-β decay or via model-dependent effects in cosmology). In this section we examine only the most sensitive techniques, which give constraints at the level of $O(1)$ eV and show potential for improvement.

4.1. Kinematic Probe: Beta Decay

The technique for detecting neutrino mass in β decay is to search for a distortion in the shape of the β spectrum in the endpoint energy region. For masses at or above 0.1 eV, distortions induced by different mass states (weighted by the relevant mixing U_{ei}) are lumped as if they were induced by a single neutrino with an effective mass given by Equation 12. Because there are very few decays in the spectrum region of interest (only 2×10^{-13} of the total rate is in the last 1 eV), precise determinations of (or limits on) m_β require a complete and accurate understanding of all of the systematic effects that can alter the shape of the spectrum (88), such as background, determination of energy loss, and atomic physics excitations.

The most sensitive recent tritium β-decay experiments have utilized magnetically collimated retarding field spectrometers to analyze the momentum of the electrons. These spectrometers achieve excellent energy resolution, $\Delta E \sim 5$ eV at 20 keV, without loss of source acceptance. The

Mainz group (89) has set the most precise limits on $m_\beta < 2.3$ eV (95% CL). A group at Troitsk using a similar system also reports an upper limit (90), but they have encountered systematic issues in their analysis that raise questions with regard to their result (88).

4.2. Dirac/Majorana Probe: Neutrinoless Double-Beta Decay

In a number of even-even nuclei, β decay is energetically forbidden, whereas double-β decay, from a nucleus of (A, Z) to $(A, Z + 2)$, is energetically allowed. In 1935 Goeppert-Mayer (91) realized that for such cases there should be an allowed, second-order weak decay process, $(A, Z) \to (A, Z + 2) + 2\bar{\nu}_e + 2e^-$, which is known as 2ν double-β decay ($2\nu2\beta$-decay). However, as noted in Section 2.3, if neutrinos are Majorana particles, neutrinoless double-β decay ($0\nu2\beta$ decay) also becomes possible: $(A, Z) \to (A, Z + 2) + 2e^-$.

The half-life for this rare process can be expressed as $[T_{1/2}^{0\nu2\beta}]^{-1} = G_{0\nu}|M_{0\nu}|^2 m_{\beta\beta}^2$, where $G_{0\nu}$ is an exactly calculable phase-space factor, $M_{0\nu}$ is the isotope-specific nuclear decay matrix element, and $m_{\beta\beta}$ is the effective Majorana mass defined in Equation 14. The presence of the unknown Majorana phases adds an additional uncertainty to the determination of $m_{\beta\beta}$, as there can be cancellations between the terms in Equation 14. In addition, the nuclear matrix elements must be calculated using either shell model techniques or quasi-particle random phase approximation methods, which at present vary up to a factor of $\sim$2 for some isotopes.

Finally, other lepton number violating processes might contribute to $0\nu2\beta$ decay, including heavy Majorana neutrino exchange, RH currents, and exchange mechanisms arising from R-parity-violating supersymmetry models. However, if $0\nu2\beta$ decay occurs, independent measurements in a series of different isotopes would allow the extraction of $m_{\beta\beta}$ and perhaps of the lepton violating interaction mechanism as well (92).

The $0\nu2\beta$-decay experimental signature would be a peak in the spectrum of energy deposited in the detector by the two electrons, at the endpoint energy determined by the mass differences between the parent and daughter nuclei. The four-body $2\nu2\beta$ decay, in contrast, would produce a continuous spectrum that would extend up to the endpoint energy. A wide variety of experimental techniques have been utilized to observe these decays, including semiconductors, cryogenic bolometers, and tracking detectors. The most sensitive experiments use the method where the source is also the detector. With typical $0\nu2\beta$-decay endpoint energies in the megaelectronvolt region, backgrounds from naturally occurring U and Th chains are a serious concern, as are a host of cosmogenically produced radioisotope activities. The $2\nu2\beta$ decay represents an irreducible background that can be made negligible by using detectors with extremely good energy resolution.

Experimental searches for both $0\nu2\beta$- and $2\nu2\beta$ decays have been carried out on a number of nuclei, including ^{48}Ca, ^{76}Ge, ^{82}Se, ^{96}Zr, ^{100}Mo, ^{116}Cd, ^{128}Te, ^{130}Te, ^{136}Xe, and ^{150}Nd. The $2\nu2\beta$ decay was first directly observed (93) in ^{82}Se in 1987 and was subsequently seen in several other nuclei. Typical $T_{1/2}^{2\nu2\beta}$ half-lives are in the range of 10^{19} to 10^{21} years (94). Except for one instance discussed below, searches for $0\nu2\beta$ decay have only set lower limits on $T_{1/2}^{0\nu2\beta}$, with values that range from 10^{21} to 10^{25} years (94). Depending on model assumptions, the 10^{24}–10^{25}-year half-lives correspond to $m_{\beta\beta}$ sensitivities in the range of 0.5 to 1 eV.

There is currently a claim from a subset of the Heidelberg–Moscow collaboration (95, 96) for the first observation of $0\nu2\beta$ decay in ^{76}Ge, with a $T_{1/2}^{0\nu\beta\beta} = (1.19^{+2.99}_{-0.50}) \times 10^{25}$ years and $m_{\beta\beta}$ in the range of 0.22 and 0.35 eV. However, a number of concerns about the measurement related to the background suppression and analysis methods have been raised (94), and the result awaits confirmation.

4.3. Cosmological Probe

The past decade has witnessed a revolution in cosmology. A new paradigm has emerged in which the dominant sources of gravity on cosmic scales are dark matter and dark energy (2). By themselves, data on CMB anisotropies from the WMAP (Wilkinson Microwave Anisotropy Probe) mission (11) are precise enough to tightly constrain even subdominant sources of gravity, including the CνB masses, and in particular the sum $\Sigma = m_1 + m_2 + m_3$. Additional observations from probing the distribution of matter (e.g., by galaxy surveys, Lyman α data) and the expansion history of the Universe (e.g., Hubble parameter, supernova luminosities) can corroborate and tighten such constraints (97).

The latest WMAP data from five years of operation (98) provide the upper limit

$$\Sigma < 1.3 \text{ eV(WMAP 5 years)}, \qquad\qquad 24.$$

which can be strengthened in the subelectronvolt range ($\Sigma < 0.61$ eV) in combination with other cosmological data (99). The limit might be pushed down to about $\Sigma < 0.2$ eV by including Lyman α data (100), but their systematics are still being debated. Although many would agree that $\Sigma < 1$ eV, consensus has not been reached on a specific subelectronvolt limit.

A final remark: Current bounds on m_β, $m_{\beta\beta}$, and Σ probe only the "degenerate mass" scenario, with $O(1)$ eV masses much larger than their splittings, $m_1 \simeq m_2 \simeq m_3 \equiv m_\nu$. In this case, Equations 12 and 13 imply that $m_\beta \simeq m_\nu \simeq \Sigma/3$, whereas Equation 14 implies that $m_{\beta\beta} \simeq f m_\nu$ where, for $\theta_{13} \simeq 0$, $f \simeq |c_{12}^2 - s_{12}^2 e^{2i\phi_2}| \simeq 0.36$–1, regardless of the Majorana phase. Therefore, the inequality $m_{\beta\beta} \leq \Sigma/3$ should hold. If one assumes the subelectronvolt bound $\Sigma < 0.61$ from Reference 99, this inequality cannot be satisfied by the values of $m_{\beta\beta} \in [0.22, 0.35]$ eV favored by the signal claimed in Reference 96; see also Reference 70 for a discussion based on earlier WMAP data.

5. OPEN QUESTIONS AND FUTURE PERSPECTIVES

Although the past decade has been a period of remarkable discovery, a series of fundamental questions remain to be addressed:

- What are the absolute masses of neutrinos and what can we learn from the hierarchy of particle masses?
- What is the value of θ_{13}, and can we discern an underlying symmetry or mechanism that gives rise to the observed neutrino mixing matrix values?
- Are neutrinos Dirac or Majorana particles?
- Is CP violated in the lepton sector, and might neutrinos offer an explanation of the observed matter to antimatter asymmetry?
- How have neutrinos shaped the evolution of the Universe?

The answers to these questions will shape an improved ν standard model and may open a window to new neutrino states and interactions while also impacting our understanding of astrophysics and cosmology. Answering these questions will require performing a broad set of experiments at accelerators, reactors, and deep underground facilities.

The first objective of future oscillation searches is to learn the value of θ_{13}. Only for $\theta_{13} \neq 0$ can one access δ via CP-odd observables as in Equation 10, as well as the neutrino mass hierarchy via matter effects (at the $\pm\Delta m^2$ scale) in Equation 11. Even if $\theta_{13} > 0$ is observed via $\nu_\mu \rightarrow \nu_e$ oscillations, it will not be easy to disentangle multiple solutions (known as clones), which could reproduce $P_{\mu e}$ at different values of θ_{13}, δ, θ_{23}, sign($\pm\Delta m^2$), a problem known as parameter degeneracy (101). Determining a single solution in the full 3ν parameter space will likely require a combination of several measurements in different oscillation channels, energy ranges, baselines, and propagation media (vacuum versus matter). The difficulty will increase with lower values of $\sin^2 2\theta_{13}$. Finally, the discovery of possible new neutrino states or interactions could profoundly change any envisaged road map. Ways to address these challenges are described below.

5.1. Neutrino Oscillation Searches: Near-Future Projects

The measurement of θ_{13} is currently being planned both at reactors and at accelerators. The two approaches are complementary: Reactors would yield a measurement of θ_{13} devoid of degeneracies, whereas accelerators could also provide a first attempt at establishing the mass hierarchy and CP violation.

Two reactor experiments are currently under construction. Double Chooz (102) will use the same reactor, experimental hall, and detection technique as the CHOOZ experiment. It will have a near detector that will greatly reduce the systematics arising from the knowledge of the reactor neutrino flux and of interaction cross sections. The far (near) detector, located 1050 m (410 m) from the reactors, consists of a central 10.1-m³ acrylic vessel filled with liquid scintillator doped with 0.1% gadolinium, surrounded by a second acrylic vessel containing pure scintillator and acting as a γ catcher. Reducing backgrounds is an important goal in these precision measurements. Uncorrelated background can arise from a random coincidence between two sources, such as ambient radioactivity or cosmogenic neutrons. Correlated background can result from muon-produced fast neutrons in the surrounding rock, with a recoil proton mimicking the e^+–n coincidence in a neutron scattering and the eventual capture of the neutron by the gadolinium. Inner and outer veto systems should reduce these backgrounds by one to two orders of magnitude down to a few tenths of a percent. The near/far detector technique will allow the reduction of the systematic uncertainties from 2.7%, achieved by CHOOZ, to less than 0.6%. The statistical uncertainty will also be reduced from 2.8% to 0.4% due to the increase in volume and the increased running time. A sensitivity to $\sin^2 2\theta_{13}$ of 0.032 can be achieved in five years.

Daya Bay (103) in China will be located near three sets of two reactors. It intends to use four detectors at two near sites (360 m and 500 m) and four detectors located in a far experimental hall (1750 m). To account for possible small differences between the near and far detectors, they will be interchanged, which will reduce the overall detector systematics from 0.18% to 0.12%. Its sensitivity to $\sin^2 2\theta_{13}$, 0.01 at 90% CL after a three-year run, will be greater than that of Double Chooz due to (a) its larger total reactor power, 17.4 GW (thermal), (b) its larger detector mass, eight 20-t detectors, and (c) its improved systematic uncertainty. Other experiments, such as RENO (Reactor Experiment for Neutrino Oscillations) (104) and Angra (105), are in the planning stages.

Two off-axis long baseline accelerator experiments, T2K (Tokai to Kamioka) (106), currently under construction, and the NOνA (NuMI Off-Axis νe Appearance Experiment) (107), currently under consideration, plan to measure $\sin^2 \theta_{13}$ using ν_e appearance in a ν_μ beam. For a detector placed on the axis of an accelerator-produced neutrino beam, the energy spectrum is broad. The decay kinematics of pions is such that observing the neutrinos at a nonzero angle to the beam axis selects a narrow energy range of neutrinos as their energy becomes, to a large extent, independent of the parent meson momentum. The energy of this beam decreases with increasing angle. Placing a detector at the appropriate off-axis angle will allow the selection of the energy spectrum suitable for maximizing an oscillation effect at a given Δm^2 and detector distance.

T2K will use the existing Super-Kamiokande detector illuminated by a 0.8-GeV neutrino beam produced at the Jaeri accelerator complex 295 km away. NOνA will place a detector off axis to the 2-GeV NuMI (Neutrinos at the Main Injector) beam at Fermilab at a distance of 810 km. The parameter for being at oscillation maximum, L/E, is essentially the same for both

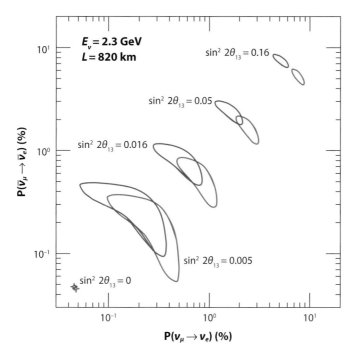

$E_\nu = 2.3$ GeV
$L = 820$ km

$\sin^2 2\theta_{13} = 0.16$

$\sin^2 2\theta_{13} = 0.05$

$\sin^2 2\theta_{13} = 0.016$

$\sin^2 2\theta_{13} = 0.005$

$\sin^2 2\theta_{13} = 0$

$P(\bar{\nu}_\mu \to \bar{\nu}_e)$ (%)

$P(\nu_\mu \to \nu_e)$ (%)

Figure 7

The correlation between the $\bar{\nu}_\mu \to \bar{\nu}_e$ and $\nu_\mu \to \nu_e$ oscillation probabilities for various values of $\sin^2 2\theta_{13}$ and for the two mass hierarchies, distinguished by red/blue colors. Changing the value of δ_{CP} moves the correlation around an ellipse. A measurement of either of the two probabilities would intercept several ellipses and would therefore result in ambiguities. A simultaneous measurement, resulting in a cross-hair, would reduce these ambiguities. Figure reproduced with the permission of S. Parke.

experiments. The beams will have a low (0.5%) ν_e contamination, as is required for a ν_e appearance experiment.

NOνA plans to build a fully active 14-kt detector consisting of planes of liquid scintillator–filled tubes. This experiment relies on an upgrade of Fermilab's Main Injector complex for an increase of the neutrino flux. Its long baseline and high energy make it more sensitive to matter effects than T2K and allow it to run with antineutrinos, thus reducing the ambiguities among the different combinations of $\sin^2 \theta_{13}$, the mass hierarchy, and δ_{CP}. **Figure 7** shows the correlation between the neutrino and antineutrino oscillation probabilities for several values of $\sin^2 2\theta_{13}$.

5.2. Oscillation Searches: Longer-Term Prospects

The construction of superbeams is being considered at both CERN and Fermilab. The proposed SPL (Superconducting Proton Linac) (108) at CERN would be a 4-MW machine with a kinetic energy up to 5 GeV. A proposed 0.5-Mt water Cherenkov detector, MEMPHYS (the Megaton Mass Physics detector) (109), would be located in a cavern off the Frejus tunnel, 130 km away. The optimal sensitivity is achieved at a neutrino energy of 350 MeV. A near detector will also be required, as in all schemes described in this section. A 90%-CL limit of 0.001 on $\sin^2 2\theta_{13}$ can be achieved (110) for a two-year neutrino run and an eight-year antineutrino run. Matter effects are not important at this energy and distance.

Augmenting the present Fermilab neutrino program is also being considered (111). One option would be to upgrade the present NuMI beam line and proceed with off-axis detectors. Another option would be to build a new beam line directed at Homestake at an increased baseline (1325 km) and thus maximize the sensitivity to the mass hierarchy. Water Cherenkov and liquid argon detectors have been studied. Because of its superior spatial resolution and granularity, which yield excellent electron/π^0 discrimination, a liquid argon detector could have three times the efficiency of a water Cherenkov; the latter does, however, use a well-proven technology. For either beam, NuMI or Homestake, a 100-kt liquid argon detector seems to be preferred. Its sensitivities—defined as the minimum values of $\sin^2 2\theta_{13}$, for which the mass hierarchy could be determined, δ_{CP} could be established to be different from 0 or π, and θ_{13} could be measured to be different from zero—were estimated assuming 60×10^{20} protons on target equally divided between neutrino and antineutrino running. A 3σ sensitivity on $\sin^2 2\theta_{13}$ of 0.002 over 50% of the range of δ_{CP}, could be reached at either NuMI or Homestake. However, the Homestake solution would result in better 3σ sensitivities for δ_{CP}, down to $\sin^2 2\theta_{13} = 0.005$ (as opposed to 0.02), and for the resolution of the mass hierarchy, down to $\sin^2 2\theta_{13} = 0.006$ (instead of 0.05).

Two possible future accelerator technologies are being considered for producing intense neutrino beams needed for high-statistics oscillation measurements. Beta beams (112, 113) would use radioactive ions decaying either via β^-, such as ^{6}He giving ν_e, or β^+, such as ^{18}Ne giving $\bar{\nu}_e$. The ions would be accelerated and injected into a racetrack-shaped storage ring whose straight sections point to the detector, boosting the $\sim$3-MeV decay neutrinos to $\sim$100 MeV. This would result in a narrowly focused forward beam. The advantages are a clean beam without an oscillated flavor intrinsic background and a neutrino energy that is tunable through the acceleration of the parent ions. One would then search for an appearance signal of ν_μ or $\bar{\nu}_\mu$ producing μ^- or μ^+ via CC interactions. A detector could be exposed simultaneously to both types of beams, which would increase its sensitivity (114). Studies indicate that for typical ion decay intensities of 10^{18} per year, sensitivities to δ_{CP} (115, 116) for a 10-year exposure of a 440-kt detector could be as low as 15°.

A neutrino factory has also been proposed (117, 118). It would produce pions using a high-intensity proton beam, let them decay to muons, cool these muons to reduce their angular and momentum spreads, accelerate the muons, and finally inject them into a storage ring; once in the storage ring they would decay, producing neutrinos pointing toward one or two far detectors. If μ^+, which decay to $e^+ + \bar{\nu}_\mu + \nu_e$, were stored, the CC interaction of the two final-state neutrinos would result in μ^+ and e^-. The signal for a $\nu_e \to \nu_\mu$ oscillation would then be the observation of μ^-, and the use of a magnetic detector would be required to determine the charge of the observed muon. If the charge of electrons could also be measured, the study of the channel $\bar{\nu}_\mu \to \bar{\nu}_e$ would allow a complementary search for CP violation. It is projected that 10^{21} $(\mu^+ + \mu^-)$ decays per year in each straight section of the storage ring may be achieved.

Experiments at two baselines would be required to avoid clone solutions resulting from a single baseline (119). Alternatively, both $\nu_e \to \nu_\mu$ and $\nu_e \to \nu_\tau$, which have opposite CP violation effects, could be studied (120), possibly with a detector using the DONUT (48) and OPERA (45) emulsion technology.

An analysis with the GLoBES (General Long-Baseline Experiment Simulator) software (121) was used to determine and compare (122) the capabilities of (a) β beams (with both types of ions accelerated to a γ of 100) in conjunction with a SPL and (b) a neutrino factory beam and T2HK, a 1-Mt version of T2K (at baselines of 3000 and 7000 km). A neutrino factory would be sensitive to smaller values of $\sin^2 2\theta_{13}$. However for values of $\sin^2 2\theta_{13}$ above 0.01 the SPL and SPL $+ \beta$ beams seem to be more appropriate. This comparison is currently being addressed by the International Scoping Study (123). Several research and development experiments are already under way. The

MERIT (Mercury Intense Target) demonstration (124) is designed to study liquid targets, whereas the MICE (Muon Ionisation Cooling Experiment) (125) and the MUCOOL (Muon Ionization Cooling) research and development (126) efforts are intended to demonstrate the feasibility of muon cooling.

5.3. Perspectives on Absolute Neutrino Masses

A next-generation tritium β-decay experiment with a sensitivity to subelectronvolt neutrino masses is being constructed by the KATRIN (Karlsruhe Tritium Neutrino experiment) collaboration (127, 128). Employing a 10-m-diameter solenoidal retarding electrostatic spectrometer ($\Delta E = 0.93$ eV) coupled to a gaseous molecular tritium source, KATRIN expects to reach an estimated sensitivity of $m_\beta = 0.20$ eV (90% CL), over an order of magnitude better than the sensitivity of the Mainz experiment.

It is difficult to envisage extending such a technique below 0.2 eV. However, in the future it might be possible to reach lower sensitivities by using a very large array of individual cryogenic bolometers with extremely high energy resolution in order to make a precision endpoint measurement. Two groups (129, 130) are investigating rhenium-based microbolometers to measure the β decay of ^{137}Re, which has a 63% abundance and a Q value of 2.6 keV. Current sensitivities with multiple (9) bolometers of 15 eV (90% CL) (130) hold out the possibility that, with improved resolution, arrays of 1000 to 10,000 such detectors [as proposed by the MARE (Microcalorimeter Arrays for a Rhenium Experiment) collaboration (131)] might be able to reach the millielectronvolt sensitivities to absolute neutrino mass.

There is renewed emphasis on new experiments searching for $0\nu2\beta$ decay. The most sensitive previous experiments had typical source masses of a few kilograms. Several collaborations, including the CUORE (Cryogenic Underground Observatory for Rare Events) (^{128}Te), the EXO (Enriched Xenon Observatory) (^{136}Xe), the GERDA (Germanium Detector Array) (^{76}Ge), and SNO+ (^{150}Nd), are currently constructing detectors which will have 2β-decay isotopes with masses in the 40-200-kg range (94). A number of other collaborations, such as CANDLES (Calcium Fluoride for the Study of Neutrinos and Dark Matters by Low Energy Spectrometer) (^{48}Ca), COBRA (Cadmium-Telluride 0-Neutrino Double-Beta Research Apparatus) (^{116}Cd), MAJORANA (^{76}Ge), and SuperNEMO (Super-Neutrino Ettore Majorana Observatory) (^{82}Se), are performing research and development aimed at demonstrating that large, tonne-scale next-generation detectors are feasible (94). Convincing evidence of the Majorana nature of neutrinos will require the observation of $0\nu2\beta$ decay in several isotopes. Likewise, because of current theoretical uncertainties with the nuclear matrix elements, it will be necessary to observe and measure $0\nu2\beta$ decay in three or four different isotopes in order to extract meaningful information on neutrino mass. Planned experiments approaching the tonne scale should have sensitivity to probe neutrino masses in the inverted hierarchy region.

New precision cosmological data from future missions such as Planck, as well as improved matter surveys from proposed missions such as the Joint Dark Energy Mission and from ground-based telescopes such as the Large Synoptic Survey Telescope, should provide improved sensitivity to the sum of neutrino masses Σ, down to the lowest possible values, $\Sigma_{min} \simeq \sqrt{\Delta m^2} \simeq 0.05$ eV (normal hierarchy) or $\Sigma_{min} \simeq 2\sqrt{\Delta m^2} \simeq 0.1$ eV (inverted hierarchy) (see References 9 and 97). The three techniques, β decay, $0\nu2\beta$ decay, and cosmology-based measurements, will provide complementary information on neutrino mass. Future results should be consistent if the assumed underlying models are correct.

5.4. Ultrahigh-Energy Astrophysical Neutrinos

The operation of large cosmic-ray arrays such as the Pierre-Auger Observatory (132), coupled with construction of dedicated high-energy neutrino detectors such as IceCube (133) in Antarctica and ANTARES (Astronomy with a Neutrino Telescope and Abyss Environmental Research) (134) in the Mediterranean Sea, will open a new window on the search for ultrahigh-energy ($>10^{15}$ eV) neutrinos from astrophysical sources and will provide new insights into astrophysics. Many models predict that neutrinos should be emitted from astrophysical point sources such as active galactic nuclei. If observed in sufficient quantity, measurements of the neutrino flavor composition can potentially probe for exotic physics such as neutrino decay and extreme long-baseline behavior (135).

5.5. Possible Detours

The existence of new (sterile) neutrino states would dramatically alter our view of leptons and would impact models of physics, astrophysics, and cosmology. Although MiniBooNE rules out the still-unexplained LSND result using a 2ν mixing model, there are more exotic models that might accommodate all the results with two or more ν_s flavors (136, 137). As θ_{13} becomes better determined, future long-baseline projects should have sufficient sensitivity to rule out or further restrict such models (138).

If θ_{13} turns out to be zero, then efforts to search for CP violation in the lepton sector will unfortunately reach a dead end, as experimental sensitivity to the CP phase will be lost if any of the three mixing matrix angles is zero (139) (see Equation 10). If θ_{13} is very small, finding answers to a number of the outstanding questions will be much more difficult.

6. CONCLUSIONS

A few years after proposing the neutrino as a desperate remedy to save basic conservation principles, Wolfgang Pauli exclaimed, "I have done a terrible thing. I have postulated a particle that cannot be detected." Having detected and measured these elusive particles from a variety of sources, we have discovered that neutrinos have interesting properties and an impact that Pauli never imagined. Neutrinos are the lightest-mass fermions, yet they impact the universe on the largest scales and may even offer an explanation of the matter-antimatter asymmetry—possibly holding the key to our very existence. In the coming decade a number of these intriguing questions will likely be resolved, and pursuing these answers will be a grand and enriching endeavor.

DISCLOSURE STATEMENT

The authors are not aware of any biases that might be perceived as affecting the objectivity of this review.

LITERATURE CITED

1. Marciano WJ. *Annu. Rev. Nucl. Part. Sci.* 41:469 (1991)
2. Yao W-M, et al. (Part. Data Group) *J. Phys. G* 33:1 (2006); Arnsler C, et al. (Part. Data Group) *Phys. Lett. B* 667:1 (2008); **http://pdg.lbl.gov/**
3. Araki T, et al. (KamLAND Collab.) *Nature* 436:499 (2005)
4. Gaisser TK, Honda M. *Annu. Rev. Nucl. Part. Sci.* 52:153 (2002)

5. Bahcall JN. *Neutrino Astrophysics.* Cambridge, UK: Cambridge Univ. Press, 567 pp. (1989); **http://www.sns.ias.edu/~jnb/**

6. Mezzacappa A. *Annu. Rev. Nucl. Part. Sci.* 55:467 (2005)

7. Learned JG, Mannheim K. *Annu. Rev. Nucl. Part. Sci.* 50:679 (2000)

8. Bahcall JN, Serenelli AM, Basu S. *Astrophys. J.* 621:L85 (2005)

9. Hannestad S. *Annu. Rev. Nucl. Part. Sci.* 56:137 (2006)

10. Steigman G. *Annu. Rev. Nucl. Part. Sci.* 57:463 (2007)

11. Spergel DN, et al. (WMAP Collab.) *Astrophys. J. Suppl.* 170:377 (2007)

12. Buchmuller W, Peccei RD, Yanagida D. *Annu. Rev. Nucl. Part. Sci.* 55:311 (2005); references therein

13. Bemporad C, Gratta G, Vogel P. *Rev. Mod. Phys.* 74:297 (2002)

14. Kopp SE. *Phys. Rep.* 439:101 (2007)

15. Pauli W. **http://www.ethbib.ethz.ch/exhibit/pauli/neutrino_e.html** (1930)

16. Fermi E. *Z. Physik* 88:161 (1934)

17. Majorana E. *Nuovo Cim.* 14:171 (1937)

18. Pontecorvo B. *Sov. Phys. JETP* 26:984 (1968)

19. Maki Z, Nakagawa M, Sakata S. *Prog. Theor. Phys.* 28:870 (1962)

20. Mohapatra RN, Smirnov AY. *Annu. Rev. Nucl. Part. Sci.* 56:569 (2006)

21. Fukugita M, Yanagida T. *Physics of Neutrinos and Applications to Astrophysics.* Berlin, Ger.: Springer, 593 pp. (2003)

22. Mohapatra RN, Pal PB. *Massive Neutrinos in Physics and Astrophysics*, Singapore: World Sci., *Lect. Notes Phys.* 72, 451 pp. (2004)

23. Giunti C, Kim CW. *Fundamentals of Neutrino Physics and Astrophysics.* Oxford: Oxford Univ. Press, 710 pp. (2007)

24. Bilenky SM, Pontecorvo B. *Phys. Rep.* 41:225 (1978)

25. Wolfenstein L. *Phys. Rev. D* 17:2369 (1978)

26. Mikheev SP, Smirnov A. *Sov. J. Nucl. Phys.* 42:913 (1985)

27. Fogli GL, Lisi E. *New J. Phys.* 6:139 (2004)

28. McKellar BHJ. *Phys. Lett. B* 97:93 (1980)

29. Bilenky SM, Petcov ST. *Rev. Mod. Phys.* 59:671 (1987)

30. Gaisser TK. *Phys. Scr.* T121:51 (2005)

31. Reines F, et al. *Phys. Rev. Lett.* 15:429 (1965)

32. Achar CV, et al. *Phys. Lett.* 18:196 (1965)

33. Hirata KS, et al. *Phys. Lett. B* 205:416 (1988)

34. Becker-Szendy R, et al. *Phys. Rev. D* 46:3720 (1992)

35. Allison WWM, et al. *Phys. Lett. B* 391:491 (1997)

36. Fukuda Y, et al. *Phys. Rev. Lett.* 81:1562 (1998)

37. Ambrosio M, et al. *Phys. Lett. B* 566:35 (2003)

38. Sanchez M, et al. *Phys. Rev. D* 68:11304 (2003)

39. Ashie Y, et al. *Phys. Rev. Lett.* 93:101801 (2004)

40. Ashie Y, et al. *Phys. Rev. D* 71:112005 (2005)

41. Abe K, et al. *Phys. Rev. Lett.* 97:171801 (2006)

42. Fukuda S, et al. *Phys. Rev. Lett.* 85:3999 (2000)

43. Ahn MH, et al. *Phys. Rev. D* 74:072003 (2006)

44. MINOS Collab. arXiv:0708.1495v2 (2007)

45. Guler M, et al. *CERN SPSC 2000–028 SPSC/P318 LNGS P25/2000* (2000)

46. Acquistapace G, et al. *CERN 98-02 INFN/AE-98/05* (1998)

47. Bailey R. *CERN-SL/99-034(DI) INFN/AE-99/05* (1999)

48. Kodama K, et al. *Nucl. Instrum. Methods A* 493:45 (2002); references therein

49. Bethe HA, Critchfield CL. *Phys. Ref.* 54:248 (1938)

50. Pontecorvo B. *Chalk River Rep. PD-205* (1946)

51. Alvarez LW. *Univ. Calif. Rad. Lab. Rep. UCRL-328* (1949)

52. Davis R. *Phys. Rev. Lett.* 12:303 (1964)

53. Bahcall JN. *Phys. Rev. Lett.* 12:300 (1964)

54. Cleveland BT, et al. *Astrophys. J.* 496:505 (1998)

55. Haxton WC. *Annu. Rev. Astron. Astrophys.* 33:459 (1995)

56. Hirata KS, et al. *Phys. Rev. Lett.* 65:1297 (1990)

57. Abdurashitov JN, et al. *Phys. Rev. C* 60:055801 (1999)

58. Hampel W, et al. *Phys. Lett. B* 447:127 (1999)

59. Kuzmin VA. *Sov. Phys. JETP* 22:1051 (1966)

60. Fukuda S, et al. *Phys. Rev. Lett.* 86:5651 (2001)

61. Altmann M, et al. *Phys. Lett. B* 490:16 (2000)

62. Hata N, Langacker P. *Phys. Rev. D* 52:420 (1995)

63. Heeger K, Robertson RG. *Phys. Rev. Lett.* 77:3720 (1996)

64. Fukuda S, et al. *Phys. Lett. B* 539:179 (2002)

65. Ahmad QR, et al. *Phys. Rev. Lett.* 87:071301 (2001); Ahmad QR, et al. *Phys. Rev. Lett.* 89:011301 (2002)

66. Ahmed SN, et al. *Phys. Rev. Lett.* 92:181301 (2004)

67. Aharmim B, et al. *Phys. Rev. C* 72:055502 (2005)

68. Aharmim B, et al. nucl-ex/0806.0989 (2008)

69. Bahcall JN, Pinsonneault MH, Basu S. *Astrophys. J.* 555:990 (2001)

70. Fogli GL, et al. *Prog. Part. Nucl. Phys.* 57:742 (2006)

71. Borexino Collaboration. *Phys. Lett. B* 658:101 (2008)

72. Abe S, et al. *Phys. Rev. Lett.* 100:221803 (2008)

73. Reines F, Cowan CL Jr. *Phys. Rev.* 92:830 (1953)

74. Cowan CL Jr, et al. *Science* 24(3212):103 (1956)

75. Apollonio M, et al. *Phys. Lett. B* 466:415 (1999)

76. Boehm F, et al. *Phys. Rev. D* 64:112001 (2001)

77. Eguchi E, et al. *Phys. Rev. Lett.* 90:021802 (2003)

78. Apollonio M, et al. *Eur. Phys. J. C* 27:331 (2003)

79. Boehm F, et al. *Phys. Rev. Lett.* 84:3764 (2000)

80. Eskut E, et al. *Nucl. Phys. B* 793:326 (2008)

81. Astier P, et al. *Nucl. Phys. B* 611:3 (2001)

82. Aguilar-Arevalo AA, et al. *Phys. Rev. D* 64:11207 (2007)

83. Aguilar-Arevalo MH, et al. *Phys. Rev. Lett.* 98:231801 (2007)

84. Maltoni M, Schwetz T, Tortola MA, Valle JWF. *New J. Phys.* 6:122 (2004)

85. Strumia A, Vissani F. hep-ph/0606054 (2006)

86. Gonzalez-Garcia MC, Maltoni M. *Phys. Rep.* 460:1 (2008)

87. Fogli GL, et al. *Phys. Rev. D* 75:053001 (2007); Addendum. hep-ph/0805.2517 (2008)

88. Wilkerson JF, Robertson RGH. In *Current Aspects of Neutrino Physics*, ed. DO Caldwell, pp. 39–64. Berlin, Ger.: Springer-Verlag (2001)

89. Kraus C, et al. *Eur. Phys. J. C* 40:447 (2005)

90. Lobashev VM, et al. *Phys. Lett. B* 460:227 (1999)

91. Goeppert-Mayer M. *Phys. Rev.* 48:512 (1935)

92. Gehman VM, Elliott SR. *J. Phys. G* 34:667 (2007)

93. Elliott SR, Hahn A, Moe MK. *Phys. Rev. Lett.* 59:2020 (1987)

94. Avignone FT III, Elliott SR, Engel J. arXiv:0708.1033v2 (2007)

95. Klapdor-Kleingrothaus HV, et al. *Phys. Lett. B* 586:198 (2004)

96. Klapdor-Kleingrothaus HV, Krivosheina IV. *Mod. Phys. Lett.* A21:1547 (2008)

97. Lesgourgues J, Pastor S. *Phys. Rep.* 429:307 (2006)

98. Dunkley J, et al. (WMAP Collab.) astro-ph/0803.0586 (2006)

99. Komatsu E, et al. (WMAP Collab.) astro-ph/0803.0547 (2008)

100. Seljak U, Slosar A, McDonald P. *JCAP* 0610:014 (2006)

101. Barger V, Marfatia D, Whisnant K. *Phys. Rev. D* 65:073023 (2002)

102. Ardellier F, et al. (Double Chooz Collab.) hep-ex/0606025v4 (2006)

103. Guo X, et al. (Daya Bay Collab.) hep-ex/0701029v1 (2007)

104. RENO Collab. **http://neutrino.snu.ac.kr/RENO**

105. Anjos JC, et al. *Nucl. Phys. B Proc. Suppl.* 155:231 (2006)

106. Hayato Y, et al. *T2K Letter of Intent.* **http://jnusrv01.kek.jp/public/t2k/** (2003)

107. Ayres DS, et al. (NOvA Collab.) hep-ex/0503053 (2005); **http://www-nova.fnal.gov** (2005)

108. Maylak M, et al. *Conceptual Design of the SPL II.* CERN Yellow Report 2006-006. **http://hal.in2p3.fr/in2p3-00089949/en/** (2006)

109. de Bellefon A, et al. (MEMPHYS Collab.) hep-ex/0607026 (2006)

110. Campagne J-E, Cazes A. *Eur. Phys. J. C* 45:643 (2006)

111. Barger V, et al. hep-ph/0705 (2007)

112. Zucchelli P. *Phys. Lett. B* 532:166 (2002)

113. Autin B, et al. *J. Phys. G: Nucl. Part. Phys.* 29:1785 (2003)

114. Campagne J-E, et al. *JHEP* 0704:003 (2007)

115. Bouchez J, Lindroos M, Mezzetto M. hep-ex/0310059 (2003)

116. Burguet-Castell J, et al. *Nucl. Phys. B* 725:306 (2005)

117. Geer S. *Phys. Rev. D* 57:6989 (1998); De Rujula A, Gavela MB, Hernandez P. *Nucl. Phys. B* 547:21 (1999)

118. Barger V, Geer G, Raja R, Whisnant K. *Phys. Rev. D* 62:073002 (2000)

119. Rigolin S. hep-ph/0407009 (2004)

120. Autiero D, et al. *Eur. Phys. J. C* 33:243 (2004)

121. Huber P, Lindner M, Winter M. *Comput. Phys. Commun.* 167:195 (2005)

122. Blondel A, et al. *Acta Phys. Polon. B* 37:2077 (2006)

123. Int. Scoping Study. **http://www.hep.ph.ic.ac.uk/iss/** (2006)

124. Bennett J, et al. *CERN-INTC 2004-16* (2004)

125. Muon Ioniz. Cool. R & D. Exp. **http://hep04.phys.iit.edu/cooldemo** (2008)

126. Muon Ioniz. Cool. R & D. Exp. **http://www.fnal.gov/projects/muon_collider/cool/cool.html** (2008)

127. Osipowicz A, et al. (KATRIN Collab.) hep-ex/0109033 (2008)

128. Weinheimer C. *Nucl. Phys. Proc. Suppl.* 168:5 (2007)

129. Galeazzi M, et al. *Phys. Rev. C* 63:014302 (2001)

130. Sisti M, et al. *Nucl. Instrum. Methods A* 520:125 (2004)

131. Monfardini A, et al. *Nucl. Instrum. Methods A* 559:346 (2006)

132. Abraham J, et al. *Nucl. Instrum. Methods A* 523:50 (2004)

133. Ahrens J, et al. *Astropart. Phys.* 20:507 (2004)

134. Aguilar JA, et al. *Astropart. Phys.* 26:314 (2006)

135. Hooper D. *Czech. J. Phys.* 56:A337 (2006)

136. Maltoni M, Schwetz T. *Phys. Rev. D* 76:093005 (2007)

137. Laveder M. *Nucl. Phys. B (Proc. Suppl.)* 168:344 (2007)

138. Dighe A, Ray S. *Phys. Rev. D* 76:113001 (2007)

139. Kayser B. In *Proc. 32nd SLAC Summer Inst. Part. Phys.*, 32nd, Menlo Park, Calif. hep-ph/0506165 (2004)

Cumulative Indexes

Contributing Authors, Volumes 49–58

Hashimoto S, 54:451–86
Haxton W, 51:261–93
Heckel BR, 53:77–121
Heinrich J, 57:145–69
Heintz U, 50:207–48
Heinz U, 49:529–79
Heiselberg H, 50:481–524
Herrmann N, 49:581–632
Hertzog DW, 54:141–74
Heßberger FP, 54:175–215
Hewett J, 52:397–424
Hinchliffe I, 50:643–78
Höcker A, 56:501–67
Hoekstra H, 58:99–123
Honda M, 52:153–99
Hooper D, 58:293–314
Hüfner J, 49:255–301
Hughes EW, 49:303–39
Hughes V, 50:i–xxxvii
Huovinen P, 56:163–206
Hyde-Wright CE, 54:217–67

J

Jacak BV, 49:529–79
Jackson J, 57:441–62
Jackson JD, 49:1–33
Jain B, 58:99–123
Janesick JR, 53:263–300
Janssens RVF, 56:53–92
Ji X, 54:413–50
Jung C, 51:451–88

K

Kachru S, 57:119–44
Kado MM, 52:65–114
Kajita T, 51:451–88
Kamionkowski M, 49:77–123
Kayser B, 49:481–527
Kettell SH, 50:249–97
Kharzeev DE, 54:487–523
Klein JR, 55:141–63
Klein SR, 55:271–310
Konigsberg J, 53:301–51
Kosowsky A, 49:77–123
Kotwal AV, 58:147–75
Krafft GA, 51:413–50;
   53:387–429
Kubodera K, 54:19–37
Kutschera W, 54:39–67

L

Laermann E, 53:163–98
Langacker P, 55:71–139
Lattimer J, 51:295–344
Learned J, 50:679–749
LeCompte T, 50:71–117
Lee T-SH, 52:23–64
Leemann CW, 51:413–50
Leino M, 54:175–215
Ligeti Z, 56:501–67
Lisa MA, 55:357–402
Lisi E, 58:343–69
Lu Z-T, 54:39–67
Luke M, 52:201–51
Lundberg B, 53:199–218
Lyons L, 57:145–69

M

Macchiavelli AO, 50:1–36
Mangano ML, 55:555–88
Mann T, 51:451–88
Mannheim K, 50:679–749
Manohar A, 50:643–78
Marciano WJ, 54:115–40;
   58:315–41
Margetis S, 50:299–342
Martoff CJ, 54:361–412
Masiero A, 51:161–87
Mathur SD, 50:153–206
McFarland KS, 49:481–527
McGaughey PL, 49:217–53
McGrew C, 51:451–88
McKeown RD, 51:189–217
Meadows B, 58:249–91
Meißner U-G, 57:33–60
Merminga L, 53:387–429
Meyer H-O, 57:1–31
Mezzacappa A, 55:467–515
Miller GA, 56:253–92
Miller ML, 57:205–43
Milner R, 55:165–228
Mohapatra RN, 56:569–628
Mori T, 58:315–41
Morse WM, 54:141–74
Moskalenko IV, 57:285–327
Moss JM, 49:217–53
Moulson M, 56:207–51
Mrówczyński S, 57:61–94
Müller B, 56:93–135

N

Nagle JL, 56:93–135
Nelson AE, 53:77–121
Neuberger H, 51:23–52
Nico JS, 55:27–69
Niwa K, 53:199–218
Nystrand J, 55:271–310

O

Olsen SL, 58:51–73
Onogi T, 54:451–86
Opper AK, 56:253–92
Oreglia M, 54:269–314

P

Page D, 56:327–74
Page SA, 56:1–52
Pandharipande V, 50:481–524
Paolone V, 53:199–218
Park T-S, 54:19–37
Peccei RD, 55:311–55
Peggs S, 52:425–71
Peng JC, 49:217–53
Perkins DH, 55:1–26
Petrov AA, 58:249–91
Phelps ME, 52:303–38
Philipsen O, 53:163–98
Pieper S, 51:53–90
Prakash M, 51:295–344
Pratt S, 55:357–402
Ptuskin VS, 57:285–327
Putnam G, 53:263–300

R

Raffelt GG, 49:163–216
Rainwater D, 53:301–51
Ramsey-Musolf MJ, 56:1–52
Reddy S, 56:327–74
Redwine RP, 52:23–64
Rehm E, 51:91–129
Reygers K, 57:205–43
Riotto A, 49:35–75
Roney JM, 58:315–41
Roodman A, 55:141–63
Rosenberg LJ, 56:293–326
Roser T, 52:425–71
Rowson P, 51:345–412

Rupak G, 58:1–25
Ruuskanen PV, 56:163–206

S

Šafařík S, 50:299–342
Saito NS, 50:525–75
Samtleben D, 57:245–83
Sanders SJ, 57:205–43
Sauer PU, 58:27–49
Sauli F, 49:341–87
Savard G, 50:119–52
Sawyer R, 51:295–344
Schäfer T, 58:1–25
Schiff D, 50:37–69
Schmaltz M, 55:229–70
Schwarz DJ, 56:441–500
Sharma A, 49:341–87
Sherrill BM, 56:53–92
Shintake T, 49:125–62
Shipsey I, 53:431–99
Shiu G, 55:71–139
Sikivie P, 56:293–326
Silvestrini L, 57:405–40
Smirnov AY, 56:569–628
Smith MS, 51:91–129
Snow WM, 55:27–69
Soffer J, 50:525–75
Soltz R, 55:357–402
Son DT, 57:95–118
Sorensen P, 58:177–205
Sphicas P, 56:375–440
Spiropulu M, 52:397–424
Staggs S, 57:245–83

Stankus P, 55:517–53
Starinets AO, 57:95–118
Stark J, 58:147–75
Steigman G, 57:463–91
Steinberg P, 57:205–43
Stelzer TJ, 55:555–88
Stephenson EJ, 56:253–92
Strikman M, 55:403–65
Strong AW, 57:285–327
Su D, 51:345–412
Swallow EC, 53:39–75

T

Tauscher L, 53:123–61
Tenenbaum P, 49:125–62
Thoma MH, 57:61–94
Thomson EJ, 58:125–46
Tiator L, 54:69–114
Tollefson K, 49:435–79
Tostevin JA, 53:219–61
Trodden M, 49:35–75
Tucker-Smith D, 55:229–70
Tully CG, 52:65–114
Turyshev SG, 58:207–48

V

van Bibber K, 56:293–326
Vanderhaeghen M, 57:171–204
van Kolck U, 52:339–96
Varnes EW, 49:435–79
Venugopalan V, 55:165–228
Verbaarschot JJM, 50:343–410

Vetter K, 57:363–404
Villalobos Baillie O, 50:299–342
Vives O, 51:161–87
Vogel P, 52:115–52
Vogelsang W, 50:525–75;
    55:165–228
Volkas R, 51:295–344
Voss R, 49:303–39

W

Weiner N, 58:75–98
Weiss C, 55:403–65
Werth G, 50:119–52
Wessels JP, 49:581–632
Wettig T, 50:343–410
Wiedemann U, 55:357–402
Wieman C, 51:261–93
Wienold T, 49:581–632
Wilkerson JF, 58:343–69
Willocq S, 51:345–412
Winstein B, 57:245–83
Winston R, 53:39–75
Wiringa R, 51:53–90
Wolfenstein L, 54:1–17

Y

Yanagida T, 55:311–55

Z

Zakharov BG, 50:37–69
Zioutas K, 56:293–326

Chapter Titles, Volumes 49–58

Astrophysics

Instrumentation and Techniques

Special Topics

RETURN TO: PHYSICS-ASTRONOMY LIBRARY
351 LeConte Hall

LOAN PERIOD 1	2	3
1-MONTH		
4	5	6

ALL BOOKS MAY BE RECALLED AFTER 7 DAYS
Books may be renewed by calling 510-642-3122

DUE AS STAMPED BELOW

FORM NO. DD 22
2M   7-10

UNIVERSITY OF CALIFORNIA, BERKELEY
Berkeley, California 94720–6000

ANNUAL REVIEWS
Intelligent Synthesis of the Scientific Literature

Annual Reviews – Your Starting Point for Research Online
http://arjournals.annualreviews.org

- Over 1150 Annual Reviews volumes—more than 26,000 critical, authoritative review articles in 35 disciplines spanning the Biomedical, Physical, and Social sciences—available online, including all Annual Reviews back volumes, dating to 1932

- Current individual subscriptions include seamless online access to full-text articles, PDFs, Reviews in Advance (as much as 6 months ahead of print publication), bibliographies, and other supplementary material in the current volume and the prior 4 years' volumes

- All articles are fully supplemented, searchable, and downloadable—see http://nucl.annualreviews.org

- Access links to the reviewed references (when available online)

- Site features include customized alerting services, citation tracking, and saved searches

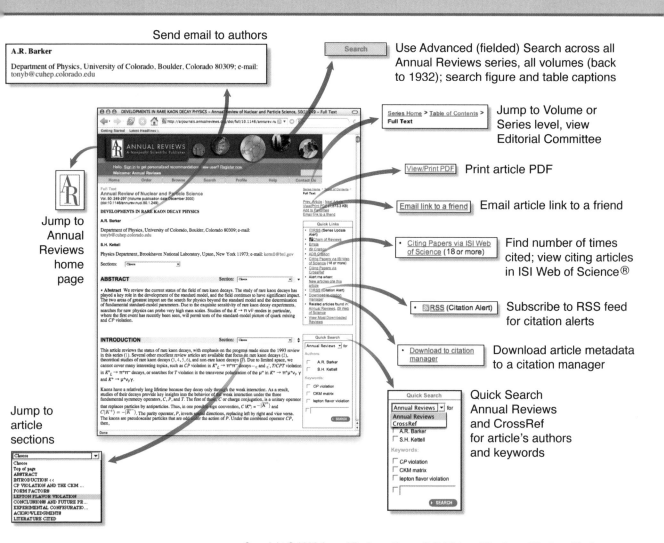

Send email to authors

A.R. Barker

Department of Physics, University of Colorado, Boulder, Colorado 80309; e-mail: tonyb@cuhep.colorado.edu

Search — Use Advanced (fielded) Search across all Annual Reviews series, all volumes (back to 1932); search figure and table captions

Series Home > Table of Contents > Full Text — Jump to Volume or Series level, view Editorial Committee

View/Print PDF — Print article PDF

Email link to a friend — Email article link to a friend

Citing Papers via ISI Web of Science (18 or more) — Find number of times cited; view citing articles in ISI Web of Science®

RSS (Citation Alert) — Subscribe to RSS feed for citation alerts

Download to citation manager — Download article metadata to a citation manager

Quick Search Annual Reviews and CrossRef for article's authors and keywords

Jump to Annual Reviews home page

Jump to article sections